THE SOCIAL FUNCTION
OF SCIENCE

The Social Function
of Science

J. D. Bernal

The M.I.T. Press

Massachusetts Institute of Technology
Cambridge, Massachusetts, and London, England

CONTENTS

PAGE

PART II: WHAT SCIENCE COULD DO

CHAPTER IX. THE TRAINING OF THE SCIENTIST

CHAPTER X. THE REORGANIZATION OF RESEARCH

CHAPTER XI. SCIENTIFIC COMMUNICATION

CHAPTER XII. THE FINANCE OF SCIENCE

CHAPTER XV. SCIENCE AND SOCIAL TRANSFORMATION

CHAPTER XVI. THE SOCIAL FUNCTION OF SCIENCE

APPENDICES

CHARTS

PREFACE

THE events of the past few years have led to a critical examination of the function of science in society. It used to be believed that the results of scientific investigation would lead to continuous progressive improvements in conditions of life; but first the War and then the economic crisis have shown that science can be used as easily for destructive and wasteful purposes, and voices have been raised demanding the cessation of scientific research as the only means of preserving a tolerable civilization. Scientists themselves, faced with these criticisms, have been forced to consider, effectively for the first time, how the work they are doing is connected with the social and economic developments which are occurring around them. This book is an attempt to analyse this connection; to investigate how far scientists, individually and collectively, are responsible for this state of affairs, and to suggest what possible steps could be taken which would lead to a fruitful and not to a destructive utilization of science.

It is necessary, to begin with, to consider the social function of science not absolutely, but as something which has grown up imperceptibly with the growth of science. Science has ceased to be the occupation of curious gentlemen or of ingenious minds supported by wealthy patrons, and has become an industry supported by large industrial monopolies and by the State. Imperceptibly this has altered the character of science from an individual to a collective basis, and has enhanced the importance of apparatus and administration. But as these developments have proceeded in an uncoordinated and haphazard manner, the result at the present day is a structure of appalling inefficiency both as to its internal organization and as to the means of application to problems of production or of welfare. If science is to be of full use to society it must first put its own house in order. This is a task of extraordinary difficulty, because of the danger of any organization of science destroying that originality and spontaneity which are essential to its progress. Science can never be administered as part of a civil service, but recent developments both here and abroad, particularly in the U.S.S.R., point to the possibility of combining freedom and efficiency in scientific organization.

The application of science furnishes other problems. Here the tendency in the past has been almost exclusively that of directing science towards improvements in material production primarily through lowering the cost and towards the development of the instruments of war. This has led not only to technological unemployment but to an almost complete neglect of those applications which would be of more immediate value to human welfare, in particular to health and domestic life. The result has been an extraordinary disproportion in the development of different sciences, the biological and still more the sociological sciences having been starved at the expense of the more immediately profitable physical and chemical sciences.

Any discussion of the application of science necessarily involves questions of economics, and we are driven to enquire how far the various economic systems now existing or proposed can give the opportunity for the maximum application of science for human welfare. Further, economics cannot be separated from politics. The advent of Fascism, the sequence of wars now raging in the world and the universal preparations for a more general and terrible war have affected scientists not only as citizens, but also through their work. Science itself, for the first time since the Renaissance, seems in danger. The scientist has begun to realize his social responsibility, but if science is to fulfil the function which its tradition demands, and to avoid the dangers which threaten it, we require an increased appreciation, both on the part of scientists and of the general public, of the intricate relations between science and contemporary life.

To make an analysis of modern science itself has become a task far beyond the means of a single mind; indeed, there is as yet no such survey even in the form of a composite work. It is even more difficult to analyse the complex relations which have grown up in the course of centuries between science, industry, Government, and general culture. Such a task would need not only a general grasp of the whole of science but the techniques and the knowledge of an economist, a historian, and a sociologist. These general statements must stand in part as an excuse for the character of this book. I am aware, and aware now far more acutely than when I began to write, of my lack of the ability, the knowledge, or the time which it needed. As a working scientist immersed in a special field, and having besides many other duties and occupations, I could never complete even the bibliographic research which the subject demanded nor give it concentrated attention for more than a few days at a time.

Accuracy both statistically and in detail should be a cardinal necessity in any general survey, but such accuracy is either not attainable at all owing to the scantiness of some of the records, or, owing to the superabundance and confusion of others, only obtainable with immense effort. No one knows, for instance, how many scientists there are in any country, except perhaps in the U.S.S.R., and how much is spent on them and by whom. What they are doing should be ascertainable, as it appears in the numbers of the thirty thousand odd scientific periodicals, but nowhere is it possible to find how and why they do it.

In describing and criticizing the conduct of scientific work I have had to depend primarily on personal experience. This is open to a double disadvantage: the experience may have been unrepresentative or the conclusions biassed. As to the first, the result of many conversations with scientists of every category in many fields convinces me that much of what I have experienced can be matched almost anywhere else in science. As to the second, it must be frankly admitted that I am biassed. I have resented the inefficiency, the frustration and the diversion of scientific effort to base ends, and indeed it was on account of this that I came to consider the relation of science to society and to attempt this book. If in detail bias may seem to lead to harsh judgments, it cannot be denied that the existence of a resentment which is widespread among scientists is itself a proof that all is not well with science. Unfortunately it is not possible in any published book to speak freely and precisely about the way science is run. The law of libel, reasons of State, and still more the unwritten code of the scientific fraternity itself forbid particular examples being held up alike for praise or blame. Charges must be general and to that degree unconvincing and lacking in substantiation. Yet if the general thesis is correct, scientists will be able to supply their own examples, while non-scientists can check the ultimate results of science by their own experience and appreciate to what extent the thesis of this book provides an explanation of how this occurs.

For those who have once seen it, the frustration of science is a very bitter thing. It shows itself as disease, enforced stupidity, misery, thankless toil, and premature death for the great majority, and an anxious, grasping, and futile life for the remainder. Science can change all this, but only science working with those social forces which understand its functions and which march to the same ends.

Against this grim but hopeful reality, the traditional piety of a pure unworldly science seems at best a phantastic escape, at worst a shameful hypocrisy. That, nevertheless, is the picture that we have been taught to make of science, while the one here presented will be unfamiliar to many and seem blasphemy to some. This book will, however, have served its purpose if it succeeds in showing that there is a problem and that on the proper relation of science and society depends the welfare of both.

In writing this book I have had the help of more people than I can name here. I owe very much to the criticisms and suggestions of my friends and colleagues, particularly H. D. Dickinson, I. Fankuchen, Julian Huxley, Joseph Needham, John Pilley and S. Zuckerman.   For much of the material, particularly the statistical material, I am indebted to the work of Mrs. Brenda Ryerson, M. V. H. Wilkins and Dr. Ruhemann, who also contributed an appendix on science in the U.S.S.R.   Finally, my special thanks are due to Miss P. S. Miller for her revision of the manuscript.

BIRKBECK COLLEGE, *September* 1938.

AFTER TWENTY-FIVE YEARS

TWENTY-FIVE years after writing *The Social Function of Science* it is interesting to look back to see how far its thesis was justified and how far any of its lessons have been learned and still hold any message for the present or the future. I would now conclude that to a very large extent the book has fulfilled its original object: to make people aware of the new function that science was acquiring then and would increasingly acquire in the future, in determining the conditions of human life and — as it is now tragically revealed — of the very existence of humanity. The events that followed very soon after its publication were to bring this home to everyone.

We are no longer concerned, as I was then, merely to vindicate the growth and use of science in modern civilization. It is there for bad or good, hence it is even more essential to understand it. In *The Social Function*, that was what I was trying to do. Yet I failed to foresee how rapidly the tendencies I had observed were to bear fruit and to what extent the prophecy I made at that time was to be fulfilled and over-fulfilled.

In *The Social Function* the scientific and technical revolution of our time was only forecast: now it is recognized by everyone. To this extent its message is obsolete or commonplace. But the task of understanding it has hardly begun, and it is going to be a very difficult task indeed, because the objects and processes we are studying move fast and much faster than our study of them. When I was revising my later book *Science in History* quite recently I became aware that after five years the main lines of current science set out in 1957 had become almost unrecognizable by 1964. The sections of the book on both the physical and biological sciences had, effectively, to be rewritten.

The scientific revolution itself has entered a new phase — it has become self-conscious. This is now recognized not only among scientists or among men of general education but in the world of private business and of state finance: research itself is the new gold-field. One lesson that I preached in *The Social Function,* the immense profitability of scientific research, has now been accepted and, in an age of commercial and international competition, acceptance by one means acceptance by all with varying degrees of delay. When a sixth of the good scientists of Britain go off to America, then even the Government is forced to recognize that it has not been looking after them properly.

Now the 'research revolution', to borrow the title of Mr. Silk's fascinating and horrifying study,* is not only a fact but a recognized fact of the time. The economics of modern states are no longer considered to be economics of a fluctuating equilibrium but economics of growth. The rate of growth of the gross national product is now taken as the index of national economic health or even of survival among the advanced industrial countries. To achieve a merely tolerable rate of increase of the national product, say about 4 per cent, depends in the first place on the amount of past research that can be applied at the time; but also the rate of increase in the future depends on the amount of research that is carried out now. Furthermore, the time lag of the application of research has greatly shortened; new ideas can come into application, especially in fields which are advancing most rapidly, like those of control mechanism, within a year or two of their first discovery.

The recognition of this led, first in the military scientific field, to a research race which is still going on and has spread now into the civil field, not only in the electrical and chemical industries but also in biology, medicine, and agriculture. In the years since *The Social Function* was written the yield per man in agriculture has multiplied three times and, correspondingly, the number of persons directly involved in agriculture has shrunk — at present only $2\frac{1}{2}$ per cent of the population of the United States and only 5 per cent in Britain. This is at a time when more than 70 per cent are occupied in agriculture in the poorer parts of the world; the difference marks a real practical achievement of the scientific revolution.

This very success, however, also marks the failure of the research revolution to spread effectively over the two-thirds of the world which are just struggling out of the old colonial regimes. The gap between the economies of the advanced industrial countries and those of the developing countries is rapidly widening. Only a small part of this can be put down to the increase in population in the developing parts of the world. Even with the increase as it is running today, at

*Silk, L. S. *The Research Revolution*. New York, 1960.

about 2 per cent per annum, this is so much less than the rate of increase in the scientific potential, which comes to more like 20 per cent per annum, that there can be no question of an automatic and independent 'catch-up' on the part of the developing countries.

Whether the gap is filled or not, however, we cannot ignore the threat of utter destruction that one aspect of the scientific revolution holds over all mankind, the destruction typified by the fission and now the fusion bomb. Concern with war has dominated the gigantic scientific efforts of the last twenty years. It has unquestionably affected the new scientific revolution, which it first stimulated and then hampered with its demands on manpower and apparatus.

Enormous changes have occurred since *The Social Function* was written, comparatively only a few years ago. It was written on the eve of the Second World War, with its vast destruction and the liberations that it brought about, especially in Asia and Africa; but more significant than the constructive aspects was the discovery of nuclear fission culminating in the atom bomb and the threat which it implies to the whole of life.* In mastering the atom something of the full power of science was made manifest, but what is equally obvious is that the powers which controlled humanity at that time, political and financial, were incapable of using the potentialities of science. They were incapable, really, even of understanding it, and the twenty years we have been spared in the atomic age are only now bringing the lesson home.

If we can survive the dangers of the immediate present we have every chance of realizing a world so different from anything we have had before that the transition is greater than any which has occurred since the first appearance of humanity. We have the potentiality of the age of abundance and leisure, but the actuality of a divided world with greater poverty, stupidity, and cruelty than it has ever known.

Between that world and the present, however, we clearly have to pass through a transitional period which will be one of great danger. The technical possibilities and, even more, the integrated control that can be achieved through the proper use of computers, cannot be fitted into the fragmented social frame of private interests and exploitation. The operational problem remains of how to effect the transition with the minimum of strain and destruction. I feel confident that the ulti-

---

* The omission of any reference to this in its constructive or destructive aspects may seem surprising, but it was deliberate. I knew very well about nuclear fission but I was warned by my friends in the Cavendish that any reference to its practical application would prevent reputable physicists from taking my book seriously.

mate pattern will, so to speak, impose itself the moment its logic is fully appreciated, but I do not minimize the danger of at least some parts of the new scientific method, especially those of mass communication and education, being used to retard this change or to deflect it.

I wrote *The Social Function* just before the Second World War. In this war the ideas that were exposed there and that were then largely theoretical were fully tested in practice. It was possible in the service of war to carry out many of the proposals for organized science and its application that I had made in the book. I summarized some of these in my paper on 'The Lessons of the War for Scientists' (see J. D. Bernal, *The Freedom of Necessity,* London, 1949):

'The freedom of scope for experimentation and assistance is a lesson which will not be lost on the scientists who experienced it. It will be of particular importance in the next few years when we are bound to suffer for lack of men to carry out the very much increased tasks which will have to be dealt with by science and where it is more than ever important that we should make the fullest use of our few capable workers. The principle first enunciated by Professor Blackett, that allocation of money to science should be made in the measure of what a competent scientist can usefully spend and not according to what he can just manage on, should be the basis for our post-war science.

'Almost equally important as a lesson of the war is the value of the greater integration which was achieved in scientific work, partly through a more rational organisation and partly through the function of an effective positive information service.'

The organization of science in wartime —
'provided what had been previously the function of the scientific societies, that is, careful discussion and interchange of scientific opinion, but it had also a much more positive function in laying out lines of attack and in determining priorities. In this way the scientific work itself could be carried out in a multiplicity of actual experimental stations — government industrial, university — and yet not lose its coherence or general direction. Further, this direction was exercised by scientists themselves, at least in the latter part of the war, and was consequently sufficiently reasonable to be for the most part acceptable to the main body of scientific workers. Out of it emerged general concepts of organization of science which will be of permanent value.'   (p. 290)

One major result of science in war was the foundation of Operational Research.

'Operational research,' I wrote, 'led not only to greater understanding in detail of the operations of war, but to a much clearer integration of different types or operations. As the war went on, combined operations, whether by land and sea, land and air, or all three together, became the rule rather than the exception and the bridge between the very diverse approaches of the different services was often effected through operational research. In this way several general principles emerged which have far wider application than merely to military operations.' (p. 297)

'The original implications of operational research are already making themselves felt in peacetime economy. In principle it amounts to the statement that any human activity and any branch of that activity is a legitimate subject for scientific study, and subsequently for modification in the light of that study. Once this is accepted in practice, which implies the provision of research workers to carry out these studies, the way is open to a new level of man's control of his environment, one in which economic and social processes become scientific through and through. This is already happening in productive industry. We are witnessing what is really a new industrial revolution in which statistical and scientific control and rational planning and design are taking the place that prime movers and simple mechanism did in the first industrial revolution. Industrial processes are now seen to represent cycles of performance in which the needs of the consumer determine production and are in turn modified by the results of that production, leading to a progressively greater degree of satisfaction at a steadily diminishing social cost.' (p. 299)

The direction implied in my major conclusion still holds.

'The most balanced and flexible plan for scientific research, how-drive: a technical, biological and social advance carried out with all the resources of the community. That such a task can be achieved has been shown by the experience of the war; but the war has shown also that it is not only possible but absolutely necessary for survival as an advanced community. A national economy, integrated through science and continually advancing by means of scientific research and development, is the basic need of the new era which we are now entering. It implies the expenditure of a much larger proportion of social effort and social resources on science than ever envisaged before.

'Those who had considered the advantages that science could bring to society had realised well before the war that the expenditure on science by society was far too small; at that time the total expenditure in this country was something of the order of one-tenth of one per cent of the national income. They could see, and they tried to point out how the increase of this proportion would bring far more rapid prosperity. In the post-war situation, however, with the leeway of destruction and disorganisation to make up and the far weaker and even perilous situation of this country, what was desirable has become an absolute necessity, and the proportion to be aimed at must be a

much higher one. . . . On the long term view we must look forward
to a fairly rapid transformation in which scientific functions — not
necessarily scientific research and development only, but scientific production and scientific administration — will absorb a progressively
larger and larger proportion of the population. From one-tenth of
one per cent we may advance to involving one, two and possibly ultimately, but in the far distant future, as much as twenty per cent of
the population in such activities. This is a logical consequence of the
increasing role of human intelligence and consciousness in the management of our society. Long before such a stage is reached, however,
the distinction between scientific and nonscientific activity will probably have largely disappeared. Already we require for the proper
functioning of our society, a certain degree of knowledge of the facts
of science and even more of its method on the part of every citizen.
The government cannot make decisions, the people cannot carry out
the decisions reached, unless they have much fuller understanding
than at present of what they are doing.'

(pp. 308-9)

The Social Function was largely a theoretical work, at least outside the academic field in which I had considerable experience. Some
of the lessons just referred to were the common lessons of the war
effort, but they also included experiences of my own in moving from
the academic world into the world of action, both industrial and military. To some extent they confirmed me in my previous opinions, but
they also showed where I had been wrong. It showed me in particular
that general statements about the unity of theory and practice had to
be studied in their own right, as part of the strategy of operational
research, a unity which we cannot hope to bring about until enough
effort and enough people are devoted to it.

These ideas have not been followed up adequately in the Western
countries although they have been in the Socialist countries. Nevertheless, the almost explosive progress of scientific invention in the
years that followed the war led in all the industrial countries to a
rapid and even to an accelerating technical and economic progress. It
was only by means of organized science that the Socialist countries,
which had in the first place fewer resources, many of which had been
destroyed in the war, particularly the great human resource represented by the millions who were killed, were able to recover and
later to run neck and neck with industrial advances of the richest
capitalist countries during the post-war period.

Three main areas of advance opened up in this post-war period,
each of which carried the promise of still far greater performance.
The first was the availability of energy in unlimited quantities, not

only beginning with atomic fission but also with the realization that the sources of conventional fuels, particularly oil, in the world were many orders of ten times greater than they had been imagined to be. At the same time the development of new methods of producing electrical energy from heat, such as magneto-hydrodynamic generation, themselves in part the product of atomic power engineering, have raised the efficiency of heat engines to the level of about 60 as against 30 per cent, thus effectively doubling the amount of energy available per unit of fuel. It was evident that the world's progress would not fail for lack of energy; in other words, that energy would be there for the taking, and with it all the materials and processes that could be formed from the universal exchangeable character of energy, effectively expressed as electrical energy. This can be used in its first form as the motive power for industry, but it can also be put to extracting metals from their ore, put to synthesizing artificial materials such as fibres and plastics and, finally, put to providing the basic requirements of agriculture in the form of fertilizers and water, in particular desalted sea water. Thus, indirectly, energy can be transformed into food, and this process will soon cease to be indirect and become a direct chemical synthesis.

The second and perhaps greater invention in its effect is the purely logical and mathematical one coming with the development of the computer. This is an example of the disproportion between the essential scientific feature of an invention and its utility. The mathematical notions behind the modern computer are no more complex than those of the computer first designed by Pascal in the seventeenth century and partly executed by Babbage in the nineteenth. What brought the idea to life again was the means to carry it out: the components, no longer wooden cogs or even metal ones, as in the earlier machines, were electrical circuits very rapidly switched, first by means of valves and magnetic circuits, and finally by means of semi-conductors. The result was not an invention of any one person — it did not require genius, but simply application of known methods to known problems. But once it came, it was to have enormous effects which are only just beginning to be seen.

The most obvious are to be shown in industry, where it has initiated a major industrial revolution of transferring to the machine not only force but also skill. In this way it can and will very rapidly put an end to one of the worst features of the first industrial revolution, the use of man as a machine minder. The social consequences of this will be enormous. Manual work is ceasing to be the basis of industry, and clerical work will soon be equally superfluous. The whole concept of work will be transformed from that of an individual and physically unpleasant or tedious task for which men and women are compensated by payment or driven to by necessity, and will become a voluntary and conscious acceptance of a definite and enjoyable role in an organized society.

It is not only industry which is affected but also the whole of administration, commercial and governmental. The clerk, sitting at his desk and totting up his columns of figures, is now being rapidly replaced by the computer. Whole cities and nations will be run by it in the future. Already many things can be done better by a computer than by a human being, and as computers are further developed that number will increase until it becomes normal to give most tasks to a computer and only reserve those tasks for human beings which at that moment it is too difficult for the computer to undertake.

A further use of computers — and ultimately a more important one — is in science itself, by making operations which are thinkable in principle but could not be carried out in practice, making automatic scientific analysis and synthesis possible. They can even effect the most intractible achievement and help in the advances of pure mathematics itself. This is a break-out of the mind that will ultimately lead to a new symbiosis between man and machine. Previously man had *used* the machines, now man and machine are one unit. They can, and indeed must, think together in the future.

The third feature of the transformation of our time that is also of great importance is the understanding on a deeper level of biological processes. The great discoveries of the mid-twentieth century, in biochemistry and in its transformation into ultra-micro-biochemistry of the interior of the cell, culminating in the elucidation of the genetic mechanism and the genetic code, are not only great intellectual triumphs but for the first time give the possibilities of conscious control of biological processes. We have already begun with the control of matters that affect us most directly, such as the cure of diseases. Clearly we must progress from that to a more general aim of the 'extension of life and the betterment of man's estate'. The first four of Bacon's *Magnalia*:

> The prolongation of life;
> The restitution of youth in some degree;
> The retardation of age;
> The curing of diseases counted incurable;

are now well on the way to realization.

All these great achievements — in power, in industry, in medicine and agriculture — are themselves only a part of what is now being seen more consciously to be the major transformation of our time, the research revolution itself. We have now arrived at the second stage, that of the development of the scientific method. To quote Bacon again:

'But above all, if a man could succeed, not in striking out some particular invention, however, useful, but in kindling a light in Nature — a light which should in its very rising touch and illuminate all the border-regions that confine upon the circle of our present knowledge; and so spreading further and further should presently disclose and bring into sight all that is most hidden and secret in the world — that man (I thought) would be the benefactor indeed of the human race — the propagator of man's empire over the universe, the champion of liberty, the conqueror and subduer of necessities.'

Bacon was talking about the scientific method itself. What has happened recently is the realization not only by scientists, who have known it for many years, but also by peoples and governments, that here is a method which in itself can be *counted on* to generate more and more of these great achievements and transformations. This is the deeper meaning of the research revolution. That revolution has begun, and it is going on faster and faster.

But that is only half the story. Research can be carried out and applied in a most disorderly and wasteful way. In *The Social Function* I estimated the efficiency of research as about 2 per cent, that is, about 2 per cent of what could have been found out and been done with the resources and men available was in fact carried out. To achieve even modest increases in efficiency, obviously something else, but something radically different is needed. We need a strategy for research which must be based on a *science of science*. This cannot be formulated by merely laying down *a priori* what the scientific method should be, as in the past, but by finding this out from what it does, through its modes of action. These modes now involve machines as well as human beings. The science of science, or the self-consciousness of science, as I have put it elsewhere, is the real drastic advance of the second part of the twentieth century. This science of science must be wide-ranging; it must include the social and economic as well as the material and technical conditions for scientific advance and for the proper use of its tools.

After these very general remarks I should like to say something on various topics which are touched on in the contributions to this volume, and also on some which are not there but which were in the original ideas of *The Social Function of Science*. I will stress only those which have gained in importance in the intervening years, and especially those of which I have had personal experience in that period.

I am not here going to refer to particular sciences, but rather to the new modes by which science advances. This means particularly scientific communication, in its wider sense the place of science in education, and the related subjects, scientific organization and finance.

The rapid growth of science, as Price has pointed out,* which is far outstripping the advance of any other field of human endeavour, has already created problems in itself, some of which were foreseen at the time *The Social Function* was written. The first problem appears as a purely technical one, that of communication between scientists, on which Coblans has given us a very informative contribution. I attempted in the post-war years, when the destruction of communications had given an admirable opportunity for reconstruction, to get this organized on the national and international level, but with striking lack of success, It is only now — when the chaos of scientific communications threatens its effective advance and results in research being repeated to discover the same things owing to lack of knowledge as to what had been done before — that it is being taken seriously.

Fortunately, at the same time, the new means of communication and of computing make it possible for the first time to deal rationally with a mass of information. Scientific communication should be an ideal field for the application of communication engineering, but this would mean a great change in tradition. What I had proposed in *The Social Function,* the effective supercession of the scientific journal, was strenuously opposed and was even condemned in *The Times* as an 'insidious and cavalier proposal' when put to the Royal Society Conference on Scientific Information in 1947. Where I was wrong was not in the direction in which improvement would come, but in over-estimating the ease with which it would happen and under-estimating the prejudices that were holding it back.

The scientific journal has effectively been killed by the rapidity of the growth of science itself. The units of scientific information will have to be collected, sifted, and sorted, largely electronically, before they can be usefully presented to those who would want to use them. This goes, in the first place, for information *inside* science; there is

---

* Most clearly in his latest book: *Big Science, Little Science.*

the further enormous field of information from the world of science to that of industry and popular enlightenment.

One very evident fact, which has increased rather than diminished in the interval, is the relatively small amount of money devoted to scientific information and communication, compared to that allocated for research itself. The distribution of scientific information will not be necessarily reformed by allocating more money to it, but it cannot be reformed at all unless more money is allocated to it.

Next to the communication of information comes the training of those who are to receive it and who are destined to carry forward knowledge and use of knowledge in the world of the future. Here again, the strictures I put on existing systems of scientific education, much resented as they were at the time, now appear almost as commonplace in the light of the new and urgent requirements for scientific and technological manpower that are put forward not only in the industrial states but in the developing ones as well.

There is no denying the existence of the problem. It has even been made a major issue in the General Election in Britain and has already led to a basic change in emphasis in education, away from the Renaissance ideal of producing a cultivated élite, to one aiming at producing administrators and possibly even governors capable of understanding and appreciating the needs of science in an industrial developing society. But the problem is far from being solved. Indeed, on the face of it it would appear to be insoluble. The amount of time available for education can be stretched only to a very limited extent, doubling it, for instance, from three years to six, but, with the output of science doubling every seven years, it is clear that entirely new methods of teaching will have to be evolved to make use of the knowledge already acquired and even more to ensure the continued rapidity of the acquisition and integration of new knowledge.

However, here the new techniques of the computer age can help. Already teaching machines are being evolved that can adapt themselves to the speed of learning of individual students, and techniques of television can also supplement to a large extent practical instruction. Here again, however, nothing effective will be done unless very much effort is devoted to research on methods of teaching science. There is a realization, which is just beginning in some of the older industrial countries, that not only a small section of a professional class needs such education, but that it must also be spread throughout the whole population. Modern automatic machinery requires highly educated personnel to watch its working, and to deduce from its performance the best way of improving it. In any case it is clear that the requirements for personnel in research and development in industry, agriculture, and medicine will be enormously increased and come to equal and in some cases surpass the number of people involved in the operation of machinery and transport. Thus the development of automation, far from decreasing the need for science, will actually increase it many-fold.

The problems of science and education are no longer limited, as they were largely at the time when *The Social Function* was written, to the advanced industrial countries. An even greater problem, with fewer means to tackle it, is that of the developing countries, which require science for their essential new task — the development of the country for the benefit of its own peoples and not, as in the past, to make its exploitation for foreign interests more efficient. Some of these problems are treated in Professor Blackett's paper, but essentially only as a means of furthering the real aim of raising the level of production and consumption in those countries to that of the industrial countries.

But the problem of the scientists themselves in the developing countries is really a separate one. It is often talked of in terms of aid and, indeed, in the short term it is clear that much of the teaching of science in these countries will have to be carried out by direct or indirect help from abroad. This is likely to be a difficult solution and one which is in many ways self-defeating. The foreign teachers are apt to stay on in the countries and not be replaced by native teachers. This is partly because their successful pupils, who go to finish their studies in advanced countries, tend to remain there rather than returning to use the skills they have acquired under the much more difficult and unrewarding circumstances of their own countries. This is one side of the 'brain drain' which affects nearly all countries adversely except at the receiving end, usually the United States.

There is a natural tendency for the kind of science taught to be the kind of science known in the industrial countries and, therefore, there is often a problem of actual unemployment in their own countries of such trained scientists. To attempt to counter this, however, may lead to an opposite error: that of training people in countries that are economically largely raw-material producers in a simplified kind of science thought to be suitable for the kind of problems they will have to meet in developing their own countries. Such an attitude, however well intentioned, is inevitably felt to be patronizing and is correspondingly resented. The hard way of self-reliance, building up without foreign teachers or advice, avoids both of these traps and has been practised with great success in China.

Quite an important criterion of the different ways of approaching science teaching is the question of language. In the early stages of colonialism and semi-colonialism the languages in which science was taught were the languages of the various imperial powers. In a colony it was one language; in a semi-colonial territory like China, where several powers were competing, there were a number of different ones — in no case the language of the country. After liberation this practice has often been continued, with the result of divorcing the scientifically educated young people from the roots of their own people and making them the more easily acceptable in foreign countries. The use of the native language, on the other hand, where it is possible, and it becomes very difficult if many languages are involved, implies an enormous work of translation and retraining of teachers, but provides a better basis for a science geared to the needs of the people. However, it inevitably adds to the language confusion of international science. It will be interesting to compare the progress in twenty years time of India and China, who adopted different methods of approach to the subject.

The idea of a kind of simplified science for developing countries has another unfortunate consequence. It inevitably strengthens the idea that international scientific co-operation is a one-way rather than a two-way process: the developing countries have as much to *give* to science as they have to take from it. In fact, it blurs the hope that, with the enormous increase in science and understanding, we shall come to the time when nine-tenths of the world and not about one-quarter, as at present, will be able to contribute to the advancement of science.

The problem of transforming the world to take account of the scientific revolution is everywhere a difficult one, and one which for the moment is growing more difficult with time; but this can only be a temporary phase. The whole problem — economic, scientific, and political — must be regarded as one of a planned operation, definite phases of advance to be kept in step by some kind of international co-ordination. Whether such a co-ordination is possible in a world dominated by divisions between capitalist and socialist economies is the great problem of our time. If the negative view is taken, as it is in China, it might appear that two radically different kinds of science will grow up in parallel, one gradually dominating and the other shrinking away. If, on the other hand, the possibility of co-existence and, even more, co-operation is admitted it may be possible to move step by step from the very limited international co-operation in science that exists today to a more complete one; it will be all the easier when the levels of production and technical advance and the political and economic systems come nearer together. Only time can resolve this difficulty, but the scientists of the world today must act on the best analysis that they can now make and push as hard as they can for the most international organization of science that can be achieved. Much has been done already, although on somewhat peripheral problems, such as meteorology, space exploration, and problems in the earth sciences, for instance, the international study of Antactica.

Some of these questions are treated in the article by Alexander King. An organization such as UNESCO is moving in this direction, though very slowly, owing to the somewhat negative policy adopted by those governments which contribute the bulk of its funds. The international scientific unions, joined together in ICSU, can be of powerful assistance in the spreading of techniques and knowledge in the several fields of science and technology.

Since I wrote *The Social Function* the Unions of ICSU have gathered new strength and extension. I have had most intimate experience in the Union of my own subject, founded in 1946, that is crystallography. I know from experience there that it is possible to build a connection between people working in the same general field, over all barriers of nationality, race and political convictions, which will enable the subject to advance in an orderly and exciting way at the same time, and where the mutual benefits of the close co-operation are most widely felt. The picture of an ordered world science, as I am convinced from this experience, is one which is quite realizable within a few years and one which indeed will be necessary if we are not to perpetuate instead a complete and frustrating chaos.

In *The Social Function* some chapters were devoted to the finance of science in the actual situation of the time and in an ideal structure of society. In view of the relatively small numbers of scientists involved at that time, the discussion was largely an academic exercise, but now, with the expenditure of tens of millions of dollars, science has entered the 'big money' field. It has been discovered, as I pointed out at the time, that we have no real criterion for estimating the amount of money that can be spent on science to provide a proper accounting system for it. It was painfully obvious that in the thirties this problem had a simple solution in principle — money spent on science was overall and in each department clearly insufficient for what could then be seen as a profitable use of science, leave alone any other social dividend which scientific advance might give, for instance, in medicine.

The Social Function was permeated with the picture of the frustration of science arising, in the first place, largely from the financial stringency in which it worked. Much of my book was taken up with arguing against this limitation. Now there is a different situation — it is the large scale of expenditure on science rather than a small scale that must be considered. During the period of the war and for the first ten years afterwards much of the expenditure on science, being predominantly military in character, was subject to very convenient principles of military finance — all sums asked for are granted, and if any questions are raised the questioner is told that for reasons of security no further information can be given. How the money was allocated and to whom were matters of state secrets. Parliaments were expected to pass military budgets and to raise the new taxation without question. It was considered that military science was sacrosanct.

This situation no longer quite exists. The immediate danger seems to have receded, though in fact the military budget is continually increasing. Now, however, some daring legislators, even in the United States are beginning to question what happens to the money. There is a definite tendency to cut scientific expenditure or, at least, to hold back its unlimited growth.

The question that has never been answered is — what, on an economic basis, is the appropriate optimal expenditure on science? Have we even the principles by which it can be assessed? In the first place there does not exist any system of scientific expenditure accountancy. Most diligent search of government publications is needed to show the proportion allocated to scientific research, to scientific development, and to actual production of weapons. There is, for instance, in *The Social Function of Science* the analysis that I attempted for the relatively meagre military expenditure of the beginning of the Second World War. In fact, scientific expenditure is an anomaly in all the traditional economic systems. It is not in the strictest sense productive at all. It is impossible to equate the amount of money spent on a scientist or a laboratory with the annual productivity of the laboratory or even of the factory with which it may be linked. Science, as I have said elsewhere, must be considered as the second differential of production. Actual production is the measure against which scientific expenditure can be judged. Extension or improvement of production by normal technical methods is the first differential of this. It represents a rate of change of the productive process. The second differential, the rate of change of that rate of change, is what scientific research produces.

This has the irritating quality of being quite unpredictable in detail. The problem of selection for development, whether to produce any profit direct or indirect, cannot be predicted until the research is carried out. This has been in the past one main reason why expenditure on science has been looked at rather critically by industrialists. There was another reason: there was no proof that anything useful that did come out of money spent on science would go to the particular firm which financed the research. This argument did not apply, of course, in the Socialist countries. Nevertheless, there, too, there was reluctance to indulge in non-calculable risks. Except in special fields like space navigation, obviously linked to rocket flight, the Soviet Union has avoided heavy spending on new types of production. Most has gone on reliable lines, such as blast furnaces, steam locomotives, large civil engineering works, rolling mills, and turbines. All this is now rapidly changing. The new drive is all for automation and computers, both in the United States and in the Soviet Union. Only where quick return sales can be made for relatively small capital expenditure, as, for instance, in transistor or television fields, had there been willingness to invest in science in a big way. It can be seen even today that the vast majority of industrial scientists are to be found in the light electrical and light chemical fields, where drugs represent the same quick turnover as do transistors.

But if the return on expenditure for individual projects in science is incalculable its total profitability is undoubted, and this is particularly true of expenditure on fundamental research. The knowledge of the behaviour and properties of matter are bound, as they are found out, to affect not one particular industry or part of an industry but all industry. We have seen in recent years the first fruits of the development of new materials, themselves rendered necessary by new machines such as jet engines. They would have been impossible to produce without the basic knowledge of solid state physics, virtually a new subject.

Further, quantum physics has given rise to the most spectacular inventions of our time, such as transistors, which have made computers possible, and masers and lasers, which should transform optics and space communication. Even space navigation is a product of fine control mechanisms, which comes more from fundamental research than from the combustion of new propellents and the aerodynamics of rocket design.

All this points to the importance of fundamental science. How should this importance be gauged? At present it accounts for something between 5 and 10 per cent of total science expenditure. Why this figure? Why not 1 per cent or 20 per cent? One of the most important tasks of the practical science of science is to get some estimate of these figures in order to build a strategy of scientific research round them. It is evident that two kinds of thought are required here. The first is a careful study and analysis of the real economics of the science of the past so as to provide the basic data on which a science policy of the future can be built; and the second is to consider the economics of a kind that includes in its thinking both the character of expenditure that occurs in an accelerating society and the element of probability of a particular scientific expenditure. I have to admit that at present this is a field more for art than for science and implies a willingness to take non-calculable risks on occasion. But we must also go as far as we can in calculating the risks, that is, in considering alternative schemes for financing scientific research on a computer and deciding roughly in which way we should be working. It is also necessary to incorporate in any system a very large amount of feed-back. This has always been an element of real strategy in military affairs, summed up in the aphorism, cut losses and reinforce successes.

At the present moment I feel that we are grossly underplaying the use of fundamental science. The quickest and also the surest returns would come from a deeper understanding of nature. Much of so-called applied science is applied obsolete science; the methods of application are even more obsolete than the science they apply. For example, building is admittedly one of the most backward parts of modern technique. Because we do not know enough about either the strength of the materials that we are using or about the reactions to the stresses, which have hitherto been incalculable, we put anything like ten times more material into the production of useful space than we need. It is called a factor of safety: it is really one of ignorance. Additional knowledge would pay enormous dividends, and yet the amount spent on fundamental research in this field is practically negligible. Of course, there are various reasons for this. The weight of technological education, the concept of good practice, together with the idea that the profits of the building industry depend on how much material is used and how slowly the building can be put up, all stand in the way. We are still using the bricks that were good enough for our Babylonian forefathers, each laboriously laid by hand. Building needs to be mechanized before it can be automized and brought into harmony with modern industry. The technical advances which I anticipate will inevitably imply economic changes of a basic nature. The scientific and computer age is necessarily a Socialist one.

It is inevitable that the whole tendency implied in *The Social*

Function is basically a humane and utilitarian one. It has often been attacked, and was attacked when it first appeared as simply 'Baconian', as implying his idea of 'the effecting of all things possible'. Now, I am as aware as anybody else of the delights of science, of the attitude in science which is also felt in mountaineering — of the need to climb Everest because 'it was there', and many of the things I have done in science would appear to have no other motivation. But even those, like Synge, who believe absolutely in science 'for the good of your soul' can, as his paper shows, presuppose that it is possible to combine science for the good of your soul with science for human welfare. He has been studying the way in which plants build up proteins and how the ruminants digest them and build up more proteins with their internal bacteria. By enjoying doing so he is in fact giving notable help to the production of protein foods so needed in tropical countries. I have no doubt myself that science can be at the same time for the good of your soul and for the benefit of humanity. The corporeal and spiritual works of mercy have to be undertaken together.

Perhaps the greatest change in the position of the scientist of twenty-five years ago and today lies in the greater self-consciousness of science and its position in society, and a greater awareness of its social function. Some of the history of this is given in Burhop's paper. It has arisen very largely from two roots, the older root being the awareness of the scientist of his own position as a worker in society, of his rights and responsibilities, exemplified in the organization of scientists not on a subject basis, as in the international scientific unions, but rather on a trade-union basis; this is the mood which has led to the creation of the World Federation of Scientific Workers under its first two Presidents, Professor F. Joliot-Curie and Professor C. F. Powell.

The second root is more political than economic. For scientists there has grown up, especially since the last war, a number of new initiatives, based less on the idea of the position of the scientist in production than on the responsibility of the scientist for the military developments of our time, particularly for the horror of the atomic and hydrogen bombs. This has given rise to a much greater consciousness of scientists, exemplified by the movements of the Pugwash Committee, arising out of the Einstein-Russell letter in July 1955, and by the parallel movements such as that initiated by Linus Pauling, the Society for the Social Responsibility of Scientists. There is no doubt that, although the membership of these groups is at the moment limited, their views are much more widely shared, and it is only fear or caution that prevents the great majority of scientists from expressing them. The important thing in this is not so much the attitude of individual scientists as the collective effort to block out at least ideal policies which would have the general direction of making science serve the preservation and not the destruction of humanity. The more scientific effort that is directed to military ends, the more resistance it will create in the minds of scientists. The awareness of the proper use of science in society is not easy to reach, and it is harder still to get agreement on it even among scientists. The scientist as citizen is not in the first place a scientist, only in the second. In the course of discussions in these and other movements he becomes aware that it is necessary to have a unitary outlook, that he cannot be torn apart by the contradictions between his science and his duty. He sees a world in which the use of science has become the dominating factor. Mankind cannot progress, cannot even exist today without science. However, far from giving him a sense of power, it emphasizes his awareness of his present weakness and futility. The powers of ignorance and greed distort science and lead it astray for war and destructive ends.

Throughout the course of the history of science the scientist individually has had to exist on sufferance; he worked, inevitably, for ignorant patrons who could not understand even what he was trying to do, and if they had they would have had little wish to further it. Now, with the scientists' growth in numbers and importance, this attitude is no longer necessary and will soon be no longer possible. Scientists also recognize their weaknesses, a lack of contact, not so much with the seats of power as with the people who can be the real beneficiaries of science. When that contact is renewed and improved we can hope to have a world where science ceases to be a threat to mankind and becomes a guarantee for a better future.

I would like to close this section by quoting two of the last paragraphs in *The Social Function*:

'In science men have learned consciously to subordinate themselves to a common purpose without losing the individuality of their achievements. Each one knows that his work depends on that of his predecessors and colleagues, and that it can only reach its fruition through the work of his successors. In science men collaborate not because they are forced to by superior authority or because they blindly follow some chosen leader, but because they realize that only in this willing collaboration can each man find his goal. Not orders, but advice determines action. Each man knows that only by advice, honestly and disinterestedly given, can his work succeed, because such advice expresses as near as may be the inexorable logic of the material world, stubbon fact. Facts cannot be forced to our desires, and freedom comes by admitting this necessity and not by pretending to ignore it.'

'These are things that have been learned painfully and incompletely in the pursuit of science. Only in the wider tasks of humanity will their full use be found.'

(pp. 415-16)

PART I

WHAT SCIENCE DOES

CHAPTER I

INTRODUCTORY

The Challenge to Science

WHAT is the social function of science? A hundred or even fifty years ago this would have seemed a strange, almost meaningless, question even to the scientist himself, far more so to the administrator or the plain citizen. If science had any function at all, which few stopped to consider, it would have been assumed to be one of universal beneficence. Science was at once the noblest flower of the human mind and the most promising source of material benefactions. While it might be doubted whether it furnished as good a liberal education as the study of the classics, there could be no doubt that its practical activities were the main basis of Progress.

Now we have a very different picture. The troubles of our times seem themselves to be a consequence of that very progress. The new methods of production which science has brought into being lead to unemployment and glut without serving to relieve the poverty and want which are as widespread in the world as ever before. At the same time, the weapons devised by the application of science have made warfare a far more immediate and more terrible risk, and have diminished almost to vanishing point that personal security which was one of the chief triumphs of civilization. Of course, all these evils and disharmonies cannot be blamed exclusively on science, but there is no denying that they would not occur in their present form if it had not been for science, and for that reason the value of science to civilization has been and is being called into question. As long as the results of science appeared, at least to the more respectable classes, as unmixed blessings, the social function of science was so much taken for granted as not to need examination. Now that science appears in a destructive as well as a constructive rôle, its social function must be examined because its very right to exist is being challenged. The scientists, and with them a number of progressively minded people, may feel that there is no case to answer and that it is only through an abuse of science that the world is in its present state. But this defence can no longer be considered to be self-evident; science must submit to examination before it can clear itself of these accusations.

The Impact of Events.—The events of the last twenty years have

1

done more than cause a different attitude towards science by people at large; they have profoundly changed the attitudes of scientists themselves towards science and have even entered the fabric of scientific thought. With what appears to be a strange coincidence, the disturbing events of the Great War, the Russian revolution, the economic crisis, the rise of Fascism, and the preparation for newer and more terrible wars have been paralleled inside the field of science by the greatest changes in theory and in general outlook that it has undergone in the past three centuries. The basis of mathematics has itself been shaken by the controversies on axiomatics and logistics. The physical world of Newton and Maxwell has been completely overturned in favour of relativity and quantum mechanics, which still remain half-understood and paradoxical theories. Biology has been revolutionized by the development of bio-chemistry and genetics. All these developments, following quickly one after another in the lifetime of individual scientists, have forced them to consider, far more deeply than in preceding centuries, the fundamental basis of their beliefs. Nor have they been spared the impact of external forces. The war, for scientists of all countries, meant using their knowledge for direct military purposes. The crisis affected them immediately, blocking scientific advance in many countries and threatening it in others. Finally, Fascism showed that even the centre of modern science could be affected by superstitions and barbarities which were thought to have been outgrown by the end of the Middle Ages.

Should Science be suppressed?—The result of all these shocks has been, not unnaturally, a state of great confusion both for the scientists themselves and for the estimation of science. Voices have been raised—and raised in such an unexpected place as the British Association—for the suppression of science, or at least for the suppression of the application of its discoveries. The Bishop of Ripon preaching the British Association sermon in 1927 said:

"... Dare I even suggest, at the risk of being lynched by some of my hearers, that the sum of human happiness outside scientific circles would not necessarily be reduced if for ten years every physical and chemical laboratory were closed and the patient and resourceful energy in them transferred to recovering the lost art of getting on together and finding the formula of making both ends meet in the scale of human life. . . ."—From *The Times* of 5th September 1927, p. 15.

The Revolt from Reason.—Not only have the material results of science been objected to, but the value of scientific thought itself has been called in question. Anti-intellectualism began to appear as the result of the impending difficulties of the social system towards the end of the nineteenth century, and found expression in the philosophies of Sorel and Bergson. Instinct and intuition came to be rated as more important than reason. To a certain extent it was the philosophers and the metaphysical scientists themselves that paved the way for the justification of the Fascist ideology of brute force under mystically inspired leadership. In the words of Mr. Woolf :

"We are living through one of these periods of struggle and decivilization, and the well-known symptoms of intellectual quackery can be observed all about us invading metaphysical thought. The symptoms are always the same, though superficially they may differ. Reason is dethroned as old-fashioned, and the man who asks for proof of a fact before he will believe it is magisterially dismissed to the bottom of the form and told to write out 500 times : 'I must not ask for proof.' The Meletoses accuse the Socrateses and Anaxagorases of blasphemous atheism. The Roman intellectual throws away his Lucretius and Greek philosophy in order to learn the truth about the universe revealed to Levantine magicians. Books and sometimes their authors are burned because they ask for proof or question the truth of someone's intuition about the nature of the universe. The mysteries of Dionysus, the abracadabra of Isis or Osiris, the worship of the sun or a sacred bull, the wisdom to be obtained by staring at your own navel or by making yourself sick before breakfast, the revelations to be obtained from the legs of tables or ectoplasm are some of the methods which at such periods have proved efficacious for penetrating the nature of the universe and of God or the Absolute. The intensity of a man's belief having been adopted as the measure of truth, the ignoble creature who still tries to use his reason, and is feeble enough to admit that he does not know what will happen to him when he dies, or why billions of stars are flaming through space, or whether his spaniel has an immortal soul, or why there is evil in the world, or what the Almighty was doing before he created the universe, and what he will be doing after the universe has come to an end—the stupid creature is hardly admitted into the society of intelligent men and decent philosophers."—*Quack Quack*, p. 166. (1)

This mysticism and abandonment of rational thought is not only a sign of popular or political disquiet; it penetrates far into the structure of science itself. The working scientist may repudiate it as firmly as ever, but scientific theories particularly those metaphysical and mystical theories which touch on the universe at large or the nature of life, which had been laughed out of court in the eighteenth and nineteenth centuries, are attempting to win their way back into scientific acceptance.

THE INTERACTION OF SCIENCE AND SOCIETY

We can no longer be blind to the fact that science is both affecting and being affected by the social changes of our time, but in order to make this awareness in any way effective, the interaction of the two needs to be analysed far more closely than has yet been done. Before beginning this analysis, which is the main task of the book, it is useful to consider the types of attitude now current as to what science is or ought to be. There are here two sharply distinct points of view which might be called the ideal and the realist pictures of science. In the first picture science appears as concerned only with the discovery and contemplation of truth; its function, as distinct from that of mythical cosmologies, is to build up a world picture that fits the facts of experience. If it is also of practical utility, so much the better, as long as its true purpose is not lost. In the second picture utility predominates; truth appears as a means for useful action and can be tested only by such action.

Science as pure Thought.—These two views are extremes: each admits of a number of variations and there is considerable common ground between the two of them. Those who hold the first view would not admit that science has any practical social function, or would allow at most that the social function of science is a relatively unimportant and subordinate one. The most usual justification which they would give for science is that it is an end in itself, a pursuit of pure knowledge for its own sake. This attitude has played a great and not altogether happy part in the history of science. It was a dominating view in classical times, and was expressed very finely in the words of Plato:

"The question is, whether the larger and more advanced part of the study tends at all to facilitate our contemplation of the essential Form of Good. Now, according to us, this is the tendency of everything that compels the soul to transfer itself to that region in which is contained the most blissful part of that real existence, which it is of the highest importance for it to behold."—*Republic*, Book VII. (2)

In its modern form this attitude towards science is not pressed as the sole, but as the main, justification of science. Science is taken as one means of finding the answer to the deepest questions which men may ask about the origin of the universe or of life, of death and the survival of the soul. The use of science for this purpose is paradoxical; what science "cannot" know rather than what it has established is made the basis of affirmations about the universe. Science cannot tell how the universe was made; therefore it must have been made by an intelligent creator. Science cannot synthesize life; therefore the origin of life is a miracle. The very indeterminacy of quantum mechanics is made an argument for human free will. In this way, modern science is being made an ally of ancient religion, and even to a large extent a substitute for it. Through the work of Jeans, Eddington, Whitehead and J. S. Haldane, assisted by the Bishop of Birmingham and Dean Inge, a new scientific mythical religion is being built up, based on the idea of a continuous creation of absolute values in an evolutionary process culminating in man.

There is no doubt that this apologetic use of science is one of its social functions in present society, but it cannot provide any justification of science as such, since equally satisfactory and equally unprovable solutions to cosmic problems can be found by the aid of simple intuition. Actually the use of science in modernist religion is an implicit admission of its importance in general culture. No religious views could expect to hold their own in cultured circles unless they were at least phrased in scientific terminology, and did not contradict the positive results of the scientific theory of the day.

In the most attenuated variant of the idealist view, science is considered to be simply an integral part of intellectual culture, a knowledge of contemporary science being as much a requisite for polite society as that of contemporary literature. The fact is, of course, that in England at any rate, this is very far from being the case, but the educationalists often seek to justify science on these grounds alone and thus to assimilate science to general humanism. Thus Sarton, the great historian of science, pleads for the humanizing of science:

"The only way of humanizing scientific labour is to inject into it a little of the historical spirit, the spirit of reverence for the past—the spirit of reverence for every witness of good-will through the ages. However abstract science may become, it is essentially human in its origin and growth. Each scientific result is a fruit of humanity, a proof of its virtue. The almost unconceivable immensity of the universe revealed by his own efforts does not dwarf man except in a purely physical way ; it gives a deeper meaning to his life and thought. Each time that we understand the world a little better, we are also able to appreciate more keenly our relationship to it. There are no natural sciences as opposed to humanities; every branch of science or learning is just as natural or as humane as you make it. Show the deep human interest of science and the study of it becomes the best vehicle of humanism one could devise; exclude that interest, teach scientific knowledge only for the sake of information and professional instruction, and the study of it, however valuable from a purely technical point of view, loses all educational value. Without history, scientific knowledge may become culturally dangerous ; combined with history, tempered with reverence, it will nourish the highest culture."
—*History of Science and the New Humanism*, p. 68.

These views of the function of science have in common with those of the classical philosophers the acceptance of science as a purely intellectual occupation, concerned, it is true, with the objective universe, rather than with the yet purer ideas of mathematics, logics and ethics, but concerned with it still in a strictly contemplative way. In spite of the fact that this is a view held by many scientists themselves, it is essentially self-contradictory. If the contemplation of the universe for its own sake were the function of science, then science as we know it now would never have existed, for the most elementary reading of the history of science shows that both the drive which led to scientific discoveries and the means by which those discoveries were made were material needs and material instruments. The fact that this view could have been held so successfully for such a long time can only be explained by the neglect, by scientists and historians of science, of the whole range of man's technical activities, though these have at least as much in common with science as the abstractions with which the great philosophers and mathematicians occupied themselves.

Science as Power.—The opposite view of science, that it was the means of obtaining practical mastery over nature through understanding it, was generally present, though deprecated, in classical times. It appears explicitly as a hope in Roger Bacon and with the men of the Renaissance, but it is first fully expressed in its modern form by Francis Bacon:

> "The roads to human power and to human knowledge lie close together, and are nearly the same; nevertheless, on account of the pernicious and inveterate habit of dwelling on abstractions, it is safer to begin and raise the sciences from those foundations which have relation to practice and let the active part be as the seal which prints and determines the contemplative counterpart."

This remained the predominant view of science for at least two hundred years:

> "What then was the end which Bacon proposed to himself? It was, to use his own emphatic expression, 'fruit.' It was the multiplying of human enjoyments and the mitigating of human sufferings. It was the relief of man's estate. . . . It was continually to give to human beings new methods, new tools and new paths. This was the object of all his speculations in every department of science, in natural philosophy, in legislation, in politics and in morals. Two words form the key of the Baconian doctrine, Utility and Progress. The ancient philosophy disdained to be useful, and was content to be stationary. It dealt largely in theories of moral perfection, which were so sublime that they never could be more than theories; in attempts to solve insoluble enigmas; in exhortations to the attainment of unattainable frames of mind. It could not condescend to the humble office of ministering to the comfort of human beings. All the schools contemned that office as degrading; some censured it as immoral."

So Macaulay wrote in the very first year of the Victorian age. To him, as to the great majority of the forward-looking people of the time, the function of science was to be a universal benefactor of humanity:

> "Ask a follower of Bacon what the new philosophy, as it was called in the time of Charles the Second, has effected for mankind, and his answer

is ready; 'It has lengthened life; it has mitigated pain; it has extinguished diseases; it has increased the fertility of the soil; it has given new securities to the mariner; it has furnished new arms to the warrior; it has spanned great rivers and estuaries with bridges of form unknown to our fathers; it has guided the thunderbolt innocuously from heaven to earth; it has lighted up the night with the splendour of the day; it has extended the range of the human vision; it has multiplied the power of the human muscles; it has accelerated motion; it has annihilated distance; it has facilitated intercourse, correspondence, all friendly offices, all despatch of business; it has enabled man to descend to the depths of the sea, to soar into the air, to penetrate securely into the noxious recesses of the earth, to traverse the land in cars which whirl along without horses, and the ocean in ships which run ten knots an hour against the wind. These are but a part of its fruits, and of its first-fruits. For it is a philosophy which never rests, which has never attained, which is ever perfect. Its law is progress. A point which yesterday was invisible is its goal to-day, and will be its starting-post to-morrow.' "—*Essay on Bacon.*

Disillusion.—A modern Macaulay would have a different and more chastened view of the fruits of science. He could point to comforts and powers far beyond the imagination of a hundred years ago, to really great steps in the conquest of disease, to the possibility of putting mankind for ever beyond the danger of famine and pestilence, but he would have to admit that the material science of the moderns had, in fact, no more solved the problem of universal wealth and happiness than had the moral science of the ancients the problem of universal virtue. War, financial chaos, voluntary destruction of goods which millions need, general under-nourishment, and the fear of still other wars more terrible than any before in history, are the pictures which must be drawn to-day of the fruits of science. It is not therefore surprising that scientists themselves are turning more and more away from the view that the development of science in itself leads automatically to a better world. Thus Sir Alfred Ewing, in his presidential address to the British Association, in 1932:

"In the present-day thinkers' attitude towards what is called mechanical progress we are conscious of a changed spirit. Admiration is tempered by criticism; complacency has given way to doubt; doubt is passing into alarm. There is a sense of perplexity and frustration, as in one who has gone a long way and finds he has taken the wrong turning. To go back is impossible: how shall he proceed? Where will he find himself if he follows this path or that? An old exponent of applied mechanics may be forgiven if he expresses something of the disillusion with which, now standing aside, he watches the sweeping pageant of discovery and invention in which he used to take unbounded delight. It is impossible not to ask, Whither does this tremendous procession tend? What, after all, is its goal? What its probable influence upon the future of the human race?

The pageant itself is a modern affair. A century ago it had barely taken form and had acquired none of the momentum which rather awes us to-day. The Industrial Revolution, as everybody knows, was of British origin; for a time our island remained the factory of the world. But soon, as was inevitable, the change of habit spread, and now every country, even China, is become more or less mechanized. The cornucopia of the engineer has been shaken over all the earth, scattering everywhere an endowment of previously unpossessed and unimagined capacities and powers. Beyond question many of these gifts are benefits to man, making life fuller, wider, healthier, richer in comforts and interests and in such happiness as material things can promote. But we are acutely aware that the engineer's gifts have been and may be grievously abused. In some there is potential tragedy as well as present burden. Man was ethically unprepared for so great a bounty. In the slow evolution of morals he is still unfit for the tremendous responsibility it entails. The command of Nature has been put into his hands, before he knows how to command himself.

I need not dwell on consequent dangers which now press themselves insistently on our attention. We are learning that in the affairs of nations, as of individuals, there must, for the sake of amity, be some sacrifice of freedom. Accepted predilections as to national sovereignty have to be abandoned if the world is to keep the peace and allow civilization to survive. Geologists tell us that in the story of evolution they can trace the records of extinct species which perished through the very amplitude and efficiency of their personal apparatus for attack and defence. This carries a lesson for consideration at Geneva. But there is another aspect of the mechanization of life which is perhaps less familiar, on which I venture, in conclusion, a very few words.

More and more does mechanical production take the place of human effort, not only in manufactures but also in all our tasks, even the primitive task of tilling the ground. So man finds this, that while he is enriched with a multitude of possessions and possibilities beyond his dreams, he is in great measure deprived of one inestimable blessing, the necessity of toil. We invent the machinery of mass-production, and for the sake of cheapening the unit we develop output on a gigantic scale. Almost automatically the machine delivers a stream of articles in the creation of which the workman has had little part. He has lost the joy of craftsmanship, the old satisfaction in something accomplished through the conscientious exercise of care and skill. In many cases unemployment is thrust upon him, an unemployment that is more saddening than any drudgery. And the world finds itself glutted with competitive commodities, produced in a quantity too great to be absorbed, though every nation strives to secure at least a home market by erecting tariff walls. . . .

We must admit that there is a sinister side even to the peaceful activities of those who, in good faith and with the best intentions, make it their business to adapt the resources of Nature to the use and convenience of man.

Where shall we look for a remedy? I cannot tell. Some may envisage a distant Utopia in which there will be perfect adjustment of labour and the fruits of labour, a fair spreading of employment and of wages and of all the commodities that machines produce. Even so, the question will remain. How is man to spend the leisure he has won by handing over nearly all his burden to an untiring mechanical slave? Dare he hope for such spiritual betterment as will qualify him to use it well? God grant that he may strive for that and attain it. It is only by seeking he will find. I cannot think that man is destined to atrophy and cease through cultivating what, after all, is one of his most God-like faculties, the creative ingenuity of the engineer."—*Nature*, 130, 349, 1932.

Escape.—Some turn away from science in sheer despair of anything being done with unregenerate human nature. Others immerse themselves more closely than ever in their actual scientific work, refusing to consider at all its social consequences because they know beforehand that they will probably be harmful. Only the fortunate few can say with G. H. Hardy in his famous apostrophe on pure mathematics:

"This subject has no practical use; that is to say, it cannot be used for promoting directly the destruction of human life or for accentuating the present inequalities in the distribution of wealth."

Many accept the subjective and somewhat cynical view that the pursuit of science is just as much of a game as bridge or crossword puzzles, but more exciting and amusing for those who have a taste in that direction. In a sense this view must always be part of the truth. There must be for any effective scientist an intrinsic appreciation and enjoyment of the actual operations he is performing, and this appreciation will not differ essentially from that of the artist or the sportsman. Rutherford used to divide science into physics and stamp collecting, but if the analogy were to be carried through, it would be reduced to "gadgeteering" and stamp collecting.

The Social Importance of Science.—These subjective views cannot however tell us what is the social function of science as a whole. We cannot expect to find this by considering only what the scientist thinks of his work or how he would like it to be regarded. He may enjoy it, may find it a noble calling or an amusing pastime, but this does not explain the immense growth of science in the modern world, or the reason why it has become the main occupation of many of the most able and intelligent men in the world to-day.

Science has plainly acquired a social importance far greater than can be due to any valuation of intellectual activities as such. It is however certainly not being used directly for human welfare. We need to find out for what it is actually being used, and this is a social and economic rather than a philosophical inquiry.

The Scientist as Worker.—For science to exist at all on its modern scale, it must be thought to have some positive value to those who

finance its activities. The scientist must live, and his work is only in
the rarest cases immediately productive. The time is long past when
the scientist was a man of independent means or earned his living at
some subsidiary trade. Scientific research is no longer, in the words
of a Cambridge professor of the last generation, "a proper occupation
for the leisure of an English gentleman." A statistical investigation
in the United States some years ago revealed that among the two
hundred most eminent scientists in the country, only two were men
of private means, and all the others held paid scientific posts. The
scientist of to-day has already become almost as much a salaried
official as the average civil servant and business executive. Even
when he works in a university he is effectively controlled, if not in
the detail, then in the general direction of research, by the interests
that control the productive processes as a whole. Scientific research
and teaching are in fact small but critically important sections of
industrial production. (3) It is to its services to industry that we
must look for the current social function of science.

Science for Profit.—The history of the development of industry,
including the peculiar governmental industry of warfare, and the
oldest industry, agriculture, shows that the essential business of
changing the process of industry in the direction of greater efficiency
and consequently of greater profitability is now being performed
almost entirely by the application of science. The three chief
technical changes that follow from the application of science are the
increasing automatism of production, the greater utilization of
materials with the elimination of waste, and the saving of capital
costs owing to more rapid turnover. The effect of the last is, however, probably more than offset by the increased capital cost of
automatic machinery. In general the result is a reduction in working
costs for the same production or more usually a greater production
for the same working costs. Science therefore is complementary to
other means of reducing costs, factory organization, speeding up of
workers or lowering of wages. How far science is used will depend
on its relative advantage compared to these other methods. These
advantages are real but they are limited, and owing to the conservatism
of producers they are by no means made use of to the full. Hence,
however much science may be stunted in its development, it never
would have reached its present importance if it had not been for its
contribution to profits. If the direct and indirect subsidies from
industry and Government were to cease, science would sink at once
to a level at least as low as that which it occupied in the Middle
Ages. This practical consideration disposes of the possibility desired
by idealist philosophers such as Bertrand Russell, of continuing to
develop science without at the same time developing industry. Quite

apart from the enormous contribution, in the way of apparatus and of problems to be solved, which industry has made to science, there is no other source from which science can be adequately financed. This connection would remain in a socialist economy, for here, with the removal of the perversion of science for profit, the need for developing production to the utmost for human welfare would be paramount. Science would therefore need to be linked more closely than ever with industry, agriculture and health.

The Institution of Science.—The result of this connection between industry and science has been, in the course of the last century, imperceptibly to turn science into an institution, one comparable with and even more important than that of the Church or the Law. It is, as they are, dependent on the existing social order, it is recruited in the main from the same section of the population and it is saturated with the ideas of the dominant classes. Yet it has acquired to a very considerable extent an organization, a life and an outlook of its own. The continued existence of this institution of science is in general far too easily taken for granted; because science in its association with industry has in the past made such enormous progress, it is assumed that this progress will automatically continue. Intrinsically, however, there is no more justification for continued progress in science than for continued progress in industry. The events of the last few years have shown us how unsafe it was to base anticipation of the future of economic development on a superficial examination of the trends of the recent past. A far deeper and longer view is necessary.

Can Science survive?—We have seen, in the course of history, institutions grow up, stagnate, and die away. How do we know that the same will not happen to science? Indeed, the greatest burst of scientific activity before the present age, the science of Hellenistic times, which had also become an institution, faded away long before the society in which it had been born was itself destroyed. How do we know that the same will not happen and, indeed, is not happening to modern science? It is not sufficient in answering these questions to make an analysis of the present situation of science. A full answer requires a knowledge of the whole history of science. Unfortunately, the history of science as an institution in relation to social and economic events has not yet been written or even attempted. Existing histories of science are little more than pious records of great men and their works, suitable perhaps for the inspiration of young workers, but not for understanding the rise and growth of science as an institution. Some attempt at such a history must, however, be made if we are to understand the significance of the institution of science as it now is and its complex relationships with other institutions and with the general activity of society. The key to the future of science lies in its past, and it is only after examining it, however cursorily, that we can begin to determine what is and what may become the social function of science.

(1) See also *The Revolt from Reason*, by Professor L. Hogben.

(2) It is interesting to note that this passage occurs immediately after one which discusses the military, and therefore to Plato the noblest of the useful aspects of science :

" It is obvious, he continued, that all that part of it which bears upon strategy does concern us. For in encamping, in occupying positions, in closing up and deploying troops, and in executing all the other manœuvres of an army in the field of battle or on the march, it will make every difference to a military man, whether he is a good geometrician, or not.

Nevertheless, I replied, a trifling knowledge of geometry and calculation will suffice for these purposes."

(3) An exception might be claimed for medicine, but in this connection the great developments of modern health services may be seen as a necessary factor for the preservation of a vast and congested industrial population.

CHAPTER II

HISTORICAL

SCIENCE, LEARNING AND CRAFT

SCIENCE as we know it is a relatively late product. It took definite form only in the sixteenth century, but its roots go back to the very beginning of civilization and even further, to the origin of human society. Modern science has a twofold origin. It derives both from the ordered speculation of the magician, priest, or philosopher, and from the practical operation and traditional lore of the craftsman. Until now, far more attention has been given to the first aspect of science than to the second, with the result that the whole progress of science has seemed more miraculous than it was in fact. The interaction of the theoretical and practical activities of man furnishes a key to the understanding of the history of science.

Primitive Science.—There was a time, no doubt, when these two aspects came together in the persons of the same men, when every man was part craftsman, part magician. Both the magical and technical aspects of primitive life have the same object: mastery over the external world however conceived, the need for getting food and avoiding pain and death. At least a third of the techniques we now use must belong to palaeolithic man: hunting, trapping, cooking, tanning and dressing skins, working in stone, wood and bone, painting and drawing. All these represent an immense advance over the animal stage and are made possible only by the development of society and of language. But the first human approach to nature could hardly be a scientific one. Man's first contact with nature would needs be through those parts of it that affected him most immediately, his own group, the animals and plants he needed for food and other products. These are, as we know now, far the most complicated parts of nature and are still to a large extent beyond our capacity to control by the use of purely scientific techniques. It was not therefore surprising, indeed it was absolutely necessary, that early man should have approached them in a very different way. In practice, other men, animals and plants could be dealt with by a gradual modification of his own animal behaviour mechanisms made possible by the productive collaboration of society. Theory was, on the other hand, a purely social product which began with language. It was thus inevitable that the external world should first be interpreted in terms of social behaviour, that is by considering animals and plants and even inanimate things as persons to be treated as aberrant members of the tribe. Logical and scientific thought at this stage would not only have been inconceivable but useless.

Agriculture and Civilization.—The first great revolution in human society came with the discovery of agriculture, starting in some small region in the Near East, and then, by a slow process which still continues, spreading over the rest of the world. Agriculture had associated with it a number of new techniques—the domestication of animals, spinning, weaving and pottery, and soon after, the use of metals. More important for the development of science were the social institutions that agriculture, for the first time, made possible, namely, trade and towns. A method of production of food that might, and often did, leave a surplus of a kind which could be stored and carried from place to place without spoiling, made it possible for an increasing number of men to live independently of food production. It also made it possible for substances other than food, magical substances at first, such as malachite and amber, then metals and building materials, to be sought for in distant places and transported to the centres of cultivation. In this way the idea of trade grew imperceptibly out of the ritual exchanges of more primitive times. But trade, even in the state of barter, requires some form of standard, and thus measure and number came into practical prominence for the first time. With measure and number came the possibility of using intellectual processes directly for practical ends, the birth of a theory not altogether divorced from reality. Number and measure required more record than memory could give, and thus brought in the art of writing, which spread from its primitive use in accounts to cover all records and to give society a coherence in time which it has never lost. It was not long before all the modern forms of trade—credit, bills of exchange, loans, and interest—had developed, and with them the appropriate mathematics, so that a pretty complete knowledge of arithmetic and algebra was needed by the business man and his clerks at least as early as 4000 B.C. (1)

The Town and the Craftsman.—More immediately, trade gave rise to that agglomeration of villages which soon became the town, drawing its sustenance from the surplus of many villages and producing a return of tools and articles of luxury. In the towns the crafts had a chance to grow, particularly the new craft of the metal worker, helped by the always urgent demand for arms, for now that agriculture allowed the accumulation of a surplus, war and dominion had become a profitable industry. From the town craftsmen in these early times, somewhere between 6000 and 4000 B.C., came the greater portion of those of the arts of life which we still use:

permanent houses of wood, brick or stone, with rooms and fire-places, baths and drains, wheeled vehicles and ships, and the simplest machines, the inclined plane, the pulley, the lathe and the screw. All these involved considerable understanding of mechanics and physics, and in the case of the metal worker's arts, of chemistry as well. Whether this was explicit or implicit at first we cannot say; we have no records other than the objects produced, but that more science than we know of may have gone to their development is suggested by the relative stagnation of those arts between 4000 B.C. and 1500 A.D., during which period the technical tradition continued for the most part unchanged through the vicissitudes of civilization except in quantity and fashion.

The Fatal Separation of Priest and Craftsman.—It may be, of course, that the solution to the main problems of living was so well found by these originators of civilization that there was little incentive to make any change. Continual war and insecurity may have checked development, but another reason may be that with the rise of towns there came a separation for the first time between the craftsman, the man of action, and the priest, the man of words. The development of writing for many centuries had been an almost exclusive priestly monopoly; the priest's life was easier and more honoured than the craftsman's, and tended to draw to it the most active intellectual spirits. Theology and metaphysics are as amusing a game as science to those who are well enough provided for not to have to concern themselves with earthly things. Once a division between the man of theory and the man of practice was well estab-lished, material progress and the development of science alike became difficult, uncertain and liable to lapses.

Astronomy.—Fortunately, there remained two fields in which theory and practice met, Astronomy and Medicine. Astronomy had its practical justification in the basic occupation of agriculture, in drawing up the calendar, and it was needed, too, by the trader and navigator in steering his way by the stars. Astronomy could not, however, be left to mere farmers and traders; not only was it too difficult, but it dealt with things above, with the region of the gods who ruled the destinies of men. Thus it must be left to priests to interpret and to foretell the will of the gods. Astronomy and science in general owe much to astrology for the impetus it gave to exact and systematic observation. Astronomy was the one field in which elementary mathematics could give an effective account of happenings in the external world. The sciences which lay behind the craftsman's operations were still too complicated for any intellectual unravelling, but the motions of the heavens seemed to happen with such perfect geometrical regularity that they could be reduced to order. This required observation and calculation, but it also required, and this is very significant for our purpose, the existence of astronomers in different places and working over long periods of time, far longer than an individual's life—a state of affairs that implies empires and stable government. Science as an institution was born in the temple observatories. The motions of the stars were regular; those of the planets and of the moon so complicated as to force the astronomer into more and more arduous efforts of interpretation in the course of which the main outlines of geometry were worked out.

Medicine.—The situation of medicine was less fortunate. A need for some way of dealing with disease was far more urgent than the need for astronomy, but the success in dealing with it was necessarily incomparably less. The doctor, before the middle of the last century, could not in fact have had any knowledge of the fundamental physiological and chemical facts on which his practice depended. A few useful things could, it is true, be done in surgery and a certain common sense used in nursing, while a small fraction of the drugs used might occasionally be of some benefit. (2) Yet the doctor remained for all his learning a medicine man whose chief function was to give hope to the patient, and to relieve his relatives of responsibility. Doctors because of their attendance on persons of wealth and importance were from the beginning among the privileged and intellectual classes. As such they did attempt to reduce their practice to some kind of theory. These theories were, if we except a few such sensible compilations as the Hippocratic code, a more pathetic misuse of mind than even theology or philosophy, but they were an attempt at science, and it is largely to doctors that we owe the practice of biological experiment and the institution of scientific education.

The Greeks and Science.—With the rise of Greek civilization, it seemed for a while that science as we know it now might have come into being. The early Greeks, particularly the Ionian Greeks, themselves pirates turned merchants, had a blend of practical interest and childish theoretic curiosity that went a long way to the clarifying of our knowledge of the universe. The Greeks were not, of course, finding out directly about the universe; what they were doing was acquiring, by fair means or foul, all the techniques of the ancient world. They had the immense advantage of coming fresh to them; they could sift from the very start the useful and enlightening from the merely traditional and magical. Recent research has shown us how little of the scientific achievements of the early Greeks were at all original, and how much was borrowed directly from Babylonian and Egyptian sources. The astronomical achievements of the Greeks could, for instance, have only been made on the basis of systematic

observations carried out for hundreds of years, during which tii.
they were untutored barbarians.

Science under the Philosophers.—The fatal division between the
man of theory and the man of action was, however, very soon apparent,
and already by the fifth century the division was more absolute in
Greece than it had been in the ancient East. Assimilation of foreign
ideas and a certain amount of technical advance went on, but it had
not the patronage of the man of power and influence. After trading
and war, politics had become the main concern of the Greek cities,
and for politics, word mastery became more important than mastery
over things. The Greek genius at its height was contemplative; it
sought to understand the world only to admire eternal truths. The
very idea of using intellect to further change was abhorrent to
Socrates and Plato; they had seen too much of it in the destructive
rivalries of the city states, and of the classes within them. Thus
Plato:

> "Science is pursued for the sake of knowledge of what eternally exists,
> and not what comes for a moment into existence and then perishes."—
> *Republic*, Book VII.

The Hellenistic Revival.—A certain reaction from this point of
view set in with the creation of the Alexandrian Empire and of the
Hellenistic states that succeeded it. Aristotle, the tutor of Alexander,
combined both practical and metaphysical elements in his general
philosophy, though only through the latter was his influence felt in
later ages. The Hellenistic monarchs favoured a more practical
science, and, indeed, this was a great period of Greek mechanics
and mathematics, although the problems to be solved were of a very
limited nature, practically confined to architecture and military
engineering. Siege warfare and naval warfare made great demands
on mechanical ingenuity. After astronomy, mechanics is the next
most easy subject to be reduced to mathematical form, and the
work of Archimedes, himself a great military artificer, shows that at
any rate the Greeks had thoroughly mastered the principles of statics.

More important from our point of view is, however, the fact that
in Alexandria science was for the first time organized, and organized
by the State. The Museum of Alexandria was a combination of
library, university and research institute; scientists became pensioners
of the State, and were no longer forced to wander in search of their
livelihood. The work of the Museum itself soon degenerated into
pedantry and mysticism. It depended for its existence on the service
it could give to the Princes, and these needs were too easily satisfied;
a multitude of slaves was always at hand for any task requiring
expenditure of energy. Nor did this period of economic expansion

last; the states were soon on the defensive, and curiosity about foreign countries, which had been one of the most promising features of Hellenistic science, disappeared. Only literary culture, philosophy and a certain amount of astronomy survived.

Islam.—Nevertheless, although the Museum degenerated and disappeared, the idea of such an institution persisted. In the next age in the history of science, that of the dominance of Islam—leaving on one side the unproductive period of the Roman Empire—several such institutions were set up and flourished for a while. At the beginning of Islamic science, the same conjunction of practical interest and theoretic curiosity as had given birth to Greek science reappeared. Islamic religion had a much more material bent than Greek philosophy. The righteous merchant, and not the husbandman, the warrior, the priest or the philosopher, was the most respected Mussulman. The Arabs ransacked the literature of Greece, Persia and India for the more theoretical aspects of knowledge, but they also paid attention to the work of the tradesmen, particularly the druggists and the metal workers. Alchemy proved as powerful a stimulus to chemistry as astrology had been to the Babylonian astronomy. Chemistry, unlike astronomy and mathematics, is a subject which can be grasped only as the result of a slowly accumulated tradition of experiments, requiring but little rationalization in the way of general theories. In fact, the early theories of chemistry added nothing of significance to the implicit ideas lying behind the operations of the early metal workers. The practical chemist knew what to do when he wanted a certain result, but he could not have known the effective reason why it worked.

The Middle Ages.—Knowledge of Islamic and Greek science was slow to trickle into the still barbarous West of the Middle Ages. For a long time it had no function to fulfil there. At first a greater need was felt for the philosophic works of Greece, as transmitted by Arabic translations, than for the more material achievements of science. The products of the Eastern craftsmen and traders—silk, steel, gems, spices and drugs—were imported for many centuries before any attempt was made to imitate their production or to discover their sources. Only here and there among scholastics do we find, as with Albertus Magnus or Roger Bacon, some inkling of the significance and human value of science. Mediaeval society had succeeded in building out of barbarism a relatively stable social system, but one based on a primitive economy, and therefore not requiring or giving any scope for advanced science. It was not so much that inventions were not made; they were not permitted to grow. In Italy in the thirteenth century, spinning machines, essentially similar to Hargreaves' jenny, were invented and actually used, but were soon suppressed by the guilds as too destructive to the livelihood of the tradesmen.

Mediaeval society by its very success in achieving static conditions made those conditions unstable. Order and security led to trade, and trade to the accumulation of wealth which was in turn incompatible with the economy of feudal government. The break first came in Italy, and it was here, too, that science in its modern form had its birth. The economic and the intellectual sides of the Renaissance reacted very intimately on one another. Rapid development of trade and manufacture, still along traditional lines, was accompanied by the rediscovery of the original Greek sources of philosophy and incidentally of science.

THE BIRTH OF MODERN SCIENCE: SCIENCE AND TRADE

The fatal gap between theory and practice, though still wide, closed at certain points. The superior craftsman by his arts became recognized and even assimila^ted into the society of the wealthy. Some of the learned and even some of the nobility deigned to interest themselves in mechanical arts. In the Italian cities of the Renaissance, the painter, the poet, the philosopher, the wandering scholar from Greece, all met together in the house of the banker or merchant prince. In 1438 the first academy of modern times was founded at Florence by Cosimo de Medici. True it was a platonic academy, but one definitely breaking away from scholastic limitations, and the prototype of the scientific academies that were to follow. Here again the conditions that occurred at the beginning of Greek and Islamic science were satisfied, but there was one significant difference. The West of Europe was a relatively poor and depopulated region; its rulers were full of desire for riches but had few natural means of acquiring them. Mining for precious metals, war and foreign trade, little distinguished from piracy, were the most easy means to hand, but in mediaeval Christendom the resources of the ancient empires in the way of man power were sadly wanting.

The Combination of Ingenuity and Learning.—It was at this point that ingenuity was at a premium. At first the ingenuity was the natural ingenuity of the craftsman or millwright. The small mining company wanted to raise ore and pump water without having to take any new partners or pay ruinous wages for hired miners and simply had to invent machines to do the work. But later, when feudal or merchant princes became the owners of mines, foundries and ships, they naturally turned to the educated men, to the artists and professors of mathematics for help, or rather the latter, seizing their chance, offered their services. Leonardo's letter to the Duke of Milan, quoted below (p. 167), may stand as a classic instance. Here he offers to construct a whole catalogue of new military machines, to manage drainage and civil engineering, and as a kind of afterthought he adds, "I am able to execute statues in marble, bronze and clay; in painting I can do as well as anyone else." In the actual event he probably owed the favour he received to his personal beauty and to his songs. This in itself shows how close together had come the callings of courtier, scholar, soldier and mechanic, a condition impossible in the Middle Ages and hardly less so in Classical Antiquity.

Technical Advance.—The growth of technique by itself was necessarily slow, not so much because individuals were incapable of improving it, but because they had little means of passing on that improvement to their successors. The need for secrecy, the inability to transmit personal skill, and the jealousy of less successful rivals powerfully reinforced through the influence of the guilds, reduced progress to a minimum. Even more potent perhaps was the inability to find capital on a sufficient scale to start new processes. Where men trained in philosophy and mathematics, having a comprehensive view of history and backed up by the most important patrons of the times, paid attention to the trades, wholly new possibilities were bound to appear. The academic scientist from the very start was free from the difficulties of the craftsman, and, in his position of adviser to princes or men of wealth, he could interest them in pushing forward schemes in the face of guild opposition.

Science built on Craft Knowledge.—Yet the entry of philosophy into practical life had less effect in its early stages on the processes of production than had the study of these processes on the development of modern science. The interests of learned men were turned not only to nature but to the works of man, and this not in the purely contemplative manner of the Greeks but with the underlying intention of improving these works for the benefit of humanity, or, at any rate, for the benefit of their patrons. A typical example of this process is the life-work of Agricola, a humanist scholar, friend of Melancthon and Erasmus, who spent his life in studying the ways of miners, became a mine-owner himself, and wrote a great treatise on mining, *De Re Metallica*, which in balance and comprehensiveness is a better technical handbook than any that has been produced before or since. In describing the age-old practices of the miner's and smelter's craft, he laid the foundations of scientific geology and chemistry, though it is not recorded that his interest in the industry produced any actual change in it. The fruits of the scientific studies of the sixteenth and seventeenth centuries did not, in fact, show themselves in technique, with the one crucial exception of navigation (3), until the time of the industrial revolution.

Italy and the First Scientific Societies.—At first, the scientists of the Renaissance worked in an isolated way or in small groups that happened to meet together in some university town or at some prince's court. They communicated by letter and, as they were so few, it was possible for any one of them to know fairly quickly of any new discoveries or theories. The idea of collaboration as a means of far more effective and rapid progress was present from the start, but was not easy to realize. Italy still led the way. The great discoverers of the fifteenth, sixteenth and early seventeenth centuries, with the exception of Kepler, were all Italians or Italian trained. The Italian universities, particularly those of Padua and Bologna, for a while remained the only ones in Europe which had not a definitely scholastic and anti-scientific bent. The first scientific academy, the Accademia dei Lincei, was founded in Rome in 1601, but within thirty years Italy, having lost her spiritual and political independence to Spain and her commercial supremacy to the nations of northern Europe, had definitely given over the lead of scientific activity.

Holland, England, and the Royal Society.—The situation in the northern countries was different. They were at the beginning of a period of prosperity, not at the end of one. The age of great princes was passing; that of merchants and manufacturers was to come. Holland and then England began to be concerned with the new knowledge which already could do so much for navigation and warfare (4) and which it was hoped might be as useful in the trades. The development of the new sciences could not be left to patrons or universities; it would have to be the work of gentlemen scientists themselves, banded together for mutual support and assistance. Thus, in England, in 1645, first arose the "invisible college" which, after the Restoration, became the Royal Society. In a similar way the private meetings in the Salon of Etienne Pascal in Paris in 1631 were recognized in 1666 as the Royal Academy of Sciences. Bacon had been the forerunner of these enterprises, and they carried with them from the start the intensely practical intentions of the *New Atlantis*. As the draft constitution of the Royal Society, drawn up by Wren, has it:

" . . . The Way to so happy a Government, we are sensible, is in no manner more facilitated than by promoting of useful Arts and Sciences, which, upon mature Inspection, are found to be the Basis of civil Communities and free Governments, and which gather Multitudes, by an Orphean Charm, into Cities, and connect them in Companies; that so, by laying in a Stock, as it were, of several Arts, and Methods of Industry, the whole Body may be supplied by a mutual Commerce of each others peculiar Faculties; and consequently that the various Miseries, and Toils of this frail Life, may, by as many various Expedients, ready at Hand, be remedied, or alleviated; and Wealth and Plenty diffused in just Proportion to every one's Industry, that is, to every one's Deserts.

And there is no Question but the same Policy that founds a City, doth nourish and increase it; since these mentioned Allurements to a Desire of Cohabitation, do not only occasion Populosity of a Country, but render it more potent and wealthy than a more populous, but more barbarous Nation; it being the same Thing, to add more Hands, or by the Assistance of Art to facilitate Labour, and bring it within the Power of the few.

Wherefore our Reason hath suggested to us, and our own Experience in our Travels in foreign Kingdoms and States, hath abundantly confirmed, that we prosecute effectually the Advancement of Natural Experimental Philosophy, especially those Parts of it which concern the Encrease of Commerce, by the Addition of useful Inventions tending to the Ease, Profit, or Health of our Subjects; which will best be accomplished by a Company of Ingenious and learned Persons, well qualified for this sort of Knowledge, to make it their principal Care and Study, and to be constituted a regular Society for this Purpose, endowed with all proper Privileges and Immunities." (Preamble of a Charter to incorporate The Royal Society; from a first Essay, and rough Draught, by Mr. Christopher Wren.)

The preamble of the Charter itself expresses these ideas in a shorter and more sober fashion:

"And whereas we are informed that a competent number of persons of eminent learning, ingenuity and honour, concording in their inclinations and studies towards this employment, have for some time accustomed themselves to meet weekly and orderly to confer about the hidden causes of things, with a design to establish certain and correct uncertain in philosophy, and have by their labour in the disquisition of Nature to prove themselves real benefactors of mankind; and that they already made a considerable progress by divers useful and remarkable discoveries, inventions and experiments in the improvement of Mathematics, Mechanics, Astronomy, Navigation, Physics and Chemistry, we have determined to grant our Royal favour, patronage, and all due encouragement to this illustrious assembly, and so beneficial and laudable an enterprise." (5)

The Discoveries and Navigation.—Yet as far as immediate practical results were concerned, the Royal Society approached closer to Swift's *Laputa* than to Bacon's *Atlantis*. Admirable studies were made of industries, but little improvement could be suggested. The great work of seventeenth-century science was to clear the way for approaching the fundamental facts of physics and chemistry. Only in astronomy could its work be brought to a final conclusion in the great syntheses which Newton made of the work of Galileo and

Kepler. Astronomy had, particularly for the seventeenth century, an enormous economic importance. World navigation, world trade, the planting of colonies, were just beginning, and here the tables of the astronomers and the pendulum and balance wheel clocks of the physicists meant the saving of ships and cargoes, and the conquest of distant empires. The first subsidized scientific institution in England was the Royal Observatory at Greenwich. (6)

The First Scientists.—The seventeenth century marked the transition between the amateur and the professional scientists. The members of the Royal Society were, for the most part, country gentlemen and men about town, though they included some great nobles and even the King himself. For most of them, the meetings of the Royal Society were a form of entertainment, from which profitable ideas might possibly be gained. Besides them, however, there were the officials of the Society, Hooke (7) and his assistants and the secretary, Oldenburg, who depended, at any rate in part, for their living on their scientific work, and for whom scientific work constituted the major occupation of their lives. Hardly less were Newton and the pietist nobleman, Boyle, scientists in the modern sense.

The Newtonian Era.—The result of the scientific work of the seventeenth century was a success, but one of an unexpected character. Science did not, as Bacon had hoped, immediately lead to a satisfaction of human wants, but it had established itself, largely through the work of Newton, as an extraordinarily effective way of quantitative calculation in the domain of mechanics and physics. The Newtonian method of reducing everything to massive particles acted on by forces seemed at the time to offer as great hopes for the advancement of science as had the inductive method of Bacon or the logical geometry of Descartes, and it had, beyond that, the immense advantage that in astronomy and mechanics, at least, it actually worked. People began to apply the Newtonian method quite improperly to the whole field of natural knowledge, and even to theology and ethics. The idea that by reason and calculation alone men could succeed in solving all their problems was one of the guiding motives of eighteenth-century philosophy, and it had passed far beyond the boundaries of scientific thought. Science had for the first time become an important cultural factor, and exerted its influence even on political events. The eighteenth century became the age of reason, and the pious and conservative Newton was to become a forerunner of the French Revolution. The immediate effect on science, however, was disastrous. Newton had done so much that it seemed hardly worth while for lesser men to do anything.

SCIENCE AND MANUFACTURE

The great scientific outburst of the seventeenth century was not maintained. It depended too much on the specially favourable conjunction of social, political and economic factors, and on the genius of too few men. From 1690 to 1750 was a relative blank in the history of science, time enough to digest but also largely to forget the great work of the seventeenth century. (8) When science again appeared in vigour, it was in very different surroundings. The gentlemen and merchants of the seventeenth century had been, in fact, too successful. The normal course of development of capital and the growth of trade had given them all they wanted. Science was a plaything of which they soon got tired. A new class was emerging, however, that of the small manufacturers who were taking advantage of the new markets won by the trade wars and of the new demands created by them to push new wares and new ways of making them. The science of the eighteenth century was from the start closely identified with the industrial revolution. Now it was no longer a question merely of science studying accepted methods of industry; the methods themselves were changing and science had to take a part in that change. It was not at first a predominating part, for it was the institution of capitalism through the breaking down of guild resistance and through the creation of available money on the one hand and property-less workers on the other, which made that development possible for the first time. The release of ever-latent human ingenuity was not primarily disciplined or inspired by science. The early development of the industrial revolution—the introduction of automatic textile machinery—was largely the work of uneducated craftsmen, but one great gift, the steam-engine, which solved the crucial problem of power, came, at least in part, from science.

The Steam-Engine.—The steam-engine has a very mixed origin; its material parents might be said to be the cannon and the pump. The awareness of the latent energy of gunpowder persistently suggested that uses other than war might be found for it, and when gunpowder proved intractable, there was a natural tendency to use the less violent agents of fire and steam. The need for power was, however, at the outset extremely restricted. For most purposes, wind and water-mills sufficed, and industry had naturally grouped itself round such sources of power, as it still does round sources of raw materials. But in the case of mines there was no such freedom. The mine had to be where the ore was, and as often as not no natural power might be available, and it was necessary either to go to the expense of using animals or men, or to abandon the working completely.

The idea of raising water by means of fire was consequently a natural one, but the crude attempts at doing this, such as that of the Marquess of Worcester, broke down because the materials able to withstand steam pressure could not at that time be made. Here science stepped in. Torricelli's discovery of the vacuum. suggested a source of power which, if cumbersome, was at any rate manageable, and after some rather fumbling attempts by scientists such as Papin, the military engineer Savery in 1695 and the Cornish tin-miner Newcomen in 1712 constructed the first practical steam-engines which could pump water out of mines on an economic basis. With an available source of power which could be set up anywhere, industry was free of all local restrictions, though it took nearly a century, and the radical improvements introduced by Watt, before this was realized economically in practice.

Science and Revolution. The Lunar Society.—The effect of this and other useful applications of science, such as Franklin's lightning conductor in 1752, made practical men see not only that in science they had a vast power which could be used profitably, but that in order to use it, it was necessary to go deeply into the secrets of nature. Towards the end of the century a lively scientific interest began to penetrate these manufacturing circles, and it was there that most of the new developments of science took place. It was in Leeds, Manchester, Birmingham, Glasgow and Philadelphia, rather than Oxford, Cambridge and London, that the science of the industrial revolution took root. Its practitioners were no longer small country gentlemen and churchmen, but dissenting ministers and quakers, and their patrons were no longer aristocrats and merchant bankers, but manufacturers. The effective centre of scientific thought in England at the end of the eighteenth century was not the Royal Society but the Lunar Society which met at Birmingham under the patronage of Boulton, Wilkinson and Wedgwood, attended by Watt, Priestley and Erasmus Darwin. (9) But science was necessary not only for directors of industry; it was also becoming increasingly desirable that the leading operatives at least should have some knowledge of scientific principles. Science, at any rate in manufacturing districts, would have to come into the scheme of education. It was useless to expect anything from universities; they had in the eighteenth century sunk to a depth of sloth, ignorance and bigotry worse than any in their history. The want was filled by the setting-up of mechanics' institutions and libraries in the centres of the new manufacturing districts. The first was, characteristically enough, in America, where Franklin founded the Philadelphia Academy in 1755. Similar institutions were founded in Manchester, Birmingham and Glasgow, and finally Count Rumford, a kind of inferior Franklin, founded the Royal Institution in London, destined to be the most famous of them all.

"In 1796 he made a 'proposal for forming in London by private sub-scription an establishment for feeding the poor, and giving them useful employment, and ·lso for furnishing food at a cheap rate to others who may stand in need of such assistance, connected with an institution for introducing and bringing forward into general use new inventions and improvements, particularly such as relate to the management of heat and the saving of fuel, and to various other mechanical contrivances by which domestic comfort and economy may be promoted.'

Rumford told his friends that he was 'deeply impressed with the neces-sity of rendering it *fashionable* to care for the poor and indigent.'

The Society for Bettering the Condition of the Poor was founded to meet the first suggestion in his agitation. The second suggestion, for the founding of a research institution, was separated from the first, as it would be 'too conspicuous and too interesting and important, to be made an *appendix* to any other existing establishment, and consequently it must stand alone, and on its own proper basis.' In 1799 the Institution was founded and private subscriptions were collected for 'a public institution for diffusing the knowledge and facilitating the general and speedy intro-duction of new and useful mechanical inventions and improvements; and also for teaching, by regular courses of philosophical lectures and experiments, the applications of the new discoveries in science to the. improvement of arts and manufactures, and in facilitating the means of procuring the comforts and conveniences of life.' Sir Joseph Banks, the President of the Royal Society, was the chairman of the managers, and Rumford was the secretary. A house was bought in Albemarle Street and its rooms converted into laboratories, lecture rooms, offices, etc.; and a flat for the accommodation of Rumford. 'A good cook was en-gaged for the improvement of culinary advancement—one object, and not the least important, for the Royal Institution.' Like all other in-stitutions founded by social idealists, its character was rapidly adapted, not to the achievement of the precise objects of the founders, but to those objects in its constitution which were of interest to classes with increasing social power. As the class of student in the public grammar schools of the fifteenth century gradually changed from orphans to the sons of princes, and as the co-operative movement of the Rochdale pioneers changed from a communal society into a business paying dividends, so the Royal Institution changed from a laboratory for the solution of the problems of the poor into an institution for the solution of the scientific problems which governing opinion of the day thought important. The solutions of the problems of science ultimately benefit the poor, but only after they have benefited the industrialists who exploit science. . . ."
—Crowther, *British Scientists of the Nineteenth Century*, pp. 35-36.

The Great Age of French Science.—In France, the eighteenth century was an age of transition from monarchical and feudal rule to a middle-class republic on the English model. Politics and philosophy took the first place, but science was also much in demand, particularly in the latter part of the century when manufacture was also developed. From the start, however, it had a more official and specifically a more military character than in England. The French artillery schools were indeed the first formal institutions at which scientific education could be acquired. The great French mathematicians and physicists at the end of the period, like Lagrange, Laplace and Monge, etc., were trained at these schools, but their most illustrious pupil was Napoleon, the first administrator to appreciate the value of science. Lavoisier was at the same time a member of the financial oligarchy of the Fermiers Généraux and the scientific head of the Government Arsenal, in the laboratory of which most of his important experiments were made. The hatred felt by the people of Paris for the administration of the Ferme was the ultimate cause of his trial and execution. The Revolution, after a check due to the immediate confusion, developed still further the eighteenth-century trends. In founding the École Polytechnique and the Bureau de Poids et Mesures, it created the first establishment of science on a fully subsidized state basis.

The Pneumatic Revolution and Chemical Industry.—The seventeenth century had for all practical purposes established the scientific basis of mechanics; the fruit of that was seen in the eighteenth century in the steam-engine and later in the locomotive. The great triumph of the eighteenth century was the reduction of chemistry from a traditional technique to a science as amenable to calculation as mechanics. This was finally achieved by Lavoisier and Dalton by bringing into traditional chemistry physical ideas mostly derived from the properties of gases. The fruits of this "Pneumatic Revolution" were seen in the nineteenth century with the development of the heavy chemical industry, in the production of soda, bleaching powder and gas. (10)

The Nineteenth-Century: Science becomes a Necessity.—Once the industrial revolution was well under way, the position of science as an integral part of civilization was secure. In a thousand ways science was necessary both in measuring and standardizing industry and in introducing economies and new processes. The fact that science was necessary to industry did not mean, however, that an industrial basis for science would arise of itself. Indeed, through the nineteenth century, in spite of the persistent demand for more science, there was difficulty in securing any adequate financial support, either for scientific research or science teaching. This was inherent in the anarchical nature of the age of capitalist expansion. There was a distrust of official institutes of any kind, particularly of Government institutes, and there was no means of raising money on a large scale for any purpose of a not immediately profitable nature. In the early part of the nineteenth century, the bulk of scientific work was still being carried on in such places as the Royal Institution, or in the private laboratories of people of means. The Royal Institution became in the time of Davy and Faraday almost the national physical and chemical institute. Yet in spite of its services to industry it was never easy to finance. In 1833, two years after the epoch-making discoveries of electrical induction, Faraday had the greatest difficulty in finding a few hundred pounds to enable the Institution to carry on. (11)

Germany enters the Field.—Meanwhile the development of science was proceeding apace in Europe. The early nineteenth century marked the peak of the French achievement in science, but from France the movement spread rapidly to Germany, now able to play, for the first time since the sixteenth century, an independent part in European culture. The reform of the German universities and the readiness with which the Germans took up the new sciences, particularly chemistry, from the French, led to so rapid a growth that by the middle of the century it was apparent that, in quantity at any rate, German science had taken the lead, and German manufacture appeared more able to assimilate the resources of science than did that of England.

Partly as a reaction to this and particularly owing to the direct influence of the German Prince Consort, science in England, by the middle of the century, began to receive official notice. A Science and Art Department was formed, and a resolute attempt was made by Royal Commissions to introduce science to the old universities and to make it an integral part of the newer universities that were being set up in provincial towns and in London. The great bulk of this new scientific work was, of course, that part of science which was of immediate utility, physics and chemistry; the biological sciences had to wait much longer for recognition. Darwin was for the best part of his life a man of private means, working in retirement; Huxley earned his living on the Geological Survey. (12)

Science as an Institution. The Idea of Pure Science.—Nevertheless, there grew up in the nineteenth century a definite institution of science. The Royal Society was revived and took up, but on a relatively much smaller scale, its functions of the seventeenth century. (13) The British Association, which was founded in 1831 largely to supersede it, gradually became the official popular mouthpiece of science. Numerous departmental societies, chemical societies, geological societies, etc., appeared spontaneously with the appropriate arrangements for publication. A scientific world appeared, consisting of professors, employees in industrial laboratories and amateurs, but in contradistinction to the scientific world of the seventeenth century, it claimed as its function only the realm of fact and not the realm of action. The great controversies of the nineteenth century, such as that of evolution, were fought out in the field of ideas. Scientists claimed no part in the direction of State or of industry. They were concerned with pure knowledge. It was a satisfactory arrangement to both parties. The industrialists made use of the work of the scientists, and generally paid them for it, though not much; the scientists had the satisfaction of knowing that they were living in an age of indefinite progress to which their labours, in a manner which it was unnecessary to examine, were contributing the largest share. At the time when science should have been most obviously connected with the development of the machine age, arose the idea of pure science: of the scientist's responsibility being limited to carrying out his own work, and leaving the results to an ideal economic system, ideal because natural and open to the free play of economic forces. This is the attitude which lies still at the back of many scientists' and laymen's ideas of science, little though it fits the state of the present-day world.

SCIENCE AND IMPERIAL EXPANSION

By 1885 a new current was setting in, and it was apparent that the development of manufacturing industry was leading to unexpected and disturbing results. Already Britain had lost the monopoly of manufacture, and was fast losing its predominance as a manufacturing country; Germany and America were formidable rivals. The Empire was invoked to save British industry by providing it with fresh fields for export, not so much now of consumable goods as of production goods, railways and machinery. An incidental result was the further development of science. To cope with the new problems of Imperial expansion, the Imperial College and the Imperial Institute were founded, and a general overhaul of scientific teaching and research was made. In Germany, however, industrialization was far more intense; science was being used on quite another scale. The Technische Hochschulen were turning out thousands of trained chemists and physicists, who were being absorbed into the laboratories of industry, and in a few years the chemistry of dye-stuffs and explosives, for which the foundations had been laid largely in France and Britain, had been captured as part of a new German industry which held the virtual monopoly of the world market.

The War.—The turning-point in the history of science occurred with the War. The War differed from previous wars in that it involved whole nations and not only armies drawn from them.

Agriculture and industry were pressed into direct war service and so was science. Of course, from earliest times science had been in demand for the arts of war more than for those of peace, not because of any particular bellicose nature of scientists, but because the demands of war are more urgent. Princes and Governments are more willing to subsidize research for war purposes than for any other because science may produce new devices which from their very novelty are of critical military importance. (But see pp. 171-3.)

Collaboration of Scientists.—The collaboration of the scientists in the late War, however, went beyond anything that had happened before. It was not a matter of the application of well-known scientific principles by a small number of technicians and inventors, but the total mobilization of the scientists in every country, for the sole purpose of increasing, during the War itself, the destructive power of modern weapons, and devising methods of protection against such advance on the opposite side. (See p. 180.) Here, at the beginning, the Germans had an advantage; not only were their scientists more numerous, but they were in much closer contact with industry than were those in the Allied countries. This was an immediate advantage, which would have proved decisive had it not been for the grave deficiency in Germany of primary raw materials, such as metals, rubber and oil. The Allied powers had to improvise scientific and industrial services during the War. In 1917 this took final form in the Department of Scientific and Industrial Research in this country, and in 1916 of the National Research Council in the United States of America. As the Report of the Department for 1932 states:

"The scheme was devised by our predecessors in office in the middle of the greatest War in history. From the outset of hostilities, it was apparent that the application of science was to play an important part in the conflict; and men of science were enlisted in the nation's army of workers with no inconsiderable effect. The circumstances of war lent force to the pleas of those who had been calling for a closer march of British industry with science, for they demonstrated, with an emphasis which had hitherto been lacking, the consequences of failure to follow up scientific discoveries capable of utilization in the industrial sphere. For example, it was soon found that this country was to an unfortunate extent largely dependent on foreign sources for some of the supplies necessary for warlike operations. Our greatest enemy of those days had secured, by application of science, a hold upon certain manufactured products which was found to be of an extent and nature to threaten our national well-being. And there was a general awakening to the fact that for success in times of peace as well as of war it was desirable that the resources of science should be utilized to the full. The perils of war furnished precepts for peace, and it was realized that on the conclusion of the conflict a situation would arise in the world of industry which would call for increased effort if British industrial supremacy was to be maintained, and if the manufactured products of the nation were to continue to hold their own in the world's markets. In anticipation of that situation, the Government of the day set up the Department of Scientific and Industrial Research and, as part of the financial provision placed at its disposal, Parliament voted a capital sum of one million pounds for the encouragement of industrial research. The most effective way of promoting this aim was the subject of careful consideration by our predecessors in consultation with leaders of industry, and the scheme of co-operative research associations was devised." (See also p. 172.)

State Science. —This extract illustrates how the War led naturally to a new and much more conscious appreciation of the function of science in a modern industrial state. It was then recognized that science could not be left entirely unorganized and dependent on ancient endowments or sporadic benefactions. The very existence of a modern industrial state in peace and war—and from the technical point of view, the problems involved are not fundamentally different— was seen to depend on the activities of organized science. The discovery of natural resources and the means for the most effective use of them depends on science and science alone. This realization, however, was by no means clear, as the passage just quoted will indicate. There were forces inherent in old institutions and habits which fought against any such rationalization of science. In practically all countries, the reorganization of science took place in a confused and half-hearted way. The governments and industry wanted it but were not prepared to pay the price, and scientists instinctively clung to the relative independence of pre-War days. Although in the War nearly all had accepted service unquestioningly, in peace it was possible to question the desirability for science to put itself entirely at the service of governments and monopolist industry. The result in nearly all countries was a compromise, one of a particularly unsatisfactory character. Science was neither organized nor independent. A multiplicity of authorities controlled it, administering a still greater multiplicity of funds. (See Chap. III.)

The post-War Period and the Crisis.—This confusion was not in itself able to check the immense productivity of scientific research. At first after the War, science, once set free from immediate technical tasks, burst into an activity which has been rarely surpassed in its history, and notably so in Germany, as if to show that the predominance which could not be won by violence might be attained in the peaceful sphere of the intellect. This lull did not survive the crisis of '29 and its political aftermath. Science almost everywhere was curtailed by economy, and the apparently unassailable position of Germany destroyed by the fanaticism of the Nazis. Since 1933 there and everywhere else the growth of armaments is further limiting and distorting the whole structure of science.

The natural inefficiency of scientists was made worse rather than better by the development of bureaucracy; science was neither free to develop according to its own intrinsic tendencies nor was it effectively directed in the service of industry. In its new phase, expenditure on science must needs be far greater than before on account of the larger scale of proportionate expenses of apparatus and the necessity of employing far more people of all different grades in organized collaboration; yet the funds provided have been everywhere, except perhaps in the United States, inadequate for such an expansion. Science was not allowed to continue in the old way nor was it effectively enabled to carry on in the new.

SCIENCE AND SOCIALISM

Meanwhile in the Soviet Union very different developments were occurring. The importance of science had grown imperceptibly in Russia with the growth of capitalism, but this importance was not formally recognized. After the Revolution of 1917, however, a great development began. In Marxist theory science had always had an important place. The ideal of Bacon—the use of science for the welfare of human beings—was indeed a guiding principle of the constructive side of Marxism. Science, it held, must be used directly for this purpose and no longer divert its service to increasing profits. In spite of the extremely slender scientific resources of Czarist Russia, of the destruction of the Great War and civil wars, of the immense sufferings and privations of the period of reconstruction, the importance of science in the U.S.S.R. continued to grow. The effective start, however, for a large-scale organization of science as an integral part of a general drive towards the improvement of conditions did not occur until the first five-year plan in 1927. From then on, both in numbers and finance, Soviet science has shown a continued and ever more rapidly increasing advance, completely unaffected by the depression that has done so much to check the progress of capitalist science. It is not to be expected in an institution such as science, which requires for its maturing years and even generations of common effort, that overwhelming success should be immediately obtainable; indeed, it will be some time before in exactness and critical ability Soviet science is able to surpass Germany or Britain. What it has done, however, is enough to show that in this new way of organizing science in the service of humanity lie possibilities for both altogether beyond those which the present indefensible and chaotic system of science and industry in the West can offer. (See pp. 221-231.)

(1) For a penetrating study of this and other aspects of the early history of science, see Professor Gordon Childe's *Man Makes Himself*, and his article in *Modern Quarterly*, No. 2.

(2) Professor L. Hogben makes the same point in *Science for the Citizen*, pp. 777-778.

(3) Ballistics might claim to share the honour with navigation, but although all the leading scientists, including Galileo and Newton, spent much time on its study, it is doubtful whether all their ingenuity was of any use to the practical gunner (see p. 169).

(4) See p. 169. Stevinus of Bruges, secretary to William the Silent, was the first scientist administrator, and by his technical and economic measures did as much as anyone to secure the independence of the United Provinces.

(5) See also note (4) p. 291.

(6) The assistance given by King Charles was not of a very spectacular kind. Mr. Weld, in his *History of the Royal Society*, makes the following remarks on its foundation :

" The King allowed £500 in money, with bricks from Tilbury Fort, where there was a spare stock, and some wood, iron and lead, from a gatehouse demolished in the Tower ; and encouraged us further with a promise of affording what more should be requisite. The foundation was laid August 10, 1675, and the work carried on so well, that the roof was laid and the building covered by Christmas.

" Mr. Baily states, ' that this Observatory was formerly a tower built by Humphrey, Duke of Gloucester, and repaired or rebuilt by Henry VIII in 1526. That it was sometimes the habitation of the younger branches of the royal family ; sometimes the residence of a favourite mistress ; sometimes a prison, and sometimes a place of defence. Mary of York, fifth daughter of Edward IV, died at the tower in Greenwich Park in 1482. Henry VIII visited " a fayre lady," whom he loved, here. In Queen Elizabeth's time it was called Mirefleur. In 1642, being then called Greenwich Castle, it was thought of so much consequence, as a place of strength, that immediate steps were ordered to be taken for securing it. After the Restoration, Charles II, in 1675, pulled down the old tower, and founded on its site the present Royal Observatory ' " (p. 254).

" Bearing in mind the apathetic conduct of the King towards the Royal Society, it will not appear extraordinary that the Observatory, so hurriedly established, was left for a period of nearly fifteen years without a single instrument being furnished by Government. Sir Jonas Moore provided Flamsteed with a sextant, two clocks, a telescope, and some books ; all the other instruments, excepting the foregoing, and those lent by the Royal Society, were made at Flamsteed's expense. ' It is true,' says Mr. Baily, ' that they had given him a house to live in, and had appropriated a precarious salary of £100 a year ; but, at the same time, although his employments were sufficiently laborious, the King had ordered that he should instruct monthly two boys from Christ Church Hospital, which was a great annoyance to him, and interfered with his proper avocations ' " (pp. 255-256).

(7) Hooke, who ranks as the greatest experimenter of the seventeenth century, was, as curator, obliged to produce two original experiments a week for the Society. He was, however, besides this, surveyor to the City of London, no sinecure after the fire, and a great architect, building Bethlehem Hospital and, almost more than Wren, St. Paul's Cathedral.

(8) This decline, which is quite clear to the scientist, coincided, as G. N. Clark has pointed out in his *Science and Social Welfare in the Age of Newton*, with a great turn of the tide in economic affairs, the ending of the period of high prices following on the opening up of America, and the beginning of a period of steady prices which lasted until the Napoleonic period. Although Professor Clark is very careful to dissociate himself from an economic view of the history of science, the coincidence is remarkably striking, and particularly so because science arose again not only when the new economic change was taking place, but precisely in those places where the change was most intense.

(9) See S. Smiles, *Life of Watt, Lives of the Engineers*, etc., also H. W. Dickinson, *Matthew Boulton*.

(10) Professor Clark seemed to be surprised that this change did not occur in the seventeenth century, and cites it as an example which proves that economic factors do not determine the actual course of science, although he admits they may influence the intensity with which scientific pursuits are carried on. In the author's opinion, it is a very good demonstration of the contrary proposition. The need for discoveries in chemistry could

only occur when old processes employing chemical means, brewery, tanning, dyeing, bleaching, had ceased to be cottage or small-scale occupations and had become large enough to make it worth while to think rationally with a view to improvement (see p. 128). This change only occurred in the eighteenth century, and therefore economic incentive for this kind of science was lacking.   On the purely scientific side, the development of chemistry needed to solve these technical problems required the previous analysis of mechanical and physical forces, particularly the study of the properties of gases, itself a product of the development of the steam-engine.   Consequently both directly and indirectly, the great revolution in chemistry was the product of economic forces.   See also Hogben's *Science for the Citizen*, Chapters VII and VIII.

(11) See Crowther, *British Physicists of the Nineteenth Century*.   See also for similar conditions in France, p. 201.

(12) In any full account these remarks would have to be extensively qualified.   There were notable advances in the mid-nineteenth century in many other fields.   In medicine there were the discoveries of anaesthetics and antiseptics, though these as well as the germ theory of disease were largely the fruit of chemical research.   In agriculture there was the work of Liebig and Bunsen, both however chemists.   The science of geology was mainly established in this period as a direct consequence of studies of mines and canal and railway surveying.   It is, however, a curious commentary on Huxley's occupation that Owen, the great palaeontologist, worked as professor at the Royal College of Surgeons.

(13) The decadence of the Royal Society in the late eighteenth and early nineteenth century was very real.   Babbage, one of the most original minds in Britain, wrote in 1830, " On the decline of science in England," and campaigned violently against the election of fellows on the ground of their wealth and social position alone.   See Hogben, *Science for the Citizen*, pp. 616 and 713.

CHAPTER III

THE EXISTING ORGANIZATION OF SCIENTIFIC RESEARCH IN BRITAIN

University, Government and Industrial Research.—We now return to the more concrete study of the present situation of scientific research. In this country, as indeed in nearly all other countries outside the U.S.S.R., scientific research is carried out in three different administrative spheres: in the universities, in Government services and in industry. The independent scientist, so important in earlier ages and even in the nineteenth century, has practically disappeared. The work is co-ordinated, in so far as it is co-ordinated at all, by the scientific societies who are also largely responsible for scientific publications and to a lesser extent by such bodies as the Medical Research Council and other grant-providing bodies.

Research in the universities has appeared as a natural outgrowth of individual investigations undertaken by the teaching staff. It is primarily concerned with pure science, although more recently in a number of universities a limited amount of applied science research has also been done. The objects of Government research are two-fold: firstly, research for the Defence Services, Army, Navy and Air Force; and secondly, research for the benefit of industry, agriculture and medicine. Both these kinds of research are necessarily largely of an applied character. The research carried on by industry is almost exclusively of this character, as the work of industrial laboratories for pure science is less developed in England than in America or Germany.

These three spheres are, however, not independent of one another. The universities tend increasingly, particularly in relation to science, to depend upon grants from Government Departments and donations from industrialists. A large proportion of scientific research workers in universities are, in fact, paid either by Government or industry. On the other hand, much of the direction of scientific work in industry and in Government Departments is carried out by men holding university posts, particularly in the higher grades, and by committees of such men with advisory functions. Governmental and industrial research are also very closely combined; the whole scheme of Research Associations is an attempt to give to industry the advantages of the centralized research facilities which the Government provides, and to share the expenses of research likely to be of assistance both to Government and industry. A particularly important Department of Government Research (War Research) is inextricably connected with the research of the armaments industry, which is itself merely one aspect of heavy industry—steel, engineering, explosives and heavy chemicals. The scientific societies, particularly the Royal Society, are at once in all three camps. Their personnel is largely drawn from the universities, they administer large Government funds for research, thus becoming in part Government Departments, and they are in close touch with the research carried out by industry.

All this will give the impression that we have a well-knit organized system of research in this country. Actually, however, all these connections have grown up through force of circumstances and for personal reasons in an entirely haphazard way, and the result in structure, if reduced to a diagram, would simply show the enormous degree of interlocking and cross-connections without any discernible plan. (1) The most effective direction of science, so far as it does exist, is not inside the framework of any of these bodies, but depends on the fact that a handful of the more important scientists in the country know one another, and between them know practically everybody else of importance in the scientific world and in the administrative and business circles which are concerned. Plans for scientific development are discussed informally, and, of course, secretly. Wealthy men are approached and persuaded privately to put up funds, somebody who knows the Prime Minister suggests that something might be done for a particular branch of research, and in this typically English way scientific research carries on.

RESEARCH IN THE UNIVERSITIES

The universities occupy the most important position in fundamental research. Indeed it would be safe to say that some four-fifths of fundamental research done in Britain is turned out in university laboratories. This has been a very gradual development, particularly on the material side. It is only in the present century that the universities have developed large and well-equipped laboratories not primarily devoted to teaching purposes. The position of the universities in respect to scientific research is in process of very rapid change. Before the War, most of the research in universities was carried out by professors, lecturers and other university teachers in their spare time, although it was coming to be understood more and more that research work was as important, if not more important, to the university as was teaching.

Research Workers.—Since the War, research has been multiplied by the addition of two classes of workers, post-graduate students and subsidized whole-time senior research workers. The competition for posts in the scientific world forces the pace in respect of qualifications. Partly owing to the influence of Germany and America, English universities introduced the Ph.D. degree for which original research is a necessary condition. Now that the Ph.D. degree is necessary for anyone aspiring to a post of any importance in the scientific world, universities are assured of a plentiful supply of young research workers who stay from two to four years. The actual number is difficult to estimate. The University Grants Committee list 1791 full-time and 936 part-time advanced students in science, technology, medicine and agriculture (for their distribution see Appendix I (*c*)), but probably less than half of these are doing research. We may reasonably take 1500 as an upper figure for junior research workers. Some of these are continuing their studies at their own expense; the majority, however, are supported partially or wholly by grants from the university or college in the form of scholarships, from the Department of Scientific and Industrial Research, or other Government bodies, and from local authorities. Besides these, there are a small but growing number, about a hundred, of senior research workers in universities. For the most part, these workers are not paid by the universities. In fact there are only about twenty research posts of this type in the country: the majority depend upon various forms of fellowships and on senior Government research awards (see p. 83).

The position of the research worker in the universities is still anomalous. He has no recognized place but is treated as part-student and part-teacher. As a result, permanent or professional research workers are still rare. It is normal for a student to spend anything from two to six years in research in universities and then drift into teaching, administration or industrial work. The effects of this anomalous position on the research workers themselves and in their work will be discussed in a later chapter.

The organization of research work in universities follows the traditional department system. The professor controls a department and advises the research workers in that department; that is, in general, he suggests the research that they should undertake, and assists and criticizes them in the course of the work. Though, of course, this is largely nominal in the case of senior research workers, in many cases the professor himself collaborates in the work of individual research workers. He sets someone to work at a problem in which he is interested, takes a larger or smaller share in the actual work, and publishes papers jointly with the research worker. This system, of course, may be of great advantage to young research workers, but it is open to the gravest abuse.

The effective direction of scientific research in universities thus rests entirely in the hands of the professors. University faculty boards or their equivalents, and the general directing authority of the university, can only interfere indirectly through their control of sums allocated to various departments. They are not sufficiently qualified to direct the actual research or to co-ordinate it with similar research in other institutions. This means in effect that fundamental scientific research is carried out in a large number (approximately 400) of independent laboratories. These, of course, vary enormously in importance. Only a few of them are equivalent to the scientific institutes of the Continent, employing some twenty to forty research workers. The majority are one or two-man departments. The importance of any laboratory depends on a number of factors. Large laboratories are found where there is a demand for much advanced teaching or for the solution of some industrial or semi-industrial problems. They are also found where the professor is a man of notable ability either in science or in the far more difficult art of securing funds for research.

There is, except in a certain limited field, a marked difference in the position of scientific research in the larger and smaller universities. In the latter, as might be expected. are to be found the majority of small laboratories as well as completely isolated research workers; it is there also that the requirements of teaching make the largest encroachments on the time for research. Occasionally, thanks to a special benefaction, a highly specialized institute of some size will be found in a small university, but for the most part the great bulk of valuable research is concentrated into a relatively small number of laboratories in the large universities. This situation intensifies the already existing disparities between universities by drawing most men of outstanding ability to those centres where that ability is likely to be useful, and still further lowering the standard of the subsidiary centres. That continual exchange of teachers and research workers between universities standing on a more or less equal basis, which was one of the best features of German university life, is almost completely absent in England. Instead there is a tendency to compete for posts in the larger universities and to retain them indefinitely when acquired.

There exists no official mechanism for co-ordinating the work done in different university laboratories. The university itself, with its multiplicity of science sections, cannot be co-ordinated except administratively, while laboratories in the same subject in different places can collaborate only on a purely voluntary basis as there is no higher administrative authority to direct their work. What co-ordination there is depends on the scientific societies.

Nature of Research done.—It is not our object here to attempt to describe the actual subjects of research carried out at universities. It is regrettable, however, that no description of these does exist; a little can be gleaned from such popular works as Julian Huxley's *Science and Social Needs*, and in detail for one university from *Cambridge University Studies*. It is, of course, nobody's business to describe the progress of science in universities or in the country at large, but the project might be worth the notice of some enterprising publisher. The conditions which determine the amount and the nature of the work done at the universities are largely historical and economical. They are historical in so far as the work carried out in any one year is generally the continuation of work of previous years, and as new professors generally inherit the more or less explicit programme of work from their predecessors. Except in the case of schools the importance of whose work is universally recognized in the scientific world, such as the work of the Cavendish Laboratory on the structure of the atomic nucleus, the limiting factor of any line of research is the possibility of getting money for it. This depends largely on the importance of the department from the teaching point of view, which is determined by the number of students attending the department, that is, effectively, by the number of posts available for students in any particular subject. The great majority of science students in universities are destined to one of four careers—engineering, industry, medicine, and teaching, of which the last absorbs far the greatest number—while a small minority will take up purely scientific research.

Research in Engineering.—The department of engineering in most universities is somewhat anomalous, being generally in closer touch with the industry than with the rest of the university. Yet in spite of this, the university course is often considered to be relatively useless, compared to shop experience, in the training of practical engineers. The fact is that most engineering departments fall between two stools. Any profound study of the fundamental principles of engineering is not considered suitable for what is in fact a technical training, but on the other hand, the departments are rarely equipped with machinery on a sufficiently modern scale to give the students any actual experience of industrial conditions.

Research in Physics and Chemistry.—The chemical industry takes far the largest share of industrial scientists and needs men with a knowledge of chemistry and physics. Consequently these departments are generally the largest and the most important in any university and they are also those most ridden by tradition. The need for training teachers still further sterilizes the university courses. The vicious circle of university and school education in respect to physics and chemistry seems impossible to break down. Universities must train people to teach the subjects which are required in school in order to satisfy the university examinations. It is this close connection with traditional teaching and with the requirements of industrial chemists, whose work is largely of a routine nature, that seriously hampers chemical research in the universities, and is making more difficult the assimilation of the new principles of chemistry which have been introduced from physics in the last ten years.

Research in Medical Subjects.—The requirements of medical students dominate the biological departments of many universities. The extent and importance of the departments of botany, zoology, physiology and bio-chemistry depend very largely upon the amount that the medical student is expected to know of these subjects. Here again, tradition is strongly enforced for the requirements of a rigid examination system. On the research side grants also come to a large extent from the Medical Research Council. In recent years the requirements of agriculture are beginning to make demands on the biological side, but the confused state of agricultural research in this country and the extremely low salaries that it offers, prevent it being effective in any ordered way.

An Unbalanced Programme of Research.—The result of these external demands is to produce a body of scientific research of an unbalanced kind, with the heavy predominance of the physical sciences, unjustified by their relative importance either in the present or in the future or by their intrinsic interest, and a definite lack of development on the biological side and still more of subjects on the boundaries of exact science, such as psychology and sociology. Some idea of this discrepancy can be seen from the tables in Appendix I (*a*) giving the number of posts for these different subjects in the universities.

This unbalanced programme of research is of crucial importance because the universities still provide practically the only opportunities in this country for fundamental research in science. There are, of course, a few independent scientific research institutes such as the Royal Institution, but so few as to make no effective difference to the general picture. The tendency is more and more for outside bodies, such as the Government, the Royal Society and the Rockefeller Foundation, to subsidize research inside universities rather than to set up institutions of a semi-independent kind. Consequently the general direction of scientific research in universities determines effectively its position in the country. In so far as research in universities is hampered and misdirected by traditional or economic factors, all other branches of scientific research are made to suffer.

SCIENTIFIC SOCIETIES

Although most fundamental scientific work is actually done in universities, its co-ordination depends entirely on voluntary associations, the scientific societies which are administered and largely paid for by the scientists themselves. In practically every subject there is a specialized society of which nearly all but the poorest research workers are members. The most important function of these societies is the publication of papers, but they also hold informal discussions and to that extent effect the general development of the subject in a purely advisory way. (2) Each worker has some idea, though usually it is an extremely imperfect one, of what is being done in his field in the various laboratories of the country and he can adapt the course of his work to this knowledge. There is, however, very little attempt in any subject to go beyond this and to suggest definite plans or programmes of work in which each laboratory would take a specific share. This type of collaboration is, in fact, only found when it is largely dictated by the nature of the work itself, that is, in the astronomical, geo-physical and meteorological fields.

The Royal Society.—Besides the special scientific societies there are two general bodies for the advancement of science—the Royal Society and the British Association—which provide the closest approach that exists in England to a parliament of scientific workers. The Royal Society, like the majority of English institutions, has in the course of its history imperceptibly changed its functions while retaining its original forms. Those that it exercises at present are of a much more limited character than was envisaged by the founders. (3) This has been largely because many of its original functions have been taken over by the specialized science societies, while its research and teaching functions have been absorbed into the university and Government Departments. The functions it retains are primarily those of an honorific body carrying on the ceremonial side of scientific intercourse, an authority responsible for the distribution of relatively important funds for research, a publishing house (4) and a semi-official advisory body to the Government on scientific questions. Recently, however, there have been signs that it intends to widen the scope of its activities in two directions: one, purely scientific, in integrating the work of allied fields of science through periodical discussions, though without going as far as considering programmes or general directives, and the other, a tendency to concern itself with the social results of scientific research. It is clear that if there were a movement towards a closer organic integration of science, the Royal Society would be formally the body most fitted to carry it out, though it may be doubted whether it would possess the necessary initiative or elasticity (see p. 399).

The British Association.—The British Association has a very different function. It furnishes the only corporate link between science as a whole and the general public. For many years the reports of its meetings have been the only expression of the results of scientific discovery that reach the public through the Press. These reports have therefore taken on the appearance of *ex cathedra* statements of the convocation of the church of science. They have always included as their most prominent feature the expression of the scientists' views on all higher matters: on philosophy, life, religion, sex and morality. The curious impression which is generally prevalent on the present state of scientific knowledge is largely due to these doubly distorted accounts. Of recent years, however, the Association has become more and more concerned with the economic, social and even political aspects of science. The scientists have been to a certain extent on trial, and it is at their Association meetings that they make their defence. In the Presidential addresses and even in some of the less specialized sessions there has been discussion, and often critical discussion, of the value of science to the community. It is clear that in the Association there are considerable possibilities for developing among scientists and the public a more acute and effective consciousness of the importance of science in social life.

GOVERNMENTAL SCIENTIFIC RESEARCH

In the promotion of scientific research the importance of the Government is second only to that of the universities. Government interest in science comes under four heads—war, industry, agriculture and health. The first two activities are closely connected, but both health and agricultural research have an indirect but none the less significant relation to the objects of war. The nature and significance of Government war research will be discussed more fully in Chapter VII; for the moment it is only necessary to say that each of the Services maintains its own research department. These are, naturally, principally of an engineering, physical and chemical nature, and the expense of these departments, even before the present armament drive, totalled nearly three million pounds, which is at least a third of the total amount of money spent on scientific research. It would be unfair, however, to take this figure without further explanation, yet it is difficult to subject it to adequate analysis (see Appendix IV).

We must assume that a great deal of the money allocated to research in the Services is spent not on strictly scientific work, that is, work in laboratories, but on trials on half or full scale of actual weapons and war machines, tanks, experimental boats, aeroplanes, etc.

The Department of Scientific and Industrial Research : the National Physical Laboratory.—The industrial research of the Government, under the direction of the Department of Scientific and Industrial Research, is more open to examination.   It falls roughly into two categories: the Governmental laboratories proper and the industrial research associations.   Of the Government laboratories, far the most important is the National Physical Laboratory which combines the functions of a central bureau of standards of every kind of unit used in commerce and industry, and a research laboratory of industrial physics. It contains, in particular, large-scale hydrodynamic and aerodynamic equipment, such as tanks and wind tunnels essential for building ships and aeroplanes.   It also contains the most complete equipment for testing the properties of materials under industrial conditions of use. Results of the work of the National Physical Laboratory are fully set out in its annual reports.   The impression produced is that the work of routine examination occupies too dominating a place, and sterilizes, so to speak, the rest of its activities.   Examination of materials or processes by a national laboratory is naturally directed towards finding defects, and the positive work of the laboratory seems to be limited to attempts to correct defects as they occur in practice.   This work is, of course, of great importance; clearly, in any system of applying scientific research it must be undertaken.   Yet it can reasonably be urged that the work of such an institution as the National Physical Laboratory should not be limited to such considerations and should be concerned just as much with the discovery of new possibilities as with the remedying of old defects.   How well this could be done is shown by those parts of the Laboratory that are most closely in touch with the Services' research, that is, the aerodynamic and the wireless sections where new processes and positive development are the directing considerations.   The National Chemical Laboratory has an even more restricted function; essentially it is an analytical laboratory assisting the Board of Trade in standardizing products from the chemical point of view.   But the Government takes little positive action in directing chemical research.

Fuel Research.—Apart from these, the two main governmental institutes are the Fuel Research Board and the Food Investigation Board.   The Fuel Research Board, on which almost as much money has been spent as on the National Physical Laboratory (see Appendix II (*a*)), has as its object the utilization of coal and in particular the production of petrol from coal, and the running of the country independently of foreign oil supplies.   Its importance consequently in the scheme for national defence need not be emphasized.   It is interesting, however, to note, in connection with the relation of Government research to industry, that the method of hydrogenation of coal developed in large part by the Fuel Research Board was not in fact operated by a Government factory, but was handed over to Imperial Chemical Industries for operation and even assisted by what amounted to a very large Government subsidy, for the petrol produced by this process was freed from a tax which accounted for four-fifths of its selling price.

Food Investigation.—The Food Investigation Board is one of the most rapidly growing of the Government's Research Departments. It has been concerned almost exclusively with methods for the preservation of food products.   Originally these were intended to be of assistance to home producers of food; actually it was found that the research introduced such effective methods of food preservation as to make transport of food from distant countries possible on a very much larger scale, and consequently to give a much larger differential advantage to Empire and foreign produce, an advantage only partly offset by tariff barriers.   A very striking point about this type of research is the extreme effectiveness of science as applied to simple processes inherited from a pre-scientific age for the storage and treatment of food.   It shows that biological engineering applied on an adequate scale is likely to have the most astonishing results, and, in collaboration with new agricultural methods, can solve, technically, the problem of food supplies of the world.   What we still lack are the social and economic adjustments needed to realize these possibilities.

Forest Products and Building.—Two further institutes deserving of notice are the Forest Products and Building Research Institutes; both have considerable promise but are held up by bureaucratic restrictions and by the anarchic character of the industries they serve.   How difficult is the position of timber research is shown clearly enough from their own report:—

" The investigatory work in the laboratory provides only the middle link of a chain of three which connects the forest in the Empire overseas with the timber user in the United Kingdom.   The three links are: (*a*) information about supplies and prices; (*b*) information about the qualities of the timbers; (*c*) marketing promotion. . . . We feel it incumbent on us to take this opportunity of reiterating our views, so that with the disappearance of the Empire Marketing Board, whose sphere of work covered all three of the links, there may be no failure to provide adequately for the first and third of them no less than for the second. To continue the work at Princes Risborough on Empire Timbers without proper intelligence concerning supplies would be to build a house without foundations. To do so without a proper marketing organization would be to build one without doors and windows. . . ."—From the Report of the Advisory Council of the D.S.I.R., 1932-33.

Since then the creation of the Colonial Forest Resources Developing Department has done something to remove these anomalies, but much still remains to be done.

The Building Research Station is unique in that in part it is concerned with the consumer as well as the producer. It has of recent years occupied itself with considerations of the convenience of dwelling-houses in respect to aspect, insulation and domestic convenience.

Research Associations.—The Research Associations of the Department of Scientific and Industrial Research were initiated towards the close of the War, with the definite objects of demonstrating to British industrialists the value of applied research and of preventing the repetition of the state of affairs in 1914, when British industry was caught napping by the more scientific industry of the Germans. A million pounds was subscribed by the Government and granted on the so-called "pound to pound" basis, *i.e.* for every pound subscribed by an industrial concern a pound was given by the Government. It was intended that by the time the million pounds were spent industry would itself realize the value of research and no further assistance of this kind would be needed. As it turned out these aims were only very partially achieved. About twenty Research Associations were set up, chiefly between the years 1918 and 1920, covering about 50 per cent. of the productive industry of the country. The other industries, for the most part old and traditional industries, thought they could get on perfectly well without science; in any case, if there was anything wrong, a protective tariff was a better help and cost nothing. After the first five years a system of diminishing Government grants was instituted but failed, whereupon a new "datum-line" system was introduced. A datum-line figure was fixed by experts for each branch of industry, and only after a sum corresponding to this figure was subscribed by the industry itself did the Government grant its "pound for pound" up to a limit of twice the datum-line figure. Thus, if full use was being made of the facility, the Government was contributing one-third of the total sum spent on industrial research. The million-pound fund was all spent, coming to an end in 1932 at the depth of the depression. There was nothing for it, if the whole of industrial research was not to be abandoned, as rubber research was for a while, but to continue the Government subvention. The situation is improving but is recognized to be still far from satisfactory. In the year ending 31st March

1936, £346,479 were spent on the Research Associations, of which £108,951 were contributed by the Government.

The chief difficulties are those of finance, for reasons that will be discussed later. The industrial contributions to the Associations are small and erratic, naturally fluctuating much with the trade cycle; those of the Government are unfortunately apt to follow the same curve. The results are a very uncertain income which prevents long-range planning of research and necessitates concentration on immediate problems, often relatively trivial. This situation is well summed up in one of the reports (1933):

> "Inadequate resources continue to hamper research associations in all directions. Problems await solution which are not formidable scientifically, provided the means exist for their appropriate approach by competent men of science. But as the means to employ sufficient staff and to provide them with the tools of their profession do not exist, the problems remain unsolved. . . .
>
> It is impossible to plan intelligently under uncertain conditions of finance, when the short view tends invariably to prevail over the long, with the result that researches which are vitally important though not immediately productive tend to be crowded out by *ad hoc* inquiry. Research Associations in short cannot carry out effectively the researches which are required in the interests of industrial progress or make plans for important sections of their programmes of work unless they can offer prospects of reasonable financial security to their scientific staffs, and they can only hope to do this if they can be assured of financial support to enable them to develop their activities over a period of years. . . .
>
> It is a scientific habit of mind and vigilant and continuous examination of manufacturing practice in the light of available technical knowledge that alone will ensure for industry the fullest advantage of new advances."

Since then, of course, the situation has greatly improved, and the income of the Research Associations, both from governmental and industrial sources, has increased rapidly (see Appendix II (c)). This has led to an attitude of complacency and to the assumption that all is for the best in British industrial science. The opportunity now exists for endowing research so as to preserve the work in progress from the effects of the next slump (see p. 317 and Appendix V). But as the authorities either believe there never will be another slump or that the system will not survive it, the chances of anything being done are remote.

The work of the Research Associations is of a more immediate technical character than that of the National Physical Laboratory or its attendant institutes. The kind of problems tackled are mostly those connected with difficulties that turn up in the course of industrial operations, such as the weaknesses of metals under certain stresses or the origin of the matt appearance of chocolate kept after a certain time. (5) Quite often, however, attention to such apparently minor problems leads to very large industrial savings. Thus an investigation into the quality of coke for iron smelting led to savings of fuel amounting to £800,000 per annum, and one on the bloom on frozen meat to savings of £300,000 per annum (see Appendix V). These examples are cited to show that even when working on an extremely restricted scale and only attempting essentially negative problems, the direct application of science to industry can lead to economies out of all proportion to the cost of research.

The existing Research Associations are shown in Appendix II (c). They fall roughly into six groups whose relative importance can be judged by the amount of money allocated to them. The greatest developments are recorded for the heavy industries, electrical industries and textiles. Engineering as such, shipbuilding, cement, brickmaking, glass and the brewing and tobacco industries are among those not represented. Many of the industries which have no Research Associations are old and traditional industries, in many cases divided into a large number of small firms which do not feel the need of scientific research or actually distrust it because they fear they will lose trade secrets.

The chemical industry is in a very different category though it also is not represented by a Research Association. Here it is rather a question of a large monopolist industry with wide international connections that prefers to manage its own research and does not require to share it with Government Departments. (6)

Research Grants.—Besides the Associations, the Department of Scientific and Industrial Research finances a number of junior and senior grants to research students, mostly in universities. Here it is frankly taking on a task which the Ministry of Education has failed to fulfil. The number of grantees is small—about eighty a year out of the two thousand honours graduates in science. Even then, however, so small is the demand for trained research workers that only a third of these go on into industrial research. This part of the Department's activities is of considerable assistance to fundamental research, for small as the number of students is, they form an appreciable addition to academic research. But the whole system is anomalous as there is no attempt at co-ordinating the work done or relating it to industrial problems. The grants themselves are so small as to produce real hardships (see p. 84), and it is very doubtful whether they fulfil the purpose for which they were intended.

It can be seen that there exists in Great Britain, through the Department of Scientific and Industrial Research, a framework covering, though very imperfectly, most industrial operations. Governmental scientific research is certainly closer to day-to-day problems than is university research. It may even be that with the present economic system it represents the best that can be done by the State to bring science into industry. One of its guiding principles has been that of conciliatory approach to industrialists, a tactful pointing-out of the advantages of research while giving full reassurances that in no case does the State wish to enter into competition with them. In this way, over the course of twenty years it has permeated the more advanced half of British industry. A more forthright policy would perhaps have failed, but it would be optimistic to claim that the results achieved fulfil anything like the requirements of a state science service even under capitalism.

MEDICAL RESEARCH

The Medical Research Council.—Besides research for the Services and the Department of Scientific and Industrial Research, the Government interests itself directly in medical and agricultural research. The Medical Research Council was founded in 1920 to co-ordinate the existing, more or less separate, subventions to medical research. Administratively the Council differs very much from the D.S.I.R., being mainly an advisory rather than an executive body, and the funds at its disposal are much smaller, at present (1938) only £195,000 per annum. Under the direct control of the Council are their institutes, of which the most important is the National Institute for Medical Research at Hampstead ; the upkeep of these accounts for £58,500. Of the remainder of their appropriation most is spent in subsidizing individual research workers throughout the country. In this there is more evidence of intelligent co-ordination than is furnished by the similar scheme of the D.S.I.R. A number of important problems are selected for research, and in some cases these are attacked by means of co-operative teams of workers. The problem of the composition of vitamin D, for instance, was satisfactorily solved by one such team of eight workers at the National Institute. A great deal of the work, however, as can be seen by the reports, is completely uncoordinated and consists of the subsidizing of research considered, in the eyes of persons of standing, to be likely to give results of medical importance. As a result much fine work gets done—the Bio-chemical Laboratory at Cambridge has, for instance, largely been subsidized from this source—but it only represents a fraction of what a more comprehensive scheme would yield.

The policy of the Medical Research Council, moreover, lacks any serious continuity. It is permanently exposed to a conflict between two different conceptions of Medical Research, the clinical and the scientific. The first view, which is now becoming predominant in the policy of the Council, is that results of immediate medical value should be aimed at and that the research workers should, as a rule, hold medical degrees. Yet the danger of too exclusively medical an outlook in the absence of a sufficiently extensive scientific background was ably pointed out by Sir F. Gowland Hopkins in his presidential address to the Royal Society in 1934. (7)

The scientific aspect of the Council's work, even at its highest development, suffers mainly from its inadequate finance and lack of comprehensive direction. (8) There is not enough money at the disposal of the Council to make it possible for it to subsidize more than a relatively small number of research workers in physiological and bio-chemical subjects at the universities. Consequently the work tends to follow individualistic and uncoordinated trends, already referred to in relation to university research. At the same time the insecurity of position common to all Government-aided scientists is made worse in this case by the difficulty of obtaining any other posts. (9) This increases the already existing pressure for medical research workers to qualify as medical practitioners, a policy of very dubious value, since the ability for research and medical practice are very different, while the taking of a medical degree in any case implies the loss of two to four years of research time.

An important subsidiary of the Medical Research Council is the Industrial Health Research Board. This body carries out investigations on many aspects of individual diseases and on conditions of work in factories, workshops and mines. When we consider that, after malnutrition, industrial conditions are the greatest cause of illness and death (10), we can see that its potential importance is enormous. As things are its scope is extremely limited by two considerations. In the first place, in order to be permitted to examine industrial conditions at all it is obliged to remain a purely consultative and neither an executive nor a propaganda body (see Note 8). It has power neither to investigate any industrial conditions nor to enforce any action in relation to them, not even to make them publicly known. In the second place, although it is no longer called the Industrial Fatigue Board, it is not yet entirely free from the suspicion that its services are invoked by employers at least as much to alter physical conditions to allow for speeding up work, as for protecting the health and comfort of the workers, and this hinders the essential active collaboration of the Trade Unions in its work.

Private Medical Research.—It is convenient at this place to consider other aspects of medical research in this country. The universities, the voluntary and municipal hospitals and various privately subsidized research institutes all contribute to medical research. Much of this research is carried out on a very small scale in individual hospitals and medical schools. The type of work, moreover, is much more clinical even than that carried out by the Medical Research Council. It is difficult to estimate the total amount of money involved, but it is unlikely to exceed £200,000 per annum. (11) If we consider that the annual cost of the treatment and maintenance of the sick is estimated at £200,000,000 per annum (12) and of this the medical profession must receive not less than £60,000,000 (13), a total expenditure of £400,000 on medical research seems ludicrously small. The essential difficulty is, however, that, although the value of medical treatment to the patient depends ultimately almost entirely on medical research, the doctor's fees are entirely independent of it; and, in fact, the greater the development and application of medical research, the more absurd seems the whole system of the practice of medicine for private profit. More relevant than this consideration is the fact that no sufficiently organized body is concerned with the development of medical research, while the completely individualistic nature of medical practice and the hopelessly inadequate finance of the voluntary hospital system makes it virtually impossible to persuade doctors themselves to contribute to any medical research scheme. (14) The Government's interest is obviously extremely lukewarm. It is actually paying more for the poison gas research of the Chemical Warfare (Defence) Department (£204,000) than for the Medical Research Council.

Needless to say, the medical research work outside the Council's activities is practically completely uncoordinated in itself and in relation to the Council's work, and the position of the research worker is correspondingly worse. The fact that in the past, when conditions no better than these prevailed, medical research has been able to achieve significant and even revolutionary results in medical practice should not be used as an excuse for present apathy and self-satisfaction. The early successes of medical research were a consequence of the discovery of the germ theory of disease which enabled acute diseases to be brought under control on the basis of the relatively slight knowledge of the mechanisms of infection and recovery. The problems of chronic diseases, which cause under modern conditions the majority of deaths, other than those due to malnutrition, are still largely unsolved and will require for their solution a much more thorough understanding of physiology. This can only come in a reasonable time if far greater efforts are made to develop medical research. If we consider that for lack of medical research thousands of people are dying unnecessarily every year and millions are suffering from disease, the condition of medical research in this country is not only a disgrace but a crime.

AGRICULTURAL RESEARCH

The situation of agricultural research is even more confused than that of medical research. Funds for agricultural research are derived from a number of different Government Departments, from local authorities, and from various voluntary societies and commercial enterprise. An attempt to co-ordinate these was made by the setting up of the Agricultural Research Council. This body was not constituted to take over and administer in a unified way the funds for agricultural research as the D.S.I.R. does in its own field, but simply to co-ordinate and prevent overlap of existing expenditure. Agricultural research work is carried out in a number of different stations throughout the country, but each of these draws its funds from many separate sources and in these circumstances the difficulties of providing any coherent scheme of agricultural research are practically insurmountable. The position is admirably summarized in a report made by the Society for Political and Economic Planning on this subject:

"The manner of spending agricultural research money in Great Britain is so curious and involved that fully to describe its working would far exceed the limits of space available. To summarize very briefly, England and Wales are divided into provinces served by seventeen agricultural colleges and research institutes, ninety per cent. of whose incomes are derived from a Government block grant of £159,000. Research institutes are autonomous, and their work is under the control of a director, with varying resources at his disposal.

The amount of support these receive from public funds, without which they could not exist, depends upon decisions reached through collaboration between five units of the central government, the Ministry of Agriculture, the Scottish Department of Agriculture, the Development Commission, the Agricultural Research Council, and the Treasury, on the one hand, and local authorities and the heads of research institutes and laboratories on the other hand.

Although the administrative picture can be clearly drawn in broad outline, there are wide variations in detail in the relationships between the various county authorities, which give an impression of considerable complexity.

Apart from the question of inadequate funds, various criticisms are levelled at the existing arrangements for agricultural research. From the farmer's standpoint it is suggested that much current research is of little or no practical value either because it is carried out without adequate appreciation of actual farming conditions, or because it deals only with particular aspects, leaving untouched others which must be dealt with before action can follow, or because it is presented in a form which the average farmer cannot understand or in a publication which he has never heard of. It is, moreover, suggested that the pattern of organization adopted is so cumbersome that it is hard for an ordinary farmer to get a prompt answer to his questions, unless they are so simple as to be answerable offhand by the adviser on the spot, who obviously cannot keep in full touch with the more specialized recent research on a large number of subjects.

The further suggestion is made, that owing to the complex division of responsibility, a somewhat elaborate etiquette has grown up in order to protect the interests of the various parties concerned, with the result that inquiries are liable to be treated with excessive caution and in a spirit of red tape, unless the people concerned happen to be personally acquainted. Again, it is maintained that the allocation of funds as between animal diseases and poultry research which are starved and fruit research which is well looked after bears no relation to the relative national importance of the agricultural industries concerned or to the urgency of their need for research assistance. The allocation of funds as between, say, basic research on the one hand and *ad hoc* research on the other, or between economic and pathological research, is criticized on the same grounds, and it is suggested that if valid reasons exist for the present allocation they should at least be publicly stated and submitted for criticism as a whole, instead of being borne on so many different votes, and so intricately entangled that only a clear-headed accountant could unravel the position. The complaint is made that there is no known quarter to which requests, suggestions, or ideas for new research lines worth following up can be forwarded with the certainty that they will be sympathetically and promptly examined, and that action will ensue where the suggestion is found to be of value.

To these and similar criticisms from the farmer's side rejoinders may be made, and further criticisms added. The research worker, for example, may claim that a very substantial contribution is being made in the face of many difficulties and widespread obstruction. He may point out that, whereas the State pays many of its medical and legal advisers salaries of £1,000 a year and upwards, very few who make a career in agricultural research can aspire to getting beyond £800, even if they get as high as that. The level of salaries being so low, and the overlapping of educational, advisory, research and administrative functions so general, it may be submitted that an underpaid and overworked staff can do no more than it is doing. Again, it may be said that effective research depends on keen and intelligent co-operation, which is not always forthcoming from farmers, who cannot expect their needs always to be sensed without taking more trouble to think out and make clear what their needs are. Finally, the research director may claim that a large proportion of his time is wasted in making and following up applications for piecemeal grants to a series of grant-giving bodies, official and unofficial, each with small resources to dole out. The administrator again may retort that the system, however cumbersome it may look on paper, has produced remarkably good results within the limits of finance and personnel available: that co-ordination is, in fact, carefully and continuously maintained by personal contact, and that while friction may occasionally occur no system of organization has yet been invented which can make two men work together if they do not want to work together.

It is not necessary to develop these arguments any further in order to show, first, that the existing system is not working as smoothly and effectively as it might, and further, that any attempt to fix blame on particular parties is bound to be futile."—*Planning*, No. 57, pp. 3-5.

It will be seen from this that the present situation of agricultural research is satisfactory neither to the Government, the farmers, nor the research workers. It is not very surprising that such a state of affairs should occur. English agriculture has remained for the most part fixed at a stage of development which in the eighteenth century represented a pioneer experiment in the production of food for profit, but in the twentieth is a sheer anachronism. The essential difficulty of agricultural research is not so much to get the work done but to see that when it is done it can be taken up in a practical way. The chief tendency in modern agriculture is to restrict output with the aim of keeping up prices. This is fundamentally incompatible with any agricultural research whatever. As Sir Daniel Hall says in *The Frustration of Science*:

"Whether as a consequence of these state interferences with agriculture or whether on account of causes more general, bound up with the world's disequilibrium, the market appears to be overloaded with all agricultural products which have more than a local sale. Wholesale prices are definitely below the general costs of production, and this low level is universally ascribed to over-production. Yet in any general sense over-production of foodstuffs should be indefinitely remote. The distinguishing feature of the consumer's demand for food is its flexibility in the matter of quality, even if we allow that the whole population is satisfied as regards quantity, which is far from being the case. The lower the family income the more is the dietary made up of cereals—wheat, rye, maize, rice— because these materials afford the cheapest sources of the energy with which the body must be furnished. As the income rises of family or community the more are cereals replaced by live-stock products—meat, milk, eggs, etc., and by vegetables and fruit. Meat and livestock products are themselves manufactured from cereals and other prime returns from the soil. Thus a superfluity of wheat can be converted into bacon or eggs, and from the energy point of view the conversion is a wasteful one; from five to ten times as much life-sustaining material is contained in the wheat as in the meat into which it can be transformed. Similarly vegetables and fruit possess a low amount of energy for the maintenance of life in proportion to their cost, *i.e.* for the quantity of labour expended in their growth, again as compared with the labour required to produce cereals. Thus for a given population the gross call upon the farmer—the total production that is needed from the land, will rise with the purchasing power and standard of living of the general public. The poorest classes consume little but cereals, which make the smallest call upon the land area and the labour of the farmer; to supply the mixed dietary of a better-class family more land, more labour, more skill, are required. From this point of view it is idle to postulate over-production of foodstuffs.

Yet over-production as measured by the actual demand and by prices does exist, and science is asked to call a halt in its endeavours to increase production. The only remedy for the situation that is being generally attempted is restriction of output. International agreements are being made to restrict the production of wheat, of sugar, and of rubber. Brazil has been burning coffee, the United States have ploughed up cotton and tobacco, and slaughtered young pigs, the Irish Free State orders the slaughtering of calves. The research workers in agricultural science, a relatively small body who have been growing by degrees in one country and another during the last half-century, and have acquired some control over nature, seem to find themselves no longer wanted in the world. Perhaps not entirely so, for if national self-sufficiency is to be the world policy, the task of growing rice, for example in Essex, will make heavy demands upon science. But there is a better way, if good is to be measured by the real wealth of the population, *i.e.* by the share of the world's resources at the disposal of the individual, and that is to apply science also to the distribution of the productive capacity of the world and to the government of its peoples.

A century ago the factory did not all at once displace the hand-loom, and in the case of agriculture the solitary worker has the additional advantage in the struggle that he is at least producing food for his family. But the final outcome cannot be in doubt; organization with capital, power, and science at command—in other words the machine—must win, provided free competition is allowed to rule. State organization of agriculture in some form has become inevitable; many branches of farming in Great Britain would perish if they were not 'nursed.' The question remains, what form shall the organization take ? We have one example before us in the Russian plan. This represents what we might call an engineer's layout to obtain maximum efficiency of production from the land, given a perfectly clean sheet as to land, labour and capital, without any hampering conditions other than those imposed by soil and climate. It is the method of industrial exploitation such as we see at work in some of the great farms of the United States and of tropical countries, raised to a higher power, from thousands to millions of acres, by the all-controlling State organization. Its aim is to secure from the soil the food and other raw materials required by the nation by the minimum employment of man-power, made effective by the application of science and machinery, thus liberating the greater proportion of the labour hitherto so employed for other forms of production which will add to the real wealth of the community. It demands for its realization a wealth of directive skill and a technique of national organization which only began to be attempted during the War. It necessitates a social revolution which no other country is prepared to carry through " (pp. 26-29).

At present some £40,000,000 per annum are spent on direct subsidies to agriculture and as much again in indirect subsidies from tariffs and so forth. At the same time an elaborate system of marketing boards has been set up mainly to prevent the farmer producing more than a stipulated amount of foodstuffs, with the net result that, as Sir John Orr points out, one-half of the population has not enough of the right kinds of food to eat. If one-fiftieth of the expenditure on agricultural subsidies went to agricultural research and the Government's powers were used to ensure that the results of the research were promptly put into immediate operation, as is done even in such relatively backward countries as Egypt, it should be possible to increase production sufficiently to provide the population with ample foodstuffs, apart from basic imports of wheat and meat, and at the same time so to lower the cost of production that farming would be profitable without subsidies. The complicated network of conservatism, prejudice and vested interest which prevents this being done is probably responsible for far more deaths and misery through sheer under-feeding than are due to the failure of the system of public health.

SCIENCE IN INDUSTRY

It is not easy to estimate the amount of scientific work being done in the laboratories of industrial firms. No survey of this work exists, and owing to its nature it is very difficult to collect any information about it. Some picture, however, can be obtained by the consideration of the number of scientific research workers employed in industry and by the output of papers contributed to scientific journals by industrial scientists. At the outset we are faced with the difficulty of distinguishing between scientists and technicians in industrial service. Many mechanical engineers, and still more electrical and chemical engineers, are necessarily in part scientists, but their work on the whole cannot be classified as scientific research as it mostly consists of translating into practical and economic terms already established scientific results. On the other hand, many trained scientists in industrial employ are occupied with precisely such tasks, consequently the number of published papers is probably more indicative of the scientific importance of industrial research than is the actual number of scientists employed. A sample analysis shows that while the number of scientists employed in industry represents some 70 per cent. of all qualified scientific workers (15), the number of papers they contribute to scientific journals is only 2 per cent. and even to technical journals only 36 per cent. of the total number of published papers (see Appendix III (b)). To these must be added the scientific information contained in patents which are for the most part taken out by industrial firms (see pp. 144-147). The great majority, however, of these patents are for technical improvements and the contribution of patent literature to scientific advance is, except in restricted fields, negligible. It is also necessary to take into account the amount of secret scientific research which is being carried on. It is inevitably quite impossible to gauge the importance of this, but it is fairly clear, if only from the objections raised by industrial firms to collective research and to detailed Government inspection, that it must be considerable.

Expenditure.—The amount of money spent on industrial research is, however, probably large compared with that spent on Government research. Naturally scarcely any figures are available, but the total may be as much as two million pounds (see Appendices II and III). Yet this total is delusive because it includes money spent on non-profit-making plant on a semi-industrial scale, an expense far greater than that of scientific research proper. Industrial scientific research is very irregularly distributed between industries and between firms in the same industry. Naturally newer industries which depend for their existence on scientific research on the whole contribute most largely to it while the older traditional industries in many cases hardly carry out any scientific research whatever (see Appendices II (*b*) and V). In most cases only the larger firms in any industry are in a position to carry out research, and consequently we may say that probably the greater part of industrial scientific research is carried out in the laboratories of a very few firms. A greater number of firms may employ one or two chemists for routine purposes, but real research requires at least five workers, and only the three hundred and fifty odd firms employing more than a thousand workers and smaller specialized firms in such trades as radio and fine chemicals can afford to do this. We may safely assume that the number of research laboratories is between three and six hundred. Of these the great majority are small laboratories, mostly occupied with routine control and development. Serious contributions to industrial research probably come from less than a dozen big firms, which have very large laboratories with a hundred to three hundred workers.

Character of Work.—It is also very difficult to assess the character of the work carried on in industrial laboratories. The dozen or so laboratories of the big electrical and chemical firms are, of course, large enough to be compared with Government laboratories, and conditions of work in them are not essentially different. Scientists of high qualifications are employed as directors, and a considerable amount of fairly fundamental work is done. There is, however, no doubt that in this respect Britain lags far behind both the Continental countries and the U.S.A. There is a tradition in British industry which is definitely inimical to science and consequently to the scope and freedom given to industrial scientific research. Few results of fundamental importance have in the past ten years emerged from any British industrial laboratory, whereas many such have come from German and American laboratories. The large new combines which have arisen in England since the War in electrical and chemical industries have patent-sharing agreements with the corresponding firms abroad, and there is an undeniable tendency to import scientific results ready made rather than to develop them in English laboratories. Needless to say, where on account of tariffs foreign firms have established British factories, practically the whole of the research work is done abroad. The Government, despite its zeal for the protection of the products and profits of British industry, would seem to have given no consideration to the safeguarding of its scientific initiative. As in 1914, only imminence of war would bring this fact to the notice of the powers that be, and it is highly probable that the occurrence of another war would find this country unable to supply an adequate number of research scientists and technicians.

Co-ordination of industrial research beyond that due to the formation of trusts and agreements between firms is virtually non-existent. This in itself leads directly to inefficiency, as there is no guarantee against overlapping; in fact, overlapping probably does occur at least twice over in the greater part of industrial research. Where, owing to governmental interference, associations of firms have been formed, as in the iron and steel trades, co-operative research is undertaken, in this case under semi-governmental control, through the Research Associations. There are, as well, informal connections between industrial scientists and the Research Associations, but owing to requirements of secrecy this does at least as much to hamper the work of the Associations as it does to assist the scientists. A large part of the time of all Associations is taken up with work for firms in the industry. Thus we may say that, taken in all, not only is the amount of money expended in industrial research in this country both by the Government and private firms ludicrously small, but also the greater proportion of what is spent is wasted on account of internal inefficiency and lack of co-ordination.

THE FINANCE OF RESEARCH

It should not be surprising, in view of what has already been said, that the finance of scientific research in this country has an extremely complicated character. Moreover, the sources of the money used for science do not correspond closely to the separate categories of administration of scientific research already enumerated. University, industrial, independent, and even Governmental research, all to a greater or lesser degree draw their funds from the same group of sources. The chief sources are the return from ancient endowments, current endowment, grants from Government and local authorities, and Industry. University science draws from all four sources. Industrial research, as already mentioned, draws from Government, or Government from industry, according to different judgments of the value of the research. It is extremely difficult to estimate actual sums of money which are available from these sources, but some of the published figures are given in Appendices II (*b*), (*c*) and III (*c*).

Endowment.—For most practical purposes the value of the ancient endowments can be neglected, as only the older universities benefit substantially from them (see Appendix I (*d*)). Here the total return from endowment is indeed considerable, amounting to nearly a million pounds a year, but most of this sum goes to maintaining university amenities and to teaching. The amount available for scientific research is probably at most a tenth of the total. The income to universities from fees does not enter into account as the fees do not in themselves suffice even to pay for the tuition and could consequently contribute nothing to the financing of research.

Current endowment is on a considerable scale, but is naturally extremely irregular in its incidence. The chief beneficiaries are the universities and, to a lesser extent, independent research institutes and hospitals. Figures here are also difficult to obtain, but some are included in the Appendix. As in the case of ancient endowments it is, of course, not clear how much of these sums could be considered to be devoted to research proper. Many gifts to the universities are for the foundation of chairs in which the function of teaching often predominates, or for the erecting of buildings in which both teaching and research take place. Endowments are apt to come in the form of large sums at irregular intervals, but there is a general tendency for them to follow the fluctuations of the trade cycle. In the case of the older universities this irregularity is not so dangerous, as they are well ballasted with ancient endowments. In other cases endowment can be an additional cause of instability and irregular development.

Government Grants.—We have already discussed the governmental contribution to scientific research. Apart from the upkeep of its own laboratories, the total Government contribution in the form of grants for students and research workers is relatively insignificant: £90,000 a year for medical research, £26,000 for industrial, and £7000 a year for agricultural research, in all £123,000. Small as these sums are, they cannot be neglected in university economy as they furnish an important part of the maintenance of research students between their graduation and the time, if it occurs, that they can take up a senior appointment. The administration, though not the amount, of expenditure of Government funds is largely in the hands of committees on which the universities are represented. Local authorities contribute on a considerable scale to the teaching side of universities, but, except for agricultural purposes, very little to the research side. This, as things are at present, is probably fortunate, as the interference of local politics in research institutions, where they are not guaranteed by the checks which are operative in Government science, are sometimes deplorable. (16)

For the most part the industrial contribution to the finance of science is confined to the subsidizing of their own laboratories. Occasionally, however, industrial firms, as apart from individuals, contribute to the endowments of universities. (17) More frequently, however, industry supports special researches which are carried out in university laboratories partly by members of the university staff and partly by research workers paid for entirely by the industry. This system has never become very widespread, for it is in some ways disadvantageous to both parties. The chief trouble is that, from the university point of view, it ties the research workers too much to the service of firms and, from the firms' point of view, it is even more difficult than in the case of their own research to see what financial returns they get out of the work. Secrecy is another difficulty. Commercial work done in universities is generally considered there to be carried out with a secrecy inappropriate to academic pursuits, while in the eyes of the firm it is dangerous to trust their workers in such a general atmosphere of free discussion as a university is supposed to provide. It is not surprising, therefore, that the largest firm in the chemical industry has been gradually withdrawing its support for research carried on in universities and centring its work where a closer eye can be kept on it. (18)

Administration.—In universities, management of the funds available for scientific research is for the most part in the hands of the same bodies as are responsible for the actual direction of research. Elsewhere, that is in Governmental or industrial research, it lies with administrative officers who need have no knowledge of science. The scientific boards of management have been brought up in an atmosphere where money has always been scarce and are consequently inclined to be over careful of expenditure for fear of finding themselves in the position where it was impossible to raise any more money. Scientific institutions very rarely borrow, having practically no security. There is relatively little pressure to acquire more funds, the most that is hoped for is to be able to get along, to offset deterioration and perhaps to allow for a very slow increase. Existing conditions are accepted without any protests because of the feeling that claims for endowment on a much larger scale would only frighten intending benefactors and give the impression that scientists were not entirely reconciled to the present state of affairs. The raising of new funds is indeed a very delicate operation and is carried on in an atmosphere of the deepest secrecy, mostly by personal contact. Public appeals are sometimes launched, but only if the ground has been well prepared and important support has been privately assured. Even in pressing the Government for increased funds, everything has to be done in the most cautious way in order that no suspicion can arise of party politics, that is, of lack of the most complete conservative orthodoxy.

Treasury Control.—Government scientific departments subject to Treasury control suffer under severe disabilities. In financing scientific research the rational method would be to allow for wide fluctuations on materials and apparatus, while retaining a fairly constant or gradually increasing contribution to salaries. This is very different from the ordinary routine expenditure of administrative departments where needs can be fairly accurately estimated beforehand. Except where the system of block grants or grants-in-aid prevails, the sum allocated every year must be spent in that year. Any failure to spend it would indicate that the department did not really need the money and would consequently have to do with less the next year. The result is alternate years of wasteful expenditure and cramped work. There is no doubt that the system of block grants, although opposed by the Treasury, would relieve the situation considerably, it being possible in these circumstances to carry over a surplus or deficit on that account in succeeding years. But the main trouble is that administrative officers, not understanding what research expenditure is for, adopt towards it an entirely arbitrary attitude, depending partly on past practice and partly on the personnel of the scientific directors.

The situation in industry shows these features in an aggravated form. Ideally, research should be free of the Treasury limitations that hamper expenditure; actually, however, research expenditure is looked at as a somewhat ornamental extra to be indulged in when the firm is doing well and ruthlessly cut in bad times. It is practically impossible to sell scientific apparatus, and consequently the only effective economies are to be obtained by sacking staff or reducing their salaries.

The Character of Research Finance.—The result of this financial system is that the money available for scientific research is apt to be invariable in amount when it should be variable, and widely variable when it should be constant. The effects of this are felt most keenly by the scientific workers themselves. Under modern conditions security is one of the prime requirements in seeking employment; there is consequently a tendency to accept scientific work where security is guaranteed, as in the universities and in parts of Government service, and to avoid posts which may carry better pay but from which dismissals are most likely just at the periods when jobs are hardest to obtain. (19) It is true that in this respect the scientific worker is no worse and possibly better off than the great bulk of manual or clerical workers. The social injustice of the system is a common injustice, but the result of this is felt not only by the scientific worker but by the whole community, through the holding up of the progress of pure, and even more of applied, science. Effective scientific investigations are not jobs to be finished in a day, a month, or even a year; ten years may often pass in a single man's work between the first ideas and their final working out. Unless there is a reasonable security for a period of this order, the chances are that many long-period researches will never be brought to an end and that even more will never be undertaken. This conspires with other tendencies, particularly in industrial science, in favour of researches yielding immediate results. Such researches are, however, of very limited utility and in the long run grossly uneconomic. It may be said that on the average the deeper the investigation the greater the profitability of any particular research. Any system of adequate development of scientific research must include a provision for secure employment.

The Character of Research Expenditure.—Before we can arrive at any idea of the amount spent on scientific research it is necessary to examine the character of that expenditure. The four most obvious categories for research expenditure are: salaries, apparatus and experimental material, upkeep (including salaries of laboratory assistants, mechanics, etc.), and buildings. For different kinds of scientific research the amounts required under these heads will vary enormously. In mathematics only salaries and a small expenditure for chalk, stationery, etc., is required, though nowadays introduction of calculating machines threatens to make a mathematics department as expensive as any other. At the other extreme, an agricultural field-station will spend far more on upkeep, including the purchase of stock, than it will on salaries. Roughly, the more practical the investigation, the more charges other than salaries will increase.

On the boundaries of applied science the situation is more complicated because of the difficulties already mentioned of separating the technician from the scientist and semi-industrial plant from scientific apparatus. In publishing accounts of scientific expenditure, therefore, it would be desirable to state in every case the proportion of salaries to total expenditure, as giving some measure of the more or less practical nature of the investigation and enabling comparisons to be made between the relative amounts of scientific work included in two different scientific appropriations. As time goes on and science becomes more complex the relative proportions of salaries will shrink in all cases. Consequently, a steady endowment of science or even a moderately increasing one may conceal an actual retrogression of scientific work. Such retrogression was, in fact, marked all over the capitalist world during the late slump and is still maintained in many countries.

The real difficulty, however, in economic assessment of science is to draw the line between expenditures on pure and on applied science.   At present when both are lumped together it is felt that science is being adequately rewarded because of the relatively large sums involved—relative, that is, to the amounts spent in the past, not to the budgets of the industries concerned.   However, as applied science is by far the most expensive, the greater part of this sum represents expenditure which is not strictly research but definite investment, the future return of which is fairly assured.   It is clearly necessary to spend money in some definite proportion on pure and applied science, but unless the sums are kept separate it will be impossible to see that the less immediately justifiable claims of fundamental research are fairly treated.

The Budget of Science

From what has already been said it can be seen that the difficulties in assessing the precise sum annually expended on scientific research are practically insurmountable.   It could only be done by changing the method of accounting of universities, Government Departments, and industrial firms, and this is unlikely to happen unless some substantial inducement, such as exempting research expenditure from income tax, is adopted.   Nevertheless, it is necessary to obtain some idea, however rough, inside which expenditure on research is likely to lie, in order to see the position of research in the national economy.

An attempt to make such an estimate for a fairly normal post-depression year, 1934, is shown below: At present (1937) the Defence Estimates would be shown much larger (£2,800,000) and there would be a corresponding increase in industrial research, but both of these must be considered as abnormal expenditure and will probably not be maintained.   Two estimates are shown.   The first or gross estimate includes everything which can possibly be called research.   Thus for the universities it assumes that half the time of all university teachers in science, medicine, technology and agriculture is spent on research and that two-thirds of departmental expenditure is used for research purposes.   In Government and industry it assumes that everything called research is research.   The net estimate attempts to allow for these assumptions by reducing the gross sums by factors corresponding to what is known of the character of the work in the different sections.   The reduction factors are by no means as drastic as they might be, they would still allow for a good deal of routine measurement and testing, but the resulting figures must give a fairly close approximation to the amount of money spent on progress in scientific knowledge and technique. The estimates are naturally of very different orders of accuracy. Only the Government figures are explicitly given. The university figures are estimated in a complicated way from those given in the University Grants Commission Report. The industrial figures are, of course, the most difficult to obtain. The bases for their estimation are the statements of research expenditure from thirty-five firms given in *Industrial Research Laboratories*, an estimate of forty-five others, based on the number of men employed, and a generous allowance for the firms who declined to give particulars. (Details are given in Appendix III (c).) This figure, therefore, is far the least reliable and may be out as much as 50 per cent. either way, but considering the rough nature of the total estimates this does not seriously matter. The actual estimates are as follows:

	Gross.	Net.
UNIVERSITIES, LEARNED SOCIETIES AND INDEPENDENT FOUNDATIONS . .	£1,500,000	£800,000
GOVERNMENT—		
Defence Services	2,000,000	80,000
Industrial Research	600,000	300,000
Medical Research	150,000	120,000
Agricultural Research . . .	200,000	150,000
INDUSTRIAL—		
Contributions to Research Associations .	200,000	100,000
Independent Research	2,000,000	400,000
TOTAL . .	£6,650,000	£1,950,000

Thus we see that the gross total is under seven million pounds and the net total under two million. These figures are useful only if we bear in mind what they stand for. An intermediate figure of four million pounds will serve for most purposes as a generous estimate of what is spent on scientific research in Great Britain. Professor Julian Huxley, who in 1934 made a survey of research in Britain, is wisely cautious in expressing an opinion on the absolute amounts of money spent on research, but his estimates are in substantial agreement with those given here :

"Research directed to industrial needs heads the list—that is, counting the money spent by Government, by university departments of applied science, and by private firms—with, I should say, nearly half the total. Research for the fighting services, not counting mere development, takes about half of what is spent on industry. Research connected with agriculture and related subjects like forestry and fisheries comes next, with a fifth or a sixth of the total; and then research connected with medicine and health, with about an eighth, or even less. And research in all other branches, together with all background research, probably does not come to a twelfth of the total, though I admit that this item is the most difficult to be sure of. As to the actual amounts, I hardly like to give any figures, as people so often quote rough estimates as if they were ascertained facts. But I should say that the total spent on research in this country is between four and six millions a year, probably nearer the lower figure."—*Scientific Research and Social Needs*, p. 255.

The total contribution of the community to all inquiries capable of changing the state of civilization is thus £4,000,000 or less. This is the amount put aside to allow for the development, apart from the mere mechanical growth, of industry and culture. A sum of this size can be appreciated only comparatively. Compared in the first place with the national income of £4,000,000,000 it represents one-tenth of 1 per cent. This certainly seems a very low percentage and at least it could be said that any increase up to tenfold of the expenditure on science would not notably interfere with the immediate consumption of the community; as it is it represents only 3 per cent. of what is spent on tobacco, 2 per cent. of what is spent on drink, and 1 per cent. of what is spent on gambling in the country. It is true that these ways of spending money, while not in themselves necessarily more enjoyable than the pursuit of science, are spread over a far larger number of people. Nevertheless the expenditure on science becomes ludicrous when we consider the enormous return in welfare which such a trifling expenditure can produce.

In a hundred years the national income has increased eightfold. This has ultimately been due to the application of relatively rudimentary science, the total cost of which can be estimated at not more than £100,000,000, probably far less. Any estimate of the precise returns of scientific expenditure is impossible to make, but they are certainly very large indeed. Fundamental science takes some considerable time before its results become commercially valuable, and when they do, the benefits are spread over a large number of industries and are consequently hard to check. But in applied science, where the proportion of returns is far less, the results are surprising enough. In Appendix IV, taken from Government figures, are shown the returns in annual savings against the total expenditure on research, including research on many other problems besides those to which the savings referred. The average return on money invested is 800 per cent. per annum. We shall discuss later why our present system of production is not able to take advantage of this immense profitability of science, but whatever the reasons are, the fact remains that we do not make use of science to anything but a very small fraction of its possible material utility.

In this respect Britain, which is a very wealthy country, is far behind others. It was estimated by President Hoover in 1926 that $200,000,000 are spent annually on scientific research in the United States. More recent figures are not available, but it is probable that not less than $300,000,000 are now spent. This is nearly ten times our gross total, but allowing for the greater national income of the United States, estimated at $50,000,000,000, it represents an expenditure of 6/10 per cent. as against our 1/10 per cent. In Germany the figures are hard to get, but the total is certainly of the same order as our own (see p. 200). In the Soviet Union, where scientific expenditure is organized far more effectively than in this country, the expenditure in 1934 was 900,000,000 roubles, amounting at official exchange rates to £36,000,000, nine times our gross expenditure, or eight-tenths of 1 per cent. as against the British contribution of one-tenth of 1 per cent. of the national income. It is essential to bring home this capital deficiency of British science, the fact that its total development in relation to national needs is grossly inadequate. The scale of expenditure on science is probably less than one-tenth of what would be reasonable and desirable in any civilized country. This is a deficiency of an entirely different order from the current deficiencies of the economic system. A recent investigation by the Engineers' Study Group, entitled *Food and the Family Budget*, claims to show that the material wants of the population of the country could be met, without notably interfering with the present grotesque system of distribution, by an increase in the national income of about 25 per cent. or 1000 million pounds per annum. (20) Compared with this the needs of science are modest. A sum of between 20 and 40 million pounds per annum, which is between ½ and 1 per cent. of the national income, would permit of an adequate expansion of science and of the general reorganization which would also be necessary. It might be found, however, that the expenditure of such sums for a few years would be by itself sufficient to raise the national income by far more than 1000 million pounds a year.

(1) See Sir W. Bragg's address, p. 66 below.

(2) There are 60 national scientific and 15 medical societies listed in the *Official Year-Book of the Scientific and Learned Societies of Great Britain and Ireland*, besides the very large number of local scientific societies. The extent of the activities of such societies and its limitations can be seen in the case of the most ambitious recent effort of organization, the Chemical Council, of which Professor Philip writes in *What Science Stands For:*

" Within the last two years a notable step has been taken towards the consolidation of the science and profession of chemistry by the formation of the Chemical Council, which is based on the three chartered organizations already mentioned (the Chemical Society, the Institute of Chemistry and the Society of Chemical Industry), as well as on the Association of British Chemical Manufacturers, representing important industrial and commercial interests. The Chemical Council, set up in the first instance for a period of seven years, aims at securing a joint foundation for undertakings which have hitherto been the concern of separate organizations, and at enlisting the support of industry in this matter. The publication of new knowledge, either in the form of original communications or in the form of summaries of papers which have already appeared, is of the first importance in a science growing so rapidly as chemistry. For every chemist, whatever be his particular field of work, some acquaintance with new views, new discoveries, new applications, is essential, and the publication of new knowledge in the appropriate form is really a concern of the whole profession. The successful prosecution of this enterprise is a vital matter also for the industries which depend for their smooth running and their progressive development on the application of chemical knowledge and the furtherance of chemical research. If the newly established Chemical Council can unite the chemical profession and the chemical industry in support of publications and other objects of similarly wide appeal, such as a central library, it will have achieved a notable advance. Its formation is the earnest of further moves in the direction of consolidation and unification of the chemical profession, such as the acquisition of adequate central premises and the establishment of a complete register of trained chemists " (pp. 58-59).

(3) Thus we find Bishop Sprat, the first historian of the Society, indicating its multifarious technical occupations :

" First they employ fellows to examine treaties, etc., of countries ; they employ others to discourse with seamen, travellers, tradesmen and merchants ; then they compose a body of questions about observable things. Then the Fellows would start correspondence with the East Indies, China, St. Helena, Teneriffe, Barbary, Morocco " . . . (p. 155).

" In this our chief and most wealthy merchants and citizens many have assisted with their presence and contributed their labours and helped correspondence ; employed factors abroad to answer enquiries ; they have laid out in all countries for observations and gifts " . . . (p. 129).

" They have proposed the composing of a catalogue of all trades works, and manufacture . . . taking notice of all physical receipts or secrets, instruments, tools, and engines, manual operations or sleights. . . . They recommended advancing the manufacture of tapestry, silkmaking, melting lead ore with pit-coal . . . making trial of English earths to see if they will (not do) for perfecting the potters art. They have compared soils and clays for making better bricks and tiles. They started the propagation of potatoes, and experiments with tobacco oil " . . . (p. 256).—Sprat, *History of the Royal Society*, 1667.

See also pp. 291, 394.

(4) Sir William Bragg alludes to these as well as to the position of the Society in the general scheme of British scientific research in his presidential address for 1936 :

" The capital value of the funds administered by the Society, if we include in them the Warren bequest, is now more than a million sterling. . . . In all the Society now directs the expenditure of about £31,000 a year on research. The direction makes a considerable demand upon the time and energies of Fellows, and it is a pleasant duty to acknowledge their willing and able service on numerous committees.

The use to be made of these moneys is to a considerable extent limited by the terms of the respective trusts. Nevertheless, there is ample opportunity for a general policy at the discretion of the Society. It is natural and right that special emphasis is laid upon general or fundamental research, so far as donors' wishes allow ; and indeed the terms in which the donors have expressed themselves are favourable to research of that kind.

It is to be observed that many other bodies possess funds which are administered for similar purposes. In a list published by the Royal Commission for the Exhibition of 1851, the Commission itself takes place as one of the oldest, and the Leverhulme Trust as one of the newest. The list includes such well-known names as the Carnegie Trust, the Halley Stewart Trust, the Beit Memorial Fellowship Trust and others. City companies are also to be found there. The Improvement of Natural Knowledge follows also on the activities of many bodies that have specific applications in view. Each branch of the Defence Services maintains its own research laboratories ; so do the Medical Research Council, the Department of Scientific and Industrial Research, the Agricultural Research Council, the Post Office and so on.

Still more closely concerned with the direct applications of Natural Knowledge are the laboratories of the country's industries. Many of these are of great and established reputation. On the whole, the industrial laboratory is some way from being as frequent a factor in industry as it ought to be, but undoubted progress has been made in recent years.

This brief enumeration of some of the agencies making for the improvement of natural knowledge will serve as a reminder that the sum total of the work done in this direction is very large. It may fall far short of what is to be hoped for, but it forms an agency which begins to acquire a certain coherence, something which can be viewed as a whole and considered in respect to its character and its effects. It is beginning to find itself, like Kipling's ship.

An immediate and obvious effect is the increase in the volume of published results. The publications of scientific societies have doubled and trebled in size; and their treasurers are in many cases hard put to it to meet the consequent additional expense. Numerous industrial publications also contain records of special investigations. There is every reason for satisfaction with the increase in natural knowledge which has followed on the encouragement of research.

In certain respects, at least, the application of the knowledge acquired is also satisfactory, though judgment on that point will vary according to the position of the observer in a very large field. There are obvious improvements in the health and general well-being of the nation, in its industries, in the strength of its trade and in its powers of defence; and these are matters of primary importance. Though they may be no more than means to an end, they and the appropriate application of knowledge are a first consideration.

To such applications every kind of research may contribute; for even those who would have it that science must be followed without thought of its usefulness must admit that it has to be very pure science indeed which only meets with its application, as a straight line meets its parallel, at infinity. In general, the encounter may be expected to come so soon that its effect has a present importance, and must be taken into account. The individual member of the Society may keep his thoughts and his experiments within an isolated region, and so contribute what is due from him as a Fellow. But the Society as a whole must take the wider view, and watch constantly the relations between scientific advance and the people who are affected by it. It accepts these responsibilities when it undertakes to administer the great sums that have been entrusted to it. In the early days of the Society the Fellows recognized duties in these respects, as the records of their Transactions show. Many of the Founders occupied important positions in the State and their science bore directly on the needs of the nation. Throughout the three centuries of its existence, the same ideals have encouraged the activities of the Society. At some times they have been less effective than at others, but their general purpose has never been blurred. The whole of the work of the Society is therefore an important part of a general effort to improve knowledge in the expectation of resultant benefit."

(5) For further details the reader can refer to the annual reports of the D.S.I.R. (H.M. Stationery Office).

(6) See minutes of evidence given by Imperial Chemical Industries before the Royal Commission on Private Manufacture of Armaments.

(7) Sir Frederick Gowland Hopkins, in his presidential address at the anniversary meeting of the Royal Society in November 1934, said (*Proceedings of the Royal Society*, Vol. 148, pp. 24-25):

" In the history of all science which has dealt with living organisms a natural sequence may be traced. There is first the purely descriptive phase with the morphological studies which ultimately tempt efforts of classification. Then comes the study of function and the endeavour to correlate function with structure. Later the nature of the materials which support structure and form have received attention, and later still, the endeavour has been made to follow the dynamic molecular events which underlie all displays of active function. Modern biophysics and biochemistry are busy upon the last task which, though not long begun, is to-day progressive and its progress is accelerating.

I am convinced that ultimately we shall attain to an adequate intellectual picture of these invisible events and of their organization in living tissues. Our thoughts will then penetrate below the surface of visualized phenomena. Disease itself will be viewed from a new standpoint. I believe indeed that even now those who think in terms of molecular events may have visions of progress denied to those whose thought is guided by the visible alone.

To the advancement of such knowledge studies of the intact body can contribute at most but very little. You will, of course, understand that I have throughout been speaking of the advancement and not the application of knowledge.

I will pause here to ask you not to look upon me as a mere obstructionist; I do not wish to see obstacles put in the way of activities in a field which, from the nature of things, must always be of much importance. I would personally like to see a Chair of Experimental

Medicine in every University capable of providing for such a Chair an adequate Clinic. More—if clinical science is to be encouraged without any discouragement of laboratory science, I would like the encouragement to be as generous as possible. I am only urging that in any planning for the future endowment of medical research proper consideration should be given to the relative magnitude of the fields in which new knowledge should be sought.

I seem to have sensed, however, the beginnings of a definite movement in this country, and indeed elsewhere, not, of course, to ignore the laboratory; but in the distribution of funds provided for medical research to endow the Clinic on a scale which might endanger the future of research in fundamental biological science. The tenor of my remarks has been due to a conviction that in the long run such a policy would sterilize advance.

I am tempted here to a quotation which I owe to Knud Faber. It is from the writings of the great French physician, Charcot. Charcot taught that clinical observation must ever remain the supreme court of justification on the Clinic itself, but he says of it that ' without scientific renovation it soon becomes a belated routine and, as it were, stereo-typed.' It was plain to Charcot, says Faber, that the fundamental sciences were the source from which clinical observation and clinical analysis must always derive their impulse for advance."

(8) A somewhat different view of the work of the Medical Research Council is furnished by the *Report on the British Health Services*, prepared by P. E. P., p. 312 :

" Clinical research has in the past been closely linked to specialized practice. In surgery, which is an art as well as a science, this is inevitable. But in some branches the function of the medical research worker and the practitioner can be separated with advantage. Medical practice and research have been yoked together partly by the fact that the rewards of the research worker were negligible. Measures have, however, lately been taken to secure for whole-time research workers salaries making it worth their while to forego the rewards of private practice. The Medical Research Council have sought with some success to secure an increase in senior posts for whole-time work and higher teaching, and thus stop the drift of young research workers into private practice. Special clinical research units have been created by the Council in leading London hospitals (referred to in Chapter V). This policy is also being pursued by the Nuffield Trustees at Oxford. Nevertheless, there is little, except love of the work, to tempt the brilliant student to devote himself to medical research once he has graduated. There is also still too little provision in some branches for the recruitment and training of research workers, although considerable numbers of scholarships and research grants are given.

The results of medical research are passed on to the students in the medical schools and to others through the specialized journals, but it is almost impossible for a general practitioner to keep up with the latest research work. However, the development of post-graduate courses and the allocation of funds by the Ministry of Health and by the Department of Health for Scotland to enable panel practitioners to attend courses, will facilitate the spread of knowledge about research results. As has been pointed out in Chapter III, the findings of research workers in the field of industrial health are not implemented or even studied by industrialists, partly because the Industrial Health Research Board is precluded from popularizing its findings by the risk of becoming involved in controversy to an extent which might impair its neutral and detached position.

In spite of a number of weaknesses, medical research is probably on the whole more comprehensive, better planned and organized, better manned and better supported financially than any other major class of research in Great Britain, apart from research in connection with defence. It has the great advantages of a vigorous tradition of leadership and team work, and a high standard of personnel in many branches. It is particularly strong on fundamental problems in physiology and pathology, but although a broad view is taken far more work is necessary upon the economic, social, psychological and population problems out of which so much unfitness arises. The additional research most needed is not purely medical, but is of a mixed and applied nature largely falling within the province of the Ministry of Health and the Department of Health for Scotland. These departments have recently done some excellent work of this type, for example, in investigating the causes of maternal mortality in England and Wales in relation to social conditions and in tracing the incidence of diseases among insured persons in Scotland. There is room for a great expansion of this type of work, which bridges the gap between the laboratory and everyday life.

An equally serious weakness of medical research is the absence of a public relations mechanism for making the public, including such special groups as factory employers and workers, aware of the gist of the many valuable discoveries waiting to be turned to good account. Research touching on broad human problems which is buried in little-read technical reports might almost as well not be done at all. The Medical Research Council raised the question in its Report for 1934-35, but there still exists nothing like adequate provision for informing the public in intelligible terms of health discoveries which vitally concern them and which have largely been made with public money. When full allowance has been made for matters on which only the medical profession need be informed, and for differences of opinion about the most suitable agency of information, it remains plain that somebody ought to be telling the public a great deal about health which no one is telling them at present."

(9) Professor Mottram comments on the financial policy of the Council as follows :
" And the way the politician regards the need for research is shown by the fact that in the financial crisis of 1931 in Great Britain, not only were the salaries of the permanent staff of the Medical Research Council reduced by 10 per cent.—which was perhaps inevitable and defensible—but the grant for research was reduced by a like amount, bringing to an end many valuable pieces of work. For an ' economy ' of some beggarly sum of £19,000 per annum, work which might have saved untold lives perished from inanition. For money is the life-blood of research. It is needed mainly to subsidize research, but it is also essential for subsidizing the research worker. Such people Great Britain and the U.S.A. can supply in abundance—in fact, there is grave danger of unemployment among their ranks and the fruits of years of training being allowed to rot unharvested. The advance of medical research is frustrated in Great Britain to-day by the parsimony of the Treasury."
—*Frustration of Science*, pp. 81, 82.

(10) J. Kuczynsky in *New Fashions of Wage Theory* has studied statistically the effects of unemployment on death rates, and found unequivocally that the slight drop in death rate is due to the disappearance of a number of diseases brought about by working conditions to an extent that overcompensates the general weakening produced by the malnutrition accompanying unemployment.

(11) Since this was written the situation has been greatly improved by the large donation given by Lord Nuffield for medical research at Oxford University. It is too early to estimate the effect of this bequest, but it would seem as if its full value would not be realized partly because the neighbourhood of Oxford hardly furnishes enough clinical material and partly because of the limited value of clinical research itself, as pointed out by Sir F. Gowland Hopkins. (7)

(12) P. E. P., *Report on the British Health Services*, p. 25.

(13) There are some 34,000 actively practising doctors. The estimated average gross income of a panel doctor is £1700, but specialists, of whom there are not less than a thousand, receive far more than this. *Op. cit.* (12).

(14) See Cronin's searching novel of the medical profession, *The Citadel*.

(15) Excluding naturally here science teachers in schools who undoubtedly form the majority of those who have taken university degrees.

(16) See the case of Mr. Hay in report of the Conference on Academic Freedom, Oxford, 1935 (Heffer).

(17) Thus new chemical laboratories at Cambridge were provided for in 1920 by the Anglo-Persian Oil Co.

(18) The following speeches in the Cambridge University Senate throw some light on the relations of the universities with industrial research. They were occasioned by an apparently innocuous regulation which was designed to place secret and commercial research under the control of the University instead of the professors, as had been the custom hitherto.
" Professor Sir W. J. Pope said that the phrasing of the proposed new Regulation I reflected the ancient academic distrust of commerce and industry : it suggested that association with such branches of activity needed to be scrutinized in every detail by the governing body of the University because of the danger that something shameful might result, such, for instance, as a young research worker being forced to hide his results to serve some sordid commercial end. It was matter for regret that such phrasing should have been used, and more particularly in view of the fact that commerce and industry, through both firms and individuals, had made immense money gifts to the University during the last twenty years, and had shown great breadth of mind and vision in the manner of making those gifts. He trusted that the Council would withdraw that regulation, which would wound, and arouse a just indignation.
Hitherto it had been customary for the head of a laboratory to seek collaboration with

industrial undertakings, such as commercial firms and research associations : the collaboration had, in general, involved the working out of some problem by a research worker paid by the industrial concern, which also paid a fee, so adjusted by the head of the department as liberally to cover the expenses, to the laboratory. In nearly all cases the research work carried out was purely academic in character, and no restrictions were placed on publication : the object of the industrial concern which bore the cost was solely to assist the University to produce men trained in research methods, who might or might not enter the scientific industries. Occasionally an employee of a large firm came to them to work out some industrial problem, and they had no concern with the fate of the information acquired when he returned to his works. The University should, however, be gratified when a worker in technological science found it advantageous to attack a few of his problems in its laboratories.

He would like to emphasize that the collaboration established in those various ways had been of incalculable value to the University : it usually provided an opening for the research worker in the industry concerned : it created a sympathy between the University Department and Industry which secured favourable consideration for Cambridge graduates when vacancies had to be filled : it had been the determining factor which had led industrial concerns to make substantial financial contributions to the University.

Professor Lowry said it was scarcely necessary for him to emphasize to what a large extent the University was indebted to commercial and industrial undertakings. He supposed that the money which had lately come to them from the American oil industry, coming through an educational trust, had lost all connexion with the industrial industry from which the funds were derived ; but that was not the case when the Department of Chemistry had received the largest benefaction which had ever been made to it in the whole of its history. That benefaction had been made by an oil company which was still carrying on business, and he was not at all certain that it had not in part been made because in the period before the War certain discoveries had been made in the chemical laboratories at Cambridge which became a vital factor in the supply of explosives during the War. He did not think it was generally realized to how large an extent the efficient work of a research department depended, except in the case perhaps of the more wealthy American universities, on funds provided not by the institution in which the research was being carried out, but from various outside sources, more particularly commercial and industrial undertakings. As an example, a friend of his, who was the head of an important laboratory in London, had at his disposal funds to the extent of £5000 per annum, derived in part from Research Associations and in part from commercial and industrial undertakings ; and there was not the slightest doubt that he would not have had his world-wide reputation as Director of the laboratory had he not had at his disposal funds of about £5000 a year, which he could employ in promoting the research in which he was interested.

As to his own laboratory, he did not think that he need say more than that commercial and industrial undertakings were spending year by year a sum which was considerably in excess of the total amount granted by the University for the whole of the Department of Chemistry."—*University Reporter*, vol. LXIV, 991, 1934.

In further debate other members of the Senate expressed their disapproval of any secret research being carried out in university laboratories, but the final result was a compromise, leaving the situation substantially unchanged.

(19) See Sir W. Bragg's speech, p. 83.

(20) Since this inquiry was made the national income has increased from £4,400,000,000 to £5,700,000,000 per annum, but owing to our unequal distribution the required £1,000,000,000 has not helped noticeably to make up the deficiencies complained of.

CHAPTER IV

SCIENCE IN EDUCATION

Science Teaching in the Past

Science came late into the educational scheme. It is not surprising that it had no place in mediaeval education, but the revival of humanism in the Renaissance left it almost as severely alone. A certain amount of mathematics could be learnt in the universities and was even taught in the navigation schools, and a little botany and chemistry in the medical schools, but that was all. The great developments of seventeenth- and eighteenth-century science took place not because of, but in spite of, the place science occupied in education. All the great scientists up to the middle of the nineteenth century were self-taught in so far as their science went, and, in spite of the precedent of Boyle and Newton, science did not take root in the older universities. At the end of the eighteenth century the only educational establishments which gave anything like an adequate training in science were the dissenting academies in England, at which Priestley and Dalton taught, and the Artillery Schools in France, at which Napoleon was a pupil. The industrial revolution enhanced the importance of science, and gradually in the nineteenth century it began to make its way into the universities and still later into the schools. Mr. Clarke, the first Professor of Mineralogy at Cambridge, acquired his Chair, one of the earliest to be given in a scientific subject, by lectures he delivered on the jewels in the high priest's breastplate. Sir James Smith, on the other hand, one of the most competent of British botanists of the day, was refused permission to teach there because he was a member neither of the University nor of the Church of England. The only evidence of science in Dr. Arnold's Rugby was the unfortunate Martin, who had turned his study into a natural history museum. (1) Science teaching had then a flavour of radicalism and met, particularly after the Darwinian controversy, a bitter religious opposition.

When science was accepted, it appeared either as an extra subject tacked on to other studies or as an alternative for those mean-souled and materialistic enough to prefer it to the classics. Even the vigorous advocacy of T. H. Huxley and his disciples has hardly sufficed to rescue it from that condition, except perhaps at Cambridge. One result of its mode of entry into the curriculum was that the method of teaching science was not developed from the way in which the early scientists had learnt their science—by apprenticeship—but followed the didactic practice which had served for humane studies; that is, it was based essentially on lessons or lectures to which was attached of necessity some provision for practical laboratory work.

The pioneers of the teaching of science imagined that its introduction into education would remove the conventionality, artificiality, and backward-lookingness which were characteristic of classical studies, but they were gravely disappointed. So, too, in their time had the humanists thought that the study of the classical authors in the original would banish at once the dull pedantry and superstition of mediaeval scholasticism. The professional schoolmaster was a match for both of them, and has almost managed to make the understanding of chemical reactions as dull and as dogmatic an affair as the reading of Virgil's *Aeneid*. The chief claim for the use of science in education is that it teaches a child something about the actual universe in which he is living, in making him acquainted with the results of scientific discovery, and at the same time teaches him how to think logically and inductively by studying scientific method. A certain limited success has been reached in the first of these aims, but practically none at all in the second.

Those privileged members of the community who have been through a secondary or public school education may be expected to know something about the elementary physics and chemistry of a hundred years ago, but they probably know hardly more than any bright boy can pick up from an interest in wireless or scientific hobbies out of school hours. As to the learning of scientific method, the whole thing is palpably a farce. Actually, for the convenience of teachers and the requirements of the examination system, it is necessary that the pupils not only do not learn scientific method but learn precisely the reverse, that is, to believe on the authority of their masters or text-books exactly what they are told and to reproduce it when asked, whether it seems nonsense to them or not. The way in which educated people respond to such quackeries as spiritualism or astrology, not to say more dangerous ones such as racial theories or currency myths, shows that fifty years of education in the method of science in Britain or Germany has produced no visible effect whatever. The only way of learning the method of science is the long and bitter way of personal experience and, until the educational or social systems are altered to make this possible, the best we can expect is the production of a minority of people who are able to acquire some of the technique of science and a still smaller minority who are able to use and develop them.

Science in Schools

If we consider the educational system in respect of science in this narrow way, abandoning for the moment as visionary the expectation that science should play an integral and leading part in all instruction from the early ages, as it already does in the Soviet Union, and concentrate only on the question of the turning out of scientific workers, the present system still presents us with the most astonishing gaps and inefficiencies. Except for some special schools catering for a negligibly small percentage of children, there is very little science taught before the age of fourteen, that is up to the time when the vast majority of the children in this country finish their education. It is true that a certain amount of nature study, which is expected to serve as a roundabout explanation of sex, is taught in the elementary schools, but it would be farcical to pretend that this was science. The school teachers are not to blame. With the best curriculum in the world it would be extremely difficult to teach science to forty children at a time. But this early limitation has serious results. In the first place, by not teaching science at the age when children's original curiosity has not yet been damped by social conventions, the best chance of arousing a sustained interest has been lost. Actually, if educators could take the time to study the teaching of science, much of it would be found adaptable to the capacities of very young children indeed. In fact, the essentials of physics, chemistry, and biology can be and have been taught to children of six who, in some cases, could not even read. (2)

But another disadvantage of this limitation is that a great many promising recruits for science are lost at this stage. This is, of course, not peculiar to science. Gray and Moschinsky's work (3) has shown that only 26 per cent. of elementary school children of outstanding ability manage to continue their education in secondary schools, and, of those who do not, many would undoubtedly be promising scientists. It is true that a few manage to get into science at a later stage by becoming laboratory assistants, but these form a negligible minority. The existence of a large number of wireless amateurs and other scientific hobbyists testifies to the fact that there exists a very large reserve of potential scientific talent.

In secondary and public schools science begins to play a part, but it is a very restricted aspect of science. An initial disadvantage is the fact that with the present educational system the secondary and public schools are obliged to teach boys of low average intelligence and consequently to waste opportunities for pushing on those of real ability. The effects of this are made apparent at the university stage. There is still a very strong prejudice which derives from the public school classical tradition against science altogether, and science masters and boys taking science are often treated as if their interests made them socially inferior. The conventions of the examination system limit science teaching to physics and chemistry, with perhaps a little biology largely for intending medical students, and a pathetic study of botany which is supposed for some mystical reason to exercise a purifying effect on the female mind. Now physics and chemistry, as required for university entrance examinations or school certificate, has been worked into one of the most repulsive routines imaginable. A vicious circle has been established between the schools and the universities by which neither can alter the curriculum because of the objections of the other. Science is taught so that a fraction of those taught it can go to the universities in order to learn to teach it in just such a way to future generations. It is true that science masters in schools have devoted an enormous amount of care and ingenuity to making the curriculum attractive, but for every boy that it attracts there must be two or three that it puts off science for ever. It is unfortunately true that those parts of science most suitable for examination subjects are the metrical parts of physics and chemistry (the attractions between magnets, the combining weights of sodium bicarbonate and sulphuric acid), and these are at the same time the most troublesome to the lazy and unmathematical boy and the most exasperating to those who are really keen on science and want to get on to those parts of the subject where something new and interesting is being found out. There is little, in fact, in school physics and chemistry that was not known a hundred years ago and much that was known three hundred years ago.

Science masters are, of course, aware of this state of affairs and have been trying in the face of apathy and obscurantism to set their house in order. A recent report (4) prepared by the Science Masters' Association on the teaching of general science goes far to meet many of the criticisms that have been made here. It contains a syllabus for a four-year course which is probably the first to have been constructed in a scientific way. Three masters listed their pupils' interests in everyday things which had scientific implications. Three others summarized fundamental scientific ideas. These two lists were woven together in the syllabus. This, though it marks a definite advance, lacks comprehensiveness and modernity. There is a good biological section but nothing on astronomy or geology. Of the ten sections into which each year in physics is divided, the first two years contain only one fact each, and the third only two facts discovered in the nineteenth century. Only in the last year does the outlook become more modern, but even then nothing later than

1890 is introduced. X-rays, wireless, and electrons are not so much as mentioned. The chemistry is worse; the whole course contains nothing not known in 1810. The whole of organic chemistry, without which biology is incomprehensible, is omitted and modern ideas on the structure of matter never even hinted at. Nevertheless, if the spirit in which this approach has been made is maintained, it is still possible to hope for a living system of school science teaching in Britain. Further advances along this line have been made by the Modern Education Committee in the United States. Their elaborate syllabus contains a fairly accurate summary of the contemporary scientific viewpoint with particular reference to the relation of science to the life of society.

SCIENCE IN THE UNIVERSITIES

The place that science teaching occupies in the universities has never been clearly thought out. One conception has obviously been that science is an alternative way of acquiring a liberal education. This attitude is reflected in the ideal of pure science which is so often held up to the students. In practice, however, science is so departmentalized and divorced from any other aspect of culture that this conception has been entirely subordinated to that of technical training. Even here, however, there is still much confusion. Science is taught as if those who are taught it will be expected to use it for some purpose in later life, whereas it is probable, though no exact figures are available, that out of every hundred students of science in the British universities, some sixty become school teachers who have simply to recapitulate what they have learned to other generations; thirty go into business, industry or Government service, where for the most part they will be occupied in routine tasks for which most of what they have learned at the university is of little use; three continue in university teaching, and the final two become research workers and have rather painfully to unlearn much of the inaccurate and out-of-date information acquired in the universities and to forget the rest.

The diversity of function of the university science schools is further complicated, particularly at Oxford and Cambridge, by the diversity of material for them to work on. In spite of the examination system the fact that access to the university is largely a matter of wealth rather than of ability (5), means that even the Honours course must start at a very low level in such sciences as physics and chemistry, which are already supposed to be learned at school, and from the beginning in all other subjects. The result is that the first two years of an ordinary university course are occupied with teaching of a quality much more suitable to upper school grades. The situation is, in fact, so paradoxical that the standard of entrance scholarship examinations at the older universities is often as high as, if not higher than, that of Honours Finals. The result of this, however, is not an unmixed evil; it means that the science student of ability is able safely to neglect his first two years' work and to acquire some general culture and knowledge of the world by mixing in student societies.

The Lecture System.—In their mode of teaching the universities carry on a tradition little changed from that of their mediaeval predecessors. There was once some justification for the lecturer whose business was to expound a crabbed text of Aristotle or Galen to pupils who would certainly find difficulty in understanding it or who were very unlikely to possess books, and it needed considerable ingenuity on the part of the barber-surgeon-demonstrator to show how the actual facts of anatomy could be reconciled with the dogmatic statements of the classical authors.

All this is past and gone, yet the method of teaching still survives and has spread from the older universities to the later foundations and even to the technical schools. The obligation of spending the whole of every morning in term listening to scientific lectures is a useless anachronism and waste of time. That is not to say that lectures have no utility whatever, but their good points could be achieved far better in other ways. A scientific lecture lies between two extremes. It may be an inspired and generalized commentary on the subject, intended to arouse interest and stimulate thought by dwelling on the present limitations rather than on the established status of knowledge and by bringing science into close relation with technical and social problems. Lectures of this kind are necessarily rare and, on the whole, deprecated as of little use for examination purposes. Actually, except for the lectures delivered occasionally by eminent visiting scientists in the universities, their place would better be taken either by papers read to scientific societies or by small tutorial classes at which there are ample opportunities for discussion.

The opposite extreme is the conscientious lecture in which all the points, particularly the numerical results and mathematical arguments required to establish them, are carefully and methodically expounded. These lectures are usually incredibly dull, but are much valued because it is realized that anyone who attends them and takes good notes can hardly fail the bookwork part of his examinations. Yet it is clear that in this case the purpose of the lecture would be much better fulfilled by the presenting of a typewritten sheet containing all the data, formulae, and arguments required, and thus forming a useful summary of the text-books. Some lecturers actually go so far as to furnish such sheets in addition to the lecture.

There exists, of course, every intermediate gradation between these two extremes, and there are many conditions in which lectures do fulfil a valuable function. Particularly in new and rapidly developing subjects the lecture may take the place of text-books which have not yet been written. New knowledge is still considered somewhat dangerous in the universities, and a scientific theory is generally thought to require a quarantine of some forty years before it is safe for elementary students. Thus an Honours degree in Natural Sciences may be acquired at Cambridge, including physics and chemistry, in which the student has not heard except incidentally of the quantum theory, first put forward in 1900. A further excuse for the maintenance of the lecture system is the opportunity it affords for showing elaborate experiments which are difficult for the student to carry out for himself. Although these have a certain theatrical value and add interest to science, the conditions for showing them are rarely suitable for a real appreciation of the technique of experimentation.

Lectures are supplemented by demonstrations or practical work. For the most part this consists in carrying out a set of prescribed experiments and practising the techniques of the use of the microscope, of quantitative and qualitative chemical analysis, and of making physical measurements. Demonstrations certainly do provide the irreducible minimum of acquaintance with the manipulative technique of science, but they do little more; even in advanced demonstration there is no going beyond the existing methods, no hint as to the use of scientific method in attacking a problem the result of which is not already known, or of making an observation of quite an unexpected kind. In so far as science is a manual art this is not the way to learn it. The methods which made the great scientists of earlier times were far more effective. The old method of apprenticeship, the watching and helping of already competent people, together with that informal kind of learning by familiarity which results from pottering about a laboratory trying to solve, perhaps very inefficiently, some problem of one's own, are likely to teach far more of scientific method than the best arranged set of demonstrations.

It is by considering these alternatives that we see that it is not only pious conservatism that has caused the present lecture and demonstration system to be retained ; any more useful alternative would be bound to be more expensive because it would increase the ratio of teachers to pupils and the amount of apparatus which each pupil would require. Now all universities are in a 'chronic state of straitened resources. They might vastly increase their standard of teaching in either of two ways: by increasing the staff and evolving not one but several courses of study for students of different ability and different ultimate profession, or they might raise the entrance standard in such a way as to leave only pupils of high intelligence. But the first would add to the expenditure while the second would diminish revenues, and so until we realize the social price we have to pay for inefficient universities we are likely to have to put up with the present teaching system.

Specialization.—Another abuse that has insensibly grown up in the teaching of science in universities has been the excessive departmentalization. When science first appeared in the universities in the nineteenth century it was in the guise of natural philosophy, but this soon gave way to separate departments of physics, chemistry, zoology, etc., while the older division of medicine still remained and became more marked. For the most part science subjects are taught separately and out of relation with one another. From their very nature there must be a certain amount of overlapping, but owing to lack of co-ordination the common parts of two subjects are often taught twice over and in a contradictory manner. Each subject is conceived of as a more or less closed body of knowledge preserving its purity not only from the world of practice but from other subjects. This results in a very considerable fossilization of the separate curricula, a process much assisted, of course, by the rigidity of the examination system.

The Curriculum.—Except on the rare occasions when a young and vigorous professor manages to acquire an important chair, the curriculum of any subject changes by an uncomfortable process of accretion and compression. Very unfortunately, from the teaching point of view, science differs from the classics by the fact that its subject-matter is always increasing while the time available to study it remains the same. The first method usually adopted for dealing with this increase is to wait a respectable time before admitting any new knowledge to the curriculum at all, on the ground that it is controversial and may need subsequent alteration. The idea that the older parts of the subject are likely to be in far greater need of drastic alteration does not easily occur to the academic mind. In any case, truth in science teaching is conveniently limited to the idea of truth for examination purposes. When at last the new element of knowledge is admitted, it is tacked on to the end of the syllabus and the rest of the subject is appropriately squashed to make room for it, the whole process resembling the old peasant method of dressing by which a new petticoat is put on every year on top of the others, in the pious expectation that one of the previous ones has now become too ragged to be of any use. The result is that every curriculum is a hotchpotch of old and new, full of internal contradictions which the teacher glosses over and the students are very rarely able to detect. The teaching of chemistry, for example, is based on the great chemical revolution of 1784 and its sequel in the atomic theory of 1808. We now possess, through the quantum theory and the development of modern physics, a far more rational and direct approach to chemical problems, but we may have to wait another fifty years before some enterprising and far-seeing chemical professor manages to sweep away the whole of the present curriculum and replace it by one which will by then be some eighty years out of date. In physics the situation is not much better. The general examination in the University of London, for instance, is on a syllabus in which most of the facts were known in 1880. It has only a passing reference to X-rays and radio-activity, and ignores the whole of modern physics completely.

Of course there is no intention on the part of university authorities to maintain out-of-date curricula, but there is a very natural inertia, and there is no provision for the periodical revision of all curricula or for the maintenance of proper relations between the curricula in different subjects. Here, as in many other aspects of university life, the examination system is largely to blame. A narrow view of the immediate interests of both teachers and students demands that examination syllabuses should remain unchanged for at any rate a number of years, in order to collect a sufficient number of standard questions on which candidates can be trained or coached. A change in the syllabus and the introduction of new and unfamiliar questions produce a strain on the teacher and on the examiner and a probable increase in the already large element of chance attached to examination results. This in itself points to another inherent weakness in the examination system; the tendency to rely on questions of fact, memory, or mechanical performance of some technique.

Examinations.—It is unfortunate that the easiest modes of testing knowledge and those which on the average will give the fairest results are precisely those that are the least valuable from the point of view of acquisition of scientific ability. If each candidate were tested by his ability to make some entirely new observation or reduce some newly observed phenomena to order, in other words, if research were made the test, we should have ideally a much surer guide to the probability of his capacity to understand and make use of science. Unfortunately, without years of tests of this sort, it would be quite impossible to distinguish between native ability and the chance cussedness of nature. Only the fool could be detected by his failure to handle the obviously easy problem or the able scientist by his ability to cope with the difficult one; the greater number of cases where the difficulties were beyond the capacities of both would have to be passed over.

Actually this method is used or is supposed to be used in the higher university degree of Doctor of Philosophy. This is granted ostensibly for research, but as a test of ability it is little more than a farce. The actual thesis is examined by one or two specialists and their judgment, whether intelligent or biassed, is supported by boards to whom the substance of the thesis is so much Greek and who sit through drowsy summer afternoons with their hands propped in a permanent gesture of acceptance of another degree and another fee to the university.

The main evil of the examination system is not so much in the examinations themselves and in the unfairness of their results, because, as is frequently pointed out, the really able can succeed even in examinations, but rather in the whole attitude of mind which the existence of examinations induces. In the days when the universities were chiefly places for the rich to idle away a few youthful happy years, they could quite rightly be treated with contempt; but where, as now, the whole career of an educated citizen from the age of ten onwards depends on his performance in a series of examinations, they have become the most powerful influence of miseducation. It is dangerous for anyone unbacked by money or a superabundance of genius to try and take examinations lightly. (6) For the rest, all knowledge must be gauged by the criterion of its value for examination purposes. This results in a deliberate shutting off of interest at just the points of uncertain knowledge where interest is most required. It is probable, though not yet proved, that owing to this, universities have acquired a definitely negative educational value and that the student has a more general and liberal outlook at the beginning of his studies than at the end. Luckily a science student is spared the worst features of the system in that the orthodoxy that is demanded of him is in general only one of fairly established fact and not, as in the humane studies, of conventional opinion.

Medical Education.—In the general picture of university science teaching two departments stand in a special position, those of medicine and engineering. Medical teaching for historical and social reasons has remained separate from the main body of science teaching. Academically, it is the elder sister of the sciences and preserves more fully than they do mediaeval traditions of teaching. Socially, the teaching of medicine is the training of a caste, to a large extent hereditary, of medical practitioners, and from this comes the exclusiveness which marks off the medical student from his fellows in the university. Medical teaching can be criticized on two grounds: the first, ably expressed by Professor Mottram in *The Frustration of Science* (7), that it is indeed a very bad training for the practice of medicine largely because of its relative neglect of the study of the common ills of men or of the bases upon which sound health can be maintained; the second that it fails, even compared with other science teaching, to present medicine as a science rather than as a traditionally academic and somewhat mystical art.

The early stages of medical training are on either count frankly farcical. The physics and chemistry and, to a large extent, the biology—certainly the botany—of the young medical student are taught without the slightest regard either for scientific method or for practical utility and are quite rightly regarded by the majority of medical students as necessary but tedious initiation ceremonies, the responses for which they have to learn with the least trouble to themselves but can then conveniently forget for the rest of their lives. The intermediate stages of anatomy and physiology are even worse. The first involves a prodigious strain on the memory in the accumulation of names of parts largely devoid of either clinical or physiological significance and separated from the knowledge of their use, which is relegated to physiology. This subject, largely owing to its connection with medicine, is in a state of such ill-ordered confusion and contradiction that it conceals most of the important lessons which the intending doctor can learn from it. The substitution for these subjects of a reasonably well-ordered morphological biochemistry with special reference to the human body will probably take years of concerted effort and be achieved in the teeth of the most violent medical opposition. Of the later stages of medical education there is nothing to say here; once the medical student has passed into the hospital he has, for the most part, left the confines of science for good.

Engineering.—The engineering departments cannot, and do not indeed, usually claim to substitute for the apprenticeship that practical engineering gives. In view of this, it seems a pity that the years a student spends in the engineering schools on acquiring a rather half-hearted introduction to engineering practice, should not be used instead for the study of mathematics, physics, and chemistry in relation to the social and economic background in which the engineer will in future have to work. It is unfortunate that those men who are, in practice, the most creative of new values of society should be at the same time deprived by these methods of education from acquiring any general culture. (8)   As in medicine there is the additional disability of an occupation rapidly becoming hereditary. Consequently the average level of ability of the students in engineering is lower than in the university as a whole, and they are cut off from the general life of the university almost as much as medical students.

THE TRAINING OF THE RESEARCH WORKER

The small proportion of university students who pass on into research still require considerable training before they are able to play a positive part in the development of science. As yet this training is not a formal one. The young research worker is expected to pick up his technique from his fellow research workers, his nominal supervisor, and his own reading and practice. This, on the whole, is not such a bad system. It is true that a little formal teaching in the method of criticism and the writing of papers would be useful, and that a number of somewhat timid and unenterprising research workers used to a rigid and didactic educational system are completely lost when suddenly left to themselves. However, as most of the early training of the research worker consists in unlearning his previous education, in learning to disbelieve what he has been told, and to distrust the arguments which were used to convince him of it, it is somewhat difficult to imagine this being officially taught.

Financial Difficulties.—The main difficulties of the young research worker are less educational than material. Up to the research standard the methods of financing education are, though grossly inadequate and unfair on the poorer student, at any rate fairly simple and straightforward to work. If the requisite excellence is reached in the prescribed examinations, application to the proper educational authorities will result in a standard scholarship grant, and this may even last over into the first year or so of research. After that the research worker is faced with an extremely complex problem for which his training has in no way fitted him. A course in the intricacies of the wangling of appointments and grants would certainly be one of the most popular and necessary courses if it could be introduced into our universities. Actually the first, and in many ways the most fruitful, years of research are clouded for the great majority of research workers by complete material insecurity. Few grants last longer than three years, many are annual, and in all cases there are far fewer grants than applicants, so that the research worker knows that, statistically, there is more probability of his having to become a schoolmaster or a routine analyst in a factory than of his being able to secure a university teaching post or to continue as a research worker. Indeed, on one tour of inspection some Government officials were as shocked at a young research worker actually stating that he expected to continue in the career of research as were the workhouse authorities when Oliver Twist asked for more.

Opportunities for Research.—There are in Britain 3 whole-time Research Professorships, of which one is attached to medical science. There are 51 senior research grants in general science with an average salary of £425 and an average tenure of 2½ years, and 37 medical research grants with an average salary of £475 and an average tenure of 3½ years. This means that an opportunity of full-time research is, on the average, offered annually to 19 research students in science out of the 1600 doing post-graduate work in science and to 12 out of the 750 doing post-graduate work in medicine. The number of junior research grants, most of which are already held by these students, is naturally larger, but impossible to assess with any accuracy. The Royal Commission for the Exhibition of 1851 lists 45 such grants yearly, of an average salary of £186, and an average tenure of 2·2 years. There are besides approximately 120 grants at an average of £140 each by the D.S.I.R., of which about 80 are granted each year, making 165 grants in all, or 100 vacancies per year. This figure is certainly low, but even if we assume that it is half as much again, 150, it would still represent only 4 per cent. of the 3700 who annually graduate in science and technology from British universities. There can be no doubt that opportunities for research are inadequate and unsatisfactory. This situation has at last received official recognition though, as yet, no steps have been taken to remedy it. Sir William Bragg in his presidential address to the Royal Society in 1936 thus referred to it:

"The position of the men, and especially of the younger men, who are encouraged by these financial aids to devote the most ingenious years of their life to scientific research must be considered by those to whom the ordering of their lives is due. Some of the most brilliant young men in the Empire are selected for a specific purpose, which purpose they undoubtedly fulfil. Good work is done, and when it is finished a fine and most useful type of man is available for further service. In a great number of cases the satisfactory opportunity of further service presents itself. But it is not always so. It is possible to find a man living on income derived from one Research Trust after another until he ceases from age or other limitations to be eligible for further aid. His work may have been excellent, and his competence as great as ever, but he finds that he must look in some new direction for his living. Academic activities may be no use to him, nor he to them. His occupation has led him up a blind alley. I am told that there is a certain tendency for men who have been employed in industry as research workers to change over, when possible, to purely administrative work which is expected to be more lasting and in the end more remunerative. There is a hint as to the true cause of the trouble. The blind alley should be a thoroughfare leading to occupations more suitable to the men and better fitted to get the best out of them. It is obvious what these occupations are. They are places of responsibility to which specialists in science are as yet but rarely admitted. There is an encouraging beginning, but it takes time to realize that the man who is in touch on one side with the growth of natural knowledge should be in close touch on the other side with the opportunities of its application.   He should be an equal in the council chamber rather than a subordinate in the waiting-room.   On the other hand, the scientific expert must himself help to take down the barricade that makes the alley blind.   This requires that his education should be much more than sufficient to make him only a laboratory man."

Nor are the actual emoluments of the young research worker really adequate.   The D.S.I.R. grants, which are the most sought after, are mere subsistence allowances, £120 a year (except at Oxford and Cambridge where £200-£250 are given).   From these every kind of deduction is made, though permission is graciously given to retain one-third (or a sixth at Oxford and Cambridge) of the money made by teaching (see p. 406).   Living on such salaries, is it surprising that the research worker is unable to broaden his interests and become other than a narrow specialist?

The Problem of Getting On.—There are, of course, in this field, as in all others, time-honoured methods; one of them is to pick your chief wisely and make yourself agreeable to him.   It does not follow that the best scientists are the best research directors; some of them are so wrapped up in their own work that they see their students for an hour or so once a year; others are so interested in their students that they are apt to forget that they have not done all the work themselves.   It is always a distressing experience for a young man to find that age and genuine eminence are not guarantees against the temptation to enjoy credit for what one has not done.   Perhaps the most convenient chiefs are those amiable scoundrels who establish a kind of symbiosis with their research workers, choose good ones with care, see that they are well supplied with apparatus, attach their own names to all their papers, and when at last they are found out, generally manage through their numerous connections to promote their protégé into a good position.   Independence of spirit is not at a premium in the scientific world.   The young research worker who remarked, when asked his views on scientific collaboration by an eminent professor at a selection committee, that he did not intend to be anybody's lackey, did not get the post, and it was years before his undoubted gifts and character began to win him any recognition, while far less able but more pliable contemporaries were already sitting in professorial chairs.

These, however, are evils common to all authoritarian systems. One more peculiarly damaging to science is the necessity incumbent upon all research workers to produce results and to see that they are published.   The young graduate just escaped from the pressure of the examination system finds he has exchanged one servitude for another, for it is on his published results by number and bulk as much as by excellence that his future depends.   The period of years that would most profitably be spent—as the great scientists were able to spend theirs—in study, meditation and apparently aimless experimentation, is denied to all research workers without means, that is, already to the great majority. The result is to stifle originality at a time when it is most fruitful and when it is still free from the later burdens of administrative and social responsibility. Another result is to burden scientific literature with masses of useless papers, which makes the task of finding good ones far more difficult than it need be.

The Profession of Research.—All this occurs because the position of the research worker is in itself an anomaly and does not as yet form part of the recognized system of things. Research had previously been carried on either by amateurs or by teachers in their spare time. The idea of a separate profession is new, as is the recognition that ability for scientific teaching and ability for research by no means always coincide. The suitable endowment of research as a separate profession would make an enormous difference. It might permit the continued flourishing of a small number of idle research workers, but at the same time it would ensure that the majority of serious workers could give themselves whole-heartedly to their work and be free from the necessities of self-seeking struggle which is now their fate. That this is a perfectly feasible aim is shown by the fact that in France the profession of research has now been recognized and provided for (see pp. 201-2 and Appendix VI).

The working scientists of to-day are the product of the system of selection and education. It is not surprising that, with such a different social and economic environment, they should be different from those who were occupied in laying the foundations of modern science. In early days the decision to occupy oneself with the study of science was a personal choice which very few people took, and then in spite of the very grave disabilities that attended the choice of such a useless vocation. (9) It restricted the practice of science to wealthy men and those who could acquire their patronage. Nowadays science is a definite profession, where at any rate a modest livelihood can be made, and as such attracts a large number of entrants. The process of selection that goes on inside scientific education is one that favours, on the one hand, technical proficiency and industry and, on the other, general social conformity. The scientist no less than the administrative employee must, if he is to be successful, get on with people of wealth and authority. Too great an interest in social or political matters is a double disadvantage, distracting from close application to work and giving rise to the general opinion of not being a sound man. There is an unwritten tradition in the scientific world, though it lacks historical justification, that really good scientists know nothing and care less about social problems, and the implication is that anyone who displays such an interest by admitting a partiality for anything but constituted authority, is equally likely to be biassed and unreliable in his scientific work.

When this attitude applies, as it increasingly does, not only to political but to almost any cultural activity outside their own fields, official science becomes generally lowbrow. Interest in the arts or literature is not exactly condemned, and indeed may be condoned as a harmless hobby, but actually writing or painting, unless it is admittedly badly done, is positively dangerous for a scientific reputation. The fault lies just as much with culture as with science. Both exhibit an ignorant contempt for the other which does neither credit. Science does, of course, like any other vital occupation, boast a certain number of distinct and vivid personalities of genuine culture and independence of spirit, but they are not typical of the profession as a whole. A certain timid subservience and conformity is a much more common characteristic. Scientists compensate for the lack of appreciation they receive as such from the external world by appearing as ordinary as possible in their daily lives and reserving the whole of their intellectual activity for the narrow sphere of a scientific speciality. The work of the scientists has revolutionized the modern world, but this has happened not because but rather in spite of the character of the scientists themselves.

Popular Science

The effectiveness of any scheme of scientific education is shown by the place science takes in everyday life. Here it is not a question of the material contribution of science in the form of inventions, because these are presented to those who use them, not as contributions of science, but as substitutes or extensions of things which existed before science. In this sense the cinema is only the play made more easily available, and the telephone a simple means of talking to one's friends. In nearly all these cases the use of the scientific appliance does not require much if any scientific knowledge and no acquaintance with scientific method. Children, with the vaguest idea of where the stations are and with no idea at all of electric oscillations, have no difficulty in getting exactly the programme they want. Nevertheless the presence on all sides of machinery and services which incorporate scientific principles inevitably forces a consciousness of science different from that of previous periods. There are, quite outside the ranks of professed scientists, thousands who have some degree of interest in science. This interest ranges from the practical mastery of some limited field of science, such as that needed for an amateur wireless operator, to the merest general interest in the wonders of science. For these there has grown up a wealth of popular scientific literature, articles, magazines and books, hardly less imposing in bulk than the literature of science itself.

Popular science is, however, almost as widely divorced from operative science as is popular music from classical music. The results of science more or less accurately or sensationally reproduced do get through, but piecemeal and leaving behind the whole method and spirit of science. The Press in Britain has never taken science seriously; with one or two notable exceptions no newspaper has even the equivalent of a scientific editor. Science news is scrappy and generally oscillates between the extremes of the sensational and the obscure. Mr. Gerald Heard thus qualifies it in his introduction to *Science Front*, 1936:

> "Science news, however, gets hardly any press, and when it does, such items as are printed come through as completely disjointed fragments. The popular papers print an account of some find simply because it seems startling—simply because it seems to upset our accepted outlook. The more serious papers in reality do no better, for when they print science news they get an expert to send in a paragraph, and he takes for granted not only that he is writing for other people as informed as he, but also that informed people, as much as uninformed, do not see or know what relationship this new piece of the jig-saw has to do with the rest of the puzzle, that puzzle which science is piecing together into one vast whole. It is hard to take an intelligent interest or anything but the most passing curiosity in such news. It is far harder to keep such pieces by us, sort, sift, and fit them until we can see where they add on to the growing front of knowledge."—*Science Front*, p. 9.

Magazines of popular science are better, but still contain for the most part amazing stories, practical hints, and an occasional accurate and serious article. There is not a single publication whose function it is to present the progress of science in a generally understandable way against a background of the economic and political developments of the time. (10) Books on popular science are far the worst. They include pedantic and generally inept compendiums of knowledge brought out presumably for the benefit of publishers, accounts of recent work horribly mangled and misunderstood by amateur scientists and best-selling sermons by the most eminent of the profession. Among them are a few books which manage to be understandable and accurate at the same time, but they do not set the tone, and the proportion of them to the rest is far smaller than in the Victorian era.

The Current Influence of Science.—The value of science in public affairs is to be gauged by its conscious effect on the ideas of the time. There is no doubt that although, taken as a whole, there is in modern Britain considerable interest in science, it does not provide an adequate popular critical background for science. There is not that give and take between scientific and popular ideas which was characteristic of previous centuries even when the circle of scientific interest was socially very restricted. There is nothing for science like the concentrated and trained appreciation with which football matches or horse races are followed; and this is not to be explained only by the lack of a financial interest in science fancying or by the intrinsic difficulties of the subject. There are finer points in cricket or billiards than are often to be found in biological or physiological arguments; while if people were really interested in science it would very soon be discovered what excellent sport could be had in backing Professor B's theory against Professor A's at ten to one. (11)

There is no getting away from it: to a large extent science has become detached from popular consciousness and the result is very bad for both. It is bad for people at large partly because living in an increasingly man-made world they are gradually falling behind in their awareness of the mechanisms that control their lives. At bottom there is not very much difference between a savage with his complete ignorance and helplessness before the natural phenomena of drought or disease and the modern man before the man-made disasters of technological unemployment and scientific warfare. Faced by the unknown and the fearful and not granted the means of understanding them, in both cases he turns to fantastic and mystical explanations. It is no accident that the present age has seen the recrudescence of superstitions such as astrology and spiritualism, which it had been thought were well dead at the end of the Middle Ages. The far more dangerous grip which demagogic fascist ideas can exercise is a measure both of popular ignorance and the need to have something to believe.

The Isolation of Science.—But it is also very bad for science. From the crudest point of view, unless people at large—and this will include wealthy benefactors and Government officials—know what the scientists are about, they can hardly be expected to provide that assistance which the scientist feels his work demands in return for its probable benefits to humanity. More subtly, however, the absence of popular understanding, interest and criticism reinforces in the scientist the already dangerous tendency to mental isolation. This does not usually take the form so often imagined, of the scientist as an other-worldly person who can only just manage to keep alive through the assistance of female relations. The isolation is that of science, not of the scientist. Apart from his subject he may appear as the most ordinary person, play golf, tell good stories and be a devoted husband and father; but his subject is "shop" and, except for twenty or so people who understand, it is something which he keeps rigidly to himself. Among people of literary culture there is almost an affectation of knowing nothing about science; nor have the scientists themselves escaped from it. In their case it refers to all other sciences than their own. It is one of the rarest things to find good general conversation on scientific topics, and this is true even when scientists are the majority of the company. This was certainly not the case when Voltaire and Mme du Châtelet conducted philosophical experiments at their house parties or when Shelley discussed chemistry and moral perfection with equal enthusiasm. Among the younger English writers of distinction there is but one who exhibits in his work any comprehension of modern science, and he has excellent family reasons for doing so.

Scientific Superstition.—The lack of a cultural background to science still further enhances the evils of scientific specialization, but at the same time it does worse by ensuring that the social influences which unconsciously enter into all but the most detailed scientific theories are not the mature reflections of a critical and cultured society but, for the most part, the commonest prejudices and super-stitions of the time, The effect of this is seen reflected back in popular science. When a public has neither the training nor the interest to follow the working of science it can still be willing to acclaim results, the more marvellous the better, and to listen to the opinions of sufficient eminence on any subject whatever. These opinions it can understand because they are usually simply its own opinions sent back with the stamp of august approval. Subjects like relativity or the origin of the universe, which are intrinsically difficult, are found eminently suitable, not for technical explanation but for providing texts on man's helplessness and ignorance and on the beneficence and intelligence of the Creator. At the same time much more significant and practically important theories of the day, such as the quantum theory, receive scant attention.

The result of this is to widen not only the gap already alluded to between the scientist and the public, but also one between scientists and popular science. The attitude of the working scientist towards such subjects as the origins of the universe and of life, or of vitalism in biology, is totally different from that expressed in books on popular science. To the scientist the picture of the disappearing reality of phenomena is so much nonsense; he knows that he can handle materials the better for the quantum theory, or biological preparations for a knowledge of bio-chemistry and genetics; he also knows that he cannot get this across because publicity for these views is so much harder to get than for the opposite ones. The result is that the public is deluded into believing that idealism rules in science at a time when materialism is winning all along the line, and at the same time the working scientist is inclined to withdraw into an exclusive self-satisfaction with his own knowledge and the ignorance and superstition of the public.

Many causes contribute to this deplorable state of affairs. To a certain degree the effective separation of science and culture was due paradoxically enough to the introduction of science teaching. Science, so to speak, has lost its amateur status and with it a great deal of public interest. No one need think for himself about science; there are always people who know about that sort of thing. The rapid development and the multiplicity of scientific discovery has a generally bewildering effect, and this is emphasized by the specialization of the scientists themselves and the myth, which is increasingly believed, that the time has gone past when any mind can profitably cover more than a small fraction of the topics of human knowledge, much less claim to have made all knowledge its province. Actually all that this belief reflects is that the methods of exposition and communication in science have not kept pace with the progress of discovery. A well-arranged system of scientific publication (the nature of which will be discussed in Chapter XI) should make it perfectly possible for every well-educated man to have a general picture of the whole field of science sufficiently detailed for him to grasp the significance of development in any part of it. For the moment he is barred from this by the obscurity of scientific jargon and the anarchy of scientific publication.

The Pre-Scientific Attitude.—The lack of proper appreciation of science is not confined to the public at large; it is particularly powerful and dangerous in the fields of administration and politics. The pre-scientific attitude here destroys most of the benefits that could be gained from the technical results of science. Of none of the more important general factors which affect human life do people think scientifically or even collect the material necessary for scientific analysis. The position is admirably stated in a *P.E.P.* (*Political and Economic Planning*) broadsheet:

"A civilization has grown up under industrialism which calls for enormous resources of knowledge in order to operate it without constant and painful breakdowns. It is hardly unfair to say that we neither possess the required knowledge, nor are we making at present any adequate effort to get it, although its provision offers no insuperable difficulties. Our whole attitude towards the obtaining and use of knowledge is still coloured by the prejudices and assumptions of a pre-scientific and pre-technical age. It is hopeless for isolated groups of people to struggle, as they have long been struggling, for a little more investigation of rents and incomes here, a little more research in psychology there, and a little more attention to educational research, social research, traffic investigation, medical research, and so forth. The trouble is something deeper than a failure to provide certain facilities. A large element in the population, educated and uneducated, has yet to recognize that the same technique which has produced electricity, wireless, aircraft, fertilizers, and new breeds of plants and animals can, if suitably adapted, produce on just as lavish a scale the social, political, and economic inventions of which we are so desperately in need. Unfortunately, whereas a first-rate process or product may be hit upon by an eccentric person in a garret and made available through comparatively small private investments of capital, a social invention from its nature often calls for raw material which has to be more or less publicly gathered. While, moreover, the industrial executive has gradually come to recognize that a product or a process does not last for ever, and that, as a matter of course, provision must be made for new patterns and new technique, there is no corresponding awareness or equipment for checking and improving the performance of, say, the machinery of government, the health services, the handling of traffic or other problems of a social or economic nature." —*Planning*, no. 17, 2nd January 1934.

The Need for Science and its Suppression.—It is, however, no accident that science is neglected both by popular thought and administration. Existing attitudes towards science are fundamental and necessary parts of our present social system. The relation between science and social life has a twofold aspect. The current needs of society evoke science to satisfy them; therefore, whatever those needs are, some science is necessary. But science thus called forth cannot fail to create new needs and to criticize old ones. In doing so it must take a part in the modification of society, greater than and different from that which it was originally called upon to play. The scientific movement which was called into being by seventeenth-century governments was to prove, in the eighteenth century, the most powerful basis for criticizing the forms of those very governments. The situation to-day shows this contradiction even more clearly. Any widespread appreciation of the results of science, of the possibilities that it offers to humanity, or of its methods of criticism cannot fail to have large social and political implications. Those forces in society that are opposed to such changes must necessarily try to prevent science overstepping its original bounds. It is to be a useful servant and not a master. Consequently science suffers at the same time an internal stimulation and an external suppression. The paradox is most clearly seen in present-day Germany where the scientist is at the same time most urgently needed to provide a basis for an autocratic economic state and for the preparation of an overwhelming military machine, and violently repudiated as a potential source of cultural Bolshevism. But the same tendencies are plainly visible in this country. Two theories of the function of science are in sharp opposition. The one is that the scientist still exists on sufferance and owes his immunity to his performing his job and refraining from meddling in politics (see p. 394). Against this we have the view championed by Julien Benda in *La Trahison des Clercs*, where the men of learning are pilloried as the chosen guardians of culture who have failed in their trust by abdicating to the forces of superstition and violence. The world to-day puts to the scientist a bitter choice between these views, but, however he chooses, it is clear that in the long run the benefits of science can only accrue to a society which is capable of understanding and accepting them in their full implications.

(1) " If we knew how to use our boys, Martin would have been seized upon and educated as a natural Philosopher. He had a passion for birds, beasts and insects, and knew more of them and their habits than anyone in Rugby ; except perhaps the Doctor, who knew everything. He was also an experimental chemist on a small scale, and had made unto himself an electric machine, from which it was his greatest pleasure and glory to administer small shocks to any small boys who were rash enough to venture into his study. And this was by no means an adventure free from excitement ; for, besides the probability of a snake dropping on to your head or twining lovingly up your leg, or a rat getting into your breeches-pocket in search of food, there was the animal and chemical odour to be faced, which always hung about the den, and the chance of being blown up in some of the many experiments which Martin was always trying with the most wondrous results in the shape of explosions and smells that mortal boy ever heard of."—*Tom Brown's Schooldays*, p. 215.

(2) Susan Isaacs, *Intellectual Growth in Young Children*, Routledge, 1930.

(3) *Sociological Review*, XXVII, p. 113, 1935. See also Hogben, *Political Arithmetic*.

(4) *The Teaching of General Science*, Report by the General Committee of the Science Masters' Association in October 1936. Murray, 1937.

(5) D. V. Glass and J. L. Gray have made a special study of the relation of opportunity to wealth in the English and Welsh Universities. (Reprinted in *Political Arithmetic*, pp. 419-470.) They point out that 27 per cent. of the male undergraduate population of the universities are ex-elementary school pupils ; only 22 per cent., however, also had a free secondary education, making a disparity in university opportunity of over forty to one in favour of boys educated in fee-paying schools. The Board of Education working on a different basis claims that 42 per cent. of university entrants come from elementary schools (see *The Times*, 5th July 1938), but the discrepancy is not important as the real advantage is more heavily weighted in favour of wealth than either figure indicates on account of the special advantages of the public schools.

(6) See Christopher Isherwood's account of his treatment of examinations in *Lions and Shadows*.

(7) Professor Mottram, himself a teacher of medicine, finds little to recommend in the present system :

" In the first place it is not too much to say that no poor person, no one without well-to-do relatives to back him, can easily enter the medical profession. A career is not open to talent unless there is financial backing. Between five and six years' training is essential before a man can take a degree in medicine, and even then he is unfitted to go out into general practice. True, there are scholarships in science to the universities, particularly the older universities, which will carry a clever student through the academic years of his training, and medical schools give scholarships to a clever student of biology, anatomy and physiology which will carry him through the years of hospital training ; but these scholarships are far too few in number. Then at the end of his training he is stranded, for he has either to purchase a practice or squat in some neighbourhood and wait for a practice to grow—a heart-breaking process if he has no private means. There are devious ways by which a man can earn sufficient to keep himself alive while his practice is growing—medical journalism, part-time service in public health work, and so on. But these are sufficiently precarious to deter any but the cleverest and most pushful of people. On the other hand, the well-to-do with moderate ability only finds his way to a practice made simple. If his father is a physician so much the better. He is pushed, pulled or crammed through the necessary examinations and steps into his father's shoes when the time comes. Many a man enters medicine because his father has a good practice and from no inherent enthusiasm for the healing art.

Second, it may be with certainty said that the academic part of the medical student's training is hopelessly inefficient. While it may be admitted that medicine is still an art and not a science, it is fairly clear that to understand and apply the modern discoveries of medical research a medical man must have a severe training in scientific method. He must develop a critical and scientific outlook. This his academic years in biology, chemistry, physics, physiology and anatomy are supposed to give him. We may confidently assert that in ninety-nine cases out of a hundred he sloughs his scientific training when he enters the wards. In fact he is often advised to forget all the physiology which he has learnt. Possibly this advice is wise, for it is to be doubted if it is of the slightest use to him. The fact is that in trying to study biology, chemistry, physics, physiology and anatomy in two and a half to three years he gets but a smattering of these subjects, and of their serious import nothing. He acquires but the bare bones of these subjects, and of their living spirit not a jot. It is only by a deep, critical study of a subject * that a man can begin to discover the spirit of scientific work. When he has finished his academic work scarcely a man is equipped to read an original article in the sciences he has studied (or shall we say ' learnt ' ?) and give a judgment upon it. Nor is he fitted to do any original work.

* Such study is possible only if a student step aside from his medical curriculum and spend a year or more upon an honours or advanced course. In Great Britain, the United States and Canada, to the writer's knowledge, there exist such courses—*e.g.* Part II of the Natural Sciences Tripos at Cambridge, the Honours School of Physiology in Oxford, the Special Honours in the University of London, the P. and B. Course in Toronto and the University of Chicago. The numbers of students who can afford to spend the necessary time and money are extremely small."—*Frustration of Science*, pp. 86-88.

(8) That this can be done is shown by the excellent cultural courses that are given at the Massachusetts Institute of Technology.

(9) For a Victorian description of the position of the research worker, see the article by Sorby in *The Endowment of Research*, London, 1876. His conclusions are worth quoting. He writes : "Original research can be carried on in a satisfactory manner only when an investigator has abundance of time for work, and freedom from those cares which interfere with reflection."

(10) *The Realist* attempted to do this for a time, *The Scientific Worker* has a certain popular as well as a professional appeal, *The Modern Quarterly* will deal critically with these aspects. But these are all rather serious publications. What we need is a good popular scientific illustrated weekly, though the new *Discovery* does something to remedy this lack.

(11) That this lack of popular interest is only apparent is shown by the immense popularity of all forms of science in the Soviet Union as shown in the Press, in the clubs, and in the parks of culture and rest. See p. 228.

CHAPTER V

THE EFFICIENCY OF SCIENTIFIC RESEARCH

ONCE we admit any function for science in society it is possible to ask whether that function is being carried out efficiently or inefficiently, whether the results obtained are the best obtainable with the human and material resources available. Our judgment of the degree of inefficiency of science will, however, largely depend on our ideas as to what the function of science is. Nevertheless, without prejudging that issue, which is the central problem of this book, it is still possible to talk of the efficiency of scientific research in relation to the different hypothetical functions of science.

Three Aims for Science: Psychological, Rational and Social.—Science as an occupation may be considered to have three aims which are not mutually exclusive: the entertainment of the scientist and the satisfaction of his native curiosity, the discovery and integrated understanding of the external world, and the application of such understanding to the problems of human welfare. We may call them the psychological, rational, and social aims of science. The social effectiveness of science will be the subject of a later chapter. What concerns us here are the other two aims.

It is clearly impossible to estimate in any strict sense the efficiency of science with respect to its psychological aim. Nevertheless, as psychological satisfaction plays an important part in the carrying on of scientific research, it needs to be taken into account in any discussion of the general efficiency of science.

That scientific research is profoundly satisfying to all who choose to undertake it is undeniable. On the whole people choose to be scientists precisely because they anticipate this satisfaction. It is not, however, of a kind peculiar to science. In almost every profession there are opportunities for the exercise of a disciplined curiosity intrinsically no different from that exhibited in scientific research. The growth of the profession of science to its present dimensions is not a sign of a spontaneous increase in the number of individuals gifted with natural curiosity, but of the realization of the value that science can bring to those who finance it. For this purpose the psychologically pre-existing natural curiosity is utilized. Science uses curiosity, it needs curiosity, but curiosity did not make science.

Oddly enough, it is not until comparatively recent times that scientists themselves have sought to justify science on the basis of the psychological satisfaction it brings. Originally science was justified because it was for the glory of God or the benefit of humanity. Although these claims really amounted to implicit acceptance of the psychological justification, explicitly they brought science into relation with divinity or utility, which were conceived to be at the times in question the general social ends of man. The scientists of the seventeenth century had obvious reasons for insisting on the utility of science, as they alone saw its possibilities and needed the external support which could only be gained by pointing out its material benefits. They had to uphold this practical aspect against detractors like Dean Swift, who ridiculed the scientists of the time for occupying themselves in vain and unprofitable fancies. Nevertheless, there is no reason to believe that the scientists did not honestly think their work of benefit to society, nor had it occurred to them that the success of science could be put to any other uses.

The Ideal of Pure Science

This early confidence began to be shaken in the nineteenth century when it became apparent that science could be, and was being, put to base uses; its place was taken by the idealism of pure science, science without thought of application or reward. Thomas Henry Huxley voices the feelings of the Victorian scientist in his persuasive prose:

" In fact, the history of physical science teaches (and we cannot too carefully take the lesson to heart) that the practical advantages, attainable through its agency, never have been, and never will be, sufficiently attractive to men inspired by the inborn genius of the interpreter of Nature, to give them courage to undergo the toils and make the sacrifices which that calling requires from its votaries. That which stirs their pulses is the love of knowledge and the joy of discovery of the causes of things sung by the old poet—the supreme delight of extending the realm of law and order ever farther towards the unattainable goals of the infinitely great and the infinitely small, between which our little race of life is run. In the course of this work, the physical philosopher, sometimes intentionally, much more often unintentionally, lights upon something which proves to be of practical value. Great is the rejoicing of those who are benefited thereby; and, for the moment, science is the Diana of all the craftsmen. But, even while the cries of jubilation resound and this flotsam and jetsam of the tide of investigation is being turned into the wages of workmen and the wealth of capitalists, the crest of the wave of scientific investigation is far away on its course over the illimitable ocean of the unknown."

" Thus, without for a moment pretending to despise the practical results of the improvement of natural knowledge, and its beneficial influence on material civilization, it must, I think, be admitted that the great ideas, some of which I have indicated, and the ethical spirit which I have endeavoured to sketch, in the few moments which remained at my disposal, constitute the real and permanent significance of natural knowledge.

If these ideas be destined, as I believe they are, to be more and more firmly established as the world grows older; if that spirit be fated, as I believe it is, to extend itself into all departments of human thought, and to become co-extensive with the range of knowledge; if, as our race approaches its maturity, it discovers, as I believe it will, that there is but one kind of knowledge and but one method of acquiring it; then we, who are still children, may justly feel it our highest duty to recognize the advisableness of improving natural knowledge, and so to aid ourselves and our successors in our course towards the noble goal which lies before mankind."—*Method and Results*, pp. 54 and 41.

In another sense the ideal of pure science was a form of snobbery, a sign of the scientist aping the don and the gentleman. An applied scientist must needs appear somewhat of a tradesman; he risked losing his amateur status. By insisting on science for its own sake the pure scientist repudiated the sordid material foundation on which his work was based.

Science as Escape.—With the general disillusionment which set in after the War even the idea of pure science began to pale. The development of psychology seemed to show that the pursuit of knowledge was simply the carrying into adult life of infantile curiosities. A grandson of Huxley, writing of scientists, can make one of his characters say:—

"I perceive now that the real charm of the intellectual life—the life devoted to erudition, to scientific research, to philosophy, to aesthetics, to criticism—is its easiness. It's the substitution of simple intellectual schemata for the complexities of reality; of still and formal death for the bewildering movements of life. It's incomparably easier to know a lot, say, about the history of art, and to have profound ideas about metaphysics and sociology than to know personally and intuitively a lot about one's fellows and to have satisfactory relations with one's friends and lovers, one's wife and children. Living's much more difficult than Sanskrit or chemistry or economics. The intellectual life is child's play; which is why intellectuals tend to become children—and then imbeciles and finally, as the political and industrial history of the last few centuries clearly demonstrates, homicidal lunatics and wild beasts. The repressed functions don't die; they deteriorate, they fester, they revert to primitiveness. But meanwhile it's much easier to be an intellectual child or lunatic or beast than a harmonious adult man. That's why (among other reasons) there's such a demand for higher education. The rush to books and universities is like the rush to the public-house. People want to drown their realization of the difficulties of living properly in this grotesque contemporary world, they want to forget their own deplorable inefficiency as artists in life. Some drown their sorrows in alcohol, but still more drown them in books and artistic dilettantism; some try to forget themselves in fornication, dancing, movies, listening-in, others in lectures and scientific hobbies. The books and lectures are better sorrow-drowners than drink and fornication; they leave no headache, none of that despairing *post coitum triste* feeling. Till quite recently, I must confess, I too took learning and philosophy and science—all the activities that are magniloquently lumped under the title of 'The Search for Truth'—very seriously. I regarded the Search for Truth as the highest of human tasks and the Searchers as the noblest of men. But in the last year or so I have begun to see that this famous Search for Truth is just an amusement, a distraction like any other, a rather refined and elaborate substitute for genuine living; and that Truth-Searchers become just as silly, infantile, and corrupt in their way as the boozers, the pure aesthetes, the business men, the Good-Timers in theirs. I also perceived that the pursuit of Truth is just a polite name for the intellectual's favourite pastime of substituting simple and therefore false abstractions for the living complexities of reality. But seeking Truth is much easier than learning the art of integral living (in which, of course, Truth-Seeking will take its due and proportionate place along with the other amusements, like skittles and mountain climbing). Which explains, though it doesn't justify, my continued and excessive indulgence in the vices of informative reading and abstract generalization. Shall I ever have the strength of mind to break myself of these indolent habits of intellectualism and devote my energies to the more serious and difficult task of living integrally? And even if I did try to break these habits, shouldn't I find that heredity was at the bottom of them and that I was congenitally incapable of living wholly and harmoniously?"—From *Point Counter Point*, by Aldous Huxley, pp. 442-4.

Here it is recognized that science is being used mainly for the enrichment of the few and the destruction of the many. Consequently its ultimate justification is that it is quite an amusing pastime. This attitude, though rarely admitted, is actually extremely widespread among scientists, particularly those in the safer and more comfortable positions. Science is one of the most absorbing and satisfying pastimes, and as such it appeals in different ways to different types of personality. To some it is a game against the unknown where one wins and no one loses, to others, more humanly minded, it is a race between different investigators as to who should first wrest the prize from nature. It has all the qualities which make millions of people addicts of the crossword puzzle or the detective story, the only difference being that the problem has been set by nature or chance and not by man, that the answers cannot be got with certainty, and when they are found often raise far more questions than the original problem.

If we examine the present state of science from this point of view, it must be admitted that on the whole it is fairly satisfactory. The only complaints of the scientists are on purely material grounds.

Given an adequate salary and fair security of tenure, together with no obligation to perform any specified tasks, the scientist would be happy enough. From what has already been said even these conditions are not available for the majority of scientists, but they are available for quite a number and they represent a perfectly attainable ideal. If the game were the only thing that mattered the major inefficiencies from other points of view—the lack of apparatus or information, the lack of any general plan or direction, and the failure to co-ordinate science with other human activities—are all immaterial. Actual material deficiencies can be considered extra hazards added to the game; overcoming them is itself the education of the scientist. The conditions of his work make it particularly convenient for him to take this point of view. But the danger of treating science purely as a game is that playing games as a life work does not often bring lasting or full satisfaction. Men require to feel that what they do has a social importance as well. Even a supreme performer such as Morphy could get no satisfaction out of his success because he could not bear to be regarded as only a chess player.

Science and Cynicism.—Nevertheless, sufficiently narrow specialization and the inclination to make the best of whatever means are available still assures to many scientists a relatively happy time. Some not so limited in their views may yet accept this attitude deliberately. "Whenever I look out at the world," a professor once remarked, "I see such misery and mess that I prefer to bury myself in my own work and to forget about things that in any case I could do nothing about." To others the psychological attitude towards scientific research leads to a cynical admission of the complete futility of science itself (1), an attitude which expresses itself in theories attempting to prove the impossibility of exact knowledge and the failure of determinism or even of a simple causality.

Ultimately this view reduces science to a more or less ornamental but, in any case, quite useless outgrowth of civilized society, yet it is clear that whatever the scientists themselves may think, there is no economic system which is willing to pay scientists just to amuse themselves. Science must pay its way just as much as any other human activity, though the payment need not always take a purely material form. The prestige of science and its moral and political influence have also to be taken into account.

THE TECHNICAL INEFFICIENCY OF SCIENCE

It is only the narrowest specialization or the most complete social cynicism that makes it possible for the scientist to accept the present conditions of scientific work with anything approaching satisfaction. Judged by our second criterion—the most rapid development of scientific knowledge as a whole—the inefficiency of the system cannot be glossed over. Most of the scientist's work is in fact wasted, either for the immediate lack of apparatus or assistants or because it is not adequately co-ordinated with other work, and finally there remains a considerable chance of its being entirely lost in the mess of unreadable scientific literature.

Bad Organization.—If we try to examine more closely the inefficiency of science as a method of discovery we find that it originates in two major defects. The first is the totally inadequate scale of finance, of which we have already spoken; the second is the inefficiency of organization which ensures that these small resources shall be to a large extent wasted. This last remark may seem to the scientist something approaching treason. Even if it were true it should not be publicly stated, for the little that science gets now it gets as the result of the belief in its effectiveness. Once it is suspected that scientists waste the money that is given to them they will not be able to get even that much. Yet the gentleman's agreement to gloss over the internal inefficiencies of science is bound to be disastrous in the long run. However carefully concealed such things are, they are always suspected and give rise to an attitude of vague distrust on the part of possible benefactors and the public at large, which is far more damaging to science than openly brought charges. In a similar way the elaborate ethical codes which oblige doctors to support one another in all circumstances and never to admit the existence of statistically inevitable errors and the equally inevitable appearances of scoundrels and fools in the profession, only results in deepening distrust of official medicine and plays into the hands of quacks and charlatans. (2) More important, however, is the consideration that without a really effective internal working organization, scientists will never be able to get for their profession the recognition they think it deserves or the additional finance which it so urgently needs.

The reason for the present situation of scientific research is not far to seek. Scientific activities have in detail grown in a spontaneous way, while the organizations to co-ordinate these activities have not been planned beforehand, but have grown up with the development of science itself, always at a slower rate than the activities they organize. This is a general picture of the development of human institutions, but in the case of science it is aggravated by peculiar factors. The personal interests of the scientists are extremely diverse, and they are at the same time far removed from those of administration. There is a natural reluctance on the part of scientists to take time away from their detailed work in order to attend to the problems of organization; consequently these are for the most part left to a small number of rather poorly paid officials and to committees of older scientists no longer in contact with contemporary movements.

The inefficiencies of scientific research are more extensive than intensive. The closer to the individual scientist and his work, the greater the degree of efficiency; the larger the field surveyed, the greater the inefficiency. The actual growth of science has been such that it is now being cluttered up and hampered by its own past and current productivity. This shows itself for the most part in the relation between different kinds of work rather than in the work itself.

Laboratory Waste of Skill.—Even in detail, however, there is considerable waste due to a large extent to false economy. Poor equipment and lack of a sufficient number of laboratory assistants and mechanics ensure that a large number of scientists spend much of their time in mechanical and routine tasks at which they are not necessarily very efficient and which, in any case, delay their proper work. It may reasonably be objected here that this is sometimes a blessing in disguise, that intensive scientific work consisting only of significant observations and manipulations is too much of a nervous strain, and that the necessity to carry out other occupations slows down the work to a pace which is more humanly desirable. Yet surely the choice of routine work should be left to the scientist himself to determine. There is no need to prevent him carrying out mechanical tasks, but he should not, in normal circumstances, be required to do them.

This situation is difficult to remedy mainly because the economic aspect of scientific work is not strictly compatible with that of a profit-making society. A scientist receiving £400 per annum may be obliged to waste three-quarters of his time because he has not an assistant costing £150 per annum. Though the arrangement is grossly inefficient, to the university or Government body concerned the difference is simply one of an expenditure of £400 or £550 per annum, and as there is no way of showing on the balance-sheet the value of the work done by the scientist, the first figure will usually be preferred. Certain traditional ratios between scientific staffs and assistants have been set up, but they are, on the average, far too low. They fail to take into account the increasing mechanization of modern science and the consequently increasing demands on extra scientific assistants. The same criticism applies with even greater force to mechanics, who are never employed in laboratories to the most advantageous extent. Here is a clear case of absolute wastage of money. A laboratory mechanic, who can make most of the simpler and special forms of apparatus required, can nearly always produce them cheaper, often at a half or a quarter the price, than their cost if purchased from scientific instrument manufacturers. In fact the only scientific equipment it really pays to buy from the manufacturers are those things which are made on a large scale because of their engineering or other uses, as for instance, all radio appliances (see p. 111).

False Economies.—Where it is financially important that scientific results should be obtained, as in the more enlightened industrial laboratories, there is generally no lack of trained assistants, but the fact that such laboratories rarely produce work of scientific value is often taken to be due to this very abundance and not to the personal and organizational factors which are so effective in sterilizing industrial science (see p. 138 *et seq.*). This argument is often combined with the praise of the sealing-wax and string school of experimental work. There is no doubt that a certain amount of direct contact with materials and the overcoming of immediate physical difficulties sorts out the effective and ineffective scientists more rapidly than the presence of numerous operatives and assistants. It is also true that many of the greatest experimental discoveries of science in the past were made with extremely crude apparatus. But from these facts one should not conclude that the material difficulties of earlier scientists were the cause of their greatness or that the creation of difficulties will automatically reproduce it. As science advances the delicacy of the phenomena it observes continually increases, and this puts a premium on the use of more and more elaborate apparatus. Moreover, as science advances, the intellectual quality of the average scientific worker must necessarily decrease, because a larger proportion of the population is occupied in science than in the past. Although the prestige of science draws to it men of ability who in former times would have entered other professions, the growth of science has been far more rapid than could be made up by any such accessions. It is consequently unfair to expect the average scientific worker to force results out of inadequate materials in the way in which the rare scientists of older times were able to do. Scientific puritanism is in the end self-defeating.

Salaries of Scientific Workers.—Something has already been said about the financial position of scientific workers, but it is worth mentioning again here because it is a factor in leading to a lowered efficiency of individual work. It is very difficult to estimate whether the pay of scientific workers is on the average adequate. We do not know, in the first place, nearly enough of what they are paid (3), but the general impression is that, although graduate students are grossly underpaid for the first few years, older workers usually receive a salary of between £300 and £600 a year, which corresponds to their modest requirements. It is probably true that for equal ability a scientific worker could add 50 per cent. or more to his salary in other fields of enterprise, but for this loss he is supposed to be compensated by the agreeable nature of his work. It is often argued that, as wealth is the only criterion of importance in modern society, science would only receive its due recognition if scientists' salaries were twice or three times what they are now. But this is confusing cause and effect; salaries are fixed by the law of supply and demand. Present society does not value science and consequently it has no reason to pay scientists any higher salaries. Moreover the scientists themselves have not up till now shown much evidence of their need for higher salaries. They have not even made any large-scale efforts to ensure them either by united action on trade-union lines or by the formation of a closed guild system which has been so successful in the case of doctors and lawyers, though the Association of Scientific Workers and the British Association of Chemists and the various scientific institutes represent steps in this direction (see p. 400). It is also somewhat doubtful whether increased pay for scientists would, on the whole, be beneficial to science, as it would certainly draw into the profession a large number of self-seeking persons for whom at present it offers little attraction: we see enough already of the damage done in science by economic competition not to wish to increase this factor.

Whatever justification there may be for the average income of the scientist, it is difficult to justify the distribution of payments between those of different categories. There is too large a spread between the upper and lower ranks of scientific incomes, although this spread is trifling compared with the general inequalities of income. Few professors earn more than £2000 per annum, and not many research posts are given to honours graduates at less than £100 a year. (4) The bodies employing scientists at such rates excuse themselves by saying that, as they can always find applicants for such posts, they are really doing a kindness to those who would otherwise be doing nothing at all. The Department of Scientific and Industrial Research in its research grants treats post-graduate research not as work for which pay is given but as training for future work, and accordingly only gives grants which are in any case small, averaging £130, when the applicant can show that he can obtain no support from his parents or grants from local authorities or elsewhere.

The spread in salaries that does exist, in particular the large jump between a lecturer's salary at £400 to £500 per annum and a professor's at £1000, is a powerful inducement to internal snobbery and place-hunting in science. A more even distribution of salaries would do much to give science the possibility of an internal democracy which would be far more capable of dealing with its tasks than its present oligarchic organization.

Another disability which is even more sharply felt is the insecurity of tenure of scientific posts, particularly of industrial posts and all junior posts. The evils of this system have already been alluded to on p. 82, but it certainly contributes to the internal inefficiency of science by the insistence it puts on the achievement of immediate and voluminous results. Too often the promising scientist dare not undertake a piece of work which would, if persevered in, make a notable contribution to the advance of science, because he is uncertain whether at the end of one year or two years he may not have to leave his position without anything tangible to show for it. In a more subtle way the general financial anxiety distracts workers, particularly young and promising workers, and prevents them from acquiring undisturbed calmness of mind which is necessary for ordered thinking.

Scientific Institutes

Under modern conditions the greater part of scientific work is carried on in a laboratory or institute containing anything from four to forty scientific workers and occupied with a number of more or less related problems. So far we have considered only the efficiency of the individual worker. That of the organization of laboratories is probably more significant for the progress of science. At present the organization of science is in a transitional stage of development; it is passing from the period when it represented a sum of individual efforts to one when it advances by conscious team-work, through which the contributions of the individual scientists are absorbed in the general result. The laboratory of to-day rather resembles a primitive factory consisting of a number of independent workers each with his own tools and supplied with some common services, such as power or materials.

We can see already a wide divergency of laboratory organization. In some laboratories almost complete isolation is the rule. Every worker keeps his room locked, and many have worked for years without knowing what problems the others are engaged on. In other laboratories a definite division of labour has already taken place. One worker, for instance, may be responsible for all the spectroscopic work, another for micro-analysis, etc., but these occupations tend on the whole to be restricted to a few specialists, the main body of research workers being relatively independent.

At present the degree of internal co-ordination depends almost entirely on the character of the director of the laboratory. At one extreme we have the autocratic laboratory in which the director treats all the investigators as personal assistants who are given set tasks to carry out from time to time; at the other the anarchic one where each worker is entirely on his own, selects his own problems and reports to the director merely as a matter of formality. The danger inherent in the first extreme is that it checks originality and gives no sense of responsibility to the assistants. It is in such laboratories that the greatest exploitation of the work of juniors for the benefit of the seniors goes on. Many scientific reputations have been made almost entirely by skilful collaboration. When, as only too often happens, the director is advanced in years as well as autocratic, the problems attacked are likely to be those which were important thirty years ago. As a result we find that in any subject the laboratories which contribute to advance in ideas, apart from routine description and experimentation, are a very small fraction of the whole.

At the opposite extreme the anarchic laboratory is open to disadvantage of a different kind. Without any kind of direction, all but the most able workers have to face the task of finding out what to do as well as doing it. They have to rely too much on their own resources which, in view of the general intractability of scientific work, may be very discouraging. Such laboratories are apt to produce scientific recluses working at their own problems in jealousy and secretive isolation.

Between these extremes we have a more co-operative arrangement in which the director and the research workers consult, formally or informally, at frequent intervals about the general progress of the work and the means of fitting individual workers into the solution of some common problem. It is clear that this last represents the closest approximation to the kind of organization which will avoid internal waste. But at present the co-operative research laboratory is rather the exception than the rule. It depends for its very existence on the presence of a director of wide foresight and one who is willing to delegate authority. Such men are still all too rare in the scientific world. Except in a very few laboratories of this type there is nothing that corresponds to a comprehensive plan or scheme of work conceived over a period of years. As it is impossible to see, except in a general way, what is being done or will be done in the laboratory, it is impossible to co-ordinate it with work done in similar laboratories in other places or in different laboratories in the same place. Consequently the attack on many general problems of science, which could be carried out by co-ordinated effort, is attempted only by scattered individuals, and the results of the work are always incomplete and have to be pieced together with difficulty from a large number of scattered sources.

University Laboratories.—What has been said so far applies in the main to all laboratory work, but special disabilities occur for laboratories in different types of institutions. The main defect of university laboratories is, with some outstanding exceptions, their small size and lack of equipment. It is from them that the sealing-wax and string theory of scientific research originated. At every turn limitation of means hampers work: new assistants cannot be taken on, years may pass before a grant is available for a piece of apparatus. Ultimately the result is so discouraging as to reduce research to a mild pottering away at problems. It would probably be no exaggeration to say that nearly half the university laboratories in this country are in this condition. This tendency is aggravated by the dispersal of effort over a large number of laboratories. Such a distribution is extremely uneconomical; there is no opportunity for common services, apparatus has to be unnecessarily duplicated, and there is a lack of contact and mutual inspiration only partly compensated for by the existence of scientific societies.

Another characteristic disability of university science is the interference of teaching with research. This is an intrinsically difficult problem and one to which no simple solution is applicable. It is almost certain that every university teacher stands to gain by undertaking some research, if only to give him the status of a genuine scientific worker in his own eyes and those of his pupils. On the other hand, every research worker stands to gain, in learning how to present his results and in appreciating the more general aspects of science, by being occupied to a certain extent in teaching. The problem is to determine the correct proportion and choice of teaching and research staff and the correct amount of time in each case to be devoted to teaching and research. As things are at present the number of teaching posts in the universities far exceeds the number of research posts, with the almost inevitable result of the occupation of teaching posts by workers whose main interest is research and who would take research posts if they were available. University teachers nearly always tend to neglect either their teaching or their research. Many of them are not suited to teaching at all; others find that the demands of teaching prevent them from giving the continuous thought and interest which is necessary for research. The situation is aggravated in the higher grades because here the demands of administration add themselves to those of teaching and research. This pressure on time necessarily leads to a preference for the greatest amount of routine work possible; stereotyped lectures, the same year after year, interfere far less than a freshly thought-out course, and changes in the curriculum or in the organization of laboratories become almost unthinkable.

Effects of Endowments.—Another difficulty to which research in the universities is particularly liable is that arising from endowments. These are not always an unmixed blessing; except in a very large university, where it is possible by suitable wangling to distribute the benefits fairly widely, they are apt to unbalance the course of studies in an entirely irrational way, some of the departments being hypertrophied and others starved. Because of the relative meanness of wealthy Englishmen, the full evils of the endowment can best be seen in the United States, but it is not only there that there is no dollar without a string to it. Even in this country the atmosphere of patronage makes itself discreetly but effectively felt. Except for the older universities, which are sufficiently well placed both in respect to old endowments and to the honour they can confer on their benefactors, the policy of the university is often controlled not so much by those who have given to it in the past as by those who may be expected to give to it in the future. The development of research in the university will depend on the ability of its professors and departmental heads to extract money from local magnates, quite as much as it does on their scientific ability. Even liberally minded chiefs hesitate to employ research workers whose activities may cause financial loss to the department. (5) These considerations are particularly potent in regard to economics and sociological research. For other sciences the selection and training of research workers is generally sufficient to prevent any unpleasantness on this score; but this is in itself a serious criticism of the system.

Government Laboratories.—The special difficulties which beset scientific research carried out under Government control are largely due to bureaucratic methods. Civil Service and Army methods of administration are essentially unsuitable for the carrying on of research. Research is always an exploration of the unknown, and its value is not to be measured by the amount of time spent on it but by the output of new ideas thought of and tested out. Regularity of hours or days, clocking in and clocking out, with an annual fortnight's holiday, is not conducive to original thought. (6) The work of a scientist requires the most irregular hours. Sometimes it may be a matter of wanting to work sixteen or twenty-four hours a day for weeks on end; at others all the time spent in the laboratory is useless and the best results would come from going to parties or climbing a mountain. Not only are the conditions of work uncongenial, but the work itself is often of a routine character. Necessarily Government laboratories must do much routine work, but in getting it done they only too often fail to make any distinction of persons, and thus both blunt the abilities of promising research workers and discourage the entry of others into the service.

The scientist in Government pay gets the worst of both worlds. He does not have academic privileges and he misses the possibilities of advancement and in many cases even the security of tenure of the Civil Servant. Higher posts are reserved for administrative grades, and thus it happens that many governmental scientific workers are directly controlled by persons who have at most a mere smattering of scientific knowledge. In future it may be worse; the subject of everyday science is being removed from the higher civil service entrance examinations. At the same time a large proportion of scientific workers are not on the permanent staff, but hold temporary posts (7) or are engaged as students or workers on special investigations. In this case insecurity of tenure is added to the other deterrents to doing any work beyond the prescribed minimum.

It is not surprising that under these conditions many good scientific workers are deterred from entering Government service, and that nearly all those who can get university posts are willing to accept them at lower salaries than the Government offers.

RESEARCH IN INDUSTRY

Secrecy.—Two factors weigh heavily against the effectiveness of scientific research in industry. One is the general atmosphere of secrecy in which it is carried out, the other the lack of freedom of the individual research worker. In so far as any inquiry is a secret one, it naturally limits all those engaged in carrying it out from effective contact with their fellow scientists either in other countries or in universities, or even, often enough, in other departments of the same firm. The degree of secrecy naturally varies considerably. Some of the bigger firms are engaged in researches which are of such general and fundamental nature that it is a positive advantage to them not to keep them secret. Yet a great many processes depending on such research are sought for with complete secrecy until the stage at which patents can be taken out. Even more processes are never patented at all but kept as secret processes. This applies particularly to chemical industries, where chance discoveries play a much larger part than they do in physical and mechanical industries. Sometimes the secrecy goes to such an extent that the whole nature of the research cannot be mentioned. Many firms, for instance, have great difficulty in obtaining technical or scientific books from libraries because they are unwilling to have their names entered as having taken out such and such a book for fear the agents of other firms should be able to trace the kind of research they are likely to be undertaking. As another example we may cite the case of *Industrial Research Laboratories*, prepared by the Association of Scientific

Workers. This contains particulars of industrial laboratories, approximate expenditure, the research workers employed, etc. In preparing
it, 450 firms undertaking research were circularized. Of these
only eighty answered, of which only thirty-five gave particulars
of expenditure, while twelve declined to give even the number of
qualified workers employed. One firm replied: "The names of
our laboratory staff are never disclosed." (See Appendix III (c).)

Such secret methods would be really effective, however unethical,
only if those turning out the secret research had a personal interest
in its secrecy. But here the system defeats itself. The general
suppression of the results of industrial scientific research by the
firms concerned has a depressing effect on the research worker. If,
either from stupidity or from a secure monopoly position, the firm
does not consider it worth while to see that improved methods are
used, then it is hardly worth the research worker's while to trouble
to devise these methods, or, in fact, to bother himself any more about
the firm than his own personal advantage dictates. It is very rarely
that the scientist is a director or even an important shareholder in
the firm; his interest in secrecy is usually limited to keeping his
job and securing a moderate rise or a small or nominal bonus for
any given piece of work. It is in fact somewhat dangerous to show
too much promise in this direction, for fear of setting up a standard
which it will afterwards be necessary to live up to. After a period
of initial enthusiasm a research worker who sees that little social or
scientific gain proceeds from his work, and is not receiving any
pecuniary advantage from it, will not be at great pains to push his
inquiries to uncomfortable lengths and is more likely to indulge in
an effective system of bluff at the firm's expense.

Lack of Freedom.—One of the greatest disabilities of the industrial
scientist is his lack of freedom. Most workers are on a contract basis.
These contracts, which the prospective employee is usually too
ignorant or too frightened to refuse, are designed almost entirely to
protect the firm. A man's intellectual output is bought for a definite
period. All his inventions and ideas, even if developed outside the
works, belong to the firm. All patents must be surrendered to them at
the rate of ten shillings a time, even when they may make thousands
of pounds. Some contracts even go so far as to prevent the worker
from taking a job in a rival firm, that is, any other firm in the trade, for
two years after leaving employment. Effectively this means that he is
permanently bound to the firm though they are not to him. Recently,
an even worse abuse has appeared. Research workers are taken on
with contracts definitely terminating at thirty or forty years of age.
They are used when they are young, bright, and cheap, and then
turned off with little prospect of employment. It is hardly worth

stressing that this is not the way to get the best out of a scientific worker. The scientific ignorance of business executives cuts both ways. It prevents the scientist being properly appreciated or rewarded, but it also prevents the firm finding out how far its scientific staff is occupied in elaborately doing nothing in particular. University scientists visiting industrial laboratories are often amazed at the ignorance, not surprising in the circumstances, of the scientists employed, but even more at the way in which this ignorance can impose on the heads of the firm.

All the disadvantages inherent in Government directed laboratories also apply with added force to those of industry. What a large firm gains in funds available for research it loses by corresponding development of bureaucracy. The freedom of the scientific worker with regard to hours and holidays is just as effectively restricted, actually often to the detriment of the work. It would be of great advantage to an industrial scientist, for instance, to work for three or four months of the year in a university laboratory, but this is very rarely done. Even opportunities for visiting scientific congresses or going to scientific lectures are considerably restricted. One very large firm went to the length of arranging that lectures specially planned in a university for industrial scientists should be held out of working hours, consequently curtailing the time for discussion which was, in fact, more valuable than the lectures themselves. There is also a natural tendency towards an excessive amount of routine work and of work from which immediate results may be expected.

Low Standard.—The general administrative inferiority of the scientist still further detracts from his being able to direct and control the general course of the application of his results, and this tends to produce a lack of interest in the work. The result of these conditions shows itself in a tendency on the part of the more ingenious and enterprising research workers in industry to drift back to university research, which they are generally willing to do even with considerable reduction of salary. Those with more pecuniary interests take minor managerial posts and the remainder accept their position, carry out their routine tasks, and do not display any excessive activity or inventiveness. The net result is, of course, that the efficiency of the work in industrial scientific laboratories is exceptionally low, especially in regard to the relatively considerable expense in apparatus. Consequently the potential value of scientific research to the firms is heavily underrated.

Under the conditions of employment in industrial science it is not surprising that industrial jobs rank in desirability at the very bottom of the scientific scale and often below school science teaching. Although there are a number of brilliant research workers who, for some reason or another, have entered and remained in industry, these are exceptional, and industrial scientists on the whole do not represent the better grades of scientific worker. This tendency is reinforced by the methods of recruiting industrial scientists. For the most part, even in the biggest firms, the selection of industrial scientists is not made by scientists but by the official responsible for all staff appointments, consequently appearance, social conformity, public school, ability at games, are all considered as well as, if not before, academic qualifications. (8) For the neglect of the last there is a certain justification in that university teaching is, for the most part, of such a character that it does little or nothing to train its students for the tasks of industrial science. Thus recruitment and conditions conspire to ensure that industrial science should be staffed mostly by amiable, gentlemanly, possibly industrious, but certainly not able or enterprising workers. (See p. 388.) The present conditions of industrial science are not likely to be easily changed, as they are due to deep-seated causes. The primary one lies in the very nature of industrial production itself. Production for profit, as will be shown in the next chapter, inevitably distorts the application of science and hence the direction of research. Competition and monopoly between them lead directly to secrecy and to the throttling of fundamental research. A more immediate cause for the peculiarly unimaginative nature of industrial research is its control by men of purely commercial temperament, generally completely ignorant of science, treating its results as commodities and the producers of those results as hired workmen. There is reason to believe that in this respect the situation is far worse than fifty years ago. Especially with the big firms control has passed from their founders who had necessarily an understanding of science, to successors who have little or none, while the setting up of new concerns of any size by scientists has been rendered practically impossible by monopoly conditions.

Some indication of the extent to which this has gone is shown by an analysis of the directors of 9 firms in the electrical and chemical industries which owe their entire existence to science, were founded by men of scientific abilities, and which between them control more than three-quarters of the industrial scientific research in the country. Only 13 of the 114 directors have any scientific qualification and these are in 5 of the firms, while 5 are in the same firm. Only one individual of all these directors is a man of known ability in the scientific world. Under such circumstances the cynical attitude of scientific workers to the higher management is understandable. It is not only that the directors do not understand science, they are on the whole, on account of the traditions of the class to which they belong or would like to belong, actively inimical to the spirit of science. (9)

SCIENTIFIC INSTRUMENTS

One great source of inefficiency in scientific research is the cost and character of scientific apparatus. Except for a small proportion of apparatus turned out by laboratory workshops the scientific worker depends for most of his material on the scientific instrument industry. This is an industry which owes its very existence to science though it also draws from two older industries, those of the glass maker and the potter. Early scientific instrument makers were either professional clock or spectacle makers, or ingenious individuals with a natural bent for science who were forced to make instruments in order to support themselves and carry out researches on their own account. To these men science owes much. It was the first Dollond who discovered the principle of the achromatic lens on which is based the whole of modern astronomy, microscopy, and photography. Watt set up in Glasgow as a scientific instrument maker, and it was the repairs he effected to the university's steam-engine model that enabled him to make the modern steam-engine a possibility. Frauenhofer and Abbe were both in the optical glass trade.

Until the beginning of the present century, however, except for optical instruments, the scientific instrument industry was on a relatively small scale, used methods of hand manufacture, and was generally in very close touch with the few scientists who used their wares. The spread of science into industry, however, resulted in an immensely increased demand for what were originally scientific instruments but had now become industrial necessities, such for instance, as all forms of electrical measuring instruments, ammeters, etc. A further fillip was given to it by the popularization of wireless, which meant an immense consumer market for what would have once been called the most delicate and complicated scientific apparatus. The result was that we have now a relatively large scientific instrument industry with an annual turnover of some six million pounds, not counting the very considerable amount of scientific instruments made by electrical companies and the chemical ware from unspecialized potters. Thus it can be seen that the industry must have an income at least three times that of scientific research itself and that, therefore, it has ceased to be primarily dependent on it.

Mass Production.—This in some ways has been a benefit to science. The greater demand for certain components of scientific apparatus has resulted in their production by mass methods, and this has so lowered their costs as to make a veritable transformation in laboratory technique. (10) On the other hand, certain policies, only too prevalent in the scientific instrument trade, are very detrimental to laboratory work. Scientific instrument manufacture is now run on a strictly commercial basis and is consequently liable to the same abuses as ordinary business. In so far as firms make apparatus for other parts of industry the standard is high, though the price is often equally so, but in producing for public consumption or consumption by non-technical users a great deal of the apparatus is unnecessary ornamentation, and the price is even higher. The most flagrant case is in apparatus intended for the medical profession. Here, of course, there is a double racket. The manufacturer knows that the doctor cannot possibly judge the real value of the article and prices it at four times the cost or over, but he is careful to give it an appearance of finish which is calculated to impress the doctor's patients and justify the charging of correspondingly inflated fees. The actual cost, for instance, of taking an X-ray photograph, including the overheads and depreciation, can rarely exceed three shillings, but a patient is lucky if he gets off under two guineas.

High Prices.—When selling more specialized apparatus directly to scientific laboratories other difficulties appear. The market, compared with the public market, is a small one, and the firms are disinclined to put themselves out about it. The result is that prices, though not relatively so high as for the more gullible public, are still sufficient to check sales and keep the market small, thus completing the vicious circle. Actually much of the apparatus used in laboratories could be made on a mass-production basis and the price cut to a fraction, often as little as one-tenth, of the present price, even allowing an equal margin of profit. This has been done in the new scientific industry of the Soviet Union (see p. 227) and also here in the wireless industry. The old conditions are allowed to continue largely because it is no one's direct interest to put a stop to them. The tradition has grown up that scientific instruments must be bought, and no university has been far-sighted enough to invest in an instrument plant of its own which would both supply its own departments and pay for itself quite handsomely into the bargain. Nearly all apparatus is bought by individual departments out of grants and generally at the retail rate. The result is that in this way universities and research institutes are paying a large subsidy to the retailers which could easily be avoided if every university or group of institutes bought through a buyer at wholesale rates. There would probably be objections to this for, in one way or another, there are probably a good many commissions flying about. However, the result of such a policy would in the long run pay universities and manufacturers alike as far more apparatus would be purchased. The present state of affairs is one of the penalties of the haphazard growth of science and of its contempt for material things.

There are usually fairly close links between instrument firms and universities, but in Britain, at any rate, the practice of gifts of apparatus from firms is rare, and consequently there is little encouragement from the laboratory end to assist the manufacturer in improving his product. The result is that, particularly for physico-chemical and biological apparatus, the actual design is often many years out of date.

LACK OF CO-ORDINATION OF RESEARCH

The inefficiency and the imperfect organization of individual research laboratories is by no means the most serious disability from which scientific research suffers. Even more important is the general lack of co-ordination between the different scientific institutes and between individual research workers in different places. The fact is that the general organization of science and the communications between its various parts have remained at a primitive level and consequently fallen far behind the requirements of the enormous expansion of scientific activity which has occurred in the last fifty years. For the most part, science still retains as its only organizational forms the learned societies which, though essential for its first development in the seventeenth century, are quite inadequate to deal with the problems of scientific advance of to-day. The essential defect of the learned society is that it is conceived of as a voluntary association of amateurs each having complete freedom of operation and meeting for mutual edification and for arranging certain common conveniences, such as published journals, to take the place of private letters. Now at one time such associations represented a great and indeed a revolutionary step, as may be judged by the immense enthusiasm and the violent opposition that they aroused. (11) The idea of a voluntary association of gentlemen of means and leisure is no longer adequate to cover the organizational requirements of modern science. Very few scientific workers in any country are now anything but salaried officials of universities, Government or industry. Their apparent freedom depends to a large extent on their ineffectiveness or the ignorance of the ruling powers as to the ultimate results of their work. Existing scientific societies do not, as we have seen, provide an adequate basis for organization, even less for initiative in the direction of research; they have become almost purely publishing houses and honorific corporations.

Informal Methods.—What organization of science there is is almost entirely informal. Workers in any given field generally get to know one another personally and arrange among themselves, when they are on friendly terms, the kind of work each of them intends to pursue and the relation of one man's work to another.

The system undoubtedly has its advantages.   It avoids rigid rules and bureaucratic "red tape," but it is at the same time liable to very grave abuses.   It provides no check against the play of personal interests.   Naturally, in science there is less incentive to jobbery than in business or politics, but there is always some, for although scientific posts do not carry substantial salaries, the scientist attaches almost childish value to the title and prestige of the position.   Bitter rivalries, sometimes personal, sometimes between the merits of different branches of science, are fought out with all the methods of private intrigue.   As the money available for science is never sufficient to satisfy more than a fraction of the demand, perpetual scrambling goes on behind the scenes for what money there is.   This is enhanced by the general secrecy that covers all these transactions; any dealings particularly with wealthy benefactors are most carefully guarded until they can be revealed as a *fait accompli*.   Anyone who is able to discover what is going on may be bought off by a share of the "swag."   The amount of energy which is put into securing, at other scientists' expense, money from a Government Department or a potential benefactor would, with an ordered organization, suffice to make such a compelling demand for such allocation for science that there would be enough for all.   The result of this lack of system is that, together with examples of successful collaborations, we find others of overlapping, brought about simply from lack of consultation.

Lack of Integration of different Sciences.—Far more important is the absence of intensive and conscious drive in science.   This is becoming much worse as a result of the recent developments by which the different sciences have come to be intrinsically closer together.   Now informal methods of co-operation, though moderately successful inside any branch of science, almost completely break down between the sciences.   There are far less occasions for members of different than of the same societies to meet one another, and when they do so specialization has so far advanced that their common topics are likely to lie outside science altogether.   Universities might be expected to supply some remedy for this state of affairs, but in practice inter-departmental jealousies are often stronger than common interests, and a professor of physics may know far more of what is going on in a physics laboratory at the other side of the globe than he does of the chemical laboratory in the next building.   The result of this is an enormous lag in the appreciation of the relevance of one field of science to another.   For instance, chemists for a quarter of a century have failed to recognize that advances in physics and crystallography require not merely the revision but the complete recasting of the fundamental structure of their science (see p. 253), nor have the mathematicians appreciated the extraordinarily rich fields offered to them in the recent studies of the development of organisms. One effect of this is to hold back science just at those very places where its advance is most needed: the regions between recognized sciences. Each faculty has developed its own informal though effective ways of raising money and finding men. Outside and between them such facilities can only slowly be built up and without them discoveries even when made cannot be followed up. It is not usually recognized how much the rate of scientific progress is held up by the lack of such material resources. Apparatus and assistants do not make science, but without them it grows in a crippled way like a starved young animal (see p. 100). The real tragedy is that men with ideas in an unrecognized field are kept short of supplies until as the result of many years' work they have achieved results which attract sufficient attention, and only then when their inventive powers have waned are they given scope. It is true that a man of sufficient ingenuity and determination can do good work on the very minimum of materials. Great scientists, such as Faraday and Pasteur, have shown this conclusively, but even then advance is often held up for years, and for one such success dozens of promising starters are discouraged and driven from active research.

The lack of contact between sciences also effectively delays the development of technique inside each science. By an intelligently organized adoption of new techniques from physics the operations of chemical analysis and synthesis might be shortened, in all, by a very large factor. In the normal course of development such improvements will take between ten and fifty years, by which time they will be obsolete in physics. What this means is that a very large fraction of the time and money spent on chemistry nowadays is sheer waste—workers are spending weeks on jobs which should only take days.

The Gerontocracy.—One pertinent objection which can always be raised to any criticism of the organization of science is that the guarantee of its efficacy is to be found in the character of the men of undoubted scientific achievement who hold high positions in the administration of research. In all professions control by the aged is a debatable subject. The advantages of experience and comparative disinterestedness, which ensure the continuity of tradition and the avoidance of rash courses and overmuch self-advertisement, can be put on one side: dislike of change, inability to seize opportunity, lack of contact with the current world on the other. In science, however, which depends for its very existence on the discovery of new things and the making of new combinations, and where initiative counts more than experience, the disadvantages of age weigh more heavily than anywhere else. Particularly in the last fifty years the advances in basic conceptions have been so rapid that the majority of older scientists are incapable of understanding, much less of advancing, their own subjects. But nearly the whole of what organization of science exists, and the vital administration of funds, is in the hands of old men. (12)   It is true that in many cases they have the perspicacity to advance younger men of ability, but the system of favour and patronage is always liable to abuse (13) and is in any case unbecoming to the character of science. The ability of a young worker is much better judged by his fellows in active science than by any committee of elders, however eminent. There is a further objection that under existing conditions eminence in science is often attained at the expense of breadth of outlook and general culture. It is partly to this that must be attributed the lack of understanding and initiative that official scientific bodies have shown in the wider questions of the social responsibilities of science.

Need Science be Organized?—A quite opposite objection to any reorganization of science is based on the recognition of this very danger of control by elder scientists. The existing anarchic state of science gives many opportunities to evade particularly obnoxious control. If objections are taken to the policy of one committee, another can be formed to do the same work under different auspices. It is felt that organization might put an end to these possibilities and perhaps more effectively than ever block unorthodox developments in science, through the danger of carrying over to that organization the principles of autocratic control. But this is not so much an objection to organization as one against existing abuse of such organization. Any new organization of science, if it is to be vital as well as effective, must bring with it the democratic principle which will ensure adequate participation in responsible control by scientific workers of every grade of seniority.

The idea that science needs any further organization is certainly one which is violently combatted by many scientists. The supporters of the present state of affairs justify their attitude by appealing to the traditional freedom of the scientist. Each man is supposed to be a judge for himself of what needs to be found out and of the best way of finding it out, and he is further supposed to be able to get hold of the means and to have the time for the investigation. But in the present state of science, these conditions no longer hold. Even if they did, the co-operation of other workers and the knowledge of taking part in a co-ordinated effort cannot fail to be of help in the work of any individual. How this could be done will be shown in later chapters.

Scientific-Publications

As science grows, the facts on which it is founded and the way of building laws and theories from them depend less and less on the direct observation of nature by the scientific worker and more and more on the previous observations of other workers and on their methods of interpretation. The very instruments of science are, as it were, material embodiments of previously achieved theories. It is consequently of critical importance that the scientist at every stage in his work should be able to reach, rapidly and in a convenient form, the results up to date of all relevant scientific knowledge. This is the function of the system of scientific publication which has grown up with the development of science itself. It is at present an enormous and chaotic structure. There are in the world to-day no less than 33,000 different scientific periodicals, probably more, for this number was given in the last (1934 edition) of the *World List of Scientific Periodicals*. Besides these there are an uncounted number of books, pamphlets and theses. Each of these periodicals fulfils, or attempts to fulfil, the needs of scientific information in a particular field in a particular country. Some, such as the journals of the academies, cover all subjects and have a world-wide circulation; others are the product of some single highly specialized institute and are only with great difficulty available outside their country of origin.

The production of scientific publications has long ago become so large that it is recognized that a scientific worker can only read a small fraction of the papers in what is itself a very small part of science. But how can he ensure that the papers he does read are those that are to be of the most value in his work or how can he be certain that he is not in fact reduplicating work already done? For this purpose there has grown up in recent years a vast system of abstracting, in which the contents of each scientific paper are reduced to a few lines. In spite of attempts at rationalization there is still an enormous amount of overlapping and gaps in abstracting work, and abstracts themselves have reached an unwieldy size. Thus American Chemical Abstracts consist every year of three volumes of 2000 pages each, with an index in addition of 1000 pages. This situation is growing rapidly worse; the number of entries in Biological Abstracts has grown from 14,506 in 1927 to 21,531 in 1934.

The Burying of Published Work.—The result is that it has become impossible for the average scientific worker, who does not wish to devote the major part of his time to reading, to keep up with the progress in his own field, and almost impossible for anyone to follow the progress of science as a whole even in the most general way. At the same time a large quantity of good scientific work may be permanently lost because it was not appreciated when it was published, and subsequently everybody has been so busy in keeping up with recent publications that there has been no time to sift through the records of the past. In part these difficulties are an inevitable result of the enormous growth of science, but in far larger part they are due to the lack of consideration which scientists are giving to the problem of communicating their results. The very bulk of scientific publications is itself delusive. It is of very unequal value; a large proportion of it, possibly as much as three-quarters, does not deserve to be published at all, and is only published for economic considerations which have nothing to do with the real interests of science. The position of every scientific worker has been made to depend far too much on the bulk rather than the quality of his scientific publications. Publication is often premature and dictated by the need of establishing priorities, itself an indication of the unnecessary struggle for existence that goes on inside the scientific world.

The number of scientific journals is altogether excessive. Each one had at its inception a certain *raison d'être*. It was founded to express the results of some new science from a point of view other than the orthodox, but in the course of time these distinctions disappear and the journal remains. A great deal in science has been sacrificed to local patriotism or personal distinction. Owing to this the circulations of the journals are all small and, as a large number of them never reach the libraries of any but the most important universities and learned societies, their purpose is for the most part lost.

The Cost of Publication.—The burden of this vast mass of publication is in itself a great handicap to scientific research. Apart from certain Government subsidies the cost of scientific publication is paid for by the scientists themselves. Very few journals, and those mostly technical, are run at a profit. The majority are supported by learned societies, and indeed put such a drain on their resources that they are rarely able to spend anything for research purposes. The cost of journals and books and subscriptions to learned societies are not usually reckoned as laboratory expenses, and the real salary of the scientist is, for this reason, always between 5 and 10 per cent. less than what he nominally receives. Besides this, owing to the knowledge that, under present conditions, it is unlikely that all those who should be interested will see any particular piece of work, the practice has grown up by which each scientist sends anything up to 200 reprints of his work to selected people, which of course imposes on him an additional and often considerable expense. This sending of reprints is in itself a hopeful sign and may, as is suggested in a later chapter, point the way to an altogether better system of communication, but at present it is inefficient and costly, as there is no relation of demand to supply for any particular paper. In particular, reprints of papers which are recognized to be important are generally quite unobtainable after a lapse of as little as a year.

It should be clear from what has already been said that the present system of scientific publication wastes both time and money and is a constant source of irritation to the scientists themselves. Efforts, it is true, are continually being made to improve it. A system of reports on progress in different fields of science is gradually spreading. The number of abstracting journals has been reduced and abstracts better classified, but these improvements hardly keep pace with the cropping up of new journals and the accumulation of unread papers. What is wanted is a far more drastic revision of the whole system of scientific communication. Some suggestions for this are contained in a subsequent chapter.

Personal Communication and Travel.—The chaos of scientific publication is not the only failure of adequate communication between scientific workers. There is a great deal in science that cannot conveniently, if at all, be included in publications. In all experimental science the techniques for obtaining measurements are almost as important as the measurements themselves, and in a similar but less tangible way, the mental techniques of particular sciences, as apart from any general scientific method, are of crucial importance to scientific advance. Now it still remains true that, in spite of the best system of publications that can be devised, physical and mental techniques can generally best be transmitted by direct experience. This is, in fact, the way that they have been for the most part handed on in the past. A new technique or even a new science is spread largely by the visits of foreign students to its place of origin and the setting-up of subsidiary schools from which further personal transmissions can be made. But although this happens, it does not happen nearly enough. Facilities for travel and for work in foreign laboratories do exist, but they are very inadequate. Expense is a serious drawback to all but the fortunate few who achieve visiting or exchange fellowships. It is most difficult for those who need it most, the workers who have three or four years' research behind them but have not a position which will give them enough to travel or live abroad on. As a result techniques spread much more slowly than they need and indeed rarely get through to the whole scientific world before they are superseded. It is a common experience in visiting laboratories to notice at the same time unsuspected improvements which have been in use for years and obsolete techniques which have survived for as long a period. To carry on with obsolete methods may often lead to the waste of years of effort, but this waste is inevitable unless much more rapid and direct personal means of communication between scientific workers is effectively organized.

The Effects of Inefficient Organization

It is extremely difficult to estimate the extent of the damage done to the progress of science by the organizational inefficiency of which we have spoken. There is no doubt, however, that it is at present one of the major factors retarding the progress of science. To put it in figures, the average efficiency cannot be much greater than 50 per cent. and may be as little as 10 per cent. That means, as things are at present, something between 50 and 90 per cent. of the money and efforts devoted to science are wasted. That is not to say that if these sources of inefficiency were removed science would advance twice to ten times as fast, because, under the present conditions of limited funds and recruitment, any substantial increase in the rate of scientific advance would bring it up against these limiting factors. The rapid growth of science in the last century is itself in part responsible for its present difficulties. The scientist has remained far too concentrated on the immediate work in hand to notice the slowly growing complexity of the organization in which he is working, and indeed, unless the difficulties appear in some form immediately hindering work, they are, for the most part, unnoticed.

The very success of science is enough to mask from the eyes of the public and even from those of scientists themselves the waste of effort in achieving those successes. The scientist does his work, science advances, applications and inventions follow in its train. All this is seen; what is not seen is that the rate of advance could be far greater than it is at present, and that it could be maintained with far less waste of time and intelligence. There are three things worth bearing in mind in judging from outside the achievements of science. Firstly, science still does attract, by the intrinsic satisfaction it brings to its followers and by its apparent disinterestedness, a large proportion of the most brilliant minds of each generation. Secondly, science is easy; far easier than anyone outside it can imagine. Once its language is learned, advances, except at some critical sticking places, come almost of themselves. For the greater part of scientific work, a minimum amount of manual dexterity, industry and honesty is all that is required. The richness of possible discovery compensates and more than compensates for the inefficiencies that hinder the actual work. For the most part, it is an Aladdin's cave. Everything is there for the taking. Thirdly, it is natural to compare the efficiency

of science to-day with that of other human activities.   In such a
comparison science does not fare so badly, because in its general
direction it is largely free from the grosser evils of economic and
political life: speculation, deliberate restriction, sharp practice and
corruption, all symptoms of the crippling effect of vested interest in
an outworn system.   On the other hand, in detail the inefficiency of
science simply reflects in an exaggerated form the inefficiency of the
economic system under which it has reached its present development.
In the commercial and industrial worlds there is, however, direct
economic incentive to efficiency in management.   Efficient methods
of running a business, even though they cost more in the way of
machinery or staff, pay because the saving on other costs is even greater.
But science, although it is an ultimate source of profit in an industrial
civilization, is in itself not profit-making.   From the business point
of view science does not pay; consequently the waste of the lives of
highly trained scientists on trivial or unnecessary work does not
appear as a loss, while any expenditure to prevent that waste represents
so much money that need not have been spent.   The progress of
science or the possibilities of its gifts to humanity are no concern of
the business world.   In view of the lack of social or economic consideration it receives, what is surprising perhaps is not so much the
inefficiency of scientific research but the fact that it carries on so
effectively and so brilliantly.

   Science in Danger.—Then why, it may be asked, do we wish an
exception made for science?   In a bad world it does as well as most.
The reason is that science is a unique product of human society
which demands, and rightly demands, special consideration.   On the
continued progress of science depends not only the realization of the
conquest of poverty and disease but all the means of significant
change in human society.   Science is, after all, a delicate process;
we do not know how much restriction and inefficiency it is able
to withstand.   More than once before in history we have seen science
flourish and die out.   It may happen again.   That is a risk neither
science nor society can afford to run.

   (1) The conflicts and difficulties that face those seeking satisfaction in science to-day
are well expressed in C. P. Snow's novel, *The Search*, at the point where the hero is finally
deciding to leave science :
   "Why had I ever been devoted to science?   And why had the devotion faded?   I
remembered arguments with Hunt and Audrey, years ago.   Intuitively, it seemed, they had
been wiser than I, though all the logic was on my side then.   What had I told Audrey
were the reasons why men did science?   I should still say much the same, except that
nowadays I should allow more for accident ; many men become scientists because it happens
to be convenient and they may as well do it as anything else.   But the real urgent drives
remain: there seemed to be three kinds.   Three kinds of reason to give to oneself, that is ;
reasons in which one must believe in order to be in harmony with the deeper thrusts.   One
can do science because one believes that practically and effectively it benefits the world.
A great many scientists have had this as their chief conscious reason: for me it never

existed and at thirty it seemed more foolish than ten years before. Because if I wanted directly to benefit the world, I should have to do what little I could to prevent western civilization falling within—shall I say twenty years. That task is more urgent than applied science. Applied science has done nothing to make it easy; and while science goes on, its world will collapse under its feet. My own part could be little enough at either; but if it were suddenly magnified indefinitely, and I was offered the choice between being associated with the cure of cancer on the one hand, or on the other, the maintenance in England and France of an additional thirty years of freedom for liberal, sane and generous thinking, I should choose the latter without a moment's hesitation.

One can do science because it represents the truth. That, or something like it, was the reason I had given in the past. So far as I had a conscious justification, it would always have been this. Yet it was not good enough, I thought, watching a red-sailed boat running between an island and the shore. Science was true in its own field; it was perfect within its restrictions. One selected one's data—set one's puzzle for oneself, as it were—and in the end solved the puzzle by showing how they fitted other data of the same kind. We know enough of the process now to see the quality of the results it can give us; we know, too, those sides of experience it can never touch. However much longer science is done, since it sets its own limits before it can begin, those limits must remain. It is rather as though one was avidly interested in all the country-side between this town and the next : one goes to science for an answer, and is given a road between the two. To think of this as the truth, to think of ' the truth ' at all as a unique ideal, seems to me mentally naïve to a degree.

Just as to think that science within its restrictions is not truthful is to be ignorant of the meaning of words. Constantine, I know, would agree with both these statements. But where we should differ is over the value to be given to this particular, restricted, scientific truth. I should hold that now its nature is established, now we know the way in which our minds determine its restrictions, that its value lies only in application; a scientific fact now does not enlighten us on the nature of all facts; its meaning we know before we find it out; it is important only that it gives us a new unit in our control of the outside world. In the days I argued with him, Constantine, however, would give scientific facts a value over and above their use—an almost mystical value, not as truth so much as knowledge. As though, somehow, if we knew enough we should have a revelation. I am probably being unjust to him; but at least nothing he has ever said, and he has said a great deal, revived my acceptance of the intrinsic value of scientific truth.

And one can also do science because one enjoys it. Naturally anyone who believes wholeheartedly, either in its use or its truth, will also enjoy it. Constantine, for example, gains more simple hedonistic enjoyment from research than most men from their chosen pleasures; and though he is the most devoted scientist I know, there are many men to whom enjoyment comes as a consequence of faith. But I think it is also possible to enjoy science without believing overmuch in its use, or having any views upon the value of its truths. Many people like unravelling puzzles. Scientific puzzles are very good ones, with reasonable prizes. So that either without examining the functions of science, being indifferent to them or taking them for granted, a number of men go in for research as they would for law; living by it, obeying its rules, and thoroughly enjoying the problem-solving process. That is a perfectly valid pleasure, among them you can find some of the most effective of scientists. They no doubt get their moments of ecstasy, as I did once in my youth, when I saw a scientific truth disclose itself in my mind; these ecstasies do not depend upon a belief in scientific values, any more than a religious ecstasy depends on a belief in God. The belief makes them the more likely to happen, perhaps; but I suspect they come to infidels as well; probably many people have had religious ecstasies besides the saints, but call them by a different name.

Perhaps this last reason, simple, uncritical enjoyment, is the commonest of all, I thought. Together with a smattering of the language of the more high-sounding motives; for almost any man who had drifted into science because he liked doing it would still preen himself if you asked why? and tell you he was solving the secrets of Nature. Well, it was a reason good enough, I had to admit. But I did not want to admit it; because, for me, I should always need faith in the results before I could enjoy. Human intricacies, I might enjoy for their own sake. But not scientific problems, unless they were important to me for something richer than themselves.

' There's nothing in it for me,' I thought.

' The wonder isn't that I'm not devoted now ; it is that I persuaded myself of it for so long.'

' I shall never get the devotion back,' I thought." (Pp. 346-9.)

(2) See A. J. Cronin's novel, *The Citadel*.

(3) The Association of Scientific Workers has been endeavouring to find this out by means of a questionnaire. The results so far have shown that the average salary rises fairly uniformly from £245 a year for the age group 20-24 to £800 a year for the age group 50-59, and it is distinctly higher at every stage in industrial than in academic work.

(4) *The University Grants Report*, 1929-1935, shows that at the latter date 669 professors, or 79 per cent., received salaries between £800 and £1400 ; 273 readers, or 73 per cent., received between £550 and £850; 1068 lecturers, or 77 per cent., between £375 and £600 ; and 702 assistant lecturers and demonstrators, or 82 per cent., received between £225 and £400. This indicates the small degree of overlap.

(5) In one provincial university a wealthy member of the governing board cut the university out of his will because the staff had been active in collecting for Spanish relief.

(6) J. G. Crowther in his interesting booklet, *Science and Life*, also remarks on this point :
" The best-known Government laboratory is the National Physical Laboratory. . . . It is one of the best equipped laboratories in Europe, and its work is thorough. Though much excellent work is done, it is difficult to believe that the resources of the laboratory in scientific ability and equipment are utilized to the best advantage.

The research staff work according to definite office hours, and the traditions of the British Civil Services have been instilled into them. They are made to feel that obedience to precedent, and the other features of this tradition, is more important than making discoveries. This situation is due to the belief that the older departments of Government are concerned with matters intrinsically more important than scientific research. The working habits of the clerks of the Treasury are thought to be the proper pattern for scientific discoverers.

Why are scientists expected to imitate the working habits of others in entirely different fields ?

It is due to the superior prestige of politics and finance. It is still generally believed that the principles of government in the contemporary world have no necessary connection with science. It is thought that politics necessarily consists of the manipulations of persons and parties, and that science is only of importance as a tool in the achievement of such aims. This view arises naturally from the philosophical principles of the present English social system.

The six hundred members of the House of Commons do not include one professional scientist whose daily work consists of scientific research, and only a handful who have graduated in science. The situation is even more reactionary than in the House of Lords, where there are two or three eminent scientific research workers. This reflects the belief that science is not of primary importance in modern society. It makes many men with scientific ability feel that science is less important than politics. They tend to drift from scientific research into the political work which enjoys more prestige " (pp. 79-80).

(7) Temporary post is often a euphemism. This is a case which has recently come before the Association of Scientific Workers :
In 1918 Mr. X was employed as a " temporary " assistant scientist ; ten years later Mr. X was still graded as " temporary." About this time a new rule was made by the employing body which, as it turned out, could be applied to Mr. X. During the economic depression of 1930-1932 Mr. X was advised on different occasions to seek another post, although also, from time to time, his director had encouraged him by remarks indicating that he was ear-marked for promotion. Finally, in 1934, Mr. X was sacked : by the application of the rule, made about ten years *after* Mr. X was first taken on as a " temporary " assistant, whereby the employment of a " temporary " assistant should terminate after he had reached his maximum salary (at that grade) for one year. There was apparently no question of Mr. X's professional ability ; merely the application of the rule, made long after Mr. X was first employed at that particular grade, and from which he had not been promoted, even after sixteen years of " temporary " employment.—*The Scientific Worker*, Vol. 9, p. 166, 1937.

(8) The candidate at the end of an interview for a research post was somewhat startled to be asked, " Do you bowl ? " The official on noticing his surprise said, " Well, you see, we don't really need another research chemist, but we could do very well with a fast bowler."

(9) J. G. Crowther in *Science and Life* comments thus on the British attitude towards science :
" The Germans began to send university-trained chemists to England about 1850 to

work in the chemical factories and learn the practical processes. These men returned to Germany, improved the processes with the aid of their superior chemical knowledge, and founded chemical firms. From the beginning, German chemical industry was owned and directed by chemists with theoretical training, and in half a century it captured important parts of the world's chemical industry.

Nevertheless, English chemical magnates could continue to live grandly on their old monopolies and accumulations of profits. They did not mind losing the initiative in industrial development, and were more concerned with securing a place in the English leisured class.

The late Fritz Haber was the greatest authority in the world on the relations between scientific research and industry. When he was asked why British industry had not found a satisfactory way of organizing these relations before the War, he attributed part of the cause to the social outlook of the British upper classes. He said that successful English business men and scientific research workers did not talk shop together when they met in clubs. Thus business men and scientists rarely knew each other as equals, and never learned the nature of each other's problems and how they could co-operate. In Germany, on the contrary, the business man was expected to talk about business, and the scientist about science. This led to mutual understanding and respect.

The British social habit on which Haber commented is a reflection of the prestige of the ideal of the leisured class in England. The English business man or scientist usually wishes to be known first as a leisured gentleman, and as a great organizer or discoverer afterwards. He uses the means provided by success to acquire the habits of the leisured classes.

Though the utilization of science in British industry has been considerably improved since the War, this class attitude still flourishes strongly, and in subtle ways has a profound influence on the growth of science in Britain " (pp. 76-77).

(10) Mass-production methods are not always, however, advantageous, especially when they lead to inflexible production. The design of X-ray tubes, for instance, has been kept unaltered for the last ten years, although much better tubes could be made, simply because this would mean considerable changes in the manufacturing plant.

(11) Thus Glanvill in his panegyric, *Plus Ultra*, on the Royal Society, wrote :

" This was a mighty design, groundedly laid, wisely exprest, and happily recommended by the Glorious Author, who began nobly, and directed with an incomparable conduct of Wit and Judgment : But to the carrying it on, it was necessary there should be many Heads and many Hands, and those formed into an Assembly, that might intercommunicate their Tryals and Observations, that might joyntly work, and joyntly consider ; that so the improvable and luciferous Phaenomena, that lie scatter'd up and down in the vast Champaign of Nature, might be aggregated and brought into a common store. This the Great man (Francis Bacon) desired, and form'd a Society of Experimenters in a Romantick Model, but could do no more. His time was not ripe for such performances.

These things therefore were consider'd also by the later Virtuosi, who several of them combined together, and set themselves on work upon this grand Design."

As a counterblast to this an anonymous author produced :

THE PLUS ULTRA

REDUCED TO A

NON PLUS :

OR,

A SPECIMEN OF SOME ANIMADVERSIONS UPON THE PLUS ULTRA

OF MR. GLANVILL

from which the following quotations are taken worthy of any modern opponent of science :

" In that Famed Work I encountred with so many *illiterate passages*, that the credit of *our Nation* seemed concerned in the refuting it. I met with Passages so destructive that, if to be concerned for the interest of the present Monarchy, the Protestant Religion, and the emolument of each private person (and not solely of Tradesmen) could warrant any one for putting Pen to paper, I ought not to be silent. I divided my Animadversions into several parts ; some whereof were to represent these Comical Wits as really ridiculous ; others were to make them odious to the Kingdom. I considered, that in those days few had patience to reade over prolixe Treatises ; as also I imagined, that the Contest would be more deeply imprinted in the minds of men, if they were excited by a variety of discourse of that nature. . . .

There is another Treatise, shewing the Original of the Colledge of Experimental Philosophers, as Campanella projected it, and containing a parallel of what He contrived (and their Historian hath persued) for the reducing of England and Holland to Popery : also a Specimen of Sundry Experiments published by several Virtuosi, that are *false or stolne*, yet boasted of as *their proper Inventions* : together with Instances of the danger that all Tradesmen will run into by the continuance of *this Assemblie*; which to manifest further, I shall here adde a Proposal designed to have been tendred, and improved into an *Act*, in this last Session of Parliament. It was delivered by Sir P. N. to an Honourable Member of the House of Commons, and by him sent unto me, adding, ' In which you may see what *they* ' *drive at*, viz. Instead of Monopolizing this or that particular Trade at a time, once for all ' to have a Monopoly for all that ever should be invented. It is proposed, that such kinde ' of pretended new Inventions relating to Mechanicks, Trades, or Manufactures, as are ' or shall be offered to the Parliament, may by them be referred to such indifferent judicious ' persons, as are like to give them a faithful Account, about the Newness, Reality, Usefulness, ' etc., of the things proposed, and whether they are like to answer the effects pretended ' to, and to make Report of the same to the Parliament.

' And the Royal Society of London for Improving of Natural Knowledge being already ' fixed into a Corporation, and the Council of the said Society consisting of 21, being by ' their Constitution under an Oath, to deal faithfully in all things belonging to the Trust ' Committed to the said Council : It is offered, that such things may be preferred to the ' said Council, and they to Report unto the Parliament.'

They that know the Men, know their meaning : and whosoever understands the Constitution of our Parliaments, is assured that they need not look out of their own number for different judicious persons, to inform the House what the Reality, Usefulness, or Newness, etc., is of Inventions ; or should the Parliament be at any time destitute of such Intelligence the Council must make better Reports then doth their Historian, or else it will be in vain to resort to them in the Case. Upon the same pretence, if they once gain this, that miscellaneous Assembly or *indifferentlie judicious Persons*, shall pretend to detect the Frauds of Trades ; and endeavour to recommend to all befitting Preferments in the University and elsewhere, the ingenious and learned : and then affairs will be brought to a fair pass. But I enlarge too far, and shall only adde, that I do remit the consideration and purport of this Project to the Tradesmen of London, who are better acquainted then I with the tendency and consequences hereof."

(12) For instance on one of the most important bodies in British Science, the Advisory Council of the Department of Scientific and Industrial Research, the average age of the members is 64 years, and no member is below 55 years of age.

(13) There are many instances of this in the history of science. The council of the Royal Society, for instance, has shown itself for a large part of its history more favourable to agreeable mediocrities than to men of genius; their treatment of Priestley and of Joule being cases in point. Nor are great scientists immune from human weaknesses, as Davy's jealousy of Faraday bears witness. If they were to be judged by their treatment of younger men, only the greatest like Pasteur or Rutherford would escape.

CHAPTER VI

THE APPLICATION OF SCIENCE

ANY account of the application of science and of the factors which determine its nature and extent is bound to be particularly difficult to give. The fact is that the application of science is so much taken for granted that the way in which it works has never been seriously looked into. Most scientists as well as laymen are content with the official myth that that part of the work of the pure scientists which may have human utility is immediately taken up by enterprising inventors and business men, and thus in the cheapest and most commodious way possible put at the disposal of the public. Any serious acquaintance with the past or present state of science and industry will show that this myth is untrue in every point, but just what is the truth is something much more difficult to find out.

The Interaction of Science and Technics.—There has always been a close interaction between the development of science and that of material techniques. Neither would be possible without the other, for without the advance of science techniques would fossilize into traditional crafts, and without the stimulus of techniques science would return again to pure pedantry. It does not follow, however, that this association is either conscious or efficient; in fact, the application of science to practical life has always been faced with the greatest difficulties and is even now, when its value is beginning to be recognized, carried on in the most haphazard and ineffective way. Lord Stamp, by no means a scathing critic of the present dispensation, characterizes the process as follows:

"All these discoveries, these scientific infants, duly born and left on the doorstep of society, get taken in and variously cared for, but on no known principle, and with no directions from the progenitors. Nor do the economists usually acknowledge any duty to study this phase, to indicate any series of tests of their value to society, or even of methods and regulation of the optimum rate of introduction of novelty. These things just 'happen' generally under the urge of profit, and of consumers' desire, in free competition, regardless of the worthiness of new desires against old, or of the shifts of production and, therefore, employment, with their social consequences. The economist rightly studies these when they happen, but he is not dogmatic about them not being allowed to happen at all in just that way on account of the social disturbance or degradation of non-economic values which they may involve."—*The Science of Social Adjustment*, p. 13.

The relation of science to the development of technical and economic activities is both a complex and a changing one. Science in the sense of rational, explicit, and cumulative human experience came late compared with the traditional, implicit, though also cumulative, techniques of the craftsman. It could not have been otherwise: understanding has to proceed from the simple to the complex, but the primitive needs of man, that have to be satisfied before he can even begin to understand, are on the most complex level. Man's first practical technical progress was in the direction of bio-chemistry in the preparation of food, and of animal psychology in the chase and ultimately the domestication of animals. Any scientific understanding of what he was doing was intrinsically impossible. In fact, even now primitive magic offers, over much of this field, as immediately useful explanations of phenomena as does science.

What can be understood rationally, on the other hand, must be simple; but it will not be worth understanding unless it is also useful. It was consequently only at the relatively late stage of civilized city life that mathematics, mechanics, and astronomy, the simplest of sciences, began to appear, when already the main techniques of human life had been fixed. Cookery, husbandry, agriculture, pottery, textile and metal work already existed in very much the same stage of development as they did at the beginning of the eighteenth century. Science did not appear as a practically useful, as contrasted with a magically useful, value until, in the new Western civilization, mechanic arts on a large scale became economically important in peace and war. Apart from navigation and gunnery, both of which involve only mechanical and optical science, industry by the end of the eighteenth century had given far more to science than science to industry. (1) This was the turning-point. Soon afterwards the development of chemical science, the next most simply understood of natural mechanisms, began to impinge on the older traditional processes of the dyer and the smith. It is effectively only in the present century that the next critical step has been taken, and the understanding of living structures through bio-chemistry and genetics has begun to affect the still older traditional processes of the cook and the farmer.

The Infiltration of Science into Industry.—The brief historic sketch may be sufficient to show the general trend of the relations between science and technique, but a deeper understanding of it requires an analysis of the contemporary mechanism of the interaction of scientific research and production. This process is necessarily dominated by the social and particularly by the economic conditions of production. At present, outside the Soviet Union, production is everywhere carried on for private profit, and the use that is made of science is primarily determined by its contributions to profit. Taken by and large, science is applied when and only when it pays.

The process of the application of science to industry has been a gradual one, though proceeding by scarcely distinguishable stages. Science can, so to speak, infiltrate itself into the industry in proportion to the simplicity of its operations. An old traditional industry can do very well without science as long as it is carried on on a small household scale, but even here science can enter to a certain extent by introducing apparatus for measurement, such as the household scales or oven thermometer. Yet the indispensability of science only appears when, owing to economic developments, the same process is attempted on a much larger scale. In the early days, for instance, baking and brewing were purely household occupations carried on by traditional methods and depending for their success partly on the tested efficacy of the tradition and partly on the individual knack of the housewife, but when tried on a larger scale tradition was of limited use, and it was impossible for the individual to have the same intimate control over the operations as before. Here science came in in its most elementary form of measurement and standardization. The old process was not changed, but various instruments—thermometers, hydrometers, saccharimeters—were introduced to ensure that the new processes followed as closely as was necessary the lines of the old.

The next stage appears when, either on account of a difficulty introduced by the change of scale or because it is desired to save money by using cheaper material or shorter working times, a change in the process appears profitable. This may be called, according to taste, improvement or adulteration, but in either case it makes demands that tradition by itself is unable to supply. Some form of experimentation is necessary, and pure rule-of-thumb trials on a large scale are likely to be ruinously expensive. But small-scale trials are essentially laboratory experiments. Indeed, the whole idea of scientific experimentation arises from the trial or assay which, as Agricola pointed out, is simply a smelting operation carried out on a small scale. To improve a process it is therefore necessary to understand it to some extent scientifically. This is a stage into which the metallurgical industry passed in the last century and from which it is only now emerging, and it is the one which the old bio-chemical industries are now beginning to enter. Its existence implies a fairly elaborate organization of industrial laboratories and a coherent body of empirical science.

From improving a process of industry the obvious next step is to control it completely, but this is only possible if the nature of the process is fully understood. This in turn implies the existence of a really adequate scientific theory. One of the greatest advances of the nineteenth century was the provision of such a theory for chemistry by which the chemical industry was enabled to develop, not as metallurgy has done and still does, by tentative and wasteful experimentation, but along definite lines of reasoning. Actually the process is never so simple. Theory often proves inadequate and practice sometimes runs ahead and needs to be caught up. In this way science and technics mutually stimulate one another. Although, for instance, the development of the steam-engine followed in its main lines from the theory of the behaviour of elastic fluids, already fixed in the seventeenth century, the actual operation of steam-engines led to results not envisaged by that theory and particularly it showed the inadequacy of the previously held scientific ideas on the nature of heat. This discrepancy in turn, once it was overcome, led to the further improvement of the steam-engine and to the invention of other heat engines.

The most complete integration of industry and science is, however, only reached when the knowledge of the fundamental nature of the processes is so extensive that it is able to lead to the development of entirely new processes unthought of, or indeed, unthinkable, by traditional methods ; as for example in the chemical syntheses of new dye-stuffs or specific drugs. The same result follows even more directly when a purely scientific discovery of a new effect is turned to some industrial use as, for instance, in the telegraph or the electric light. In these cases we have an industry scientific through and through, an industry which owes its inception as well as its development to science. The leading modern examples of these are the electrical industries, both for the production and distribution of power and for the improvement of communications.

Now these different degrees of application of science to industry are naturally not static categories. As science and industry advance together a greater share is taken by the scientific and a lesser one by the traditional aspects of industry. But the rate of development is necessarily very uneven in different industries, depending on the intrinsic difficulties which the processes involved present to scientific description, as, for instance, in cooking and animal husbandry, but also largely on the relatively backward economic state of these traditional industries. Here, again, the dominant consideration is the economic one. It has, up till now, been more convenient to concentrate production, and hence scientific research, on heavy industry and the production of goods that can be made in large quantities in factories. The needs of the producer in the form of economy of operation have dominated those of the consumer. If the same amount of time and money had been spent on investigating and improving production of the conveniences of life, particularly in the way of food and health services, as has been spent on machine production, we should already be far advanced not only in living a fuller life, but also in having much more understanding of biological problems.

The Time Lag in the Application of Science.—One of the most noticeable features of the application of new discoveries to practical purposes is the great lag that has existed and still exists between the time of the first discovery and the beginning of its practical utilization.   In the early stages of the development of science such a lag may be considered inevitable.   Thus we need not be surprised at the lapse of nearly a hundred years between the first discovery of the vacuum and its utilization in the form of an atmospheric steam-engine.   But even when the utility of science was fully realized the lag still persisted.   Thus in 1831 Faraday discovered the principle of electro-magnetic induction and made the first dynamo by which electrical current was produced by mechanical forces.   However, it was not until fifty years later that the first commercial dynamo was operated, and not until 1881 that Edison constructed the first public supply station.   The lag still persists to this day.   The possibilities of X-ray analysis of materials, for instance, first revealed by von Laue in 1912, have remained still largely unused in industry.   To understand the cause of this lag is a very difficult problem involving scientific, technical, and economic factors.   The explanation also will differ very much in different cases, for the lag is by no means uniform.   Sometimes, even long ago, a discovery or invention has been taken up almost instantaneously and spread rapidly.   Such was the case with gunpowder and printing. (2)

The scientific and technical reasons for the lag can be rapidly disposed of.   We may even eliminate the first by counting as the moment of the discovery the one in which the new phenomenon has not only been observed but accepted as part of current scientific knowledge.   Thus, for instance, we do not usually consider that X-rays and wireless were discovered in the eighteenth century, when these phenomena were first noted, but a century later when they take a definite place in the scientific world.   The technical difficulties are more serious.   The translation from a laboratory discovery to a practical operation involves a change of scale and intensity, and can only be effectively carried out when materials with the different properties required by the change of scale are available.   Thus, high-pressure steam-engines, intrinsically simpler in their working than vacuum steam-engines, had to wait for nearly a hundred years because the metals available would not stand the necessary pressure. Yet the technical factor is not often the limiting one.   Technical difficulties can, to a large extent, be overcome by the expenditure of time and money, or more accurately by money alone, for time is money.   It is in economic factors that we shall find the explanation for the slowness of taking up the results of scientific work and for the general character of the practical applications of science.

The position is summed up by Bernhard J. Stern as follows :

" The most potent of the cultural factors are clearly economic: Efforts to maintain economic advantage and hegemony over competing classes, and over competitors in the same industry and rivals for the same market in allied fields; costs of introducing the new method or product, which in its early form is usually crude and unstandardized, and but one of a number of innovations designed to solve the specific problem at hand; the losses incurred through the depreciation of machinery and goods made obsolete by the innovation; the unwieldy structure and the rigidity of large-scale corporate enterprises that hesitate to disturb a market which already yields profits through restricted production; the difficulties of small-scale enterprise to make the necessary capital investments; the stultifying influence of capitalist crises; and labor's efforts within a profit system to prevent being victimized by technological unemployment, by loss of skill, by speed-up and lowered wages.   There are also political factors that have their own dynamics of functioning which may be directed to impede technological change, as for example the restricting influence of nationalism; faulty patent legislation and judicial decisions justifying suppression; the system of issuing 'perpetual' franchises; the power of dominant industrial groups to control legislation to their interests as against beneficial innovations that imperil their profits."—*Technological Trends and National Policy*, pp. 59-60. (3)

THE PROFITABILITY OF SCIENCE

It must be remembered that the idea of a conscious application of science in any direct way to human welfare is a comparatively recent phenomenon, and that even now it is not being attempted outside the Soviet Union and a few philanthropic organizations. What has been, and is being, done instead is the utilization of science as one of the variable factors in industrial or agricultural production for profit.   Science is thought of and paid for in proportion to its contribution to increased value of products or reduction of costs. Now the fundamental difficulty already alluded to is that the profitability of new developments due to science is generally both doubtful and delayed.   It is impossible to see, or it is impossible for the commercially minded to see, at the very outset of a scientific discovery whether or no it is going to be profitable.   To take it up involves an element of risk, and the more removed in appearance the discovery is from practical commercial processes, the greater that element of risk and the smaller the probability of the development of the discovery on a commercial basis. The risk is, of course, a double one: firstly, that the discovery or invention will not work, and secondly, that, if it does, it may so easily be pirated, in spite of patent regulations (see p. 144), that the profit will go to others than those who have first put money into it.

Difficulties in Financing Research.—This is what leads to the paradoxical situation that the application of scientific research, which can yield a greater return than any other form of investment, is always difficult and sometimes impossible to finance. When we consider that the returns of organized research have been shown to be about 800 per cent. per annum (see p. 64 and Appendix V) the paradox becomes positively incredible until we remember that such a profit is no use in business. The risks even then might still be worth taking for such a prize, but it is nobody's business to see that they are. The capital market is not, in fact, in the least designed for financing such long-term speculative investment as the development of invention is likely to be. Indeed, far from assisting, it is tending to become more and more a factor blocking technical progress. The following analysis, which I owe to Mr. H. D. Dickinson, shows why this is so:

"The organization for investment (banks, issuing houses, the Stock Exchange, etc.) is stereotyped in a certain pattern with a purely commercial outlook. It does not serve the ends of industry as distinct from commerce very effectively; as can be seen from the perennial complaint that there exists no efficient machinery for financing long period and intermediate period development of industry—meaning by industry the application of known processes—(See the Macmillan Report)—and that as a consequence firms that are not large enough in scale and scope or variety of products to finance their own expansion out of profits are unable to get the necessary funds. This applies *a fortiori* to scientific research. The working of the capital market is still hampered by its historical connection with the trading voyage and the Bill of Exchange. The Stock Exchange exists to facilitate dealing in *existing* investments, and this *incidentally* helps to make it easier to launch new ventures, but it takes little direct part in the making of new investments. Banks, insurance companies, financial houses, investment trusts, promoting syndicates, outside brokers and share-pushers, etc., comprise between them the capital market. . . . What interest any of these possess in financing new applications of science is extremely small. They have no technical competence to judge the possibility of any such proposition, and therefore must rely on paid experts. It is therefore not to be expected that they will often *initiate* developments in this field." (4)

Two further factors militate against easy financing of scientific applications put forward independently of existing large firms. First, the amounts of money involved are ludicrously small compared with

usual financial deals, a matter at the most of £100,000 instead of
a few millions; consequently, being a rather unusual type of investment, it is hardly worth while to take up, and few firms can even be
bothered to consider it at all. Second, there is only a very short
part of the trade cycle during which it would be worth while to put
any money into such a problematical long-range investment as
scientific research. During boom conditions far more can be made
in speculation, and in a slump no one is going to risk his money.
The consequence is that the development of new applications of
science is left more and more to existing firms and particularly to
large monopoly undertakings who alone can afford to tackle the
more important lines (see note p. 138).

Against this reluctance to invest in the development of scientific
ideas must be put the inducement to such investment. Now as we
have already shown, in discussing the discoveries themselves, the
progress of science in any field is some function of the amount of
money spent in that field. It is not, of course, proportional to that
amount of money, but it is true that if money is not available no
progress will be made. The same consideration holds for the application of science, only here the amounts of money required are much
larger because experiments are on a large scale and involve heavier
capital outlay and running costs, and there are also technical difficulties already mentioned to be overcome. To get the application
at all under these conditions the risk of loss must be offset by very
large economies to be secured in the case of success. These will
mostly come when the application is aimed at satisfying an already
urgent economic need, and even more so when it is concerned in
preventing a known source of loss.

The Conditions for Practical Success.—The study of the history of
technology shows that the application of a scientific idea has usually
come in a field of immediate profitability, which may often not be
the one in which it is ultimately most valuable. Thus mechanical
weaving was first applied to ribbon weaving and only much later
to cloth, while steam power was applied successively to garden
fountains, mine pumping and, last of all, to the driving of machinery.

The demand for immediate profitability blocks the application of
science at the very outset, where the possible rate of development
is greatest. For example, in the case already cited of electric power,
practically nothing was done in the first ten years because there was
no immediately profitable use for electric current. In the forties
there was a certain development of direct current machines for electro-
plating. It was not until the seventies, when arc lighting was
introduced, first for lighthouses and then for street lighting, that
really important developments began to take place. But it needed

incandescent lighting for domestic use to introduce the central electrical power station which first made apparent the multiplicity of uses to which freely available electric current could be put. It is true that in all this time there were technical difficulties to be overcome, but it would be fair to say that if the effort and the money available for electric developments in 1880 to 1890 had been available earlier something between a half and two-thirds of the time of this development might have been saved and the technical progress of industry correspondingly accelerated.

The Problem of Scale.—There is one intrinsic difficulty in all such blind economic developments of discovery. The full profitability of any application can only be realized if it is carried out on a large scale. On the other hand, the technical difficulties of large-scale production are far greater than for small-scale production and may, in fact, be insuperable unless a good deal of intermediate scale work has been done, and this in itself is generally costly and rarely profitable. Thus, for instance, we have the apparent paradox that any source of power to be economical must be on a large scale; for human muscle can, and still does, supply small sources most economically. To be on a large scale requires large moving parts which offer the maximum difficulties in construction and efficient working. Thus the first steam-engine had cylinder diameters ten times and more than those of modern aeroplane engines of practically a thousand times the power. They were consequently ill-made and extremely inefficient, and errors of half an inch in the bore were not unusual. In these circumstances the economic advantage of the steam-engine had to be overwhelming before it could be introduced at all. The initial stages of application have to wait, therefore, until some profitable intermediate stage use has been found. The electro-plating industry supplied this for electric power, the watering of gentlemen's gardens provided it for the steam-engines; both were essentially small-scale and luxury utilities.

Waste and Frustration of Invention.—Another aspect of the intrinsic economic difficulties of scientific application is that an application is always most inefficient at the beginning and requires use to improve it. But the demand for it, on the other hand, is also least at the beginning and increases with the success of the method. The result is that a new idea will be held up at the wrong time and will develop very slowly and then, when it has reached the critical point of profitability, it will suddenly be forced to undergo the most intensive development. (5) From a social point of view all this is incredibly wasteful. In the early or pioneer stages of development most of the original work is done, and this has been largely starved for want of funds, while the pioneer's time, which could be used for other applications and inventions, is wasted in struggles against inadequate apparatus and financial difficulties. The knowledge of this is in fact a very strong deterrent to any but the most resolute or fanatical minds. Almost every scientist of ability has once or many times thought of practical applications of his work, but has not cared to face the prospect of dropping his scientific work to engage on the uncertain struggle which this attempt would certainly entail. But once the application is successful, the pace at which improvement is forced is also wasteful because, owing to the lack of previous preparation, men of suitable training and intelligence cannot be had in sufficient numbers, and the results obtained are consequently far smaller, in proportion to the money expended, than if the process had been carried out in an orderly manner.

Constructive and Remedial Applications.—Naturally the character of the application itself determines to a considerable extent the ease and the rapidity of its industrial utilization. We may distinguish a positive or constructive application of science from its negative or remedial application. In the first, science shows how to make new things such as the aeroplane or the cinema. In the second, science is called in to remove known inconveniences such as corrosion in metals, or plagues of locusts. In the first case science is offering a new gift to humanity. The economic problem is to find an effective demand to carry the invention through its earlier stages. Here, where the social need for application is greatest, it is most difficult under the existing economic system to get the application made at all.

Where science is functioning in industry or agriculture in its remedial, rather than its constructive, aspect the conditions are not so bad. A certain difficulty is encountered or a definite source of waste needs to be eliminated. With a recognized need and means to carry out the research, the problem can often be solved by the application of already known facts of science; indeed, it is in this way that scientists have won in the past, and still win, recognition for science in industry. A classical example was the discovery of the Davy lamp. This was a case of a definitely formulated demand for a lamp that would not cause an explosion if placed in fire-damp. Davy had little difficulty in finding the solution by the application of simple scientific principles though Stephenson, who knew the mines, had also discovered it empirically. The results were not, however, quite what might have been expected. According to Crowther:

"The safety-lamp allowed the coal industry to grow rapidly. It did not diminish the number of miners killed because it greatly increased the number exposed to danger by making deeper and larger mines workable. Davy refused to patent the invention because his 'sole object was to

serve the cause of humanity.' The chief effect of his invention was to increase the wealth of the owners and bring more men into the mines and expose them to the dangers of which fire-damp is one only. Hence Davy's lamp was more important as an instrument of economics than of safety."
—*Nineteenth Century Scientists*, pp. 62-3.

In many important cases, however, things are not so easy, and here the very insistence on immediate and practical results defeats its object. The practical problem may prove to require for its solution knowledge not already available and possibly of a fundamental character. But the pursuit of such knowledge, however valuable from the point of view of science, seems to those who pay for it too far removed from the immediate subject of inquiry. Thus an immense amount, probably the greater part, of industrial scientific research, from being too closely tied to its practical aspects, is immediately wasteful in the sense of failing to achieve the desired results. But it is even more wasteful in the long run, by holding up the stimulus to the general development of science that such inquiries, properly carried out, would entail. We find, for instance, that enormous sums of money are spent on detailed metallurgical research and comparatively trifling sums on scientific research into the nature of the metallic state, which would, if energetically developed, not only save an immense amount of the time and money spent on the first kind of research, but speed up the whole process of the rational use of metals as well. (6)

A very large number of applications of science fall into either the constructive or remedial categories, according to whether the point of view is technical or economic. These are the production of processes, materials or machinery, whose functions are economic, radically new technically, but fulfilling, from the moment they appear, the function of cost-saving. The steam-engine itself in its early stages when it just stepped into the shoes of the horse is a typical example, the use of the mercury arc rectifier is another. The main obstacle to this form of application is the difficulty, in an anarchical system of production, of bringing together scientific possibilities and technical needs. It is probably here that the greatest immediate possibilities for industrial advance lie. How these possibilities could be liberated will be discussed in a later chapter.

INDUSTRIAL COMPETITION AND RESEARCH

A number of other factors conspire, with those already mentioned, to interfere with the smooth application of the results of scientific discovery. Overwhelmingly in the last century, and to a large extent even now, the industry of the country, and even more so its agriculture, is carried on by a large number of small and virtually independent units. Now for scientific research to be of any value in application, a certain minimum of time and money must always be expended. As a figure for this minimum we may take roughly the expenses of one scientific worker plus equipment and assistance for about five years, and a certain amount of experimental plant and working capital to run it. Altogether the total expenditure will hardly be less than £4000. The savings effected by the expenditure of this £4000, if the research is successful, may well be of the order of £40,000 per annum. But the research may not be successful, or it may require the further expenditure of a similar sum for another five years before it becomes so. If the money is not forthcoming this may mean a dead loss. The probability of its not being successful is non-insurable and can be covered only by enlarging the amount of the research done and consequently the expense, which may well be beyond the resources of the small firm. Of course, on classical economic theory, it is for the different entrepreneurs to take the risks individually and for the lucky ones to be suitably rewarded. Effectively, however, the risk of unsuccessful research is sufficient to deter the great majority of commercial firms of small capacity from undertaking any research whatever. The fluctuations of the trade cycle make this much worse. Research is a long-period venture, as we have already seen (p. 61). But a small firm cannot carry its research through the trough of a depression. Research is, after all, the easiest item to scrap. In boom time, on the other hand, small firms are much too occupied in making hay while the sun shines to bother much about research.

Another consideration is that, even if the research is successfully completed and leads to a marked reduction of costs, this reduction will only show itself in increased profits for the firm undertaking the research if the results of the research are kept secret, and if a sufficient number of other firms do not undertake similar research successfully and thus lower the price of the product. Even if a patent is applied for, royalties on it, quite apart from the risks of litigation, may not amount to what is considered a sufficient return on the original outlay. All this tends to discourage firms from undertaking research, and puts a premium on secret, and consequently on inefficient, research if they do so. The position is even worse in agriculture. Here, for research to have any value, it must be undertaken on a very large and expensive scale, and the risks of failure are also considerably greater. Consequently practically no farmers ever engage in research and only the wealthiest landowners occasionally do so. It was in order to remedy these necessary evils of small-scale industry that the Research Associations and Agricultural Stations were set up by the Government. But, as has been pointed out, they cover only about half of the industries, those already the most progressive, and consequently they are able to be of assistance only to a minority of firms. In view of the enormous advantages which science can offer to industry, it is clear that the system of competitive industry is one which, under present conditions, most effectively retards technical progress. (7)

MONOPOLY AND RESEARCH

It is, however, not competitive but monopolistic industry which now controls the main applications of science. Under mono-polistic conditions, whether in the form of a single firm or a large number of firms with price-fixing and process-sharing agreements, there is the possibility of expending large sums on research. Indeed, at the present moment in Britain, probably four-fifths of industrial research, outside that carried on by the Government, is undertaken by no more than ten large firms. In Germany the position was even further developed, and the research laboratories of large in-dustrial combines such as the I.G. Farben Industrie became more important centres of research than even Government or university institutions. The existence of a monopoly eliminates many of the economic objections that hinder research carried out by small firms. It is clear that the total beneficial results of research must here accrue to the firm, and the large scale of the operations will ensure that, however much individual researches fail to achieve commercial results, these failures will be compensated by the success of others. The very size of industrial research laboratories itself increases efficiency in that it makes co-operative research possible. The small, one- or two-man research institutions represent probably the most inefficient way of spending money on research. On the other hand, it does not follow that the larger the laboratory the more efficient it will be. According to the nature of the subject and the variety of different kinds of research that must be combined into any one investigation, there is probably an optimum size for any applied scientific institute, and that optimum size is sometimes exceeded in industrial laboratories, particularly on the Continent. In the Soviet Union the tendency in the beginning was towards such very large research institutions, but after a few years' work it was realized that the administrative difficulties involved were too great, and there was a danger that the task of scientific co-operation absorbed too much of the time available for research; with the result that a return is now being made to the smaller, five-to-twenty man research institute.

Lack of Incentive.—Some of the difficulties facing industrial research under monopoly conditions have already been discussed, particularly the tendency to treat the research department as equivalent to any works commercial department and to stifle it effectively by bureaucratic methods. These defects are only a symptom of a more fundamental difficulty. Under competitive conditions research into the application of science is fraught with serious risks, but there is, on the other hand, a very large incentive to carry out such research, for if it is successful and sufficiently well guarded it will give a competitive advantage which may make all the difference between success and bankruptcy. Under monopoly conditions, on the other hand, the risks of research have practically disappeared, but to a large extent so also has the incentive. (8) Scientific research becomes, under these conditions, only one of a number of means of increasing profits and not necessarily a very important one. Certainly application of science can reduce working costs, but so can rationalization and speed-up schemes, and the main difficulty under monopoly conditions is rather to secure markets at high prices than to improve methods of manufacture. Consequently the money spent on advertisements always exceeds by many times that spent on research.

It is difficult to obtain detailed figures, but it is known that press advertising alone accounts for an annual expenditure of £35,000,000. Circular and poster advertising cannot be much less. The press advertising of patent medicines alone, the majority of which are a cruel fraud on people kept in ignorance of science, amounts to £2,800,000, more than is spent by the Government and Industry combined on scientific research (see p. 155).

Obsolescence.—A further difficulty that meets the application of science under monopoly conditions is the large scale of undertakings and the consequent danger of heavy capital losses through obsolescence. One effect that scientific research is bound to have, especially in industries which have been run on traditional lines, is to increase the efficiency immensely, and to do so at a rapidly increasing rate. But this means that the plant laid down at any stage of development of production will certainly be out of date in a few years and may actually be so before it starts production at all. This has been regarded as a very real evil. According to Lord Stamp:

"The second kind of balance which is vital to economic progress, and which may be ruined by over-rapid innovation, is that between obsolescence and depreciation. To be effective nearly all scientific advance for economic progress has to be embodied in capital forms, more and more elaborate, large and costly. The productivity of such apparatus and plant per man involved becomes greater, and even allowing for the men employed in making the machinery or process, the total satisfaction is continually produced with less and less human effort. Now it used to be said of British machinery that it was made good enough to last for ever and long after it became old-fashiored, whereas American machines were made to be worn out much earlier, and were thus cheaper, and they could be immediately replaced by capital assets containing the latest devices. If the period of physical life and fashionable life can be made to correspond, there is greatest economy and security of capital. But if the expensive embodiment of the latest science can be outmoded and superseded long before it is worn out, there is waste of capital, loss of interest, and resultant insecurity of business and investment. The factor of physical safety alone means that each embodiment must be really durable, even if roughly finished, and, therefore, it is impossible wholly to reduce physical life to probable 'obsolescent' life. In this way an over-rapid series of innovations may mean the scrapping or unprofitability of much excellent capital for very small marginal gains. A responsible socialist community would see each time that the gain was worth while, but competitive individuals are only just beginning to get collective responsibility. Suppose the *Queen Mary* attracts a profitable contingent for two years only, when a lucky invention in a new and rival vessel attracts all her passengers at a slightly lower fare. Here is progress in one typical sense, but the small net advantage to be secured by individuals as free-lance *consumers* may be dearly purchased by large dislocations or loss of capital reacting even upon those same individuals as *producers*.

Now, if the innovation were very striking, and were reflected in working costs, the margin of difference between the old working costs and the new working costs may be large enough to pay interest on the new capital employed, and also to amortize the cost of the unrealized life of the asset displaced. A locomotive may have many years of useful life left, but a new type *may* provide a margin by lower working costs not only sufficient to make one adopt it on normal renewal, but also to pay for the premature scrapping of the old type. The major part of modern innovation is, however, of the type which does *not* pay the costs of obsolescence and proceed by orderly and natural physical renewal of substitution.

A similar type of argument applies to the capital expenditure generally of all kinds on a district, which can be amortized over the whole economic activity of that area, such as a colliery area, but which is wasted if a dislocation occurs by the adoption of some innovation stimulating rival activity in another place. Consider the effect upon Lancashire of the discovery that the boasted natural advantage of humidity for spinning and weaving can be produced artificially elsewhere, and, moreover, to a better degree of uniformity.

The rate of introduction of new methods and the consequent impact upon employment may depend upon the size and character of the business unit. If all the producing plants for a particular market were under one control, or under a co-ordinated arrangement, the rate of introduction of a new labour-saving device will be governed by the simple consideration already referred to. It can be introduced with each renewal programme for each replacement of an obsolete unit, and therefore without waste of capital through premature obsolescence. But this applies only to small advantages. If the advantages are large, the difference in working costs for a given production between the old and the new types will be so considerable as to cover all charges as indicated above. In neither case, then, is there any waste of capital, and the absorption of the new idea is orderly in time. Again, the obsolescence occurring within a single establishment dominating supply can be absorbed into current costs. Owen Young said recently: 'Broadly speaking, there has not been a time during the past fifty years when anything manufactured by the General Electric Company was not, to some extent at least, obsolete by the time that it was put in service.' (9) It is quite clear that this process in the hands of a single unit can be reflected as a general part of continuous costs of production, and it is not necessary to assume that at no time in the fifty years could the Company make profits and pay dividends because it was meeting obsolescence payments."—From *The Science of Social Adjustment*, pp. 34-7.

This quotation shows clearly how the dangers of obsolescence to the individual producers, though not necessarily to the consumers, are much increased by unlimited competition. A new process may be swiftly copied, thus forcing all users of the old process to scrap their plant. The effect of economic anarchy in holding up technical advance and making what advance there is in as wasteful a way as possible, is apparent through the whole argument. The advantage of monopoly control is that for it there is no intrinsic necessity to change the plant until it is worn out, or until the business expands sufficiently to switch over to new plant and to drop production on the older plant. Monopoly, by its control of obsolescence, tends to retard progress more effectively than does competition. Mass-production methods intensify this conservative attitude. It is difficult enough to change design in detail in mass-produced articles—far more difficult when the change involved requires an entirely new lay-out of plant. One large monopoly in this country has the practice of writing off 50 per cent. per annum on new plant. That is, no new plant is put down unless it can hope to pay for itself out of profits in two years. If it keeps going longer, everything it makes is sheer profit. It is easy to see from this both the immense profitability of applied science and the heavy restriction it suffers from monopoly. (10)

The Stifling of Research

The immediate reaction to the dangers of obsolescence has been not to attempt to extend the scope and rationalize the procedures of the application of science to industry, but to check the development of science in order not to cause the embarrassing difficulties of obsolescence. The process takes two forms: the stifling of existing invention and the choking of new invention by restricting research. Naturally it is extremely difficult to get concrete instances of the first practice, but it has been long alleged, and recently in the most authoritative quarters. Thus, in his presidential address to the Engineering Section of the British Association at Nottingham (1937), Sir Alexander Gibb stated:

> " Of course here, as always in research, it is the case that the greater the success of research, the more immediate and drastic the effect on existing plant and equipment. That is where the rub sometimes lies. Millions are necessarily sunk in fixed assets, which may in a year or two be made obsolete by the development of new methods. Obsolescence is indeed so rapid nowadays that is it not unusual for new plant to be written off in four years; and many valuable inventions have been bought up by vested interests and suppressed in order to save the greater loss that their exploitation would involve to already operating plant. It is therefore not surprising that there is not always an enthusiasm for unrestricted research or a readiness to praise it. But it is a short-sighted policy."
>
> Address delivered at the meeting of the British Association for the Advancement of Science in Nottingham.—*Report of the British Association*, Sept. 1937, pp. 158-9.

Nature (11) has suggested a public inquiry into this question, but it may be doubted whether it would be more productive of positive results than the Royal Commission on the Private Manufacture of Arms, and for very similar reasons.

In the United States people are more outspoken. Thus in the Government report on *Technological Trends and National Policy* we find:

> " Competition between entrepreneurs, although it led to wasteful anarchic production and marketing, to some extent stimulated a response to technological innovation to keep ahead of competitors. But in the degree to which monopoly in the setting of the profit system is able to control prices, standardize products, and restrict production, alertness to technological change is diminished, a brake is put on inventions and their applications.

William M. Grosvenor has, in Chemical Markets, expressed the sentiments of modern corporate management toward the utilization of new inventions:

> ' I have even seen the lines of progress that were most promising for the public benefit, wholly neglected or positively forbidden just because they might revolutionize the industry. We have no right to expect a corporation to cut its own throat from purely eleemosynary motives. . . . Why should a corporation spend its earnings and deprive its stockholders of dividends to develop something that will upset its own market or junk all its present equipment . . . when development is directed by trained and experienced men responsible to stockholders for expenditures, they have little inducement to try to supersede that which they are paid to develop and improve.' . . .

The results upon technological invention of excessive rigidity of monopolistic enterprise, arising from its fear of imperilling its heavy investments, especially in durable goods, and from its elaborate mechanics of functioning, was noted before the Oldfield Hearings on Patents in 1912, by Louis D. Brandeis:

'These great organizations are constitutionally unprogressive. They will not take on the big thing. Take the gas companies of this country; they would not touch the electric light. Take the telegraph company, the Western Union Telegraph Co., they would not touch the telephone. Neither the telephone company nor the telegraph company would touch wireless telegraphy. Now, you would have supposed that in each one of these instances those concerns if they had the ordinary progressiveness of Americans would have said at once, "We ought to go forward and develop this." But they turned it down, and it was necessary in each one of those instances, in order to promote those great and revolutionizing inventions, to take entirely new capital "' (pp. 62-3).

As to actual suppression of invention, we have the evidence of the Federal Communications Commission:

" In 1937, the Federal Communications Commission declared that the Bell Telephone System suppressed 3,400 unused patents in order to forestall competition. Of these, 1,307, it said, were 'patents voluntarily shelved by the American company and its patent-holding subsidiaries for competitive purposes.' In answer to the company's declaration that the other 2,126 patents were not used because of 'superior alternatives available,' the Commission reported: 'This is a type of patent shelving or patent suppression which results from excessive patent protection acquired for the purpose of suppressing competition. The Bell System has at all times suppressed competition in wire telephony or telegraphy through patents. It has always withheld licences to competitors in wire telephony or telegraphy under its telephone and telephonic appliance patents, and this exclusion is extended to patents covering any type of construction. Moreover the Bell System has added to its . . . patents any patent that might be of value to its competitors. This policy resulted in the acquisition of a large number of patents covering alternative devices and methods for which the Bell System has no need. . . . Provisions tending to suppress development are found to be present in patent licence contracts between the Western Electric Co. and independent manufacturing companies.' "
—*Technological Trends*, p. 50.

The second practice, the restriction of research, is by its very nature impossible to bring home, since no firm is under obligation to spend money on research, but there can be no serious doubt that it is a most important factor in holding up the advance of applied science. This is especially so in connection with research which is liable to interfere with productive methods in which a large amount of capital has been sunk. A notable example is the relative slowness with which electric gas-tube lighting has been developed. (12) Any really effective general use of this method of illumination would have the effect not only of reducing to one-third or one-quarter the demand for electric power for the same degree of illumination, but also of rendering useless to a large extent the capital sunk in production of ordinary electric-light bulbs. Only when large new demands for cheap illumination appear, such as those introduced by modern street-lighting plans or display illumination of buildings, is the problem of developing electric gas lighting seriously taken up. With a relatively small expenditure on research the achievements of to-day could have been reached twenty or thirty years ago and we would now be that amount ahead.

Another example is the failure until comparatively recently to develop research into aluminium and other light metals. The production of these metals is in the hands of rigid monopolies concerned with keeping a high price on a relatively low output. (13) At that price aluminium cannot compete successfully with steel for many articles, *e.g.* motor-cars, in which its use would be more appropriate. As research designed drastically to lower the price of aluminium would probably result in its production from low-grade materials such as clay, without involving as at present the use of electric power in large quantities, the result of improvements would be, sooner or later, to break the monopoly. Consequently such research has not been encouraged. Recently, however, owing to the enormous stimulation of aircraft production brought about by universal war preparations, aluminium and magnesium alloys have been at a premium and Governments have been obliged to take up the question of their production as an urgent national necessity. We may therefore expect to see in the next few years very rapid strides in the methods of production of aluminium and ultimately a correspondingly rapid fall in its price (see p. 363).

It is always difficult to estimate the degree to which the application of research is actually hampered, because we have no means of measuring what has been done against what could be done even with the same expenditure of time and money. But the fact that the lag of application already mentioned still persists in spite of enormously increased facilities for consciously directing and controlling the application of science, indicates the presence of restricting forces which are growing almost as rapidly.

Patents.—A further factor which seriously complicates the process of the application of science is the law of patents. Though originally intended to protect the public from the ill effects of new processes badly carried out (14), patents are now considered to be either a reward to the inventor or the result of a bargain between him and society. This they may have been in the past, but there can be no doubt that to-day they lamentably fail to fulfil this function and hinder far more than they help the progress of invention. In practice, quite apart from customary abuses, patents more often than not fail to provide a reward to the original inventor and hold up rather than facilitate the development of the invention. (15)

The patent laws envisage a state of small independent producers with inventors capable of finding their own capital.   It is doubtful whether for any major invention this has ever been the case.   Even in the eighteenth century Watt had to go into partnership with Boulton, who had to use all his influence and spend £70,000 before either saw a penny back on the steam-engine.   It is certainly not the case now.   The individual inventor still exists, but he has increasing difficulties in finding a capitalist (see p. 132) and has to put up with worse and worse terms.   The great majority of patents are taken up by corporations.   This is not only because, for reasons already discussed, only large firms can now afford to apply science, but because of the patent law itself, which is now so complicated that only those with the longest purses can hope to defend a patent against its certain infringement.   The game can, of course, be worked both ways.   Big firms may be willing rather than go to law to buy up patents, whether valuable or not, that seem to be in their way, and the taking out of obstructive patents (Dr. Levinstein (16) estimates some 95 per cent. of patents to be obstructive) is one of the safest forms of legal blackmail.

In large firms it is usually stipulated that the rights to all inventions by any employee rest with the firm (see p. 108).   Whether the original inventor receives any reward is an act of grace depending on the management, and is the exception rather than the rule.   He is fortunate if he makes even a very small share of the ultimate profits.   Thus, whether he is independent or not, the object of patents in rewarding the inventor is now rarely achieved.   While failing to reward the inventor, the existing patent law usually operates to the serious disadvantage of the public.   Even such a conservative critic as Lord Stamp points out that the period of protection is far too long in modern conditions:

"For example, assuming the theory of social interest in an invention holds good, it is defeated if the patent system enables the invention to be withheld from commercial use.   If separate patents can be obtained by others for fine and not radical distinctions, competitive wastage, without commensurate social advantage, may result.   More pertinent to my inquiry is the *period of protection*.   This is commonly fourteen or fifteen years, up to twenty in some cases.   This was conceived to be a proper term under conditions when the pace of life was slower and the cycle of change much longer.   The true question is whether this period is still the ideal one we should choose if we were starting *de novo* under modern conditions. If under the old conditions the average effective life of an idea before its supersession was thirty years, then ideas had half their life under private and half under social control. Now if we alter the life cycle to fifteen years without changing the patent conditions, we have the extraordinary result that effective ideas will, on the average, be living their whole lives under patent conditions, and social control is virtually confined to the superseded ones. It is *prima facie* inconceivable that the terms of a true bargain between society and the individual made in the light of conditions a century ago would be the ones we should choose if we started without preconceived notions to fit the conditions of to-day. It may well be that the ideal period should not be uniform, but have some relation to the amount of capital in the plant involved. Certainly the complications of obtaining patents under many different Governments cannot be incurable. Even to cover the British Empire it is necessary to file over fifty patent applications. The theory of patent law was, moreover, elaborated before the days when the majority of discoveries emerged from large industrial laboratories through employees. United States authorities allege that the system

> ' permits the creation of monopolies beyond the scope of a given patent and prevents the use of new inventions for the general good . . . if it be said that the scrapping of existing equipment is wasteful, the *decision thereon* should not be left with the monopolistic interests but with *an impartial authority which* would take into consideration the whole scheme of *interests involved.*'

In general the discoverer of pure scientific ideas gets no protection or reward—this goes only to inventors who think out the applications."— *The Science of Social Adjustment*, pp. 151-3.

The holding of patents not in order to work but to prevent the working of processes is another widespread abuse, as also is their use to hold the community up to ransom. This has been particularly vicious in the case of medicine where, under patents, research can be stifled and the prices of really valuable drugs can be held up for years, effectively dooming poorer sufferers to death.

The taking out of patents by scientists is a practice on which opinion is much divided. The general ethics of the profession is definitely against it. It is felt that in the first place no individual scientist can honestly claim such an exclusive right to a discovery as entitles him to sole profit from it, and in the second, that a scientist has no right to block in any way the progress of application. On the other hand, it is felt only just that science should receive some return for the new values it gives to the community. The first difficulty could be, and has been, overcome by the taking out of patents by institutions rather than individuals, but this only enhances the second difficulty. With the present ill-designed and corruptly worked patent system the danger of obstruction is always present.   The injustice remains.   Science has done more than any other single factor in the creation of modern values, yet scientists, both individually and corporately, are debarred from claiming a share of the wealth they have produced.

CO-OPERATIVE INDUSTRIAL RESEARCH

The failure, for economic reasons, of either large or small firms to make adequate use of scientific research has led in many countries to the development of Governmental industrial research.   The advantage of Governmental intervention in research is primarily that it overcomes the difficulties that small firms have in getting any research done at all.   By combining together in research associations they are able, industry by industry, to collect sufficient funds to carry on fairly comprehensive schemes of research.

It has, however, been extremely difficult to raise money for such co-operative research.   This has been partly because of the lack of appreciation of scientific research in any form, but mainly because the chief competitive value of research is lost if carried out in this way.   All subscribing firms, and to a certain extent all the firms in an industry, gain equally from research carried out in the Research Associations. Competitive advantage is almost completely eliminated.   If there is a reduction of costs in these circumstances it may often show itself in reduced prices and consequently not lead to any increased profits, unless the conditions in the industry are already monopolistic or semi-monopolistic, that is, when there is an open or tacit agreement between the firms not to use any improved methods in competition with one another.   The incompatibility of the present economic system with any research carried out in the public interest is shown by the extreme difficulty which has been experienced in persuading industries to take up such research, as witnessed in almost every report of the Department of Scientific and Industrial Research (see pp. 46, 318).   But the opposition to the extension of Governmental research does not only come from this side.   Many of the functions which would be best filled by such laboratories are now filled by the work of private consultants whose profession, though usually precarious, has lucrative possibilities.   At first sight a really comprehensive system of industrial research would seem disastrous to them, though in reality the enhanced value that this would give to science would be bound to turn to their advantage.   Similar objections are raised by veterinary practitioners to the extension of agricultural research, particularly in the vital question of advice given to farmers. It is the lack of any thought-out policy of research that has allowed

these vested interests in ignorance to grow up, but in this research
has only followed the existing chaos of productive organization.

For political as well as economic reasons there is also on the part of
Governments an extreme reluctance to take any active part in research
on the application of science. If a Governmental laboratory arrives
at any result which could have commercial value, it is not in a position
to exploit it, rather it is definitely prevented from either selling the
process to an industrial firm or operating it on its own account.
The general principle is laid down that in no circumstances, outside
military requirements in war time, should Government Departments
compete in production with industrial enterprise. (17)   The inevitable result is that the attitude of Government institutions towards
applications of research is almost entirely negative. They have no
incentive towards the extension of applications, and they consequently
tend to concern themselves with answering specific demands of
industries, particularly in dealing with those cases where it is only a
matter of finding the remedy for some recognized difficulty in
industrial production. Thus Governmental scientific research is not,
outside the Soviet Union, capable of providing either the impetus
towards the new application of science or the rational control and
direction of such applications as there are.

Inter-industrial Competition.—There are, besides the simple effects
of competition and monopoly in industry, other factors affecting the
application of science. Even where effective monopolies prevent
competition over a whole field of industry there still remains the
competition between industries. This competition in itself acts
sometimes in favour of and sometimes against the effective application
of scientific research. If the requirements, both of individual consumers and of industries, were fixed and invariable there would be
no particular incentive to any section of industry to improve the
quality of its product. In the long course of traditional industry
such a state of equilibrium might be ultimately attained in which,
for every purpose, one and only one material or implement would
be suitable. Under conditions of developing industry, on the other
hand, for a variety of causes there is an increasing tendency for
alternative materials, and the industries supplying these are necessarily
in competition with one another. In this competition success depends
on improvement of quality or reduction of price, and consequently
there is an incentive to engage in scientific research in order to gain
the market from a rival material or at least to preserve a share in it.
Unfortunately the problem is not quite as simple as this. The
producers of the older material, entrenched behind its established
position, will not, in general, think of engaging in research until the
rival has appeared, if even then, and the result is that they will be

faced with losses and perhaps extinction before they are able to examine and improve their own processes. Thus in the last century the native growers of indigo and the merchants who collected and distributed their product were promptly ruined by the appearance of aniline dyes. It is said that one million Hindu agricultural labourers died of starvation. (18) Yet it is not at all clear that, with rationalization of marketing and biological research on yield, the natural product might not have been cheaper in the long run. To a certain extent this lesson has been learned. To-day, for instance, the lac industry, threatened by the appearance of synthetic plastics, is devoting a certain amount of money to research into the improvement of lac products and the possibility of new uses for them.   But it is particularly difficult to maintain such research on the basis of a falling market.

On the other hand, the existence of entirely independent financial interests concerned with producing alternative products leads to a state of affairs in which each product is boosted for the benefit of those in the industry and without consideration of the proper part the product should play in a balanced structure.   Thus, for instance, cement and steel interests compete in a most anarchic way in the field of building, and there is no impartial central authority to determine what the best combination of steel and cement would be for different purposes.   When such estimates are made by architectural or other societies they have no prospect of being put into action if they are against the interests of either of the industries concerned.   The essential difficulty that inter-industrial competition imposes on research is that it departmentalizes it and prevents that thorough interplay between different aspects of application of science that are the most fruitful of new results.   The existence of this type of competition is in itself a condemnation of an economic system that of its very nature cannot plan production as a whole in the interests of the people.   In the place of such planning we have Government interference, but almost always in support of one or other of the rival interests. (19)   How little the public interest is considered in this matter is shown by the fact that in the whole elaboration of tariffs, quotas, forced mergers, marketing schemes, etc., little or no provision is made for research to improve the products or lower their cost to the public.

ECONOMIC NATIONALISM AND RESEARCH

Of all recent tendencies, however, the development of economic nationalism has been most dangerous to the application of science to human welfare. Economic nationalism represents a use of non-economic factors, and particularly political control, to protect and extend the markets of industries in the different capitalist countries by means of protection, subsidies, or currency manipulation. It is obvious from a business point of view that the results which might be achieved by scientific research are apparently much more easily obtained by Government interference, with the additional advantage of costing nothing to the industries concerned. The immediate effect is the same as that of monopoly in lowering the incentive to improve production. There are, however, far worse effects. One of these, the increasing diversion of scientific research to war applications, is dealt with in a separate chapter. Another is the way in which economic nationalism interferes with the international character of science, beginning with applied and passing on to fundamental scientific research. Under economic nationalism the results of scientific research tend to become merely a national asset.

Secrecy, already bad enough inside the commercial world of each country, assumes the far more dangerous form of State secrecy. In each country parallel researches are being pushed, which, even with the inevitable leakages, means an immense reduplication of effort. To do the same piece of work over in more than two places (two may be justified as a check) not only divides the available manpower but deprives it of the extra advantages which would come through free intercourse, mutual stimulation, and the exchange of ideas. The logical end to economic nationalism in science is one in which the scientist becomes a servant, or more accurately a slave, of the State and science itself becomes part of national propaganda. We are already hearing of German physics. Nothing is more likely in the long run to destroy science than such a state of affairs (see p. 210 *et seq.*). The practical evils of secrecy are bad enough, but the damage done to the scientists themselves and the spirit in which they carry on their work is far worse. Suspicion and self-seeking become the order of the day. With no check from publication and free criticism the most arrant nonsense is likely to receive official sanction. Teaching will become an initiation into mysteries, and science will degenerate into the kind of cabbalistic alchemy it was in the decay of the Roman Empire. The content may be richer and the practical applications may be preserved, but the power of breaking the seal of the unknown may be as fatally lost as it was in the Middle Ages.

Secrecy.—The growth of modern science coincided with a definite rejection of the idea of secrecy. It is nowhere expressed more clearly than by Réaumur in his book, *L'Art de convertir le fer forgé en acier.* Here he published openly the principles of steel-making which he had discovered experimentally, though it had been a secret in the trade for two or three thousand years. For this he justifies himself in the following terms, which are worth quoting at length:

"Des reproches tout opposés & ausquels je me trouve flatté d'avoir à
repondre, sont ceux qui me furent faits après les Assemblées de l'Academie
que je viens de citer; il y eût gens qui trouvèrent étrange que j'eusse
publié des secrets, qui ne devoient pas etre revelés; d'autres auroient voulu
qu'ils eussent été confiés à des Compagnies qui en auroient fait usage, &
qui travaillant pour leur utilité propre, auroient aussi travaillé pour le bien
general du Royaume. Les sentiments que suppose la premiere façon
de penser, ne sont pas assés nobles, pour qu'on puisse même se glorifier
d'en avoir de directement contraires; ne sont ils pas même contre l'équité
naturelle? est-il bien sûr que nos découvertes soient si fort à nous que le
Public n'y ait pas droit, qu'elles ne lui appartiennent pas en quelque sorte?
nous devons tous, c'est notre premier devoir, concourir au bien general
de la Societé; qui y manque, quand il peut y contribuer de quelque chose,
& qui y manque, quand il ne lui en coûteroit que de parler, manque à un
devoir essentiel, et dans les circonstances les plus odieuses. Ce principe
étant certain, resteroit il bien des circonstances, où nous soions absolument
Maîtres de nos découvertes?

Il est vrai qu'on se plaint depuis long-temps du peu de retour du Public,
de ce qu'il ne recompense pas même de ses éloges, ce qui lui est une fois
connu; un secret tant qu'il est caché est regardé comme merveilleux, est-il
divulgué, on dit n'est-ce que cela: on cherche à montrer qu'on le sçavoit
auparavant, les plus legeres traces, les moindres ressemblances en sont
prises pour des preuves. C'est ce qui a fourni pretexte à divers Sçavans
de se reserver des connoissances; & à d'autres d'envelopper celles qu'ils sem-
bloient communiquer de façon à faire acheter cher le plaisir de les acquerir.
Quand ces plaintes seroient fondées, l'injustice du Public supposée aussi
certaine, aussi generale, que quelques Auteurs le pretendent, en seroit-on
autorisé à se reserver ce qui peut lui être utile? Le Medecin seroit-il en
droit de refuser du secours dans un danger pressant à des malades dont il
n'auroit aucune reconnoissance à attendre, & dont même l'ingratitude lui
seroit connue? Les avantages de l'esprit interessent-ils moins que ceux
du corps? Les connoissances justement appretiées, ne sont-elles pas le
bien le plus réel? Je dirai même plus, c'est que ne publier pas ses recherches aussi clairement qu'on le peut, n'en montrer qu'une partie, &
vouloir faire deviner le reste, c'est à mon sens se rendre responsable du
temps qu'on fait perdre à des Lecteurs. Je voudrois que les Hommes
n'admirassent point ceux, qui semblent avoir plus cherché à se faire ad-
mirer qu'à être utiles . . .

Mais pour reprendre la seconde objection dont j'ai parlé, il s'est trouvé
gens qui n'ont pas approuvé que les decouvertes qui font l'objet de ces
Memoires eussent été rendues publiques; ils auroient voulu qu'elles
eussent été conservées au Royaume; que nous eussions imité les exemples de
mystere, peu loüables à mon sens, que nous donnent quelques-uns de nos
Voisins. Nous nous devons premierement à notre Patrie, mais nous nous
devons aussi au reste du monde; ceux qui travaillent pour perfectionner
les Sciences et les Arts, doivent même se regarder commes les citoyens du
monde entier. Après tout si les recherches de ces Memoires ont les
succés qui me les ont fait tenter, il n'est point de Pays qui en puisse
tirer autant d'avantages que le Royaume; il pourra à l'avenir se passer des

aciers fins, dont il se fournit à present dans les Pays étrangers. Et cela pourtant en supposant qu'on ne negligera pas, comme nous ne faisons que trop souvent, de tirer parti de ce qui se trouve parmi nous; en supposant qu'on n'abandonnera pas des établissements aussi legerement qu'on les aura entrepris." (20)

In this he shows himself at the same time a true scientist and a true patriot. The two principles which he enunciates—that the work of the discoverer belongs to society and that those who work for science and art are citizens of the world—have been the guiding principles of the relation of science and society from then on and are only now once again in danger.

The idea of National Science is, of course, as old as modern science itself; the Royal Society, the Académie des Sciences, the Prussian and Russian Academies were all founded for the purpose of fostering national talent in science and also quite explicitly for the improvement of national trade and manufactures. But in early days these dangers were obviated by the much greater freedom with which scientists lived and worked in countries other than their own and by the prestige value which patronage of science conferred on the rulers of the states, a prestige dependent on open publication. The danger now is that in Governments obsessed by an autarchic economy and preparations for totalitarian war the value of science should appear in its narrowest economic form. Research into making substitutes both for industrial materials and foodstuffs derived from abroad has already, and not only in Germany, assumed immense importance. As this would be unnecessary in a rational world economy, it represents an unfortunate diversion of scientific ingenuity. Now that the control of scientific research, as that of the Government itself, is so much in the hands of large monopoly firms, the pressure to divert it to these ends may be too much for the free and open tradition of science to resist.

International Monopolies.—The tendencies of economic nationalism are to a certain extent offset by those of international monopolies. These are, more properly speaking, voluntary international associations or cartels of national monopolies with a field of collaboration usually limited to price fixing, agreeing to mark out exclusive selling zones or to share sales organization and, what is most important, for science-sharing patents and secrets. The laboratories of different firms in the same cartel are supposed to be in contact with one another; at any rate, their results are mutually available. In practice, however, the greater part of the research is usually concentrated in one of the firms of the cartel, and the remainder are almost entirely dependent on them for their results. Thus in the chemical industry a greater amount of work is done by the German member of the cartel, I. G. Farben

Industrie, than by either of the others. In 1935 I. G. were responsible for 555 new patent processes, Du Ponts for 508 (1936), and I.C.I. (Imperial Chemical Industries) responsible only for 270. Nevertheless, world-wide international cartels are being gradually and surely replaced by limited industrial blocs connected politically with different groupings of powerful states. Inside of these there is a certain interchange of scientific and technical information, but between them there is increasing rivalry with corresponding development of secrecy and lack of co-operation. What we are in fact seeing is the mobilization of science and technics in preparation for a forthcoming war, and this in addition to those direct aspects of war preparations which will be considered in the next chapter.

THE DISTORTION OF INDUSTRIAL RESEARCH

Most of the factors that have been discussed so far are such as to hamper any effective application of science whatever. But that is only part of the story. The application of scientific research is limited not only in quantity but also in kind. The whole trend of application, and with it the whole trend of scientific research, is distorted by the nature of the effective demand characteristic of our present economic system. From the point of view of human welfare, there is an altogether undue weight placed on production goods and heavy industry and very little on consumers' goods and general welfare. Even where such research is done its effect is often vitiated by commercial considerations. (21)

This applies particularly to research for the production of commodities used by a public whose technical knowledge is at a minimum and who are most exposed to the deceptions of advertising campaigns. The object of commerce in respect to the consumer is not to provide him with the best goods at the lowest prices, but the cheapest goods at the highest prices that can be maintained by restriction of competition. The main tendency of production of consumption goods nowadays is that of producing articles which, on account of various superficial attractions, lend themselves most suitably to selling, rather than of the most durable and economical kind. They must also wear out as quickly as possible in order to prevent a saturation of the market and to establish replacement production at the highest possible figure. Scientific research in industry is actually being directed mainly to producing shoddy and easily sold articles. Such a typical product, for instance, as the motor-car would appear within the last few years to have improved enormously in performance and decreased at the same time in price. Yet it has done so to a far less extent than the possibilities of the new mass-production methods would justify, and the improvements it has undergone are not those which would have yielded the maximum of convenience and the minimum of expenditure to the owners. Apart from durability and ease of repair, which are deliberately kept at a minimum and even diminished, economy and efficiency are sacrificed to smoothness and high top speeds. It would be possible technically to produce cars at something like half the price and half the running costs, and which would last twice as long as those produced at present. But it is considered, possibly quite wrongly, that this would knock the bottom out of the car market. (22) In these circumstances it is not surprising that research in the matter of motor-car production is largely misdirected.

An interesting example of the difficulties facing research in the industries which cater for both intermediate producers and the general consumer is shown in the case of radio valves. In satisfying the conditions with respect to performance of the valve necessary to ensure its sale at all, it is very difficult to make a valve which has not a probable life as long as or longer than the wireless set in which it is incorporated. But the result of this is that the valve manufacturers cannot sell a large number of valves to the consuming public, but are obliged to supply a smaller number to the set makers at very much lower prices or make sets themselves. This situation sets a premium on research tending to worsen rather than improve the product.

The same is true of the greater amount of research devoted to production of direct consumption goods. As far as proprietary articles are concerned—and a greater and greater portion of consumption goods are proprietary—the consumer, owing to the multiplicity of brands and the ballyhoo of advertisement, has effectively no choice. This development, incidentally, is fast washing away one of the last foundation-stones of orthodox economics. Research in this case itself often becomes part of advertisement, and is turned to meretricious if not downright fraudulent ends. How often do we not see a brand of cigarettes or patent food sold by the picture of the white-coated scientist bent over his microscope or gazing earnestly at a test-tube? One often wonders what the men themselves would say if they were allowed to open their mouths in public. What can be done, however, with very limited means is shown by the work of the Consumers' Research Council in the United States. Here a society has been able to give its members some accurate information on the relative utility of products in the market and to pillory fraudulent brands. This eminently social service is prevented from being given to consumers at large by libel laws. The legalized conspiracy to deceive the public is even more effective in this country. Harmful and useless patent medicines flourish for years because it is not safe to reveal their known constituents. (23)   And here behind the law stand the newspaper trusts with their dependence on advertisement revenue.   Even the extremely moderate and uninvidious advertisement of the British Medical Association, giving warning against the dangers of unpasteurized milk, was refused by most of the big newspapers.   Actually if only part of the immense sum—some fifty to a hundred times that available for all scientific research—that is at present spent on advertisement alone, were made available for scientific research into which types of goods were capable of giving the greatest satisfaction, human amenities could be increased at a progressively decreasing cost in human effort.   At present, however, such considerations are Utopian.   Production for profit introduces such an enormous distortion in the direction in which scientific results are applied that no increase in the funds or in the efficiency of organization of applied scientific research could by itself sensibly improve the situation.   Although we are accustomed to think of the present as a period of increasingly important applications of science it is probable that, compared with what might be effected with the knowledge and men available, the application of science is much less satisfactory than at any time in the last three hundred years.   The position can only improve if we can concurrently develop science and redirect productive processes for welfare and not for profit.

Science and Human Welfare

All this, of course, rests on the assumption that a rapid application of science can increase human welfare.   This is precisely what is disputed by romantic reactionaries and conservative economists. The case of the romantic reactionaries rests on a total rejection of the present results of science and therefore of science itself.   This rejection is based on an unresolved confusion between a dislike for the undoubted evils of contemporary civilization—the satanic mills, the unemployment, the destruction of the countryside—and an idealization of the mediaeval world which is usually seen from the castle rather than from the hut.   The failure to distinguish between the necessary effects of science and its abuse under capitalism is a natural one. The frustration of science and its possibilities are not easy to see unless they are pointed out, while the most conclusive proof, the actual demonstration of the use of science for human welfare, which is beginning to show its effect in the Soviet Union, is obscured by a barrage of suppression and propaganda.   It is unlikely, however, that either analysis or demonstration are likely to affect romantic objectors to science.   They have a conscious dislike for rational thinking and their feelings are usually too deep for argument.   We could afford to ignore them altogether if they were not made use of as a focus of Fascist demagogic appeal to youth.

The conservative economists have, however, a rational case, though a rather strange one. Rapid industrial change due to the prompt application of science is disturbing to the existing economic system. As, to them, the economic system is the best possible, it cannot be at fault, it is the distressing effects of the impact of science—which incidentally is part of the same economic system—that need to be lessened. Technical progress requires to be slowed down to the absorptive capacity of the system. To state the problem so crudely would be, however, to lay the system itself open to attack, so that the reasons for restraint have to be put down to the necessary economic disequilibrium and the strains on conservative human nature or on society.

The three main results of what is taken to be an over-rapid application of science are technological unemployment, high obsolescence charges and economic instability. Further, it is maintained that the plenty which the application of science might be expected to bring is illusory, as it takes account only of technical and not of economic factors. Now no one will deny that the unemployment and the instability exist and that the plenty does not, but how much the application of science has to do with it is another matter. No doubt they are the product of the impact of science on a society unable to assimilate it, but the amount directly chargeable to current science is a relatively minor part.

Technological Unemployment.—Lord Stamp, who could hardly be called a protagonist of rapid industrial advance, is inclined to think that the unemployment caused by science has been exaggerated:

"At any given moment the impact of science is always causing some unemployment, but at that same time the constructive additional employment following upon past expired impacts is being enjoyed. But it is easy to exaggerate the amount of the balance of net technological unemployment. For industrial disequilibrium arises in many ways, having nothing whatever to do with science. Changes of fashion, exhaustion of resources, differential growth in population, changing duties and tariffs, the psychological booms and depressions of trade through monetary and other causes, all disturb equilibrium, and, therefore, contract and expand employment in particular places.

Our analytical knowledge of unemployment is bringing home the fact that, like capital accumulation, it is the result of many forces. A recent official report indicated that a quite unexpected amount or percentage of unemployment would be present even in boom times. We know already that there may be a shortage of required labour in a district where there is an 8 or 10 per cent. figure of unemployment. So in Great Britain there may well be a million unemployed in what we should call good times—it is part of the price we pay for the high standard of life secured by those who retain employment. For a level of real wage may be high enough to prevent everyone being employable at that wage—though that is by no means the whole economic story of unemployment. Of this number probably 200,000 would be practically unemployable on any ordinary basis—the 'hard core,' as it is called. Perhaps seven or eight hundred thousand form the perpetual body, changing incessantly as to its unit composition, and consisting of workers undergoing transition from job to job, from place to place, from industry to industry, with seasonal occupations—the elements of 'frictional' unemployment through different causes. Out of this number I should hazard that not more than 250,000 would be unemployed through the particular disturbing element of net scientific innovation.

This is the maximum charge that should be laid at the door of science, except in special times, such as after a war, when the ordinary application of new scientific ideas day by day has been delayed, and all the postponed changes tend to come with a rush. At any given moment, of course, the technological unemployment that could be computed from the potentiality of new processes over displaced ones appears to be much greater. But such figures are *gross*, and from them must be deducted all recent employment in producing new things or larger production of old things, due to science. If we are presenting science with part of the responsible account of frictional unemployment at any moment, it will be the total technological reduction due to new processes, and displacement due to altered directions of demand, less the total new employment created by new objects of demand. This has to be remembered when we are being frightened by the new machine that does with one man what formerly engaged ten."—*The Science of Social Adjustment*, pp. 41-2.

Two hundred and fifty thousand is a large number of men, but it is only a sixth of the unemployment in good times or a tenth in bad. In this respect, therefore, it would seem more important to remedy the major instabilities of the economic system rather than to attempt to hold up scientific advance, and in any case that 250,000 represents the unemployment due to science under conditions where no effort whatever is being made to co-ordinate the labour lost from obsolete production and that gained in new production. As Lord Stamp says:

" It may well be assumed that, taken throughout, the gains of society as a whole from the rapid advance are ample enough to cover a charge for consequential damages. But society is not consciously doing anything to regulate the rate of change to an optimum point in the net balance between gain and damage."—*The Science of Social Adjustment*, p. 45.

If the problem were intelligently tackled in a sensible economic system by introducing new methods of production in an ordered way—using perhaps some of the devices mentioned in a later chapter—then technological unemployment might be entirely abolished. (24)

The same may be said of obsolescence cost. It is largely due to the anarchic methods of financing and introducing new processes. These are not unalterable, though Lord Stamp, and with him most conservative economists, seem to think that they are:

" Scientists often look at the problem of practical application as if getting it as rapidly as possible were the only factor to be considered in social advantage, and this difference in the position of monopoly or single management in their ability to ' hold up ' new ideas is treated as a frustration in itself. Thus it has been said: 'the danger of obsolescence is a great preventative of fundamental application to science. Large firms tend to be excessively rigid in the structures of production.' Supposing that the obsolescence in question is a real factor of cost, it would fall to be reckoned with in the computation for transition, whatever the form of society, and even if the personal 'profit' incentive were inoperative. It cannot be spirited away."—*The Science of Social Adjustment*, pp. 42-3.

Apart from the change in economic factors two technical devices could do much to " spirit away " obsolescence costs without holding up new ideas. One is the provision of nurseries or pilot plants in which innovations in production are developed to the stage when they can be brought into full production. The other is the designing of industrial plant deliberately on flexible lines so that change can take place with the minimum of capital loss. Both these will be discussed in Chapters X and XII.

The economic instability of the present system can hardly be charged directly on to science even by its worst enemies. The truth that their charges contain, however, is that the present economic system and the advance of science cannot for much longer go on together. Either science will be stifled and the system itself go down in war and barbarism, or the system will have to be changed to let science get on with its job.

The Impossibility of Plenty.—The final defence of the conservative economist is that the welfare, which it would seem could be brought about by the application of science, is illusory; that though technically possible it is barred by economic and political reasons not easily seen by the scientist:

"Enormous potentialities are seen by scientists waiting for adoption for human benefit, under a form of society quicker to realize their advantage, readier to raise the capital required, readier to pay any price for dislocation, and to adjust the framework of society accordingly. A formidable list of these potentialities can be prepared, and there is little doubt that with a mentality adjusted for change, society could advance much more rapidly. But there is a real distinction between the methods of adopting whatever it is decided to adopt, and the larger question of a more thoroughgoing adoption. In proportion as we can improve the impact of the present amount of innovation, we can face the problem of a larger amount or faster rate. Unless most scientific discoveries happen to come within the scope of the profit motive, and it is worth someone's while to supply them to the community, or unless the community can be made sufficiently scientifically minded to include this particular demand among their general commercial demands, or in substitution for others, nothing happens—the potential never becomes actual. . . .

Scientists see very clearly how, if politicians were more intelligent, if business men were more disinterested, and had more social responsibility, if governments were more fearless, far-sighted, and flexible, our knowledge could be more fully and quickly used to the great advantage of the standard of life and health—the long lag could be avoided, and we should work for social ends. It means, says Dr. Julian Huxley, 'the replacement of the present socially irresponsible financial control by socially responsible bodies.' Also, it obviously involves very considerable alterations in the structure and objectives of society, and in the occupations and pre-occupations of its individuals. . . .

It can be conceived that a socialistic organization of society could obviate such of the maladjustments as depend upon gains and risks of absorption not being in the same hands, and a theoretic technique can be worked out for the most profitable rate of absorption of scientific invention having regard to invested capital, and skill and local interests. It is sufficient to say that it needs a *tour de force* of assumptions to make it function without hopelessly impairing that central feature of economic progress, viz. individual choice by the consumer in the direction of his demands, and an equally exalted view of the perfectibility of social organiza-tion and political wisdom. But in the field of international relations and foreign trade, which alone can give full effect to scientific discovery, it demands qualities far beyond anything yet attainable."—*The Science of Social Adjustment*, pp. 48-52.

Now these arguments may be conclusive as to the impossibility of plenty in a capitalist society, but as arguments against plenty under socialism they are refuted by the actual experience of the U.S.S.R. The difficulties mentioned may prevent the system from working well or all at once, but it can work and it does. Lord Stamp's basic argument against the possibility of achieving plenty by the application of science is that effective demand is no larger than what is at present produced, and that with fall in population and closing up of overseas outlets it is bound to grow smaller still. The implicit assumption is always the continuance of the existing economic and social system. It is to this that we owe the character of effective demand. People want things all right, but the system won't let them earn money to pay for them. The population falls because people have little to hope for and much to fear. The obstacles to the achievement of plenty are real enough, but they are political and economic, not technical obstacles. Given the will and the understanding they can be overcome.

(1) This was so much taken for granted in the seventeenth century that the scientist was then concerned to claim that science might in the future be useful to industry. Thus Boyle wrote a treatise, *That the Goods of Mankind May Be Increased by the Naturalist's Insight into Trades*, from which the following extracts are taken :

". . . I shall conclude this, by observing to you, that as you are, I hope, satisfied, that experimental philosophy may not only itself be advanced by an inspection into trades, but may advance them too ; so the happy influence it may have on them is none of the least ways, by which the naturalist may make it useful to promote the empire of man. For that the due management of divers trades is manifestly of concern to the publick, may appear by those many of our English statute laws yet in force, for the regulating of the trades of tanners, brick burners, and divers other mechanical professions, in which the law-givers have not scorned to descend to set down very particular rules and instructions."

" I might add, if I had the leisure, some reasons, why I despair not, that in time the husbandman may, by the assistance of the naturalist, be able to advance his profession by a therapeutical part, which may extend not only to the animal productions of the ground, and to the vegetable ones ; but (in a large acception of the term) to the distempers of the ground itself. For if the causes of the barrenness of soils in general, and of their indisposition to cherish particular plants or animals, were by the philosopher's sagacity discovered, I see not why many of those defects may not be removed by rational applications and proper ways of cure ; as well as we see inconveniences remedied in many other inanimate bodies, without excepting the close and stubborn metalline ones themselves."

" The naturalist may increase the power and goods of mankind upon the account of trades, not only by meliorating those that are already found out, but by introducing new ones, partly such as are in an absolute sense newly invented, and partly such as are unknown in those places, into which he brings them into request. For it were injurious both to nature and to man, to imagine, that the riches of the one, and the industry of the other, are so exhausted but, that they be brought to afford new kinds of employment to the hands of tradesmen, if philosophical heads were studiously employed to make discoveries of them. And here I consider, that in many cases, a trade differs from an experiment, not so much in the nature of the thing, as in its having had the luck to be applied to human uses, or by a company of artificers made their business, in order to their profit ; which are things extrinsical, and accidental to the experiment itself. To illustrate this by an example ; the flashing explosion made by the mixture of nitre, brimstone and charcoal, whilst it past not farther than the laboratory of the monk, to whom the invention is imputed, was but an experiment, but when once the great (though unhappy) use that might be made of it, was taken notice of, and mechanical people resolved to make it their profession and business, to make improvements and applications of it ; this single experiment gave birth to more than one trade ; as namely, those of powder-makers, founders of ordnance, gunners (both for artillery and mortar pieces), gunsmiths ; under which name are comprised several sorts of artificers, as the makers of muskets, small pistols, common barrels, screwed barrels, and other varieties not here to be insisted on.

The discovery of the magnetical needle's property to respect the poles has given occasion to the art of making sea-compasses, as they call them, which in London is grown to be a particular and distinct trade. And divers other examples may be given to the same purpose ; especially where mechanical tools and contrivances co-operate with the discovery of nature's production. So that oftentimes a very few mathematical speculations, or as few physical observations, being promoted by the contrivance of instruments, and the practice of handicrafts men, are turned into trades as we see, that a few dioptrical theories lighting into mechanical hands, have introduced into the world the manufactures of spectacle makers, and of the makers of those excellent engines, telescopes, and microscopes."

(2) An estimate of the average length of lag of application is made by S. C. Gilfillan in a most interesting article on the " Prediction of Inventions " in the United States Government report on *Technological Trends* :

" Taking 19 inventions voted most useful, introduced in 1888-1913, the average intervals were : Between when the invention was first merely thought of, and the first working model or patent, 176 years ; thence to the first practical use, 24 years ; to commercial success, 14 years ; to important use, 12 years, or say 50 years from the first serious work on the invention. Again, in the study of the most important inventions of the last generation before 1930, in Recent Social Trends, a median lapse was found of 33 years, between the ' conception date ' corresponding to the second above, and the date of commercial success. Searching for exceptions, it is hardly possible to find an invention which became important in less than 10 years from the time it or some fully equivalent substitute was worked on, and few did in less than 20. Here is, then, an excellent rule of prediction for the present study—to predict only inventions already born, whose physical possibility has therefore been demonstrated, but which are usually not yet practical, and whose future significance is not commonly appreciated " (p. 19).

(3) For a penetrating study of economic checks to technological advance, see Stern's article in *Science and Society* (U.S.A.), vol. 2, p. 3.

(4) " Charles F. Kettering, vice-president and director of research of the General Motors Corporation, likewise stated in this connection in 1927 :

' Bankers regard research as most dangerous and a thing that makes banking hazardous, due to the rapid changes it brings about in industry.' " (*Technological Trends*, p. 63.)

(5) This situation is well understood, but little or nothing has been done to remedy it. Sir James Henderson, speaking at the British Association in 1936, comments as follows :

" It is generally thought that industries are on the look-out for new inventions, but the type of invention which chiefly interests them is one which will reduce their working costs and which generally leads to increased unemployment. This has been almost the only type of invention for which there has been a demand since the War. Industry is essentially a commercial concern, and its leaders are commercial men interested in their dividends, and in conserving their capital except in so far as it can increase their output.

After an invention has been developed to the commercial stage, there is little difficulty in finding capital to work it. It is much easier to find £25,000 or more for the commercial working than it is to find £5000 for the development. Yet the profits on the development of a successful invention are very great, the sale of the foreign rights alone recouping the promoter many times over.

In pre-War days there were a number of rich men who acted as promoters of inventions, but, since the War, possibly due to the heavy taxation or to other causes, such men are very scarce, and a new generation of capitalists has arisen who have not yet had their attention drawn to this lucrative type of investment or else have not the necessary economic vision to see its possibilities."

(6) W. L. Bragg's lectures on " Some Scientific Problems of Industry " at the Royal Institution, in March and April 1938.

(7) The difficulties of small firms where no facilities for joint research exist are shown in the United States Government report on *Technological Trends* :

" During the depression, progress has gone forward in the development of what is generally known as the small manufacturers' high tension equipment. . . . The small manufacturers are greatly handicapped by not having at their disposal any facilities for testing high-voltage equipment, such facilities being away beyond the financial means of the small manufacturer. Those who are responsible for maintaining service on high-voltage lines naturally desire to have all parts subjected to severe tests before they use them, but the small manufacturers have not the means to build expensive testing institutions and therefore are working under a considerable handicap " (pp. 279-280).

(8) The failure of the research laboratories of large corporations to play their part in production of technological advances is commented on in *Technological Trends* :

" It is often argued that the establishment of laboratories and research associations by large corporations and cartels disproves the charge of inflexibility of giant industry. But these relatively few research departments give the corporations greater control over the innovations that might disturb the market. According to Grosvenor, only 12 out of the 75 most important inventions made between 1889 and 1929 were products of corporations' research " (pp. 63-4).

(9) Fiftieth anniversary meeting of the General Electric Company at Schenectady.

(10) The seriousness of obsolescence in the United States is shown by estimates published in the report on *Technological Trends* :

" In 1934 the trade journal *Power* made a study of 454 ' better-than-average ' industrial power plants constituting nearly 10 per cent. of industrial prime mover capacity and found 62 per cent. of the equipment was over 10 years old, while 25 per cent. was over 20 years. Some of the older equipment was presumably used as stand-by plant for emergencies, but the bulk of the older equipment was regarded as obsolete to such an extent that, by re-placing it by facilities of the most advanced design, 50 cents could be saved, on the average, out of each dollar spent in the older plants for industrial power. In 1935 the *American Machinist* made a study of the obsolescence of metal-working equipment, concluding that, because of the rapid improvement in machine design, metal-working equipment was as a rule obsolete if not produced within the last 10 years. It took an inventory of the age of such machinery and found that 65 per cent. of all the metal-working equipment in the country was over 10 years old and presumably obsolete. The Interstate Commerce Commission records indicate that 61 per cent. of the steam locomotives in the country were built over 20 years ago. These figures suggest the magnitude of capital obsolescence.

Further light on the magnitude of capital obsolescence is thrown by the estimates of the potential machinery requirements of all industry made in 1935 by the Machinery and Allied Products Institute. This institute made an extensive survey, sampling the requirements of industries covering over 85 per cent. of all industry, and on the basis of this survey, estimated that the potential machinery requirements of all industry amounted to over 18 billion dollars worth. Of this amount over 10 billion consisted of new equipment to replace old equipment, which was for the most part obsolete.

Obsolescence surveys like the ones above referred to clearly indicate the magnitude of capital obsolescence. Yet the social implications of capital obsolescence have received very little study and a whole series of questions are waiting to be answered. When equipment becomes obsolete and therefore loses value, who suffers a loss ? Does obsolescence involve a social cost or only a business cost ? Is capital obsolescence a cause of industrial maladjustment ? Does the existence of extensive obsolete equipment prevent the using of better industrial techniques ? Can the risks of capital obsolescence be reduced without impeding the use of better techniques ? Should the losses due to capital obsolescence be distributed throughout industry ? So little is known of the actual impact of capital obsolescence on industrial activity that no answer can be given to these questions. Yet they are questions forced on us by our rapidly improving technology and deserve the most careful study. Capital obsolescence and all that it involves needs to be extensively studied if the full social implications of current trends of improving technology are to be appreciated and the problems presented by improving technology are to be met " (pp. 12-13).

(11) " Towards the conclusion of his address, Sir A. Gibbs attracted attention to the fact that the greater the success of research, the more immediate and drastic is its effect on existing plant and equipment. He says, ' Millions are necessarily sunk in fixed assets, which may in a year or two be made obsolete by the development of new methods,' and he declares that many valuable inventions have been bought up by vested interests and suppressed in order to save the greater loss that their exploitation would involve to already operating plant. This particular allegation has been made so often that it is difficult to believe there is not a good deal of truth in it. The lack of data of specific instances of inventions being purchased only to be promptly strangled is, however, a great handicap to any assessment of what the nation has lost and may lose by such a practice."— *Nature*, Vol. 140, p. 438, 1937.

(12) The first electric tube sign dates back to 1744. See Crowther, *Famous American Men of Science*, p. 67.

(13) " In 1937, the United States Attorney General's office charged that ' By virtue of its 100 per cent. monopoly of the production and sale of alumina and virgin aluminium in the United States, Aluminium Co. has acquired and is maintaining a monopolistic control of the production and sale of alumina, aluminium, aluminium sheet, alloy sheet, basic fabricated products, and through them of products manufactured therefrom, sold in interstate and foreign commerce, and possesses the power to fix arbitrary, discriminatory, and unreasonable prices and to extend and perpetually maintain said monopolistic control and to exclude others who would, except for said monopolistic control, engage in competition with Aluminium Co. in the production and sale of bauxite, alumina, virgin aluminium, and aluminium products manufactured therefrom. Because new enterprises desiring to engage in the aluminium industry would be placed at the mercy of a single powerful corporation controlling essential raw materials, and because of the great hazard necessarily involved in venturing into a business so completely monopolized by Aluminium Co. and its wholly owned subsidiaries, said monopolistic control has had and will continue to have the direct and immediate effect of suppressing and preventing substantial competition which would otherwise arise in the production and sale in interstate and foreign commerce of bauxite, alumina, aluminium, and aluminium products manufactured therefrom, and is inimical to the public interest.' "—*Technological Trends*, p. 55.

(14) See Lord Stamp in *Science of Social Adjustment*.

(15) " Judicial decisions in United States courts have sanctioned the suppression of patents in decisions which are of primary importance when resistance to technological change in the United States is being appraised. In 1896 the judgment of the court was

that the patentee ' may reserve to himself the exclusive use of his invention or discovery. . . . His title is exclusive, and so clearly with the constitutional provisions in respect of private property that he is neither bound to use his discovery himself, nor to permit others to use it.' When this decision was reaffirmed in 1909, it was declared that ' the public has no right to compel the use of patented devices or of unpatented devices when that is inconsistent with fundamental rules of property.' Technological progress is thus inextricably made dependent upon property rights interpreted in terms of individual rights and the rights of a specific industry as against the interests of the community. In practice, this interpretation benefits large corporations. For it is the consistent experience of inventors that they are helpless to promote their patents independently in fields which are dominated by such corporations. A chief obstacle is, of course, lack of capital to put their plans in operation. They find themselves involved in costly infringement suits, and harassed by interference procedures, which oblige them to sell their patents to the large-scale enterprises with concentrated capital resources, and in this way take a chance at their suppression. Patent pools often keep the benefit of patents within a small circle of corporations and restrain independents from their use, thus preventing broad technological advance. The rule of monopolies in technological change suggests at once an analogy with the restraining influence of the medieval guilds."—*Technological Trends*, p. 3.

(16) Levinstein, *British Patent Laws, Ancient and Modern*.

(17) The Medical Research Council has by its sponsoring of chemo-therapeutic research partially broken this rule, and in doing so raised considerable opposition on the ground that this is the proper field of the chemical manufacturers.

(18) See Crowther, *Science and Life*, pp. 33-4.

(19) The rapid changes in policy on the relative values of oil production from coal by various processes illustrated this point.

(20) (Trans.) " Altogether opposite reproaches, which I feel flattered at having to answer, were made to me after the meeting of the Academy. There were people who found it strange that I had published secrets which should not have been revealed. Others would have wished that they had been confined to companies who could have used them, and who, working for their own profit, would have also worked for the general good of the kingdom. The sentiments which were implied in the first way of thinking are not noble enough for one even to be able to pride oneself on having directly opposite ones. Are not they even against natural equity ? Is it really certain that our discoveries are so much our own that the public has not the right to them, that they do not in some way belong to it ? Should not we all, is it not our first duty to assist the common good of society ? Anyone who fails to do so when he could contribute anything, and particularly when it is only a matter of speaking out, fails in an essential duty and in most odious circumstances. This principle being certain, are there many circumstances where we can be said to be absolute masters of our discoveries ? It is true that for a long time there have been complaints of the ingratitude of the public which does not even reward with its praises facts when once they become known to it. A secret, as long as it is concealed, is considered marvellous ; once divulged, they say ' Is that all it was ? ' They try to show that they knew it before, and the slightest traces, the most remote resemblances, are snatched at as proofs. This is what furnishes the pretext for divers learned men to reserve their knowledge, and for others to envelop that which they pretend to communicate in such a way as to make people buy dear the pleasure of acquiring them. Even if these complaints, founded on the injustice of the public, were as certain and as general as some authors claim, would one be justified in keeping to oneself what might be useful ? Would the doctor have the right to refuse help in great danger to patients from whom he could expect no gratitude, and even whose ingratitude was already known to him ? Are advantages of the mind less vital than those of the body ? Is not knowledge, justly appreciated, the most real possession ? I will say more. Not to publish one's researches as clearly as one can, only to show part of them, and make people guess at the rest, is, to my way of thinking, to make oneself responsible for one's readers' waste of time. I would wish that men did not admire those who seem to have sought more to make themselves admired than to be useful. But to take up the second objection of which I have spoken, there were people who did not approve that the discoveries which were the objects of these Memoirs should have been public ; they would have wished them to be reserved for the kingdom, that we should have imitated the examples of mystery— little to be praised, to my way of thinking—that are given to us by some of our neighbours. We have a duty in the first place to our country, but we also have a duty to the rest of the world, and those who work for the perfectioning of science and the arts must consider

themselves as citizens of the whole world. After all, if the researches of these Memoirs have the success which made me undertake them, there is no country which can get as much advantage out of them as this kingdom. It can in future do without the fine steel which it imports at present from foreign countries, but that is supposing that we do not neglect, as we do only too often, to make use of our own resources, and supposing that we do not abandon attempts as lightly as we take them up."—*L'Art de convertir le fer forgé en acier*, par Monsieur de Réaumur, 1722.

(21) Julian Huxley alludes to this in *Scientific Research and Social Needs* :

" The bulk of research in progress in this country is organized from the production end—that is to say, it is organized and planned with a view to improving efficiency in technical processes and reducing cost to the producer or to the State. There ought to be much more research organized from the consumption end—directed towards the needs of the individual citizen as an individual and as a citizen. . . . Of course, there is some research done from the consumption angle—a lot of the work in the Research Boards under the D.S.I.R. is of this sort—in regard to building, for instance, or radio, and, of course, a great deal of medical research. But other problems are not taken up at all, or only get tackled piecemeal, because of this general producer bias in research " (pp. 256-7).

(22) *Tools of To-morrow*, by Norton Leonard.

(23) See *Fact*, No. 14, where the scandal of Patent Medicines has for the first time been effectively exposed.

(24) An interesting attempt to estimate the extent of technological unemployment in the United States is made by D. Weintraub in *Technological Trends*, pp. 78 *et seq.* He estimated that a fluctuating number of workers, rising in depression conditions to as much as 14 per cent. of those employed, are unemployed for technological reasons.

CHAPTER VII

SCIENCE AND WAR

THE application of scientific knowledge to war is of such importance as to require separate consideration. The scientists and the public at large have recently begun to realize what an enormous proportion of the efforts of science are being turned to the purpose of pure destruction, and how the character of modern war has acquired a more than ever horrible aspect on account of the application of scientific discoveries. We know, for instance, that in Britain the amount of money spent annually by the Government on war research is approximately three million pounds, or more than a half of the money spent on all other forms of research, and that many of these also have direct and indirect military value. In detail, the amount of money spent on poison-gas research alone is nearly as great as the total contribution of the Government to medical research. In almost every country scientists are being pressed into the service of war industries and classified for various military occupations if that war comes. All these seem new and sinister developments, but the connection of science and war is by no means a new phenomenon ; the novelty is in the general recognition that this is not the proper function of science.

SCIENCE AND WAR IN HISTORY

Science and warfare have always been most closely linked; in fact, except for a certain portion of the nineteenth century, it may fairly be claimed that the majority of significant technical and scientific advances owe their origin directly to military or naval requirements. This is not due to any mystical affinity between science and war, but to the more elementary considerations that the urgency of war needs, expressed in willingness to incur expenditure, are greater than those of any civil needs, and that in war novelty is at a premium. A change in technique leading to the production of new or better weapons may make the critical difference between victory and defeat. This has been so from the very earliest times. We know the elaborateness of the military engineering of the Babylonians; originally, indeed, the word engineer implied military engineer, for there were no others. In Greece, with its relatively backward technical development, mathematics was valued for its military uses, though these were somewhat restricted, as the passage from Plato already quoted (p. 12) shows.

In the Alexandrian period the application of science to war was much more conscious. The Museum at Alexandria concentrated on the production of improved siege engines and catapults, while the achievements of Archimedes with long-distance burning glasses are, whether true or not, significant as to the tasks the mathematician in the service of a city ruler was expected to perform. Needless to say, in so far as war needs were helped by science, they helped science, primarily by providing funds to keep the scientists alive, and secondly by providing difficult problems on which to focus attention and to check in practice scientific speculation.

Gunpowder.—A new and important connection between science and war appeared at the breakdown of the Middle Ages with the introduction or discovery of gunpowder, itself a product of the half-technical, half-scientific study of salt mixtures. The introduction of gunpowder produced striking repercussions in the art of war, and through it on the economic developments which tended to the break-up of Feudalism. War became more expensive and needed far more technical skill, and both these needs played into the hands of the townsmen and the kings whom they supported against the nobles. The professional soldiers did not take kindly to it in theory. An amusing sidelight on this is furnished by Froissart's account of the battle of Crécy, which, in the original version, ran as follows:

"The English remained still and let off some bombards that they had, to frighten the Genoese."

In a later version, written when Froissart was seeking the favour of the English court, all mention of the bombards was omitted. It was felt that somehow it showed the English up as unsporting. This is the version, redounding to the virtue of the English long-bow men, that has gone down to posterity in our school-books. We can see from this that the attitude of contemptuous exploitation of the technician by the military caste is no new thing.

Gunpowder was to help science in many different ways. Not only did the need for the improvement in the quality of powder, the make of guns, and the accuracy of fire, provide sustenance for chemists and mathematicians, but the problems they raised became the focal points of the developments of science. The chemical process of explosion led to inquiries into the nature of combustion and the properties of gases, upon which, in the seventeenth and eighteenth centuries, the modern theories of chemistry were to be based. In their physical aspect the phenomena of explosion led to the study of expansion of gases and thus to the steam-engine, though this was suggested even more directly by the idea of harnessing the terrific force that was seen to drive the ball out of the cannon to the less violent function of doing useful civil work.   The making of cannon provided an enormous stimulus to the metal and mining industries and led correspondingly to the development of inorganic chemistry and metallurgy.   The great technical developments of South Germany and North Italy in the fifteenth century, where the bases of mechanical industry, capitalist economics and modern science are all to be found, were largely due to the concentrated war demand for guns and precious metals. (1)

Artillery and the Renaissance.—At least as revolutionary were the new ideas on mechanics which were inspired by the flight of the cannon ball.   Until artillery appeared, dynamics in the modern sense could not exist at all.   A body moved only if it was being steadily pushed or naturally falling.   The first break from this idea occurred just at the time of the introduction of cannons, when Buridan suggested that a projectile was imbued with a new kind of force or *vis viva*.   This consideration was developed further by a number of artillerymen and mathematicians, including two of the greatest of scientists, Leonardo da Vinci and Galileo, both of whom were concerned directly with military affairs.   Leonardo's letter in applying for a post with the Duke of Milan is the classical example of the necessary connection of the scientist with war:

"Having, most illustrious Sir, seen and considered the experiments of all those who profess to be masters in the art of invention of the apparatus of war, and having found that their instruments do not differ materially from those in general use, I make known to your Excellency certain secrets of my own, briefly enumerated as follows:

(1) I have a process for the construction of very light bridges, capable of easy transport, by means of which the enemy may be pursued and put to flight; and of others more solid, which will resist both fire and sword, and which are easily lowered or raised. I know also of a means to burn and destroy hostile bridges.

(2) In case of the investment of a place, I know how to drain moats and construct scaling ladders and other such apparatus.

(3) Item; if, by reason of its elevation or strength, it is not possible to bombard a hostile position, I have a means of destruction by mining provided the foundations of the fortress are not of rock.

(4) I know also how to make light cannon easy of transport capable of ejecting inflammable matter, the smoke from which would cause terror, destruction and confusion among the enemy.

(5) Item; by means of narrow and tortuous subterranean tunnels, dug without noise, I am able to create a passage to inaccessible places, even under rivers.

(6) Item; I know how to construct secure and covered wagons for the transport of guns into the enemy's lines, and not to be impeded by ever so dense a mass, and behind which infantry can follow without danger.

(7) I can make cannon, mortars, and engines of fire, etc., of form both useful and beautiful, and different from those at present in use.

(8) Or, if the use of cannon happens to be impracticable, I can replace them by catapults and other admirable projecting weapons at present unknown; in short, where such is the case, I am able to devise endless means of attack.

(9) And, if the combat should be at sea, I have numerous most powerful engines both for attack and defence; and ships which are gun-proof and fire-proof; and also powders and inflammables.

(10) In times of peace, I believe that I can compete with anyone in architecture, and in the construction of both public and private monuments and in the building of canals; I am able to execute statues in marble, bronze and clay; in painting I can do as well as anyone else. In particular, I will undertake to execute the bronze horse in the eternal memory of your father and of the very illustrious house of Sforza, and if any of the above-mentioned things appear to you impossible or impracticable, I will offer to make an attempt at it in your park or in any other place which your Excellency may please to choose, to which I commend myself in all humility."—Codex Atlantico, Fol. 391 r.

Whether Leonardo's interests were or were not predominantly military is not the question, though the large proportion of military figures in his notebooks suggested that they were so. What is relevant is that only by his claiming military abilities could he have obtained so important a post. Galileo was himself professor of military science at the University of Pavia, and was able to sell his invention of the telescope to the Venetian Signory solely on account of its value in naval warfare (2). Sometimes, however, early scientists felt disturbed at this misuse of their efforts; thus Tartaglia, who laid the foundation of ballistics, remarks in his preface to *L'Art de jecter les bombes*:

"When I was living in the town of Verona in the year 1531, one of my intimate friends, master of ordnance at the old castle, a man of experience, very skilful in his art, and who was gifted with excellent qualities, asked me one day my opinion how to aim a piece of artillery to give it its greatest range. Although I had no practical knowledge whatever of artillery, for I have never in my life shot a single round with firearms, arquebus, bombard or escopette, nevertheless, desirous as I was to be agreeable to my friend, I promised him shortly to give him an answer to his question. (Follows an account of how he set about to tackle the problem, etc.)

As the result of this I had the intention of writing a treatise on the art of artillery, and to bring it to a degree of perfection capable of directing fire in all circumstances, assisted only by a few particular experiments: for as Aristotle says in the seventh book of the *Physica*, Section 20, 'particular experiments are the basis of universal science.'

But, since then, one day meditating to myself, it had seemed to me that it was a thing blameworthy, shameful and barbarous, worthy of severe punishment before God and man, to wish to bring to perfection an art damageable to one's neighbour and destructive to the human race, and especially to Christian men in the continual wars that they wage on one another. Consequently, not only did I altogether neglect the study of this matter and turned to others, but I even tore up and burnt everything which I had calculated and written on the subject, ashamed and full of remorse for the time I had spent on it, and well decided never to communicate in writing that which against my will had remained in my memory, either to please a friend or in teaching of these matters which are a grave sin and shipwreck of the soul.'

The imminent invasion of Italy by the Turks, who, as it happened, were instigated by his Most Christian Majesty the King of France, caused him to change his mind:

"To-day however, in the sight of the ferocious wolf preparing to set on our flock, and of our pastors united for the common defence, it does not seem to me any longer proper to hold these things hid, and I have resolved to publish them partly in writing, partly by word of mouth, for the benefit of Christians so that all should be in better state either to attack the common enemy or to defend themselves against him. I regret very much at the moment having given up this work, for I am certain that had I persevered I would have found things of the greatest value, as I hope yet to find . . . I hope that your Lordships will not disdain to receive this work of mine so as better to instruct the artillerymen of your most illustrious government in the theory of their art, and to render them more apt in its practice."

Actually Tartaglia's work and that of nearly all ballistic theorists were of little use in artillery practice, but proved very useful to the development of mechanics. It was left to Newton to combine the new ideas of dynamics derived from the problems set by artillery practice with those of astronomy. Astronomy itself was, at this time, in a state of active development in relation to the needs of navigation, and was thus of part military, part commercial nature. It was not only in astronomy and dynamics that science was linked to war; we owe much of modern physics to the development of vacuum technique and of frictional electricity by Otto von Guericke, quartermaster-general of Gustavus Adolphus in the Thirty Years' War, who was able to use his position to carry out large-scale experiments. (3)

War and the Industrial Revolution.—The connection between science and war continued unbroken into modern times. Lavoisier, the father of modern chemistry, was the head of the " Régie des Poudres " at the French arsenal. The French artillery schools furnished in the eighteenth century the only places where science was systematically taught. It was here that most of the great mathematicians and physicists of the late eighteenth and early nineteenth centuries received their training. Another product of these schools was Napoleon, the first military man to profit by scientific education, a fact not unconnected with his success. The great technical developments of the eighteenth and nineteenth centuries, particularly the large-scale smelting of iron by means of coal, and the introduction of the steam-engine, were directly due to the needs for artillery which the increasingly large scale of war demanded. The accurate boring of steam-engine cylinders, which made all the difference in practice between the efficient engines of Watt and the earlier atmospheric engines, was due to the improvements introduced by Wilkinson, who was able to make them on account of his experience in the boring of cannon. From the same field comes Rumford's discovery of the mechanical equivalent of heat, which was to furnish the basic theory for all heat engines.

The Nineteenth Century.—The long peace of the early nineteenth century diminished the relative though not the absolute importance of war for science. The locomotive engine, for instance, is one of the few major inventions which owes little to any military inspiration, and the development of dyes proved as important a stimulus to chemistry as that of explosives, though the chemistry of the two was closely connected. Towards the end of the century, however, particularly after the Franco-Prussian War and the development of imperialist rivalry, war began to become again increasingly important in its relation to science. The heavy metal industry was coming to depend, to an increasing amount, on orders for gun and battleship construction, while the new chemical industry was being built up in such a way as to provide explosives on a hitherto inconceivable scale. The large-scale production of steel, the technical development which almost more than any other has made modern mechanical civilization possible, was directly due to war needs. Bessemer had invented a rifled cannon in 1854, at the beginning of the Crimean War, but could find no iron strong enough to resist the strain and was thus led to begin his successful researches on steel production. At the same time improvements in methods of communication and transport, telephone, wireless, motor transport and, above all, the aeroplane, were revolutionizing the possibilities of co-ordinating and directing the movements of millions of men at a time, while improvements in methods of food storage and in medical services could enable such millions to live for years without being ravaged by famine and disease.

The full significance of what this meant for warfare was not realized until the experience of the last War. Before then, although a few far-sighted scientists realized the prospect that their work was piling up for mankind, most were comforted with the thought that science had now made war so terrible that no nation would dream of engaging in it. Joule, the discoverer of the mechanical equivalent of heat, had few illusions on the score of the contribution of science to war, though his attitude in respect to his own country was as qualified as that of Tartaglia:

"Such then are the legitimate objects of science. It is deeply to be regretted that another and most unworthy object has been introduced and has gradually and alarmingly increased in prominence. This is the improvement of the art of war and the implements of mutual destruction. I know there are those who think that these improvements will tend to put an end to war by making it more destructive. I cannot think that such an opinion is based on common sense. I believe war will not only be more destructive, but be carried on with greater ferocity. Individual campaigns will doubtless be short as well as decisive, but this will necessarily cause that rapid rise and fall of states and unsettling of boundaries and constitutions which must eventually deteriorate civilization itself and render peace impossible. And thus by applying itself to an improper object science may eventually fall by its own hand. In reference to this subject we must also deplore the prostitution of science for the aggrandisement of individuals and nations, the result being that the weaker is destroyed and the stronger race is established on its ruins. In making the above remarks I allude to war generally, I intend no disparagement of the efforts being made to secure the integrity and liberties of Great Britain. These have been forced upon us and it is matter of congratulation that we are not responsible for the present military attitude of Europe."—From Crowther, *British Scientists of the Nineteenth Century*, p. 140.

Science in the Great War.—Great as were the technical and scientific preparations for the War, they were found to be quite inadequate to stand up against the actual conditions of warfare as they developed. During the War scientists found themselves for the first time not a luxury but a necessity to their respective Governments. It is true that at the beginning they were used wastefully. Moseley, who might have become the greatest experimental physicist of the century in England, was allowed to go out to Gallipoli and get killed. A leading physicist in England who offered to organize a meteorological service for the Army was informed that the British soldier fought in all weathers, and it was only after the appalling carnage of offensives in the Flanders mud that such a service was instituted. (4) As the War went on, however, scientists were used at home for perfecting the existing means of destruction, for developing new weapons, and for countering the new developments in the enemy countries. Aerial and chemical warfare were two of the blessings which the science of the War period produced. But scientific research carried on under war conditions was incredibly wasteful. With inadequate materials and preparation, new processes had to be devised and put into action within a few weeks. Naturally a terrific waste of material ensued and also a great loss of life. In the Allied countries, the development of the production of poison gases to counter those produced by the Germans was rushed through, regardless of the death or disablement of chemists and workers. Similarly the development of the aeroplane made enormous strides, but only at an immense cost in both material and men. (5) In spite of this it was clear that under the stimulus of war it was possible to increase the rate of application of science by many times what had appeared to be the limit of peace-time activity. This showed that the progress of science had been limited in peace not by any intrinsic factors but rather by external economic and political factors.

War creates State-organized Science.—It was soon apparent outside Germany that the development of science, and particularly the number of trained scientists, was entirely inadequate to the requirements of the military situation. With far less natural resources the Germans had been able to take the technical as well as the military initiative through the greater part of the War. It is significant that the Germans lost one man killed to two among the Allies and brought down six aeroplanes for every one they lost. Thus the War, and only the War, could bring home to Governments the critical importance of scientific research in modern economy. This was recognized in Britain by the formation of the Department of Scientific and Industrial Research, the foundation of which was largely inspired by the need for military preparation in peace time. Thus in the report for 1933 we find:

" The circumstances of war lent force to the pleas of those who had been calling for a closer march of British Industry with science, for they demonstrated, with an emphasis that had hitherto been lacking, the consequences of failure to follow up scientific discoveries capable of utilization in the industrial sphere. For example, it was soon found that this country was to an unfortunate extent largely dependent on foreign sources for some of the supplies necessary for war-like operations. Our greatest enemy of those days had secured, by application of science, a hold upon certain manufactured products which was found to be of an extent and nature to threaten our national well-being. And there was a general awakening to the fact that for success in times of peace as well as of war it was desirable that the resources of science should be utilized to the full. The perils of war furnished precepts for peace." . . . (See also p. 30.)

In the peace treaties the victorious Allies tried to ensure the permanency of their power by annexing the science of the Germans. As, however, Government officials and industrialists conceived of science more as a collection of magic recipes than an activity with the widest ramifications through the economic structure, all they did was to acquire the secret for making a few dyes and explosives, in order to save their own scientists the trouble of finding them out for themselves, and left the German scientists to the task of reversing, by their devotion to work, the military balance that force of arms had overthrown.

War Research To-Day

The years since the War have marked an increasing preoccupation with scientific preparations for a future and imminent war. In all countries science is looked on by Governments as a useful military adjunct, and in some this is practically its only function. This is reflected in the relatively enormous budgetary appropriations for war research, not only by Governments but by industrial firms. There are only three industries large enough and sufficiently under monopoly control to be able to afford scientific research on an adequate scale. These are the heavy metal, the chemical, and the electrical industries, and the first two of these are largely and increasingly concerned with war production. It would not be unfair to say that something between one-third and one-half of the money spent on scientific research in Britain is spent directly or indirectly on war research, and probably, though the figures are more difficult to find, as much or more is spent in other countries. And this in peace time. In war time it is quite clear that practically all research would be absorbed for war purposes.

What is War Research?—The task of determining exactly what is or is not war research has now become almost an impossible one. Very naturally, in countries where pacifist opinion is still allowed to express itself, attempts are made by the authorities to minimize the expenditure on war research. This is usually done by pointing out how in a number of cases research for military purposes turns out to have commercial value and is ultimately beneficial to the community. (6) Of this we have already given some examples from the past. Those that are cited now are the usefulness of explosive research for blasting in mines and quarries, and of poison gas for the destruction of insect pests. But the fact that swords can be, and are occasionally, beaten into ploughshares is only half the story. It is equally true that apparently civilian research can be turned to war uses. The fact is that we are emerging from a period when war was a specialized task affecting a small portion of the community, and are now reverting to one in which every member of the community, tribe, or nation is primarily a warrior. Under modern industrial conditions war is no longer fought only by the men in the field of battle but by the whole national industrial complex. The indirectness of participation is a very convenient mask, because it enables the attacks of pacifists to be diverted on to what is probably the least essential part of war—the actual front-line fighting. Nevertheless it is convenient to distinguish between direct and indirect application of science to modern warfare.

The Mechanization of War.—One of the characteristic features that appeared in the Great War and which has been very much intensified since, is the mechanization of all forms of warfare. The result is that to carry on war at all requires material equipment, not only in the form of rifles and cannon as in older forms of warfare, but also of machine-guns, tanks, and aeroplanes. These in turn require correspondingly greater supplies of explosives, petrol, and poison gas. To provide them at all requires a far heavier capital expenditure than in any previous war, but to keep them going for any length of time under war conditions, they must be supplied by an active and efficient industry employing far more men than are occupied in the fighting forces. It follows at once that only highly industrial countries can wage modern war effectively. This fact can be concealed by such countries waging war by proxy, employing the nationals of other countries to do the fighting, and supplying them continuously with modern armaments and munitions. An example was the war between Bolivia and Paraguay, countries which of themselves are incapable of producing any effective armaments. This war was fought partly as a struggle for economic advantages between rival national economic groups in Britain and America, partly to provide profits for armament manufacturers, and partly to enable the efficiency of modern weapons to be tested out in practice under war conditions. The Spanish war illustrates still another method, that of attempting to change the Government of a State by supplying an intractable minority with arms. What happens when a highly industrial country engages in war with one lacking either industry or the backing of another industrial country has been tragically seen in the Abyssinian war. The success, therefore, of a country in war depends on the size and efficiency of its normal peace-time industry. There are, in fact, only seven Powers in the world that may be considered really effective in this respect, though in very different degrees: the United States, the Soviet Union, Britain,

Germany, France, Japan, and Italy. Everything which tends to strengthen national industry and improve the efficiency and economy of its processes increases its military strength. To this extent all national industrial research is potentially war research. This has been very clearly seen in the case of Germany, where the minimum of change was required to convert the whole apparatus of civil industrial research into one openly directed to war purposes (see p. 217).

Science and Armaments

Heavy Industry.—Naturally all departments of industry are not equally involved in war preparations, but those that are chiefly so are the key industries of the nation—the heavy metal, the engineering, and chemical industries. These are also the industries which absorb the greatest amount of scientific research. We have seen how in the last few years the heavy metal industry in Europe has raised itself from the depths of depression almost entirely on war orders. (7) The need of the production of guns, battleships, and tanks, which all employ enormous quantities of steel in their construction, has proved the greatest stimulus to research into the properties of metals. The expenditure of the British Iron and Steel Federation on co-operative research, apart from research carried on in individual firms, leapt from £5000 in 1932, to £22,500 in 1936.

Aeroplane Production.—In the engineering industry, particularly in transport, the pressure of war needs is just as clearly felt. Some kinds of heavy transport, trucks, tractors, etc., can be used practically indiscriminately for war or peace purposes, and it is difficult to assess the proportion of the research that goes into their manufacture that can be ascribed to war needs. It is entirely otherwise, however, with aeroplanes. Almost from the beginning the aeroplane has been developed and subsidized primarily for war uses. Even before the present rearmament boom, four-fifths of all the aeroplanes in England were military aeroplanes (8), and, in countries such as Germany, where these had been forbidden, civil aviation was deliberately developed with the object of switching over to military aviation at a suitable moment. Aviation research is accordingly of immediate military importance in practically every country. An indication of this is the increasing difficulties which are being put up for any degree of collaboration in air research between different countries. There remains, of course, some show of collaboration; new machine designs are advertised and their prestige value exploited, but the best designs are withheld from publication until they have become virtually obsolete. Thus every country hopes to be several years ahead of all other countries when war begins. The aeroplane industry being an almost entirely scientific industry in the sense discussed above, and also being in a state of rapid development, requires a far greater proportion of research than any of the older established industries. We find, in fact, that in most countries aeronautical research is the most highly developed and well subsidized of all forms of industrial research. Thus, quite apart from the military air research stations in Britain on which £727,500 was spent in 1937, a very large part of the National Physical Laboratory is devoted to aero-dynamic studies, and even in universities the study of aero-dynamics takes a prominent place. (9)

The Chemical Industry.—The chemical industry occupies an increasingly important position in the preparation and carrying on of modern warfare. But it is particularly in the case of the chemical industry that it is most difficult to disentangle how far its research is directed to civil or military ends. The military materials, which are or can be furnished by the chemical industry, are explosives, poison gases, rubber, petrol, and other motor oils. No war can be carried on for any length of time without supplies of these materials in vastly greater quantities than those used in peace time. (10) All of them have alternative uses, but only in the case of poison gases do the war-time so predominate over the peace-time uses that relatively little is produced in peace time. Explosives are in constant demand for mining and quarrying operations as well as for many purposes of civil engineering. Rubber and petrol at first sight hardly seem to come into the scope of the chemical industry. They are, however, natural products of which the sources are very unevenly distributed. Thus, of the great Powers, the U.S.A. and the U.S.S.R. both lack sources of rubber, while Britain and France lack sources of petrol, and Germany, Italy, and Japan lack sources of both. In these circumstances scientific research has been feverishly occupied ever since the War with providing artificial means for producing both these substances. The ease with which raw rubber can be produced in plantations would, in any rationally organized world, make synthetic rubber uneconomic to produce, and the same can be said of petrol made from coal. It may, of course, be that after spending millions of pounds on research and experimental plant, new methods for making these substances at a cost comparable to the natural ones may be found, or even that new materials or fuels superior to the natural products may be produced. Here it is relevant merely to point out how much scientific research is diverted in directions which, though apparently commercial, owe almost their entire existence to war demands. (11)

Explosives and Poison Gas.—Both the processes and the materials required for making the more direct war chemicals, explosives, and gases have little that is specialized about them. The primary ingredients for explosives are nitric and sulphuric acids, coal-tar derivatives such as toluene, and various cellulose materials. All of these have very considerable peace-time uses. But the desire to secure sufficient of them for war purposes has been a very conscious stimulus to research in alternative methods of producing them. Originally the sulphur needed for sulphuric acid was obtained from high-grade sulphur ores, pyrites, or native sulphur deposits, but these were too localized to be safe war-time sources. Italy, Spain, and the United States between them provide the bulk of the direct sulphur ores. There has consequently been a drive to obtain sulphur from low-grade sources such as the widely distributed gypsum. With the processes now in use no large industrial country can be starved of sulphuric acid. At one time the problem of nitric acid supply was the most acute. As the raw nitrate came almost exclusively from Chile, only the powers with control of the sea could get hold of it in war time. This position was, however, completely reversed in the last war by Haber's development of the utilization of nitrogen from the air. By this method so much nitrate was produced not only during but after the War that the natural source was for a while completely put out of action by the competition. Of course nitrates have, quite apart from their uses in war, an extremely valuable peace-time application as fertilizers, but owing to the poverty of agricultural producers the supply far outran the demand for this purpose, and a really great war will be necessary to put the synthetic nitrate industry on its feet again. (12)

The situation in the case of poison gases is very much the same: the natural materials required in addition to those already mentioned are chlorine, which can be got from salt or sea water, and arsenic, which is fairly widely obtainable. The intermediary products for producing poison gas are all common articles of trade, consequently in the production of poison gas only the last stages of research need be directed towards military ends; for the others the manufacturers of poison gas can rely on common chemical experience. Another characteristic which makes the chemical industry more immediately military in character than the other industries is the relative ease and rapidity with which it can be converted from peace-time to war-time uses. Machinery for making big guns and battleships cannot be rapidly improvised. Even that required for making aeroplanes in large numbers needs some months for preparing the necessary tools, jigs, etc., but the chemical industry can switch over to war purposes in a matter of two or three weeks at the outside.

Thus we can see that three of the main industries in every modern country, the heavy metal, engineering, and chemical industries, are in their construction so closely connected with production for war purposes that it is impossible to separate in a clear-cut technical way the military from the civil portions of such industries.   This is the problem, for instance, that had baffled not only well-meant efforts at taking the profits out of war, but the Governments themselves. (13) When they try to reduce costs charged to them by munition manufacturers, they always find these can be passed on to the producers of so many intermediate products linked to the same trusts that it is practically impossible to effect any economies.   It is equally difficult to distinguish precisely whether any fundamental or applied research, tending to the improvement of heavy industry generally, will not be of considerable military value.

National Food Supplies

It is, however, not only in industry that productive forces are developed with an eye to war needs.   Almost equally important in modern warfare is the maintenance of food supplies, and since the last war every country has made desperate efforts to see that as far as possible it has the food supply needed for a prolonged war within its own boundaries.   This tendency cuts right across the nineteenth-century developments which tended to concentrate large populations in industrial areas and feed them by the surplus products of more or less mechanized farming in less developed countries.   The idea at the back of the doctrine of free trade was that every product should be produced in that region which was most suited to it, either climatically or on account of the existence of certain industrial techniques.   Any change from this implied an uneconomic distribution of effort, and could, in fact, only be carried on administratively by the use of heavy tariffs and subsidies, and socially by preventing people in industrial countries having enough food or other necessities in times of peace, so that they might hope to have just enough to live on in war time. In this new development science has been called on to perform an important subsidiary task, that of increasing the amount of animal and plant products under conditions more or less unfavourable to them, such, for instance, as the growing of sugar-beet in England (14), or the conversion of mountain-sides to pasture in order to put pastures under wheat cultivation.   The problem of the storage of food has also received great attention.   But the outcome of research into this has had a result different from that originally intended.   Although assisting home food production it has made the importation of food from distant countries still more easy, and has necessitated the imposition of further tariffs and quotas.

There are, however, in the very countries where the policy of national food sufficiency is most urged, three powerful factors operating against it and largely nullifying the effects of this drive. In the first place, the powerful economic factor is that failure to buy food from undeveloped countries reacts on the economies of these countries in such a way as to prevent their purchase of the finished goods from the manufacturing country, and consequently produces such a loss of profit and unemployment as to offset considerably the potential military advantage of home production. Even Germany, which under the Nazi régime set itself most definitely to become independent of foreign food products, has been obliged to import the food surplus of most of the small central European states in order to provide markets for its own manufacturers. The second countering tendency is the existence of colonial dependencies, largely producing food and other raw materials, which necessarily compete with any developments of home production. This has been clearly seen in the case of the British Empire, where the confusion arising from a desire to support the home farmer and the Empire simultaneously disturbs the minds of conservatives. The third objection is largely political. Really effective production of food requires not only scientific research into agriculture but a rational organization of agricultural practice, and this necessarily means the complete transformation of ancient agricultural methods. In particular it strikes both at the landlord and the small independent peasant or tenant-proprietor, who are the main bulwark of reactionary Governments throughout the world. The result of these conflicting tendencies is to produce the maximum of expenditure and confusion and the minimum of practical results. Subsidies are poured out in plenty and go into the pockets of large landowners and farmers. Research is carried out but not put into practice, and the population gets less food at higher prices. Nevertheless, although the amounts spent on research into food production is trifling compared with the subsidies paid out to inefficient producers, they do represent a very considerable proportion of funds available to scientific research as a whole. Agricultural, biological, bio-chemical, and even medical research are all beneficiaries.

The modern progress in biological research and its applications in food production in many parts of the world, notably in the Soviet Union and in Javanese sugar-cane plantations, show that technically the problem of food production is solved and only awaits economic and political reorganization to make it a reality. It would even be possible, though a large waste of effort, to develop scientific methods of intensive food production, coupled, to a certain extent, with artificial foods (see Chapter XIV), in order to make even badly situated countries such as England produce the whole food requirements of the population. The fact that this possibility exists has been twisted into the statement that the advances of science have made internationalism unnecessary and into the advocacy of complete national economy and cultural segregation. This view is not confined to Fascists. Excess of Little England radicalism has driven even Professor Hogben to advocate it as a means of removing the causes of war through abandoning all those foreign national interests which the existence of world trade necessitates.

"If we escape a speedy nemesis of sentimental internationalism, there remains only one consistent policy which would rally progressive forces in this country to the task of social reconstruction and, as our Quaker friends say, take away the occasion for war. If we do not escape it, the only party which can hope to survive will be the one which has striven for the policy which would have made war unnecessary. The rational plan is to mobilize the healthy sentiment which modest and fertile people have for their own surroundings and kin in a national constructive effort to socialize all the resources of scientific knowledge available for making Britain progressively more isolated from Europe and the Empire. A progressive party with this programme could hope to gain support from the large section of the salaried classes for whom the prospect of nationalizing bankrupt industries has no appeal. Alternatively liberals and socialists can continue to compete in professions of international goodwill forcing us on to a universal cataclysm of unimaginable destructive consequences, while leaving us an easy prey to dictators. Even if the doctrine of natural sites were an eternal truth, the growth of national sentiment in our time is indisputable. Inescapably, we have to choose between two alternatives. We can use this sentiment for mobilizing the general will to socialize technical resources which private enterprise has failed to exploit in the interests of social welfare. We can see it used, as Hitler is using it, to drive us headlong towards barbarism and war."—Lancelot Hogben in *The Retreat from Reason* (pp. 40-41).

Unfortunately, in practice, the political forces driving to national self-sufficiency are precisely those driving to the greatest expansion of military and naval power, and in the present political constitution of the world the capacity of a nation to live on its own resources can only be regarded as one aspect, and by no means only a defensive one, of war preparation.

The Diversion of Research to War Uses

The relative importance of war considerations in determining the direction of scientific research is well seen by an analysis of Governmental expenditure on research. If we take first of all the net expenditure of the Department of Scientific and Industrial Research in 1936-37 we find the largest sum, £105,000, devoted to the

National Physical Laboratory in which three of the most important departments, metallurgy, aero-dynamics, and radio, have a more or less direct war importance. It is also quite obvious from examining their reports that these are the departments which are most active and best run. The next greatest expenditure is £22,000 on fuel research, largely concerned with hydrogenation and the production of motor fuels from coal, also of direct war importance. £38,000 goes to food investigation, mostly concerned with methods of preservation. Thus in the aggregate, out of the total expenditure of the Department—£460,000 (apart from grants to Research Associations)—about £160,000, or at any rate more than a third, can be credited to war and is fairly closely connected with possible war uses, while there is no doubt whatever that it is just those parts of the work that receive the greatest attention from governing bodies and have the greatest prospects of rapid development. (15)

Military Research.—Military research, properly speaking, is something more than research tending to increase war potential through greater industrial efficiency and independence of foreign supplies. It is concerned with devising and testing out aggressive and defensive weapons, and it is this that absorbs the large sums mentioned at the beginning of the chapter. (16) Two characteristics separate such research from all the rest of science. It is consciously directed towards a social end, that is, towards the most rapid, effective and terrifying means of death and destruction, and, secondly, it is carried on under conditions of extreme secrecy. Both these characteristics tend to separate military research, at any rate in peace time, from the main body of science. In the production of new weapons very different considerations apply from those that hold for new productive machinery. Technical perfection and ability to stand rough usage weigh far more than any economic considerations. In some ways, therefore, the designers of military machinery are far freer in the application of ideas than those in civil employ. But if money is not a factor, time is. Unless the search for new weapons is carried on at the highest pitch of speed there is the danger of falling behind and consequently of wasting all the money previously spent on research. Obsolescence, which is present to a large extent in ordinary industry, is here far worse and leads to much greater waste in research. Not only is obsolescence automatically produced by the conditions of military production, but this is greatly enhanced by the activities of commercial armament makers. Whereas in commerce an invention will be held back if it is likely to lead to the scrapping of quantities of valuable plant, in military affairs, since the tax-payer has to pay the cost, the more scrapping there is the better. Every new device means new orders for the manufacturer, and the Government has the burden of disposing of the obsolete military material for the benefit of the wars of backward nations. There are, of course, opposite influences at work. The traditional stupidity and conservatism of military authorities themselves impose a check on the development of new weapons, but once an important country can be persuaded to take them up the others are bound to follow, and the close connections between directors of armament firms and high army and navy officials often have the effect of diminishing their dislike of innovations. (17)

War research presents an even more distorted picture of rush, waste, secrecy and overlapping than does the worst industrial research. It is therefore not surprising that it adds to its inefficiencies in peace time the handicap of not attracting the best brains and consequently of still further diminishing its efficiency. Even in countries where science is forcibly enlisted into war service, as in modern Germany, we may suspect that a very considerable amount of tacit sabotage goes on. It is only if scientists think that their work is likely, ultimately, to result in the good of humanity that they will produce anything spontaneous or novel in the way of military inventions. As it is, there must be thousands of ingenious scientists who could quite easily think out enormous improvements in present methods both of attack and defence, and may even have privately done so, but prefer to keep their ideas to themselves either from humanitarian reasons or because of their opinion of the Government of their country.

The Scientist in War.—In war time, of course, it has generally been possible to persuade the scientist that his country's cause is just and that consequently he may devote himself without conscientious scruples to improving the art of war—and his choice is made the easier by the alternatives of prison or of a still more unpleasant direct military servitude. The attitude of scientists during the last war has seemed, in retrospect, a most pathetic spectacle. Every shred of scientific internationalism was lost, and scientists were not content with helping material destruction, but were obliged to vilify the scientists and even the science of enemy countries. In an editorial in *Nature* the late Sir William Ramsay, one of the most distinguished chemists of his time, could write in 1915:

"The aim of science is the acquisition of knowledge of the unknown; the aim of applied science, the bettering of the lot of the human race. German ideals are infinitely far removed from the conception of the true man of science; and the methods by which they propose to secure what they regard as the good of humanity are, to all right-thinking men, repugnant. These views are not confined to the Prussian ruling caste, although in it they find active expression: they are the soul of the people. . . .

The motto of the Allies must be 'Never again.' Not merely must the dangerous and insufferable despotism which has eaten like a cancer into the morals of the German nation be annihilated, but all possibility of its resuscitation must be made hopeless. The nation, in the elegant words of one of its distinguished representatives, must be 'bled white.'

Will the progress of science be thereby retarded? I think not. The greatest advances in scientific thought have not been made by members of the German race; nor have the earlier applications of science had Germany for their origin. So far as we can see at present, the restriction of the Teutons will relieve the world from a deluge of mediocrity. Much of their previous reputation has been due to Hebrews resident among them; and we may safely trust that race to persist in vitality and intellectual activity."—*Nature*, Vol. 94, p. 138 (1915).

This is in itself a disturbing symptom, for throughout all past history science has been considered to be above the conflict. For instance, in the middle of the Napoleonic Wars the greatest English chemist, Davy, not only was permitted to visit France but was honoured by Napoleon himself, even though some of his work had been of military utility.

Totalitarian War Preparation.—Our present state is one intermediate between peace and war. Everywhere war preparations are going on with ever-increasing intensity, dominating economic and political life. Already in Spain war has reached Europe. The problems of war research have become of the greatest urgency, and more and more scientists are being enlisted to work on them. But scientists are not only being asked to assist in war research, they are being given a new part in the carrying out of war itself. Modern warfare differs from all wars of the past, even from the Great War, in that the whole of the population is required to take part in it and all are exposed to similar dangers. Aerial attack spares no one, and in the new task of protecting the population from such attack, scientists are expected to collaborate in the practical work of defence, particularly in gas defence. This demand is, more than anything else, bringing the scientist of to-day up against the realities of the present war situation. It would seem in itself sufficiently absurd and horrible that he should have to spend his time and intelligence in an attempt to shield himself and his fellow-citizens against a danger which, but for science, would not have existed. Looking closer, he sees that the problem of defence against aerial attack is not merely military and technical, but economic and political as well, and that it is political and economic considerations that make it not so much the hideous necessity that it would be in any case as a shameful deception and hypocrisy.

Air Raid Defence.—The problem of defence against air attack can be divided into two stages—active and passive defence. Active defence is concerned with preventing aeroplanes from reaching their objectives or from returning after having reached them. It comprises the policy of raids on enemy aerodromes or on the civil population as reprisals, and various forms of interception by fighting planes, anti-aircraft guns, and balloon barrages. Most military experts are inclined to think that none of these forms taken separately, or all of them together, are likely to do more than hamper to a certain extent bombing raids between Powers of approximately the same military and industrial strength. Aeroplanes are relatively easily made, and enthusiastic young men to fly them are almost as easily found. Events in Spain have shown that two of the military hypotheses on which the effectiveness of this kind of defence was based are groundless. It had been claimed that in future wars air attacks would be limited to military objectives, including, of course, factories. Modern air forces, however, show no reluctance to bomb centres of civilian population simply for the moral or terroristic effect (18), and not only to bomb them but to machine-gun fleeing civilians. Nor have, as it had been hoped, heavy casualties inflicted on raiding forces deterred further raids, though they have reduced the frequency of successful ones.

The Protection of the Civil Population.—Although scientists are involved in almost every element of modern aerial strategy, it is not in this active defence that their collaboration is most sought. It is realized that possibilities for victory in future wars lie with the country that can longest preserve the working capacity and the morale of its civil population, and that, while it may be impossible to prevent air raids occurring, the damage they do might be minimized. The methods proposed in various countries, particularly in Germany and Britain, for these purposes show very clearly, however, both the essentially military aims of aerial defence and the extremely limited class outlook of the people who design them. (19) So far passive defence has been developed in a most chaotic manner and without any regard to the relative risks that would be involved in a modern air attack. High explosive bombs are the greatest danger and gas the least, yet nearly all measures are designed for protection against gas and for dealing with gas casualties. They would not even be effective against those large concentrations of gas which would be the only way in which it would be worth while to put it down. No protection at all is being offered against high explosive and little against incendiary bombs. The amount of money laid aside for Air Raid Precautions, £32,000,000, against nearly £2,000,000,000 for potentially aggressive armament is a measure of the importance which is attached to the defence of the civil population. Moreover, these schemes, inadequate as they are, weigh heaviest on the poorer section of the population and at the same time offer them the least protection. These are the people who are closest to the targets of attack, factories and transport centres, and who also, as the experiences of Spain and China have tragically shown, are deliberately selected as victims. They lack the means of building private shelters or of escaping to their country houses in their cars. It is apparently imagined that if the wealthy can be assured of a relative immunity the war spirit can be kept up.

Actually, the technical problems of passive defence are not insoluble; perfect defence is, of course, impossible, but a fair measure of defence could be obtained by wholesal evacuation for the duration of the war of most women and chi. en to country districts, nightly evacuation of most of the remaining population, and by the provision of fire-, bomb-, and gas-proof shelters with forced ventilation for the remainder. Such precautions, however, could not be adopted by any country in which the privileges of private property were retained, as houses, food, and means of transport would all have to be communally administered. Nor, it must be admitted, is the prospect of life permanently under the shadow of aerial warfare at all a pleasant one. Comparative safety could only be obtained at immense social cost, and it is doubtful if any of the values of civilization could be retained for long under such conditions. Present schemes, however, though they may involve a cost almost as great, offer no such security. The dangers of modern warfare are not so much, as popular writers like to make out, that of a sudden destruction of all civilized life, but rather, owing to the approximate equality of the forces of offence and defence, of a long-drawn-out destructive struggle in which hunger, exposure and disease and the demoralization accompanying them will destroy civilization as effectively as any sudden cataclysm. Naturally Governments do not inform the people of these probabilities. All schemes, however ineffective, are put out together with the impression that aerial attack can be borne without more than mild inconvenience, and the scientists are being asked effectively to abet this general deception. Those who have stood out against this and exposed the baselessness of the claims of precautions afforded are denounced as scaremongers and their pronouncements smothered in heavy official reassurances. (20)

THE SCIENTIST FACES THE PROBLEM OF WAR

Nevertheless, whether by partaking in or protesting against schemes for aerial defence, the scientists are brought very much more closely up against the problems of peace and war. Opinions which would have before been considered right and proper, and against which no voice of protest was raised, have now begun to be questioned and even denounced. The millions who had suffered in the last War are aware that to a large extent their sufferings were directly due to scientific developments, and that science, far from having brought benefits to mankind, is in fact proving its worst enemy. The value of science itself has been put in question, and at last scientists have been forced to take notice of the outcry.   Among the younger scientists, particularly, the feeling has begun to grow up, and is gaining daily in strength, that the application of science to war is the worst prostitution of their profession.   More than anything else the question of science and war has made scientists look beyond the field of their own inquiries and discoveries to the social uses to which these discoveries are put.

One of the results of this has been a much greater reluctance than heretofore among scientists voluntarily to assist in military research, and a strong feeling that in doing so they are in some way violating the spirit of science.   The position has not been reached, largely owing to the lack of organization of scientific workers, where a complete boycott of war research can be declared.   In the present state of the world it is even doubtful whether such a policy would have good results, for the immediate first effect would be to put democratic countries at a disadvantage in regard to Fascist ones.   What can and is being done, however, is the alignment of scientists as active partners of all peace forces.   Particularly in France and Britain, numbers of scientists, and among them some of the most eminent, are taking an active part in democratic movements aimed at the prevention of war and the creation of conditions under which war will be impossible.

Scientists organize for Peace.—A notable step forward has been taken by the Science Commission of the International Peace Campaign at its Congress in Brussels in 1936.   There scientists from thirteen countries met together to discuss the responsibilities of scientists in face of the war situation.   The discussion largely turned on the question of participation of scientists in war or war preparations.   It is clear that here there are three different trends of opinion: those who would join in such activities in all circumstances either because of the superior interests of the State or because in their opinion the scientist has no business to concern himself with the result of his work; those who, on the other hand, will in no circumstances have anything to do with war work or war preparations ; and, finally, the larger but rather indefinite body of those whose participation would depend on the circumstances of the war or its preparation—whether in their opinion it was intended or likely to further or hinder the general cause of peace.   It is becoming increasingly clear that the nations are faced with the alternatives of developing purely nationalist and ultimately fascist policies supported by increasingly burdensome armaments or joining together to enforce peace by collective action.   Both will require the use or at least the preparation of military measures, but many scientists who are not prepared willingly to support the first alternative will give their services freely to the second. The resolutions adopted at the Congress, given in the Appendix, did not go as far as this, but expressed the points common to pacifist and non-pacifist scientists. They did not call on all scientists to refuse to have anything to do with war preparations, but only to support those who did so against victimization. The most positive function, however, was that of research and propaganda. Research needed to be carried out as to the causes of war and the precise part science had to play in it, while propaganda explaining the results of such research needed to be carried on among scientists and the public at large. Since the Congress, work has gone on along these lines in various countries. In England a national committee has been formed, and active local groups exist in London, Cambridge, Oxford, and Manchester. It must be admitted, however, that in the face of the steadily worsening war situation these efforts seem pitiably feeble. The scientists are, in fact, for reasons which will be discussed later, unlikely as things stand to be able to effect much by themselves in the cause of peace. It is true that they occupy a critically important position, but they are most unlikely to make use of it. They are too isolated and too much under the influence of the social forces surrounding them. Before any effective stand of scientists against war can be made it will be necessary to develop a far greater understanding than exists at present between scientists and the society in which they live. War cannot effectively be combated unless its social and economic nature is fully understood, and scientists are a long way yet from this understanding. On the other side, unless citizens and their elected bodies come to understand much more clearly the function that science actually performs in peace and war, and the one it could play if properly organized, it will be impossible to separate the constructive and the destructive aspects of science.

(1) Both Agricola and Biringuccio, the leading experts on mining and metallurgy in the early sixteenth century, pay great attention to the military value of the products.

(2) Thus we find in his collected letters, Vol. I, a letter to the Doge, Leonardo Donato, dated 24th August 1609, and a further comment in a letter to his friend, Benedetto Landucci, on 29th August 1609 :

To Leonardo Donato. " I have made a telescope, a thing for every maritime and terrestrial affair and an undertaking of inestimable worth. One is able to discover enemy sails and fleets at a greater distance than customary, so that we can discover him (the enemy) two hours or more before he discovers us, and by distinguishing the number and quality of the vessels judge of his force whether to set out to chase him, or to fight, or to run away. . . . Also on land can one look into the squares, buildings and defences of the enemy from some distant vantage point and even in open country see and distinguish particularly to our great advantage all his movements and preparations. There are besides many other uses, clearly remarked by any person with judgment. And so, considering it worthy of being received by your Serenity and esteemed as useful, I have determined to present it to you and leave to you the decision about this discovery—ordering and providing according to what seems opportune to your prudence, whether or not it be manufactured."

To Benedetto Landucci. " Perceiving of what great utility such an instrument would prove in naval and military operations, and seeing that his serenity greatly desired to possess it, I resolved four days ago to go to the palace and present it to the Doge as a free gift."

As a result he was given a stipend of 1000 ducats and professorship for life.

Professor Hogben in *Science for the Citizen* has confused this story, which he attributes to me, with the other I told him at the same time of Galileo's offer of the method of determining longitude by Jupiter's satellites, which he developed later and offered in the first place, in 1616, to the King of Spain in a letter containing the following passage :

" Briefly, this is a great and illustrious undertaking, because it concerns a very noble subject regarding the perfect description of the art of navigation. And the means by which it proceeds are admirable—employing the movements of aspects of stars observed through an instrument which by so much perfects the most noble of our senses. In this matter I have done as much as God has permitted me. The rest is not my undertaking, for I have neither ports nor islands, nor provinces nor realms, nor even ships to go visiting there. It is the enterprise for a great monarch, one gifted with a truly royal spirit, who wants, by favouring it, to add to the immortality of his name and make it seen written for all future centuries on all the pictures of the seas and land. No other crown in the world to-day is more fit for that than Spain." (13th November 1616, Letter 1,235.)

His terms being unacceptable—he demanded a grandeeship and a very large sum of money— towards the end of his life he offered the same invention to the States General in Holland in a letter—equally unavailing—which contrasts somewhat amusingly with the former in its appeal to democratic sentiment.

June 1637. To Realio, Amsterdam.

" I have chosen to present it to these illustrious gentlemen, rather than to some absolute prince, because when the prince alone be not capable of understanding this machine, as almost always happens, having to rely on the advice of others, very often not very intelligent, that sentiment, which very seldom is absent from human minds, that is, not willingly to see another exalted above oneself, causes the ill-advised prince to despise the offer, and the offerer, instead of rewards and thanks, gets from it only trouble and contempt. But in a republic, when the deliberations depend on the opinion of many, a small number and even a single one of the powerful rulers, moderately knowledgeable about the proposed matter, may give the others courage to lend their consent and concur in embracing the undertaking. (Vol. 14.)

(3) See Crowther, *Science and Life*, p. 44.

(4) It was rather the pressure of the scientists themselves than any demand for their services from the military authorities that led to their utilization in the War, as the following quotation from an editorial in *Nature* shows :

" The publication of the total number of casualties during the last ten months ought to convince the nation that this war is one in which we cannot afford to give odds ; and that all the force of scientific ingenuity and scientific organization must be concentrated upon the military and naval operations. There are hundreds of men of science in the country whose energies and expert knowledge are not being effectively used. We should possess a scientific corps, with men investigating at the Front as well as at home, instead of one or two committees advising officials as to possible means of offence or defence. When a man of science of such distinguished eminence as Professor J. A. Fleming can say, as he does in *The Times* of June 15, that after ten months of scientific warfare he has never been asked to co-operate in any experimental work or place any of his expert knowledge at the disposal of the forces of the Crown, though he is anxious to give such assistance, it is evident that the people in authority cannot understand the value of the scientific forces which it cheerfully neglects. Not a day passes but we are asked by men of science how they can devote their knowledge to national needs ; and there is no ready answer. The organization of the scientific intellect of the country is essential, yet almost nothing has yet been done towards its accomplishment.

It seems necessary, in considering how national needs may be met, to separate the invention of new methods of offence or defence from an increase in the supply of high explosive shell which has loomed so large in the newspapers. The novelty of the conditions and the unconventionality of the methods employed in this war carry the first problem outside the grooves in which naval and military engineers have hitherto worked ; and the united efforts of civilians and Service men will be required for its solution. The necessity has arisen for surveying the whole scientific field to discover methods of destruction which we may use ourselves or from which our men look to us for protection. It is not enough that the Government should call in a scientific expert to advise in respect of what has occurred ; they must be ready to meet it when it does occur."—*Nature*, Vol. 95, p. 419 (1915).

(5) Thus in Crowther's article in *The Frustration of Science* we find :
" Do the considerable technical advances made during the War have a reasonable relation to the increase in the cost of aviation ? In 1914 the fastest recorded speed was 126·5 m.p.h. In 1920 it was 188 m.p.h. In 1914 the longest recorded time an aeroplane had stayed in the air was 24 hours 12 minutes. In 1920 the longest recorded time was 24 hours 19 minutes. In 1914 the highest recorded flight was 25,756 feet ; in 1920 it was 33,113 feet. The longest straight flight had grown from 646 miles to 1940 miles. Can an improvement of 61·5 m.p.h. in speed, of 7 minutes in duration, of 7357 feet in height, and 1294 miles in straight distance be regarded as adequate to a world expenditure of £1,000,000,000 ? " (p. 34).

(6) See correspondence in *Nature* on the subject of the Union of Democratic Control's pamphlet, "Patriotism Ltd.," *Nature*, Vol. 133, February and April 1934.

(7) The net profits of Vickers rose between 1932 and 1937 from £529,038 to £1,351,056, while the value of their shares rose from 6s. 1½d. in 1933 to 32s. 9d. in 1937.

(8) Even as far back as 1935 it could be said :
" The aviation industry has now become an armament industry and little else, most of the 234 machines and the 40 engines exported in 1933 were destined for military service. Now under our new programme the military function becomes overwhelmingly the chief one. More new military aeroplanes are actually to be produced this year (1500) than the whole of the civil fleet at present in existence—1200 aeroplanes including sports and pleasure craft."—*Manchester Guardian*, 24th May 1935.

(9) Thus in Cambridge in 1935 Sir John Siddeley, a notable aeroplane manufacturer, gave £10,000 for assistance in aeronautical research. This caused some controversy, because at the time it was felt, though the authorities denied it, that it was a contribution to war research in the university.

(10) " The manufacture of chemical warfare agents demands the existence of a heavy industry, which is more important for this purpose than the fine chemical industries. These heavy chemicals are such substances as sulphuric, nitric and hydrochloric acids, liquid chlorine bleaching powder, caustic soda and soda ash.
The details of manufacture of these materials are given elsewhere in this paper, but it should be stated here that the primary raw materials are : coal, limestone, salt, sulphur or sulphur compounds : given these and the necessary agricultural resources to yield alcohol, not only the important marketable chemicals can be produced (both organic and inorganic) but also most of the important war gases. The only additions to this list to make it complete for war gas manufacture are white arsenic and bromine."
See evidence given by the Union of Democratic Control before the Royal Commission for the Private Manufacture of and Trading in Arms. Minutes of the Evidence, 7 and 8, Appendix, p. 182.

(11) Thus in Britain hydrogenation plant for coal was set up in 1927 at a cost of £3,000,000 after years of experimentation, but it could only operate with the help of a large Government subsidy. Synthetic rubber has been successfully produced in the Soviet Union, U.S.A., and Germany.

(12) The overproduction of nitric acid in peace has resulted in the conversion of the Tennessee Valley Authority Muscle Shoals plant from the production of nitrates to that of phosphates. It could, however, easily be reconverted to nitrate production in times of war.

(13) These difficulties are well illustrated in the questioning of the I.C.I. representatives in the minutes of the Royal Commission for the Private Manufacture of and Trading in Arms, paragraphs 2712-2756.

(14) Sir Daniel Hall states in *The Frustration of Science*, pp. 25, 26 :
". . . all the evidence points to the greater economic efficiency of sugar production from the sugar cane in tropical and semi-tropical countries, as compared with beet in temperate latitudes. Yet by complicated fiscal arrangements beet growing is being maintained and expanded in European countries, and even Great Britain at immense expense is endeavouring to establish this alien industry, which on the existing evidence has no economic future."

(15) How wide the net of war research is thrown is revealed in a speech of Mr. Geoffrey Lloyd on 16th November 1937, objecting to unofficial scientific criticism of air-raid defence plans :
" I want to emphasize that the Government do not merely depend on their own technical advisers in this matter (defence against poison gas), highly competent though those technical advisers are, because I think hon. Members with knowledge of this subject will agree that the Chemical Defence Research Department of the Committee of Imperial Defence at the end of the War was regarded as the most efficient department of that kind in the whole

world ; but, in addition to these experts, the Government have the advice of upwards of 100 distinguished outside scientists and technical chemists ; in fact, I think it is true to say that the leading scientists of the country in this field are members of the Chemical Defence Committee."

(16) The detailed expenditure for the different services is shown in Appendix IV. There an attempt has been made to separate from the gross total, £2,800,000, attributed to research in the estimates, the part that represents the work of scientists. This amounts to no less than £1,535,500. Only a small fraction of this work is a contribution to scientific knowledge. The transfer to civil research of this sum and of the work of the 842 scientists engaged, would almost double the existing potential of science. This is a measure of what war costs science in peace time.

(17) " One of the most serious abuses of private manufacture arises from the association of Government officials and the arms industry. This association of Government servants with armaments firms, both because the Government is the only home market and because licences are required for the export market, is inherent in the system.

The knowledge possessed by Government officials is plainly of great use to the arms industry, and it is a well-known fact that the officials in the fighting services and in other administrative departments not infrequently pass on retirement or before into the service of these firms " (p. 198). Statement of evidence submitted by Union of Democratic Control.

" I do suggest that the system whereby those who are responsible for contracts or for engineering design or whatever it may be, should subsequently and habitually go over to the armament firms, is a very undesirable system. . . .

Any system which allows a man to be placed in a position where his duty and his interests may conflict is a bad system, and for that reason we call your attention to this state of affairs, and we say it is very undesirable that it should continue to exist, and we say that in certain cases it has given rise to trouble " (p. 140). Sir William Jowitt.

Extract from Minutes of the Evidence, Nos. 7 and 8, taken before the Royal Commission on the Private Manufacture of and Trading in Arms, Wednesday, 17th July 1935.

(18) Even when they do not bomb them on purpose they may destroy them just as easily by mistake, as the tragedy of Shanghai has shown.

(19) " We must have, in the first place, an Air Force strong enough to maintain the initiative in air fighting ; secondly, anti-aircraft guns, supported by searchlights and the other methods of modern detection, far more numerous and far more accurate than any we possessed in the War ; and, thirdly, on the ground, a system of air-raid precautions that will achieve two objectives : that will, in the first place, ensure the country against panic and, in the second place, will ensure that the services of the country, without which a civilized community cannot exist, will continue to be maintained. An Air Force that is deficient in either of these two fields is in a position of direct inferiority to an Air Force that is supported in these two fields. An Air Force may have the same number of first-line machines as that of a hostile Power, but if it is not supported by an effective system of anti-aircraft guns and searchlights and an organization on the ground, it will have a greater difficulty in preventing a panic and a rupture in the national life than that Air Force which is not in a position of this inferiority.

Further than that, it will be impeded at every turn in carrying out its tactics and its strategy. Inevitably, if there is no effective ground organization, when an air attack takes place there will be such an outcry from the various centres of population for local defence that the Air Force will be tied down to the local defence of this or that centre of industry or population. How well I remember, when I was at the Air Ministry, Lord Trenchard, the pioneer of air strategy, saying to me over and over again, ' The Air Force that is tied down to local defence will not be able to maintain its initiative and strategy. It is an Air Force that has lost the air war.' I claim that an Air Force that is not supported by this ground organization will almost inevitably be tied down to local defence, and will find itself in a position of great inferiority to an Air Force supported from the ground. It is essential, therefore, that we now organize a comprehensive plan, as complete as can reasonably be effected, of ground organization, and, by organizing it, we shall be able to go far to guarantee the country against panic and the stoppage of national life, and we shall be able to enable the Fighting Services to sustain their proper tactics and strategy."

(Sir Samuel Hoare, 15th November 1937. House of Commons.)

(20) The conclusions of the group of Cambridge scientists on this question are set out in *Protection of the Public from Aerial Attack* (Gollancz, 1937) and more recently in *Air Raid Protection: The Facts* (Fact, No. 13, 1938), and J. B. S. Haldane, *A.R.P.* (Gollancz, 1938).

CHAPTER VIII

INTERNATIONAL SCIENCE

Science and Culture in the Past

The internationalism of science is one of its most specific characteristics. Science has been from the start international in the sense that men of scientific temper even in most primitive times were willing to learn from others in different tribes or races. The wide diffusion of cultures of all stages shows how effective was this mechanism of culture contact. In later times, when natural barriers separated civilizations or when religious or national animosities divided the civilized world into hostile camps, the scientist vied with the trader in breaking down these barriers. The history of the main stream of modern science, transmitted as it was from Babylonian to Greek, from Greek to Arab, and from Arab to Frank, shows how effective this process has been. The Jesuits in China found that their most ready means to acceptance in the Imperial Court were the astronomy and mathematics which they brought with them. Not until the eighteenth and nineteenth centuries, however, was the full international conception of science consciously realized. The idea that the discoveries of science, whether speculative or useful, were at the disposal of all who could make use of them, and were not to be guarded as private or national secrets, marks the emergence of modern science. It was finely expressed by Réaumur in the passage already quoted (p. 151). The only nationalism shown then was the desire of each court to acquire for the ornament and utility of the country as many famous scientists as it could, irrespective of their nationality. Science in Germany and Russia appeared in the eighteenth century as grafts of science from France and Holland. Intercourse was remarkably free, and took place equally easily in peace and in war.

International Science To-day.—Internationalism in science was maintained and even increased throughout the nineteenth century, but the present century has marked a definite retrogression. Science, while still remaining international, has begun to suffer from the general tendency towards national exclusiveness, and the unity of the scientific world is being seriously threatened. In this chapter an attempt is made to give some picture of this aspect of contemporary science, to describe the divisions of science and its degree of development in different countries. Such description to be adequate would require a book of its own, which could only be written by one who had worked for long periods in many different countries. The author can claim no such experience, and therefore all that will be attempted here is a general and admittedly superficial sketch of how science in other countries appears to an English scientist with an average experience of the scientific centres of Europe but none at all of those outside it. The science of non-European countries is judged only from published work and conversations with visiting scientists. It is not, and it does not claim to be, an adequate description or appreciation of the problems, difficulties, and achievements of science throughout the world.

Subject to these qualifications it is still worth while to make some attempt to discuss scientific developments in the different parts of the contemporary world, if only to correct and implement the descriptions and criticisms of the organization and application of science which here have been drawn almost exclusively from science in Britain. It is necessary to examine how far these conclusions have more than limited application, how far the problems raised there are problems for British science or for science at large. The main character of the answer cannot be seriously questioned. Science in Britain is typical in many ways of advancing science in a large industrial country. The history of science shows that its growth follows, in the main, the general directions of economic development, and that the degree and scale in which science is pursued is roughly proportional to commercial and industrial activity. The leading industrial countries of the world are also the leading scientific countries. The great division between the two rival economic and political systems—capitalism and socialism—are reflected in the very different relations of science to social and productive enterprise outside and inside the Soviet Union. But apart from this major distinction, there exist national characteristics in scientific work depending not only on economic development but also on more purely historical and traditional factors.

The Problem of Language

One decisive factor has been the dividing up of science into spheres of internal comprehensibility, relatively separated from one another by the barrier of language. To a large extent this question of common language has played its part in a parallel way in the division of science and in the birth of modern nationalities. The full internationalism of science was only realized at the very beginning of the new science in the sixteenth and early seventeenth centuries. Although nationalities and central governments were appearing, the learned world still preserved a very considerable homogeneity. Latin provided an accepted universal language, and little but the difficulties of travel hindered a man born anywhere in Christendom from occupying an important place at any court. Important local schools of science existed, such as those of Padua or Bologna, but they were visited on equal terms by natives of all European countries. Copernicus, Vesalius, and Harvey belong essentially not to their respective countries, but to universal science centred at that time in Italy. In the great period of scientific advance, however, nationalism was beginning to appear. Galileo wrote his major political works not in Latin but in popular Italian, and this contributed notably to his trial and condemnation. Stevinus was breaking definitely with the older tradition by introducing Dutch as the ideal language for science, while Descartes effected the union between science and polite French literature. The English were more conservative. Newton was still writing in Latin though he was almost immediately translated into English. In Germany, which took to science late, the national aspect was stressed from the beginning. Leibnitz gave his enthusiastic support both to the introduction of science into Germany and to the movement for developing the German language, until then only used in theological literature.

Thus by the time science was well started and needed most a good means of common communication, national considerations had destroyed that possibility by virtually abolishing the use of Latin. It was, on the other hand, quite impossible to write science effectively even in all of the European languages, for the great majority of them were too restricted in their scope and had hardly developed a literature of their own. Consequently, there grew up a number of scientific regions transcending national boundaries and centring on those countries which were most prominent in the development of science. These acted as focal points around which gathered new centres of science in the smaller and more backward European countries or ultimately beyond the confines of Europe altogether. In this way the world has come to be divided into a number of scientific regions inside which communication with a common language is relatively easy, but between which there is an increasing tendency towards separation. This separation is, however, still relatively small, as the subject specialization of science cuts across the national barriers. International societies of scientists of the separate sciences are as important as and in some cases more important than national academies of all sciences. Nevertheless, the language barrier is a very serious one. The scientist must spend a great deal of his time in becoming perfect in a number of languages, or he must be prepared to forgo the reading of much original work which will only reach him later, if at all, in translation. This difficulty has suggested at various periods to many minds the necessity for an international scientific language, the possibilities of which will be discussed in a later chapter.

THE SCIENTIFIC WORLD AND ITS DIVISIONS

The linguistic and cultural conditions have resulted in the setting up of circles of scientific intercommunication, necessarily fewer in number than the number of different languages, and basing themselves on the leadership of the great industrialized countries of the world. These circles are not fixed; they vary with the political and economic fortunes of the nations and are at the moment in a state of extreme flux, due, in the last phase, to the emergence of an aggressive national socialism in Germany and its direct reaction upon science. For the purposes of description, however, it is difficult to take these rapid fluctuations into account, and what follows would apply in the main to the division of science in the period 1920 to 1933.

The chief scientific circles of the world are the Anglo-American and the German. After them come the French and the Soviet circles. The Anglo-American circle shows a well-discernible division between the British and American sides, but one much less important than that which separates it from the other circles. It covers not only the British Empire and the United States but also partially Scandinavia, the Netherlands, China, and Japan. The German circle is, or was, far more closely knit than the others. Inside it there was not only an exchange of information but also a very considerable freedom of personal movement, so that professorships could be given indiscriminately inside or outside Germany to any citizen of the nations in the circle. These included not only Germany and Austria but most of Scandinavia, Switzerland, and other central European countries. The French circle, once predominant in science, is now much shrunk in relative importance. It is practically confined to France, Belgium, and to part of Switzerland, Poland, and South America. The Russian or, more accurately, the Soviet circle is a new creation. Before the Revolution Russian science was a small subsidiary of German and French science, now it has definitely set up on its own, and the output of scientific publications in the Soviet Union already greatly surpasses that of France and is rapidly approaching the production of the German circle. It may seem inaccurate to speak of it as a circle, as so far it is confined to the Soviet

Union, but the development inside the Soviet Union has not only been that of Russian science but also the introduction of science to all the other nationalities that now make up the Union. Unfortunately, language difficulties operate most powerfully in the case of Soviet science to prevent communication with other scientific circles. The difficulties of learning Russian add very considerably to the existing political barriers in preventing Soviet science from receiving adequate recognition from outside and enabling it to play its full part in the development of international science. The position of Italian science is somewhat anomalous. In itself it is not important enough to rank with the other circles, but, largely for internal political reasons, it will not join any of the existing ones even to the extent of publishing papers in foreign periodicals or in an Italian periodical in foreign languages, as is the practice in the Soviet Union.

The existence of circles of scientific communication only partially overcomes the difficulties of national science. For the purpose of education and in order to provide intelligible science inside countries with languages different from any of the four leading languages, a national scientific literature has to be kept up. Thus Japan, for instance, besides publishing papers in English or German periodicals and papers in English or German in Japanese periodicals, has an extensive purely Japanese scientific literature almost completely unintelligible to the outside world. This is a practice which is justifiable, though unfortunate, in countries such as Japan or Poland with a large scientific output, but which becomes almost ridiculous in the smaller European countries where far more has to be translated into the native vernacular than can be produced by native scientists.

National Characteristics in Science.—So far we have dealt with international divisions of science which are largely artificial and necessitated by language considerations. More significant are national characters of science and the different relations which exist between science and society in different countries. As has been already said, these intrinsic characters are very complex, but they are nevertheless to a considerable extent analysable into the resultants of a number of distinguishable causes. To attribute them in a mystical way to the soul of the nation or the blood of the race, as is the fashion with Fascist ministers of education, is sheer obscurantism and does not help us at all in understanding the various ways in which these different characters can work together for advancing science as a whole.

We may distinguish in different countries different grades of scientific development. Firstly, there is the science in industrial countries with a long scientific and industrial history, whether world Powers, such as Britain, France, Germany and Italy, or the smaller countries historically of equal intellectual importance, Scandinavia, the Netherlands and Switzerland. Secondly, there is the science of countries recently industrialized on a large scale, such as the United States, Japan, and the Soviet Union. Thirdly, we must notice the development of science in backward and largely peasant states of Europe and Asia. Actually it will be more convenient to omit the Soviet Union from this classification and deal with it separately on account of the completely different relation between science and society which exists in capitalist and socialist economies.

Science in the Older Industrial Countries

The description of the organization of science in Britain is typical for that of industrial countries of long standing. There science and industry have grown up more or less unconsciously together, and the result is an extremely complex network of relations without any appearance of an ordered plan. It compensates for its inefficiency in formal organization by its traditions and by the presence of personal and class relations between scientific, industrial, and Government circles. Science in these countries benefits from tradition to the extent that certain standards of performance are almost instinctively adhered to, thereby avoiding what is always a danger to the development of science, too great self-assertion and self-advertisement of individual scientists, which easily pass into charlatanry. On the other hand, the traditional attitude towards science has a very sterilizing effect. Age and experience are at a premium as against enthusiasm and enterprise. The control of science in all these countries is in the hands of a relatively small number of older scientists, out of touch with modern developments. Nevertheless it must be said that the accumulated valuable traditions, the existence of schools in the separate sciences, and the relative freedom from either economic or political pressure that individual scientists enjoy, or rather used to enjoy in the case of Germany, still result in the production in these countries of the great majority of new and valuable fundamental scientific discoveries. They are still the focal points of scientific advance, and it is to their laboratories that scientists of other less developed countries come when they wish to set up their own schools. Within this first group each national science has its own specific characteristics, depending on a great complex of historical, social, and academic considerations. These differences are necessarily extremely difficult to define, but they have played a very important part in the development of science, each characteristic tradition of science having its own valuable contribution to make to the general advance.

English Science.—The character of English science is one which can be seen to have persisted ever since the seventeenth century. It is predominantly, as contrasted with German or French science, practical and analogical. In England, more than in any other country, science is felt rather than thought. Imagination is concrete and visual. Faraday thinks in terms of tubes of force which are imagined to behave very much as if they were made of rubber. Rutherford explores the atom as if it were a kind of coconut shy at a village fair, throws particles at it and looks to see what bits fall out. The great question for the English scientist is "How does it work?" Of the three great theoreticians of English science only Newton was an Englishman, and he was as much a practical experimentalist as a theorist. Maxwell was a Scotsman, and Dirac, most purely theoretical of them all, is French. What has given such enormous success to English science is largely just this practical predilection and robust common sense. Nature, at any rate, up till very recently, generally turned out to operate at least as simply as a human workman, and those who attributed to it mysteries and subtleties merely tangled themselves in their own ingenuity. A defect of the English is their almost complete lack of systematic thinking. Science to them consists of a number of successful raids into the unknown. It presents no coherent picture; theory is looked on suspiciously and speculation not encouraged. These disadvantages are more apparent now than they were in the last century. The greater part of the easy bits of science in which English methods were so successful have already been done, and much of science can only yield to methods of thinking and working which are very different from crude common sense and for which mechanical models are very little help. The great revolution in physics found England, except in the person of Dirac, very much behind other countries, although the fundamental empirical basis of the revolution was largely laid in England. We may, however, owing to the influx of German refugees, be able to graft on to the English stock the capacity for dealing with the more difficult theoretical problems.

The material and organizational character of English science has already been dealt with. It is only recalled here to contrast it with other countries. Actually, relative to its wealth and importance in world affairs, England spends very little on science and makes less use of its potential scientists than do any other of the great Powers The proportion of the population between the ages of 19 and 21 attending universities is less in England than in any other large country in Europe, and far less than that in the United States of

America, as can be seen in the following table. Scotland in this respect shows very much more favourably.

Country.	No. of Students (full time).	Estimated number of young men and women aged 19-21, as nearly as possible at the same time.	Percentage.
England and Wales .	40,465 (1936)	2,100,000	1·9%
Scotland . .	10,064 (1936)	260,000	3·8%
Germany . .	116,154 (1932)	3,000,000	3·9%
,, (see p. 217)	67,082 (1936)	3,000,000	2·2%
France . . .	82,655 (1932)	1,900,000	4·3%
U.S.S.R. . .	524,800 (1936)	10,000,000	5·2%
U.S.A. . . .	989,757 (1932)	6,600,000	15·0%

English science has behind it a great tradition and noble achievements. It is still in full vigour, but there is a danger that unless steps are taken to develop it on an adequate scale for modern conditions it will fall far behind the science of other and new countries.

Science in pre-Nazi Germany.—Before the Nazi seizure of power German science might not unreasonably claim, or at least dispute with English science, the leadership of the world of knowledge. Those permanent characters which gave German science this position have, we at least hope, not been destroyed but merely eclipsed by the present regimentation of science. For adequate comparison with English science we must take the science of pre-Nazi Germany. German science, for all its extent and profundity, was of relatively late growth. Although German technics were already ahead of the rest of Europe in the fifteenth century, Germany was deprived by the religious wars of the cohesion which powerful mercantile and political States like England, Holland, and France enjoyed at the time when science was being born in these countries. German science was accordingly confined to barren theological arguments and fanciful alchemical theorizings. At the beginning of the eighteenth century it could still be claimed that Leibnitz was the whole academy in his own person. The birth of German science we owe to French importations under the vigorous patronage of Frederick the Great. The imprint of that patronage remained in German science and was the source of its strength and weakness. From the beginning it was official in nature, but, while the universities in other countries still in the nineteenth century despised science, the German universities allowed it to develop and provided in that development for many of the methods of organization which have now spread to the whole scientific world. The research school and the research institute, a great deal of laboratory technique, the publication of specialized scientific journals, are all primarily due to German initiative.

The great development of German science in the nineteenth century was due largely to its association with the tradition of German learning and to the great prestige that official recognition gave to the scientist, a recognition that had to be fought for in England and France. At the same time, however, as the advantages of this powerful and systematic development of State science came the disadvantages: firstly, the traditions of patient and somewhat pedantic scholarship, the multiplication of recorded facts and commentaries on them; and secondly, the greater difficulties suffered by men of originality and unorthodox genius such as Koch, Ohm, or Frauenhofer. The greatest advantage of German science occurred only towards the end of the nineteenth century, coincidentally with the delayed onset of the industrial revolution. In England, and to a large extent even in America, the practical business man despised the mere theoretical scientist; in Germany he respected him and made use of him. The great development of the German chemical industry, which is still, in spite of war and depression, the most important in the world, depended upon this close linkage between the industrialists and the new theoretical chemists. The interests of the State were also involved. It was in Germany that the full value of science in war preparation was first realized, and the considerable opposition to it from the military caste did not prevent the German Army of 1914 from being the only one which had any effective scientific backing. Science accordingly had many reasons for official support, which took the form, not so much of large money appropriations, as of the development of an effectively organized teaching system of elementary and advanced science. By 1914 the Germans were in science quantitatively well ahead of the rest of the world; qualitatively they were at least the equals of any other country. It was largely due to this development that Germany held out for so long against the rest of the world. Both the major applications of chemistry that occurred during the period—the Haber process of fixation of nitrogen for explosives, and the chief new weapon of modern war, poison gas—originated from Germany.

It was after the War, when a defeated and starved Germany took her place again in the unstable community of nations, that occurred the most brilliant period in the history of German science. What had been lost on the material side was compensated by the freedom of the new researches and the energy with which they were followed. The War was scarcely over when Einstein's relativity theory received its convincing confirmation, and it is one of the ironies of history that this achievement, which effectively rehabilitated German science from the Allied slanders of the War years, should have been one which was made by a man afterwards hounded out of the country and deprived of his citizenship. But the relativity theory, great as it was, was only part of the revolution in physical thought that culminated in the new quantum mechanics in 1925, an achievement largely due to German science, though England and France both played their parts. If the Weimar Republic is remembered for nothing else, it will be remembered as the Government under which these and many other great scientific developments took place.

Before the depression came to shatter that society, already undermined by the effects of war and unresolved social struggles, Germany was leading the way in organized scientific research. Yet the total sums spent on German science were relatively small. It is estimated that in 1930 (1) 10,000,000 Rm. came directly from the Reich Government and approximately 20,000,000 Rm. from the states Governments for scientific research (exclusive of military research). Taking the mark as then worth twenty to the pound this is equivalent to a total Government contribution of £1,500,000 as against about £1,200,000 in Britain reckoned in the same way. If we allow as a sheer guess that industrial research took between twice and three times as much we have a total of between £4,500,000 and £6,000,000, about the same as that for science in Britain, but the national income being 70,000,000,000 Rm. or £3,500,000,000, the proportion devoted to science lay probably between 0·13 and 0·17 per cent., or roughly half as much again as in England.

Perhaps more important than this state-supported science was the practice, which was beginning in Germany before the depression, of linking science with heavy industry in a way that seemed to rival the place of the universities in its development. The prototype of these links were the Kaiser Wilhelm Gesellschaft institutes in Berlin and elsewhere. These, though founded before the War by an association of business men, showed from the outset a broad grasp of the need of industry for science. They were devoted to fundamental researches and not tied to the narrower industrial ends as has been the tendency with Research Associations in England. Besides this, large chemical and engineering firms were setting up research departments equipped in a way that no university could approach. They were employing in these departments not simply young research workers but professors of international reputation who were expected to devote only part of their time to investigations profitable to the firm and the rest to researches of a fundamental character. To those who did not understand either the political instability of the liberal regime or the economic unsoundness of the system of large capital monopolies, Germany seemed to point the way to the most fruitful developments in the application of science. Yet within two or three years all this was swept away, half the most eminent scientists exiled, degraded or imprisoned, and most of the laboratories occupied with trivial or warlike tasks.

Science in France.—French science has had a glorious history but a very uneven one. Growing up with English and Dutch science in the seventeenth century, it had always a more official and centralized character. This did not in the early days hamper its growth, and it was vigorous enough at the end of the eighteenth century not only to survive the Revolution, though with the loss of Lavoisier, but also to enter as a result of it into its most glorious period. L'École Polytechnique, founded in 1794, was the first teaching institute in applied science. Patronized by Napoleon for its civil as much as its military advantages, it produced such a crop of able men that in the early nineteenth century French science undoubtedly led the world. But this advance was not maintained; compared with that of other countries French science became less and less important, though throwing up men of notable genius. The reason for this seems to lie largely in the bureaucratic narrowness and parsimony of the bourgeois governments, whether royal, imperial, or republican. The achievements of the great French scientists were made in spite of these disadvantages of which they were very conscious. Pasteur and the Curies, for instance, struggled all their lives for adequate support for research. (2) All through the period, however, French science never lost its distinguishing characteristics—the extreme lucidity and beauty of its presentations. It was not thought that was lacking but the material means to make that thought productive. In the first quarter of the twentieth century French science had fallen to the third or fourth place and suffered from a kind of inner discouragement. The War had been a very heavy blow, both in men and resources, and nowhere more than in France was science under the control of the older men.

Nevertheless, in the last few years, a change for the better can be discerned. It began to be realized, first of all by the industrialists, that modern science was a thing that had to be undertaken on a far larger scale, both in men and materials, than had hitherto sufficed; new institutes were founded and the stage was set for a great advance. The economic and political repercussions of the depression had on science in France precisely the opposite effect of that in Germany. Warned by German example and by their own experience of Fascism, the French scientists began to take part in the political movements of the time, but they did not on that account become any less scientists; rather they demanded that science should take its due place in the creation of a free and humane world. The advent to power of the Front Populaire, to which their work had notably contributed, brought into being much more favourable conditions for scientific

development.   A new council of science was created under the charge
of the veteran scientist and democrat Jean Perrin, assisted by Curie
Joliot.   They have in a short time not only increased the funds
available for research but made research itself a profession and not a
mere annex to teaching.   (See Appendix VI.)   But the changes are
far more than administrative.   The scientific workers themselves,
collaborating in their new trade unions, are achieving a consciousness
of their needs and of their function in society.   When we consider
that these changes are taking place at a time when the threat of war
and political upheavals are greater than ever before, it is impossible
not to see in them evidences of a powerful movement of resurgence
in science.

   Science in Holland, Belgium, Switzerland, and Scandinavia.—Some
of the smaller countries of Europe—Switzerland, Belgium, Holland,
and Scandinavia—have a tradition of scientific work which dates from
the great period of the seventeenth century.   Although no one of
them is large enough in itself to be able, in these days, to take a lead
in scientific thought, their relative freedom from the political pre-
occupations that have distorted science in the larger countries has
given them a much more continuous tradition and sustained high
standard.   This, together with the high level of general education
which all of these countries enjoy, has resulted in a type of scientific
work of great value, much greater in proportion to the population
than that of the larger countries.   The scientist in these small
countries is a respected member of society and, if he has an international
reputation, he may rank in importance above national politicians—
a state of affairs impossible in the larger countries.   It would be
difficult to characterize without much deeper knowledge the scientific
work of these countries, dependent as they necessarily are, on account
of their size, more on personalities than in larger countries.   Individual
scientific workers have generally been influenced by one or other of the
larger continental schools and carry the imprint of that school into the
work of their own country.   On the whole, except in Belgium, it is the
influence of the German school which has predominated, but largely
without its official character and its philosophic profundities.   The
finance of Denmark, however, requires special mention.   Here we have
the possibly unique case of a large firm, the Carlsberg Breweries, being
bequeathed *in toto* by its founders, J. C. Jacobsen and Karl Jacobsen,
for the support of scientific research and art.   The annual revenue
of the foundation is substantial.   That devoted to science amounts to
1,310,000 kroner, or £58,527, a large sum for such a small country.

   Science in Austria and Czecho-Slovakia.—Science in the old
Austro-Hungarian Empire cannot be considered as distinct from
German science.   There was always complete interchange of ideas

and personnel between the two countries, and the preponderating influence of the Church had in the later years ceased to be any effective brake on science. Needless to say, science in Austro-Hungary was less well organized or endowed than in Germany. But Austrian science had a brilliance of its own and maintained itself in a small and impoverished country with notable distinction. For five years it remained the last representative of the traditional free German science. Now in its turn it has been crushed as brutally as and even more swiftly than German science. In a few days eighty-eight professors and one hundred and sixty-eight research workers were dismissed, exiled or imprisoned, and Austria lost at one blow nearly all those men of science who had won international fame.

The old tradition continues now only in Czecho-Slovakia, and there it is threatened both by the imminence of war and the internal disruption fostered by the Nazis.

Science in Poland, Hungary, and the Balkans.—Of the eastern European countries only Poland possessed a native scientific culture; in others all that is left are feeble offshoots of German science. As long as they remain agricultural countries tyrannized over by small military governing cliques, science is not likely to develop. Even in Poland, where the pursuit of science was associated with national and revolutionary aspirations, science is now distinctly suspect on political grounds, depressed economically and disturbed internally by anti-Semitic agitations.

Science in Spain and Latin America.—Science in the remaining countries in Europe is in no better state. The present condition of Italian science will be dealt with in discussing the effects of Fascism on science. In spite of its ancient and distinguished tradition and the brilliance of certain individual scientists, it plays but little part in the modern world of science. The situation in Spain is far worse, but holds out a greater promise. Under many centuries of clerical domination, Spain never had the chance of developing science which was given to the other countries in Europe. The Spanish Church judged, and judged correctly, that the increased interest in science was a symptom of liberalism, and successfully held it down through the obscure and unhappy struggles of the nineteenth century, though brilliant individuals like Cajal (3) did manage to break through. During the present century, however, the Church's hold was slackening and, led by a band of heroic pioneers, a definite movement towards the development of science began in Spain. It even achieved, in the last days of the monarchy, some official recognition, as typified in the creation of the University City of Madrid, lately destroyed by the self-appointed saviours of Spanish civilization. Luckily those of the scientists who were not occupied in fighting for their liberty were safely evacuated, and we can be sure that the new spirit of enterprise and hope that has sustained republican Spain through the present struggle will, when it is successful, lead to a great development of Spanish science. (4)

Science in Latin America has, until a comparatively recent date, suffered from the same disabilities as afflicted the mother country. In the colonial days, particularly at the beginning, something was done in natural history and mining, but the interest soon faded out and the revolution and civil wars which followed during most of the nineteenth century were not conducive to the development of science. In the present century, however, under the influence of the U.S.A. and of resurgent liberal thought, a renaissance in science from which much can be hoped is beginning, and already, particularly in Mexico and the Argentine, notable developments have been made in medicine, biology, and archaeology.

SCIENCE IN THE UNITED STATES

It would be an impertinence for anyone who has not lived and worked in the United States to attempt to give any critical appreciation of the organization and effectiveness of science there. The remarks which follow are merely intended to indicate the place which America seems to occupy in the world of science. The rebirth of active physical science in the late eighteenth century, when the great seventeenth-century advance had worn itself out, was due to one of the greatest of Americans, Benjamin Franklin, and the influence of his inspiration is seen in the practical and utilitarian character of that development. Franklin was the inspirer not only of the English scientific societies of the eighteenth century but also of the French. The early Americans had, however, more business to attend to than science, and it is not surprising that in the early nineteenth century, while they were creating their states and spreading their frontiers towards the West, American science did not appear in the forefront of world science. (5) The American contribution was, on the other hand, very notable in relation to the application of science. The world owes most of its fundamental mechanical devices, to instance only the sewing-machine, the reaper, and the typewriter, to American enterprise. The Americans possessed the English empirical character with far more scope and more incentive for practical activity. The inventiveness of the Americans is no doubt closely connected with their great natural resources, coupled with shortage of labour. In the latter half of the century, however, when the result of the enterprise of the pioneers began to show itself in the increased wealth and in the development of large-scale industry, a corresponding change took place in American science. This was partly aided by two factors: the widespread system of American education, including the foundation of enormous free universities (6), and the effect of the immigration of some of the most energetic liberal minds from nearly every European country. The growth of American science necessarily followed to some degree that of American scholarship. There was, during the last century, a tendency to copy European models, particularly German models. Before a distinct American school had sprung up, science in the U.S. represented an amalgam of English and German practice and theory. America had distinguished scientists, particularly the great Willard Gibbs, but it is only in the present century that she is beginning to found schools of science. (7)

The opportunity for a specific American contribution came with the change, affecting nearly all aspects of science, towards larger and larger working units and the increasing need for expensive apparatus. A certain proportion of the wealth, which in the process of building up the industry of the States had accumulated into a very few hands, flowed back to science, so that all through the present century there can be no doubt but that American science has been by far the best endowed in the world. At the same time there was no shortage of able workers capable of making use of these facilities. In astronomy, particularly, where only the largest and most expensive telescopes are capable of discovering really new aspects of space, America soon gained supremacy. This success has been followed up in many branches of physics, in medicine, cytology, genetics and animal behaviour. At the same time the big new industrial firms were engaging in technical research, only to be paralleled in Germany, and employing distinguished scientists who were also doing fundamental work. The idea of industrial research may indeed be said to have originated in America with Edison's Menlo Park laboratory. This was still, however, essentially applied research; the laboratory of the General Electric Company at Schenectady may well claim to be a pioneer of the fundamental research laboratory in industry.

As might be expected, however, from the particularly individualist features of American development, the state of science there showed many of the signs of uncoordination that were observable on a similar scale in Britain. Some attempt at reform has been made by the creation of a National Research Council which initiates and to a certain extent directs positive co-ordinated projects of research in definite fields. But it controls only a small fraction of the sums available for research and has otherwise a merely advisory capacity. Another important co-ordinating body is the American Association for the Advancement of Science, the counterpart of the British Association. It has a somewhat greater importance as the annual

meetings of many leading scientific societies are held together under
its auspices. For the finance and effective direction of science, far
more important are the big research foundations such as the Rockefeller, Carnegie, or the Guggenheim. The functioning of these
foundations as seen from abroad would seem in some ways a model of
how to spend money wisely on science. Nevertheless, they are liable
to criticism on certain grounds. In the first place, the foundations,
being purely benevolent institutes, can have no claims made on them,
merely requests, and this puts a premium on a plausible seeker for
research grants and penalizes the man or institute who has less
abilities in the art of the courtier. There is a great tendency to
spend on the more advertised or more advertisable parts of science
and thus to create quite a false set of values. Finally, the awards are
arbitrary and insecure. Neither researches nor men can count on
support for much longer than five years, and five years is a very
short time in the development of scientific ideas. The chief objection,
however, is that, although many of the administrative boards are
controlled by scientists, the distribution of the money is not determined
in any way by an organized consensus of scientific opinion. There
can be no doubt but that, great as are the benefits that have come
from the grants of these bodies, the waste of money has been greater
than in almost any other form of scientific expenditure.

The expenditure on science in the United States is colossal. If
we take the figure quoted above (p. 65), and it cannot be far wrong,
the annual expenditure on academic, governmental, and industrial
research is $300,000,000 or £60,000,000. This represents ten times
what is spent in Britain and probably more than is being spent in the
rest of the world outside the Soviet Union. But it is quite clear that
here the law of diminishing returns is operating. However great
the contribution of American science may be, it can scarcely claim to
be contributing to the advance of science ten times as much as English
or German science. Part of this difference may lie in the more lavish
scale of remuneration and, particularly, of apparatus and buildings.
But some must be put to the account of American science itself. The
position of the scientist cannot fail to be influenced by the existing
values outside science, particularly those of the struggle for success and
the importance of publicity. Although the better of the American
scientists are free from these influences, it is quite clear, from the
quality of the bulk of the work published in America, that they are
not without an effect. American publications are if anything slightly
more bulky than corresponding German ones, but, whereas in Germany one feels that it is just thoroughness for thoroughness' sake,
in America there is a suspicion that the position of a man may depend
on the bulk of his published work. The advertisement side of research,

however, is characteristically American and is by no means uniformly bad for science. While British firms consider it a distinguishing mark that they follow traditional methods and even go to the extent of concealing the fact that they do any research work at all, in America research has an advertisement value both to the firm and to the university which undertakes it. This enables a good deal of purely scientific work, whose direct utility value would be small, to be done. On the other hand, it places an undoubted emphasis on branches of science which have high publicity value, such as astronomy, the interior of the atom, the nature of life, or the curing of the more dreaded diseases, to the detriment of other and equally important branches of science. Taken in all, we can say that American science represents probably the best that can be done for science in a social system based on a mixture of private enterprise and monopoly. It can achieve great things, but it will never, as long as this system is in force, be able to achieve a success proportional to the resources available either in men or materials.

SCIENCE IN THE EAST

Until the end of the nineteenth century the pursuit of science was almost entirely confined to Western Europeans either in their American colonies or at home. The older civilizations of the East had, it is true, learned men, but they followed the established traditions which were for the most part on a level, and largely identical, with those held in Europe at the beginning of the Renaissance. Here science was suddenly and abruptly introduced along with other trappings of the more potent industrial civilization. The development of science in non-European countries differed greatly according to the degree of political and economic control held by the imperial Powers. The two extremes might be seen in India and Japan. In India there had been a long and unbroken, though lately decadent, tradition of science. The Indian mathematicians had made notable contributions to the general development of mathematics. With English rule new ideas and new methods of education were introduced, but they were introduced in opposition to the older learning, and resulted at first in a more definite split between traditional and foreign knowledge. Moreover, the education introduced from Britain was far more classical and literary than scientific in character.

Science in India.—Effectively science in India only began in the twentieth century. We can say with certainty that there are latent in India great possibilities for scientific development; the mathematics of Ramanujan and the physics of Bose and Raman have already shown that Indian scientists can reach the first ranks. Nevertheless, the difficulties under which Indian science suffers will preclude, as long as they last, any large-scale development, or, more particularly, any serious influence of science on Indian culture. It is inevitable that in science as in other aspects of life the Indians should feel the need for national self-assertion, but this attitude is always an uneasy one. The Indian scientist must, in the first place, learn his science through English channels and be subjected to the patronizing and insulting habits of the English to their subject races. The reaction to this breeds a mixture of submissiveness and arrogance that between them inevitably affect the quality of the scientific work. Indian science is noted at the same time for the originality of many of its conceptions and experimental processes, and for extreme unreliability and lack of critical faculty in carrying out the work itself.

Needless to say, Indian science, like everything in India except the English Civil Service and the Army, is starved of funds. The total annual sum available for scientific research in India is probably not more than £250,000, which would be equivalent to $\frac{1}{50}$ of a penny per head of population, or 0·015 per cent. of the miserable national income of £1,700,000,000. Yet there is hardly any country in the world that needs the application of science more than India. In order to release the enormous potentialities for scientific development in the Indian people, it would be necessary to transform them into a self-reliant and free community. Probably the best workers for Indian science to-day are not the scientists but the political agitators who are struggling towards this end.

Science in Japan.—The situation of science in Japan provides a very remarkable contrast. The Japanese were quick enough to take over the military advances of the Western Powers together with the mechanical technique sufficient to support them, and thus have been able to beat Europe at its own game of aggression and robbery. It was plain to the exquisitely literal and rational Japanese minds that it was through science that the Westerners had obtained these extremely valuable powers, and therefore Japan must have science; but the attempt to produce science by mere imitation has only had a limited success. It is true that industrial and Government laboratories and institutes in Japan are probably larger, better financed and better organized in relation to the wealth of the community than in any other part of the world, but the value of the work coming from these institutes is more open to doubt. True, Japan has already produced a number of notable figures in science such, for instance, as Noguchi, but the great bulk of Japanese work seems to suffer in an exaggerated way from the defects of both German and American science. It is over-elaborate, pedantic, and without imagination, and unfortunately, in many cases, it is also uncritical and inaccurate. It is unfair to blame the Japanese scientists for this. In a country where dangerous thoughts are being persecuted with increasing severity, originality in science will hardly be at a premium. Where science is used more openly and cynically even than in Europe for purposes of war research and for trying to find the absolute minimum of food on which factory workers can exist, it is unlikely to attract the best minds to do the best work. Of recent years there has been a notable though underground reaction against this official and military science. The younger Japanese scientists are beginning to be aware of the social implications of their work, and are thinking for themselves outside the orbit of the imperial and military myth of Shinto, or of its more violent modern forms such as Kodo. If, in the revolutions that threaten East as much as West, the Japanese people should ever acquire any peace or freedom we may expect here also a great improvement in the quality of scientific work.

Science in China.—The last few years have witnessed the beginning of an independent development of science in China. Throughout most of recorded history China has been one of the three or four great centres of civilization, and for the greater part of this time the one which possessed the highest political and technical developments. It would be interesting to inquire how it was, in fact, that the appearance of modern science and the technical revolution that followed it did not occur in China rather than in the West. Probably it was the very satisfactory equilibrium of agricultural life with a classically educated governing class, an ample supply of necessities and luxuries and of the labour necessary to produce them, that removed from China the need for developing technical improvements beyond a certain point. However that may be, once the West had got ahead technically it was practically impossible for Chinese culture to produce a science of its own without complete reorganization, and, indeed, the first effect of Western contact was to reinforce, as a kind of defensive measure, the conservatism of Chinese culture. The tragic story of Western interference in China throughout the nineteenth century with its trade wars, struggle for concessions, and destruction of ordered government, prevented the development of science in China as effectively, though in quite a different way, as it prevented that of India.

The Chinese were never in a position of sufficient independence to be able, if they had wished to do so, to import Western technique and Western science wholesale as did the Japanese. Only since 1925, with the rise of the Kuo Min Tang, has there been any movement for national science in China outside the missionary colleges. In many ways the new Chinese science is an offshoot of American science, owing to the enlightened attitude of the U.S.A.

Government in relation to the Boxer indemnity. So far little of great importance or originality has been produced, but a reason for hope lies in the extremely high quality of traditional Chinese workmanship. At the moment the devastating war, in which the aggressor aims particularly at centres of science and learning (8), has diverted the best minds to other tasks, but from what has been done it is possible to see that Chinese cultural traditions, suitably modified, give an extraordinarily good basis for scientific work. Indeed, with the care, steadiness, and sense of balance shown in all other forms of Chinese culture, there is reason to believe that China may have at least as great a contribution to make to the development of science as the West, if not a greater.

Science in Islamic Countries.—There are also signs of a renaissance of science in the Islamic world. For the first six centuries Islam was the chief agent in spreading and developing Greek science. It had still very considerable possibilities when its cultural advance was checked by the Mongol and Turkish invasions. As in China, the immediate effect of the impact of Western science was an increased conservatism, which still holds in the majority of independent or semi-independent Moslem states. Recently, however, in Egypt, Syria, Turkey and in Central Asia under the Soviet regime there are definite signs of change. In Turkey science is being pushed with the same ruthless spirit of improvement as the other more spectacular reforms of the Ghazi. Old Turkish universities have been improved and new ones founded, and Turkey ranked after Britain and the U.S.A. as the chief haven of refuge of German-Jewish scholars, though in the recent wave of nationalism most of these have been driven out again. It is too early to say anything of the results of this policy, but if it is successful it is bound to have very great repercussions on the whole of the Moslem world. Once it can be shown to be compatible with, or better still to assist, national liberation, the conservative forces of theology will no longer be able to resist its advance.

SCIENCE AND FASCISM

Any survey of the situation of science in the countries hitherto mentioned would show a degree of uniformity far exceeding the differences among the modes of organization. Rich countries have much science, poor ones little. But science itself appears as a common cultural form marking the general acceptance of what was Western civilization and has now become world civilization. We have seen everywhere science developing with the development of industry and becoming more and more closely linked with monopoly capitalism and national economic systems. So far, however, this has happened without any drastic interference with the internal growth of science or any attack on its fundamental principles of free inquiry and publication. But this state of affairs is no longer universal. With the advent of Fascism a direct attack has been launched on these principles and one which, if it is permitted to spread, threatens the progress and even the very existence of science.

Fascism is essentially an attempt to maintain an unstable and discredited system of private or monopoly production by a combination of physical force and mystical demagogy. Science is involved in both these aspects. The ideal of Fascism is the nation, or, better still, the race and the empire, a convenient way of including the inhabitants of still unconquered territories. The national economy, the national spirit, require to be particularly fostered. Science is valued in so far as it does this, and distorted or destroyed if it appears to weaken it. In this aspect Fascism simply drives to their logical conclusion the tendencies of economic and intellectual nationalism, already observable in all capitalist countries. The first duty of the scientist ceases to be the discovery of truth or the well-being of mankind and becomes the service of his nation in peace and war. And peace becomes more and more simply a preparation for war.

Science in Fascist Italy.—Fascism first arose in Italy, but in a less thorough way than it did subsequently in Germany. Science here was to be used rather than transformed. The Italian scientist is tolerated or even assisted in the national interest, and a certain material advancement of science is possible through the setting up of technical institutes designed primarily for the purpose of national economy with a very definite eye to making the country independent of foreign supplies in times of war. There has, however, been relatively little direct interference with the content of scientific thought, at least outside the scope of the human sciences. Naturally, history has been distorted, and the tendency to stress the humanitarian rather than the military side of it reversed. In sociology and economics the tendency has been merely conservative. All progressive thought has been suppressed in the interests of both Church and State, but nothing palpably ridiculous has been put in its place as has been done in Germany. The main effect on the scientists has been their isolation from the world of science. Apart from a number of exceedingly well-organized international congresses aimed at impressing on the outer world the care which Mussolini takes for the advancement of science, the Italian scientists have been largely cut off from their fellow scientists abroad, partly on account of political unreliability and partly from lack of means to travel. Another difficulty is the language barrier. To maintain national prestige Italian science must be published in Italian; but this has already ceased to be a well-known language, so the proviso effectively prevents full use being made of the one remaining channel of communication. (9) The result has been that Italian science has remained at the relatively low level that it occupied in the early part of the century, and has in no way tended to recapture the distinction of its old tradition. In suppressing liberalism, Fascism has succeeded in crushing the spirit of science which has always in Italy been closely related to it.

Nazi Science.—The state of Italian science illustrates merely the first step of a destructive process which can be seen in full blast in Germany to-day. The destruction of science in Germany, if it can be maintained for many more years, may be one of the major tragedies in the development of civilization, for German science, unlike that of Italy, occupied a key position. It was not so much that German scientists were in the front rank of discovery, but that Germany had taken on the task of the systematization and codification of all science, so that the record of the progress of human knowledge was largely in German hands. What has been done cannot be lost, but it will not be easy to improvise in other countries the mechanism of a comprehensive and thorough record of scientific advance. Even more than this perhaps is the destruction of the spirit of German science, the appreciation of a patient and exact determination of the structure of the world, the belief in the intrinsic value of pure scientific truth.

Germany, unlike Italy, was a great industrial country, qualitatively the most important in the world. Its population had an intellectual tradition and a taste for liberty without having had much exercise in the use of it. The economic and political crisis which brought about the advent of Fascism was correspondingly far deeper than that which occurred in Italy, and the type of Fascism that appeared there was necessarily of a far more violent and reactionary character. The control of material factors alone could not be sufficient for the leaders of German Fascism; they must, in order to gain and retain power, control and modify ideas as well. Conquest had to be made not only of the German state but also of the German soul. The whole of the claims on which the Nazis' seizure of power were based were so palpably irrational and incapable of standing scientific analysis that if they were to be maintained it could only be by enthroning irrationality over reason and reducing scientific criticism to impotence. Yet this negative side was not enough; simply to deny palpable truths would have left a mental vacuum; it was necessary to assert, and assert with a hitherto unachieved violence, palpable untruths. Unfortunately, there was to be found, in Germany particularly, a whole set of beliefs that could be substituted for those of reason and science.

There had always been a strong undercurrent of mystical irrationality in German thought. It is indeed true that rationalism itself was a liberal importation from France, carried out, ironically enough, by that arch-hero of the Nazis, Frederick the Great. From the German mystics to the philosophers of the eighteenth and nineteenth centuries, the tendency to confuse the obscure with the profound had never disappeared, but it had generally been inspired by a combination of benevolence and docility, especially in relation to the State. This mode of thinking, or rather refusing to think, was seized on by the Nazis and turned in the direction of glorifying the twin ideas of race and war. The Germans were to be compensated for their miserable enslavement to their own monopolists, and by the subjection of those monopolists to their rivals in other countries, by the idea that they were inherently superior and were destined to rule the world if they would submit in the interval to the necessary discipline, preparation, and struggle.

In effect what has been done is to retain the material and economic forms of capitalism, indeed to enforce them by destroying trade unions and by making the employer the Führer of his works, while rejecting contemptuously the ideals that have been used to justify their existence. To support capitalism they have had to throw out the liberal theory which was once its justification. They are obliged to go even further and repudiate openly two ideals which have existed in the world since the appearance of the great empires first made them conceivable: the brotherhood of man and the importance of the individual. To preserve the gains of greed and the lust for power of a few, they have reversed the values on which not only liberal but Christian society is ostensibly founded. (10) The ideals of blood and soil which take their place have no scientific backing; it is therefore necessary that science should be distorted to give them one. Now it must be admitted that what has passed for scientific truth has been and is to-day largely composed of the irrational prejudices which the scientists themselves take in from their cultural environment. But the whole progress of science has consisted in the detection and the refutation of these prejudices. The discoveries of the motion of the earth and of the origin of species are the crucial examples of the triumph of reason and practice over feeling. It is another business altogether to try and reverse this process and to demand in the name of the State that old prejudices should be revived and put in the place of new discoveries. Any body of scientists that accepts such dictation effectively signs its death-warrant. Yet this is precisely what the German scientists have been made to do. What integrity still remains must be of a secret and anti-Nazi character and is in constant danger of being crushed out of existence by the activities of the secret police.

It was admittedly not very difficult for the Nazis to win the loyalty or at least the obedience of the scientists—far easier, in fact, than to get that of the Churches. For that most of the blame must be laid on the character and training of the scientist; too immersed in his work, too tied to the state and industrial machine, too imbued with an easily imposed patriotism. Further, they were split very cleverly by the singling out for attack of the Jews and socialists. (11)

The Persecution of the Jews.—Naturally, even with the rapidity and brutality of Nazi methods, the spirit of German science could not be destroyed all at once. The attack on it had to take several forms, the first and most dramatic being the expulsion of the Jews from science. The peculiar tragedy of the Jewish people is that whenever they are tolerated sufficiently long to enable them to devote their talents to socially useful tasks they are sooner or later made the scapegoat for all the misfortunes of the countries in which they happen to live. The intensity of the struggle and the restricted opportunities which the Jews have had to endure through history, together with a traditional reverence for learning, give them certain advantages in the pursuit of learned occupations which result, in practice, in a larger proportion of Jews to Gentiles in the learned professions than in the population at large. Even in Germany this proportion did not mean that the Jews occupied a predominating place in any of these professions, but they were noticeable and disliked by the more stupid and unsuccessful members. These prejudices, which had hitherto in Germany, as they have in countries such as England, been restrained by the common sense and tolerance of the majority inside and outside the professions, were now turned into an official dogma backed by the whole force of law and the violence of black and brown shirts brought up on little else than anti-Jew and anti-Communist propaganda.

It was particularly in science that the Jews had acquired an honourable and important position. Their expulsion was an immediate and heavy blow to German science, though it may ultimately turn to the advantage of science in other countries. The attack on the Jews, however, went further and deeper. It was decided not only to persecute them but their ideas, and Jewish ideas were found to include almost every form of clear thinking. If in logic, mathematics, or physics everything a Jew did must necessarily have been wrong, the whole edifice of science would have to be taken to pieces and rebuilt with diminished and incongruous materials. This is the task which the Nazi philosophers are now attempting to undertake, with results to-day which appear to the outside world as ludicrous or disgusting.

Thus Stark, the veteran anti-Semite and now most honoured representative of German science, writes in *Nature*:

" When in what follows I speak of two principal types of mentality in physics, my observations are founded on experience. I have inquired into the mental characteristics that have led the great physicists of the past to their discoveries, and in the course of the forty years of my scientific life I have observed very many more or less successful contemporary physicists and authors of theories and of books, in an endeavour to discern the main-spring of their work. On the basis of this wide experience I have come to recognize that there are two main types of mental attitude among workers in the field of physics.

The pragmatic spirit, from which have sprung the creations of successful discoveries both past and present, is directed towards reality, its aim is to ascertain the laws governing already known phenomena and to discover new phenomena and bodies as yet unknown. . . .

The physicist of the dogmatic school operates in quite a different manner in the field of physics, he starts out from ideas that have arisen primarily in his own brain, or from arbitrary definitions of relationships between symbols to which general and so also physical significance can be ascribed. By logical and mathematical operations he combines them and so derives results in the form of mathematical formulæ. . . .

The relativistic theories of Einstein, which are based on an arbitrary definition of space and time co-ordinates or their differentials, constitute an equally obvious example of the product of the dogmatic spirit. Another example of this kind is the wave-mechanical theory of Schrödinger. By an amazing feat of physico-mathematical acrobatics he obtains as a final result first a differential equation. He then asks what sort of physical significance the function that occurs in his equation may have, and for this he makes the suggestion according to which the electron is arbitrarily smeared in a large spatial region round about the atom. In characteristic fashion, however, other dogmatic physicists (Born, Jordan, Heisenberg, Sommerfeld) give to¯the Schrödinger function another dogmatic signi-ficance, contrary to fundamental laws of experience. They make the electron dance round the atom in an irregular manner and allow it to act externally as though it were simultaneously present at every point round the atom with a charge corresponding to the statistical duration of its sojourn at each point. . . .

I have taken the field against the dogmatic spirit in Germany because I have been able to observe repeatedly its crippling and damaging effect on the development of physical research in this country. In this conflict I have also directed my efforts against the damaging influence of Jews in German science, because I regard them as the chief exponents and propa-gandists of the dogmatic spirit.

This reference brings me to the national aspect of the mental outlook of men of science in research. It can be adduced from the history of science that the founders of research in physics, and the great discoverers from Galileo and Newton to the physical pioneers of our own time, were almost exclusively Aryans, predominantly of the Nordic race. From this

·we may conclude that the predisposition towards pragmatic thinking occurs most frequently in men of the Nordic race. If we examine the originators, representatives and propagandists of modern dogmatic theories, we find amongst them a preponderance of men of Jewish descent. If we remember in addition that Jews played a decisive part in the foundation of theological dogmatism and that the authors and propagandists of Marxism and communistic dogmas are for the most part Jews, we must establish and recognize the fact that the natural inclination to dogmatic thought appears with especial frequency in people of Jewish origin."— *Nature*, Vol. 141, pp. 770-72.

In his original article in *Das schwarze Korps*, the organ of the S.S., he was far more outspoken:

"There is one sphere in particular where we meet the spirit of the 'White Jews' in its most intensive form and where what is common between the outlook of the 'White Jews' and Jewish teaching and tradition can be directly proved, namely, in Science. To purge science from its Jewish spirit is our most urgent task. For science represents a key position from which intellectual Judaism can always regain a significant influence on all spheres of national life. Thus it is characteristic that in a time which brings fresh tasks to German medicine and which awaits decisive achievements in the fields of heredity, race-hygiene and public health, our medical journals should, in the space of six months, publish from a total of 2138 articles, 1085 from foreign authors, including 116 from Russians of the U.S.S.R. These articles of foreign origin scarcely concern themselves with those problems which seem so urgent to us. Under the cover of the term 'exchange of experience' there lurks that doctrine of internationality of science which the Jewish spirit has always propagated, because it provides the basis for unlimited self-glorification." (15th July, 1937.)

The persecution of the Jews has had the greatest repercussions abroad, but far more cruel has been the fate of communists, socialists, pacifists and liberals in the learned world. For them it has not only been the loss of position, but in many cases the brutalities of the concentration camp.

The Dragooning of Science.—These measures would in themselves have been sufficiently crippling to German science, but they were, in effect, extended far more widely. For one actual victimized research worker or teacher there must have been many others who dared not expose themselves by attempting to maintain the standard of objectivity which is anathema to the Nazi State. The standardization (Gleichgeschaltung) of the universities and technical institutes shows the same tendency. Not only have all elected officials from the rector downwards been replaced by those nominated by the Nazi party, but also high in the administration is placed a pure Nazi functionary, rarely a person of any knowledge of science and generally one who has been brought up to despise intellectual activities as such. One of the great advantages of the German scientist, his feeling of being an important and respected person in the community, is now lost. Scientific work is carried on largely through its own inertia; the scientist goes on working until some reason is found either on racial or political grounds for objecting to him or the work. The first effect of this has been to destroy the spontaneous character of scientific work; originality has become dangerous.

The full effects of the system, however, will not be apparent until the next generation of scientists, for it is in the teaching of science that the Nazi State most specifically interferes. In the first place, the number of students has been drastically cut down (12), quite apart from the barring of the universities to Jewish students. The essentially middle- and upper-class origin of the students has been further emphasized, and the number of worker or peasant students in the universities has now fallen to a mere handful. The Nazi reform of the universities has, moreover, made effective teaching of those students that are allowed, more and more impossible. Labour service and conscription have taken away years of potential work, and in that work the emphasis is now all on body and character rather than on intelligence.

"The State must throw the whole weight of its educational machinery not into pumping its children full of knowledge, but into producing absolutely healthy bodies. The development of mental capacity is only of secondary importance. Our first aim must be the development of character, especially of will-power, and a readiness to take responsibility; scientific training follows far behind."—Hitler, *Mein Kampf*, p. 542.

A good party member "whose eyes shine when the name of the Leader is mentioned," who can carry on his military exercises and fight duels for his honour in the old approved Prussian style, has become the ideal student. Intellectual tendencies, in particular any approach to critical objectivity, are definite bars to advancement. If this system were to last for a generation it could be counted on to dissipate completely the great German scientific tradition.

All Science for War.—It might have seemed simpler not to attempt even a pretence at science. It is quite clear that, from the point of view of the philosophy of blood and soil, science is fundamentally unnecessary. But deliberate intellectual barbarism, the conscious repudiation of the European tradition of culture as un-German, is only one side of the Nazi movement. The other, and increasingly predominant side, is the development of German world power. It is in the field of science that these two aspects appear in the most glaring contradiction. It would be very grand if the German youth could defy the world and establish their superiority by their naked strength. Unfortunately, present-day warfare requires machinery and a heavy economic backing, and for these science is necessary. The Nazis are faced with the paradox of having to maintain their strength by the use of methods which they despise. The survival of German science depends on the need which the military and economic state has for its work. There is, however, the greatest confusion as to how much and what kind of science is needed for this purpose. German technique has for years been one of the highest in the world; it is based on science but does not, if it has simply to maintain itself, require any further application of it. On the other hand, if military successes are to be gained and the country made independent of all foreign sources of supply, it is necessary not only to maintain but also to improve and create new technical means, and for this science cannot be dispensed with. It can, however, be sharply limited to the attainment of these ends. There has been, consequently, a deliberate policy of turning science into Wehrwissenschaft, of encouraging those researches, and those researches only, which tend to direct or indirect military ends. This has been the aim of the Führer from the beginning, as shown by the following quotations from *Mein Kampf*:

"In science, too, the racial state should see a means to foster national pride. Not only world history, but the whole history of culture must be taught from this point of view. An inventor must not only appear great as an inventor, but greater still as a member of the national community. The admiration of each great deed must be transformed into pride that the lucky performer belongs to one's own people.

Systematically, the curriculum must be built up along these lines and education so handled that the youth, on leaving school, is neither a semi-pacifist, a democrat or the like, but a whole-hearted German" (p. 473).

"Let us educate the German people from their youth up with that exclusive recognition of the rights of their own nation and cease to taint the heart of the child with the curse of 'objectivity' even in matters which concern the preservation of his own personality" (p. 124).

"The racial state will have to consider the mental training of after-school youths as its own task as well as their physical training, and carry it through in state institutions. This training can in its outline already be the preparation for the later military service. . . . The Army will be looked upon as the last and supreme school of national education . . . here he must learn to be silent . . . also if necessary to suffer injustice in silence" (pp. 458-59).

The Rector of Frankfurt University, Dr. Ernst Krieck, puts it even more plainly:

"What is the purpose of university education? It is not objective science which is the purpose of our university training, but the heroic science of the soldier, the militant and fighting science." — *L'École Hitlerienne et l'Étranger*, 1937.

Thus, in the course of physics in the university, the greatest importance is not now given to the fundamental theories of space or of atomic structure, which are condemned as Jewish, but to ballistics and mechanics. Chemistry fits itself naturally into the task of providing explosives, poison gases and substitute raw materials, while in biology the importance of developing German-grown foodstuffs becomes the most important practical aim. (13)

Under the cover of war science a good deal of genuine research does manage to creep in. The few good scientists who are left behind actually gain materially from the suppression of their colleagues, but there is a shortage of younger men and an atmosphere of growing anxiety.

The Distortion of Science.—This distortion of science for war affects mainly the more exact sciences. Over the remaining field there is a distortion of a different and even more destructive character. The great Nazi myth of race superiority and the necessity for military struggle have to be given a scientific basis, and the whole of biology, psychology, and the social sciences need to be distorted for this purpose. In the latter cases the twisting of accepted facts has to be on such a grand scale as to destroy the science completely, and yet it has been possible to find a number of respectable German scientists who have apparently willingly subscribed to these theses. It is also true that they have been advanced by the more reactionary scientists in other countries. Indeed, the great majority of Nazi ideas are foreign importations, their most fundamental concept—that of the superior and destined race—being purely Jewish in origin. Most of the advances made in the last fifty years in anthropology and sociology have been effectively wiped out in Germany. Much cruder explanations are needed to justify the barbarous penal code, with its reversion to retributive punishment, which has been reintroduced in Germany. These are admirably supplied by the new race science of which the following are authoritative expositions:

"Blood and soil, as fundamental forces of life, are, however, the symbols of the national-political point of view and of the heroic style of life. By them the ground is prepared for a new form of education . . . What does blood mean to us? We cannot rest satisfied with the teachings of physics, chemistry, or medicine. From the earliest dawn of the race, this blood, this shadowy stream of life, has had a symbolic significance and leads us into the realms of metaphysics. Blood is the builder of the body, and also the source of the spirit of the race. In blood lurks our ancestral inheritance, in blood is embodied the race, from blood arise the character and destiny of man; blood is to man the hidden undercurrent, the symbol of the current of life from which man can arise and ascend to the regions of light, of spirit, and of knowledge."—E. Krieck, *Nationalpolitische Erziehung*, Leipzig, 1933.

"National Socialism is characterized by an heroic attitude towards all problems of existence. This heroic attitude derives from one single but all-decisive profession of faith, namely, blood and character. Race and soul are merely different designations for one and the same thing. This is paralleled by the rise of a new science, a new scientific discovery which we call race science. From a high enough perspective this new science is discerned to be no more than a far-reaching attempt to attain German self-consciousness."—A. Rosenberg.

Quoted by Robert A. Brady in *The Spirit and Structure of German Fascism*, p. 60.

"The ideas of Adolf Hitler contain the final truths of every possible scientific knowledge. . . . National-Socialism provided the only remaining possibility of working scientifically in Germany. . . . In our opinion there can be only one starting-point for the German historian of law as for all scientists; the duty to conceive of German history as nothing but the pre-history of German-National-Socialism. . . . We believe that every scientific work (whose purpose is after all to serve the investigation of truth) must coincide in its results with the starting-point of National-Socialism. The programme of the National-Socialist Party has consequently become the only basis for all scientific investigation. . . . The true Front spirit is more important than scientific discussion. . . ."—Reichminister Franck, Leader of the German Jurists, in a speech made at Tübingen in October 1936.

In all these fields a new difficulty arises. It is relatively easy to suppress and distort science at home, but German prestige abroad also needs to be maintained and increased, and it is clear that if the process of distorting science reaches its logical conclusion, the scientists in Germany and outside it will be talking different languages. The Nazi answer to this difficulty is characteristically simple and crude. Not content with distorting it in their own country they wish science to be distorted abroad. At the recent Penological Conference, for instance, they managed to achieve, by packing it with German delegates, a vote in favour of German penal theory, and it is intended that all international congresses held in Germany or outside it, if possible, should be used to glorify the Nazi state. How it can be done even abroad is shown by the barring of Professor Zondek, one of the most celebrated of biochemists, from a congress in Amsterdam, simply by a threat of the withdrawal of the whole German delegation. Here Nazi policy is attacking science at its most cardinal point, but up till now the traditions of international politeness among scientists have prevented any effective rejoinder or vindication of the world scientific tradition of objectivity.

Science in Danger.—The existence of Fascism is a double danger to science. Wherever it is allowed to spread its power science is destroyed, as the tragedy of Austria has shown us only too clearly.

But besides this, the influence of its ideas spreads into other countries. They reinforce everywhere the forces of obscurantism and injure the spirit of science. Already in every country in Europe and even in America anti-Semitism is growing, and with it the idea of nationalism in science. The development of science in Fascist countries is a clear indication of the fundamental incompatibility between either the theory or the application of science, and the tendencies of capitalist, economic, and political development. Capitalism in its later stages is incapable of bearing objective examination; the scientist becomes necessarily a critic and criticism cannot be tolerated. The scientist must therefore hold his tongue or lose his place. If he does the first, he ceases effectively to be a scientist and is incapable of transmitting the tradition of science; but if he does not, science will as certainly and more rapidly come to an end. It is easy for a scientist, in what is still a bourgeois democracy, to look with superior horror at what is happening to science under Fascism. But the fate of science in his own country is at the moment still hanging in the balance and it depends on factors quite outside the scope of science itself. Unless the scientist is aware of these factors and knows how to use his weight in influencing them, his position is simply that of the sheep awaiting his turn with the butcher. Luckily, the awareness of this state of affairs is growing, with results which will be examined in a later chapter.

Science and Socialism

The relationships between science and society depend fundamentally on the principles of organization of society itself. Up till now in discussing science in all countries there have been the same basic social assumptions, those of capitalism. Apart from a more or less restrictive state machinery whose function is essentially to maintain the economic system, human lives and human relations are dominated either by the need to earn a living by working or by the possibility of employing workers for profit. Inside this structure autonomous traditions of religion, literature, and science have grown up, but they are in the last instance dependent on their fitting in with the general scheme. They must effectively pay their way. We have examined the relation of science to this social environment and have shown how its main line of development has been determined by the needs, not of the great mass of the population, but of those producing for profit. It must be recognized that this motive has led to an increase in our knowledge of the universe greater and more rapid than that produced by any previous social form. But it must also be recognized that the development of science and technique themselves have opened to us vistas of possible human betterment which the existing system is quite unable to make use of, together with possibilities of human destruction which the existing system is using only too well.

Science in the Soviet Union.—For the last twenty years the prevailing social system has not been universal. There has existed in the world a country in which the basic method of production and social relations have been quite different and consequently the relations of science to society have been so too. The Soviet Union differs from all previous civilizations in having been to a large extent thought out beforehand and in being man's first conscious effort to mould the very framework of his own social activities. The basis of these conceptions lay in the criticism of developing capitalism which was carried out over the last hundred years by Marx, Engels, and Lenin. Marx was brought up in the tradition of the rapidly growing science of the nineteenth century; he saw the possibilities it was holding out to mankind, but, unlike others who also saw them, he understood how and why those possibilities were unlikely to be realized. The corner-stone of the Marxist state is the utilization of human knowledge, science, and technique, directly for human welfare. Consequently when Lenin managed to achieve this state and to defend it in the first few critical years against the attacks of the rest of the world, one of the first considerations was how to realize this use of science in practice. Marx had understood much more clearly than the contemporary scientists how close was the relation between the theories of science and their practice in the arts. (14) He saw how this unconscious connection between theory and practice could be made conscious and would need to be made conscious if either were to develop fully. Engels, who was a life-long student of contemporary science, had elaborated these ideas more fully (15), and Lenin, in the period of his exile, had spent a great portion of his time on an analysis and criticism of the later scientific developments. (16) Consequently, even before the struggle of the Civil War and the Famine were over, the new Soviet State had started building up science with a conscious direction and plan.

Science before the Revolution.—The difficulties were immense. Science had always been, since its first introduction to Russia by Catherine the Great, a particularly exotic and unassimilated part of the Czarist State. For the great mass of the population it did not exist at all. There was always a suspicion of liberalism about it, and it was only tolerated and to a limited extent fostered by the authorities in order to provide the minimum necessary for the civil service and the army, and to present a show to the rest of Europe that in the possession of an academy Russia was as civilized as any other country. The great Russian scientists, such as Lomonosov, Mendeleyev, Kovalevsky or Pavlov, managed to do their work rather in spite of than because of the official organization. Russian science was extremely dependent on science abroad, particularly German and French science. Not only were many foreign scientists and technicians in Russian employ, but practically all scientific apparatus was imported. It is true that just before the War the new Russian bourgeoisie began to demand science and even set up a free university in which it was taught, and from which many of the first generation of Soviet scientists graduated. But this movement had no appreciable effect on the country as a whole. (17) Naturally, the War, the Revolution, the Civil War, and the Famine did not improve matters. A number of the older and more conservative scientists escaped from the country; others died of disease or hunger; many refused to collaborate with the new system or collaborated half-heartedly and uncomprehendingly. From the remainder, with practically no help from outside, the Soviet Union had to build up a new and greater science.

Early Struggles.—Luckily, when the scientists saw that the new Government intended to give to science a scope and importance out of all relation to that which it had previously held, and that they were really free for the first time to achieve what they wanted, they made up by their energy and enthusiasm for their lack of numbers. They were faced at the outset with a double task: that of creating a Soviet science and Soviet technique and, at the same time, helping to solve the immediate problems of reconstruction. Funds and men were placed at their disposal, but in many cases the needed apparatus could not be bought and the men were completely untrained. What was achieved in the period 1917 to 1927 and how it was achieved will be worth the most careful study in the future, because it will reveal the extreme viability of science when removed from the restrictions which weigh on it in countries at a far higher scientific level. In the next decade progress was assured; the development of science marched hand in hand with industry and was closely linked with it, and the new universities and schools began to turn out trained, or, at any rate, partly trained, scientists in incomparably larger numbers than there had been before. (18) It became possible to start new work, not merely to continue old researches, and, for the first time, Soviet science began to make a notable contribution to certain branches of world science.

The Scale of Soviet Science.—It would be impossible in the scope of this book to indicate with any adequacy the organization and achievements of Soviet science. We have already one or two studies on the subject. (19) What is necessary, however, is to show in what way this organization differs from that in other countries, the difficulties it had and still has to face, and what lessons can be drawn from it for the organization of science in the world. The first striking character of Soviet science is the scale of its operations. The Budget for science in 1934 was a thousand million roubles. Without attempting to estimate the purchasing power of this sum, it represents at least 1 per cent. of the national income at the time, a sum relatively three times as great as that spent in the U.S.A. and ten times as great as that spent in Britain.

This constitutes the practical recognition that science is to be taken no longer as a luxury but as an essential part of the social fabric. Science is in fact, in the Soviet Union, linked closely at every stage to the productive processes, but it is linked to them in a way quite different from the connection that it has in other countries. The prime practical object of Soviet science is the satisfaction of human needs, either directly or indirectly, and not the increasing profitability of production. Necessarily a concern for human needs involves the improving of production processes, and in so far as it does so Soviet science will tend to shorten these processes and reduce their effective costliness in terms of human effort. In doing this, however, it proceeds in a very different way from that of the application of science in a capitalist economy. In the first place the worker, as such, is an integral part of any change in productive processes. His health and comfort are not to be interfered with in the interests of apparently more economical working. (20) Even more important than this is that the workers are encouraged in every way to assist actively in the application of science to industry. The union of theory and practice which exists under capitalism is limited to a collaboration between academic scientists and engineers; the workmen are hands to execute orders, not to think. Nor have they any incentive to do so, for the value of the improvement will go to the employers and the chances are that their own work will be made harder as a result. In the Soviet Union the great Stakhanov movement is an impressive proof of the possibility of workers themselves taking a leading part in transforming the processes of industry (see Appendix VII).

Planning Science.—The other chief difference is that Soviet science is completely integrated. The problems are not faced separately but as an interconnected whole. The development of science is pushed forward according to a plan, and that plan itself forms only a part of the wider plan of material and cultural advance. Naturally the planning of science possesses quite another order of definiteness than does the planning of any kind of production. The field in which science works contains far too many surprises for it to be possible to estimate in advance what is going to be found, or what can or cannot be done. These difficulties are overcome by planning not for the results of science, which cannot be anticipated, but for research surveys of definite fields in which valuable results may reasonably be expected. Its main feature is the distribution of the resources available for science between the various branches and institutes for scientific research in a proportion that seems likely to give the best results both from the point of view of immediate improvement of production and from the longer range view of the development of a more adequate Soviet science. The nature of the problem which is set the scientists in the Soviet Union is indicated by the programme for the next few years' work presented by the Academy of Sciences, the supreme controlling organization:

"The work of the Academy in the immediate future is to aid the State-Planning Commission in the drawing up of the third Five-Year Plan. The main efforts of the Academy's various institutes will be directed towards the solution of ten specific problems, outlined at a Session held last March. (Needless to say, these problems do not comprise the whole work of the Academy, but, for the moment, they are the leading and dominant ones.) The ten key problems on which the Academy is to concentrate in connection with the third Five-Year Plan are the following:

(1) To develop geological, geochemical, and geophysical methods of prospecting for useful minerals, particularly tin, rare metals and oil.

(2) To solve the problem of electric power transmission by creating on a scientific basis a unified electric power system throughout the U.S.S.R., with high-voltage transmission.

(3) To rationalize and extend the use of natural gas and by-product gas from industrial plants (although Soviet resources of natural gas are greater than those of the United States, extraction is one-fiftieth of that of the latter country).

(4) To find a new type of fuel for internal combustion engines (a study will be made of chain reactions and explosion processes, the internal combustion motor and electric automobiles).

(5) To rationalize the technological processes in chemistry and metallurgy; to work out scientific means for the better utilization of equipment and increasing output.

(6) To help attain the objective of raising the grain yield of the country from 7000 million poods to 8000 million poods (one pood equals 36 lb. avoirdupois) by laying the basis for a further increase in fertility. (This will involve research in seed selection, soil chemistry, plant biology, fertilizers, and the mechanization of agriculture.)

(7) To establish scientific bases for the development of animal husbandry and fisheries.

(8) To develop telemechanics (long-distance control of machinery) and to extend automatic processes in industry through application of theoretical physics.

(9) To draw up the balance-sheet of the national economy of the U.S.S.R. so as to serve as a scientific basis for the third Five-Year Plan.

(10) To study the history of the peoples of the U.S.S.R.

By its work on these ten leading problems, the Academy of Sciences will furnish the scientific foundations on which the State-Planning Commission will build the unified plan for the national economy. As the supreme scientific body in the country, the Academy is charged with the duty of setting the general trend for research in accordance with the immediate and vital problems of the State, also with the function of co-ordinating the plans of the various research institutes with the general State plan.

This does not mean that the Academy will attempt to lay down detailed programmes for its 40 research institutes and the 800 research institutes controlled by the different commissariats. Nor that research will be confined to the ten problems enumerated. It does mean, however, that lesser problems will be subordinated to questions which are of vital need to the country as a whole."—*Anglo-Soviet Journal*, Vol. I., No. 5, p. 14.

The programme is definitely technical, but with it goes the carrying out of longer range and less definable fundamental research in electricity, the structure of solids and liquids, the nature of chemical reactions, plant and animal physiology, etc.

Organization.—The organization of Soviet science is somewhat complex and is by no means yet fixed. In the early stages many improvisations were made, some of which have been retained and others dropped. The present structure is still to a large extent flexible. The general direction of scientific work throughout the Union is in the hands of the Academy, but the research institutions under the Academy represent only a small proportion of the research carried on throughout the country. The main bulk of research is carried on by the university research laboratories and by the research institutions under the control of the different Commissariats, such as those of Heavy Industry, Light Industry, Food Supply, Health, Agriculture, etc. The Academy, which was originally built on the model of the French and Prussian Academies as an honorific body for distinguished scientists, has expanded its work, not by adding to its members, but by making each member responsible for one or more institutions in his own particular sphere. Although the number of members is only 90, the number of scientific workers in the institutions of the Academy is more than 4000.

The main function of the university and technical schools is, of course, educational, but each has its research laboratories which are linked very closely with those of the Academy. More important still, however, are the research institutions attached to industry, various metal institutions, silicate, fibre, etc. These are not industrial institutions in the narrow sense but are occupied with basic problems connected with the industry and include in them scientists of great distinction. On another level are the innumerable works laboratories and field agricultural stations. The responsibility for the finance of the institutions and works laboratories falls on the commissariats, and it is their needs that determine the line of research to be undertaken. From the scientific point of view the research institutions in industry and agriculture are closely linked with the Academy, and the separation which exists in Britain between academic and industrial science is largely non-existent.

The idea behind the organization is that there should be a two-way flow of problems and solutions. The problems of industry put in a precise form by works laboratories are passed on to the technical institutes. In so far as their solution falls within the scope of existing technical knowledge, they are solved there. But if some more fundamental ignorance of the working of nature is revealed, this is passed on to the Academy. Thus industry serves to present science with new and original problems. At the same time any fundamental discoveries made in the universities or the Academy are immediately transmitted to the industrial laboratories so that anything which can be turned to useful purposes may be used in practice as soon as possible. A beautiful example of this integrated working is shown by Vavilov's bureau of plant industry. There the economic need for producing varieties of plants to suit the multiple climates and conditions of soil in different parts of the Union has led to a very thorough development of genetic principles, and also, through the investigation of wild varieties of cultivated plants, to the discovery of the centres of domestication and consequently of civilization in distant pre-history, at the same time as providing a number of new plants and crosses of great practical value. Many similar cases could be given, but for the most part they are to be found in Crowther's *Soviet Science*.

How the System Works.—The detailed carrying on of scientific work, apparatus, laboratories, etc., does not differ fundamentally in the Soviet Union from that outside it. There is an interesting development, however, in the production of apparatus, which, instead of being left to individual firms, with the resultant high prices and small turnover, is centred in the institutes themselves, which permits a rationalization of production and a consequent cheapening and multiplying of scientific apparatus so that in nearly every field the Soviet Union has become independent of foreign apparatus, a feat which is all the more remarkable in that there was practically no scientific apparatus made in the country before the Revolution.

In the question of personnel, however, and internal management of scientific research, there are totally different ideas at work. In a few years many changes have taken place, and the present inner organization is the result of the modifications usual in all enterprises in the Soviet Union. In the light of the experience of the peculiar needs of scientific research, it is a combination of individual responsibility and collective consultation. The director of the institute is responsible for the general work of the institute, and its finance and administration, even where these last two functions are vested in a different person. He alone takes ultimate decisions. The main work of the institute is planned out by the discussion among the workers themselves in their own meetings, and these workers include not only the scientific staff but what would count in other countries as mechanics and assistants. At the beginning of the year the general planning of work is discussed; it is then taken by the director or the representatives for modification in the light of plans of other institutes or of the needs of industry or education, and after a series of negotiations a short plan is approved and the budget is fixed. Necessarily the plans are left somewhat vague, particularly in relation to time of fulfilment, but some account of the work done and that still to do is expected at definite intervals. (21) In the author's experience this scheme is capable of working extremely well in general, where the director and the staff are naturally willing to work together, but in other circumstances it may be the cause of friction and inefficiency. Luckily, at the rate at which Soviet science grows, those personal struggles, which seem to be inevitable between scientists of different temperaments or beliefs, need not lead to the same embitterment that they do in other countries, because, owing to the rapid expansion of science, there is always the possibility of the aggrieved or misunderstood junior setting up an institute of his own.

Science in Education and Popular Culture.—Science in the Soviet Union is, however, by no means only or even mainly a question of research. The Marxists have always conceived of a society thoroughly permeated by science, one in which science becomes a corner-stone of education and culture. Consequently, one of the most noticeable things in the Soviet Union is the place of science in education and even more so in popular interest. Science both in its theoretical and practical aspects is taught from the very beginning in the schools and, though considerable time is left for literary interests, it dominates the higher stages. The teaching of the universities both in science and technics is extremely thorough and effective, while the number of students is of course out of all proportion to that existing before the Revolution, and higher in relation to the population than it is in technically far more advanced countries, such as Britain or Germany. The difficulties of setting up this educational system were immense, as the few teachers that were to be found were also needed for the more immediate tasks of scientific and industrial research. In the earlier stages the need was so great that many of the students were sent out after short courses, very incompletely trained, but this no longer occurs. Actually the training is prolonged on English standards; a five-year university course followed by three years learning research is needed before the final degree. The enormous advantage which Soviet education has over that of other countries, with the partial exception of the U.S.A., is that it is able to draw on the intelligence available in the whole of the population and not only on that of a certain section of it, arbitrarily marked off by wealth. There can be no doubt that once the system has had time to get under way we shall have a body of intelligent scientific workers not to be paralleled elsewhere in the world.

Even more striking, however, than the educational system is the great interest in science shown by the adult population. This is marked, among other ways, by the great sale of scientific books— not only popular books on science, but also practical and serious scientific works and technical handbooks. The main aim of the former is not, as with us, to cause the reader to meditate on the mysteries of the universe, but to show how men can use science to struggle with nature and improve their conditions. (22) Almost every scientific book of any importance, however difficult, is trans- lated into Russian, and has an extensive sale. Thus, the first edition of Dirac's *Quantum Mechanics* sold 3000 copies in Russia in a few months and only 2000 of the English edition in three years. Scientific news of discoveries or the proceedings of con- gresses are given the same prominence and arouse the same interest as news about royalty, crime, or football matches in England. The recreation parks run scientific side-shows which are always well patronized, and every visitor to the Union notices the insatiable curiosity which the people evince for anything of a technical or scientific nature. Two things have contributed to this attitude. The first is that the power and interest of science is suddenly opened to a population to whom hitherto it was a closed book, and the effect is the same, though greater than at the other periods of transference of a learned tradition, as between the Egyptians and the Greeks, or the Greeks and the Arabs. The other is that the latent hostility to science which exists in the minds of workers in capitalist states is here completely absent; they need fear no longer that science will be used to simplify production and throw them out of work or to devise weapons for their destruction. It has become their science, to be used by them for themselves.

Character of Soviet Science.—It is still too early to talk of the char- acter or achievement of Soviet science. The first generation of Soviet scientists, those who have been trained from the beginning in its philosophy and aims, have as yet had no time to contribute to world science. What has been done is the work of men trained in the old regime and working under the conditions of the new. We must balance here the material and technical disadvantages against the much greater scope which society gives to their work. Only a few of the older scientists have had the vision to see this scope and to make full use of it. They have organized research work on a vast scale and have been able in this way to do things which would be impossible for the isolated research worker. But there are very few of them; consequently present-day science in the Soviet Union is very uneven in character. In certain fields, particularly in animal psychology with the school of Pavlov, in animal and plant breeding, in geology and soil science, in physical chemistry, crystal physics, aerodynamics, and branches of mathematics, the Soviet scientists have already made their mark on world science. In others, notably in the central science of chemistry, they are still behindhand. (23)

The qualitative characteristic of the work is chiefly its originality, particularly in the choice of problems, and this can be put down directly to the new trend towards choosing problems connected with experience. Soviet science is able to pick up and illuminate aspects of common experience which have never been touched by science before, not because they were difficult or obscure but because they lay outside the conventional tradition of science. Thus, for instance, Rehbinder's work showing that hardness is a surface phenomenon depending on the medium, was no more than bringing the light of science to the technical processes known to the New Stone Age, but no one had thought of applying science to it before. (24)

On the other side, the great disadvantage is the lack of sufficiently rigid criticism, but this again is to be expected. A critical attitude is the fruit of long experience and well-established schools, its absence one of the faults of youthful enthusiasm which only time and experience can correct. (25) A certain part is played here by the long period in which Soviet science was cut off from the rest of the world and the degree in which political, financial, and language barriers still cut it off to-day. It is only by the comparison of the work of a very large number of scientists in different places that a fully critical attitude can be developed.

Dialectical Materialism and Science.—There is one aspect of Soviet science which is most incomprehensible to outside observers: its relations to philosophy, and in particular to dialectical materialism. In other countries science had, it seemed, been able to get on perfectly well without philosophy, especially in England where philosophy, like religion in polite circles, was hardly ever mentioned in connection with science. This, any student of the history of science will see, is simply because the basic philosophy of modern science was thrashed out in the violent days of the seventeenth century and has been accepted tacitly since as a good working basis for empirical advance. Now the very setting up of the Soviet State was the result of a challenge to this philosophy in Marx's work, and it is only natural that seventeenth-century philosophy along with Western science would be impossible to take over in the Soviet Union. Yet no other thought-out philosophical interpretation of science existed. Marx, Engels, and Lenin had, it is true, sketched outlines for such a system, but though they studied science they were not scientists and were in any case too busy as revolutionaries. The result is that Soviet science has been finding out its philosophy in the process of its growth, and this has been a lively and at times almost a violent process. (26) It has been complicated by the fact that the older scientists were, naturally enough, uncomprehending and even hostile to the new ideas, while the younger ones lacked sufficient scientific knowledge to illustrate their arguments effectively.

It is impossible here to discuss these arguments: only those who have gone into the question can see what a wealth of suggestive ideas and what new tools for research and for systematization lie waiting to be used in the new methods. It will be for the scientists of the Soviet Union, and it may be hoped of other countries as well, to carry out these revaluations and other transformations of science. It need hardly be said that dialectical materialism is in no sense a substitute for science; it is no royal road to knowledge. Induction and proof remain as they were; hence the accusations of the detractors of the Soviet Union—that Marxism is a dogma imposed on and distorting the findings of science—is palpably absurd, as anyone who bothers to look into the writings of Marx, Engels, or Lenin can see in a moment. But dialectical materialism can, on the other hand, do two things: suggest the directions of thought which are likely to be particularly fruitful in results, and integrate and organize different branches of scientific research in relation to one another and to the social processes of which they form a part. It is the working out of this transformation of present-day science into something that includes it and goes beyond it that is the chief interest for humanity in the scientific work of the Soviet Union.

(1) M. Polanyi, *Deutsche Volkswirt*, 23rd May 1930.
(2) His plea for laboratories, refused by the *Moniteur* but published in 1867 as a pamphlet, marks the realization of the need for the endowment of research :
". . . Les conceptions les plus hardies, les spéculations les plus légitimes, écrivait-il, ne prennent un corps et une âme que le jour où elles sont consacrées par l'observation et l'expérience. Laboratoires et découvertes sont des termes corrélatifs. Supprimez les laboratoires, les sciences physiques deviendront l'image de la stérilité et de la mort. Elles ne seront plus que des sciences d'enseignement, limitées et impuissantes, et non des sciences

de progrès et d'avenir. Rendez-leur les laboratoires, et avec eux reparaîtra la vie, sa fécondité et sa puissance. Hors de leurs laboratoires, le physicien et le chimiste sont des soldats sans armes sur le champ de bataille. La déduction de ces principes est évidente : si les conquêtes utiles à l'humanité touchent votre cœur, si vous restez confondu devant les effets surprenants de la télégraphie électrique, du daguerréotype, de l'anesthésie et de tant d'autres découvertes admirables; si vous êtes jaloux de la part que votre pays peut revendiquer dans l'épanouissement de ces merveilles, prenez intérêt, je vous en conjure, à ces demeures sacrées que l'on désigne du nom expressif de *laboratoires*. Demandez qu'on les multiplie et qu'on les orne : ce sont les temples de l'avenir, de la richesse et du bien-être. C'est là que l'humanité grandit, se fortifie et devient meilleure. Elle y apprend à lire dans les œuvres de la nature, œuvres de progrès et d'harmonie universelle, tandis que ses œuvres à elles sont trop souvent celles de la barbarie, du fanatisme et de la destruction.

Il est des peuples sur lesquelles a passé le souffle salutaire de ces vérités. Depuis trente ans, l'Allemagne s'est couverte de vastes et riches laboratoires et chaque jour en voit naître de nouveaux. Berlin et Bonn achèvent la construction de deux palais d'une valeur de quatre millions, destinés l'un et l'autre aux études chimiques. Saint-Pétersbourg a consacré trois millions à un institut physiologique. L'Angleterre, l'Amérique, l'Autriche et la Bavière ont fait les plus généreux sacrifices. . . . L'Italie a marché un instant dans cette voie.

Et la France ?

La France n'est pas encore à l'œuvre. . . .

Qui voudra me croire quand j'affirmerai qu'il n'y a pas, au budget de l'instruction publique, un denier affecté aux progrès des sciences physiques par les laboratoires ; que c'est grâce à une fiction et à une tolérance administrative que les savants, envisagés comme professeurs, peuvent prélever sur le trésor public quelques-unes des dépenses de leurs travaux personnels, au détriment des allocations destinées aux frais de leur enseignement ? "—From *La Vie de Pasteur*, by René Vallery-Radot, p. 215.

His plea had some results, but how much still needed to be done in the present century is movingly shown in the *Life of Madame Curie*, by her daughter Eve.

(3) For his struggles against obscurantism see *Recollections of My Life*, S. Ramon y Cajal.

(4) Spanish scientists are still at their work. In spite of war, aerial bombardments and the shortage of all necessaries they continue to research and even to publish their work. All scientists except those wishing to remain were evacuated from Madrid first to Valencia and afterwards to Barcelona, and were given means to continue their work. Numerous papers have been published, for example those of Professor Barañaga in mathematics, Professor Moles in chemistry, Professor Duperrier in physics and Dr. Zulueta in genetics.

(5) See, however, Crowther, *Famous American Men of Science*.

(6) Almost inevitably the standard of these is very low and research there is severely hindered by the altogether excessive amount of teaching required. But attempts are being made to remedy this state of affairs. See Flexner, *Universities, American, English, German*, and *Report on Academic Curricula*. Another peculiarly American development is that of the popular museums which not only carry out research but send important expeditions to all quarters of the world.

(7) The reasons for this are discussed by Crowther (above).

(8) The extent of the destruction can be gauged from the fact that after six months of undeclared war, 20 universities and more than 80 schools had been destroyed by bombing, and 70,000 students had been forced to fly to the interior ; while throughout the Japanese occupation, in those centres of teaching which remain, the whole curriculum has been revised to suit the Japanese masters and the students are expected to celebrate victories won against their fellow-countrymen.

(9) How artificial the language question is was shown amusingly over the matter of Italian participation in an international scientific publication where the adherence of the Italians was made conditional either on the use of Italian as well as German, French, and English, or alternatively, the dropping of French to secure parity.

(10) In a letter from the secretary of the Sacred Congregation of Seminaries and Universities at Rome to Cardinal Baudrillart on 13th April 1938, there are enumerated eight false assertions which teachers are urged to refute :

1. That human races through their natural and immutable characters are so different that the humblest of them is further from the highest than it is from the highest animal species.
2. That it is necessary, by all possible means, to conserve and cultivate the vigour of the race and the purity of the blood ; everything leading to this result being on that account alone praiseworthy and permissible.

3. That all intellectual and moral qualities of man have their principal origin in the blood, the seat of the racial character.
4. That the chief object of education is to develop racial character and to inspire the mind with a burning love for one's own race as the supremest good.
5. That religion itself depends on racial law and must be adapted to it.
6. That the first source and supreme rule of all legal systems is racial instinct.
7. That all that exists is the Cosmos or Universe, itself a living being, and all things including man are only diverse and changing forms of this universal existence.
8. That every man only exists through the State and for the State. Everything which he owns he holds only as a grant from the State.

(11) How it was possible to get the German scientists to submit so easily to the Nazis is discussed in R. A. Brady's *Spirit and Structure of German Fascism* :

"Such in general was the situation in German science which the Nazis found when they assumed control of the political apparatus of Germany. Into their programme for co-ordinating all ideas, organizations, and activities in all fields, the research and scientific posture of affairs in 1933 fitted perfectly. Hence, nothing fundamental has been changed as to scope and to method. They have merely capitalized on the trends in force by insisting upon even closer working alliances between the separate fields of research and practice, and co-ordinated all activities to fit the purposes of the Nazi state.

But if the ' co-ordination ' is of the sort described—a co-ordination which seems to run so directly counter to the techniques, the criteria, and the moods of science itself—why have not the scientists revolted *en masse?* The answer is to be found in the fact that the typical scientist is not, either by virtue of his training or vocation, much more inclined to uphold scientific laws and methods of analysis, *so far as social applications are concerned,* and outside his *own narrow field,* than is the most ignorant layman on the street. Furthermore, the number of scientists and scholars in any capitalist country who can be found ready to identify their interests with the ' common man,' and with organized labour, can be counted in extremely small numbers. One of the most naïve ideas ever expressed by a reputable economist was Veblen's notion that the interests of engineers and scientists in workmanship and efficiency would lead them naturally, if not inevitably, to ally themselves with labour's interest in maximizing output and improving standards of living. There is not the slightest ground for believing that any so-called ' soviet of engineers ' in capitalistic countries would be any more progressive than the most conservative club of business men.

It would unduly prolong this discussion to go into the reasons here why this is so unfortunately true. But it may be worth pointing out that the very nature and purpose of the Nazi drive was such as to take full advantage of the rigorousness in scientific criteria commonly accepted as basic in the various fields. As one proceeds from the more mature natural sciences of physics and chemistry, on through biology, psychology, and finally to the so-called ' social sciences,' the number of variables increases, the range of relative facts grows more numerous, the key problems become more and more complex, and the element of *biased motive and preconceived opinion* grows steadily more influential. It is in the natural sciences that the Nazis have the least interest in changing science and scientists—here applications are to the heavy industries, the techniques and equipment of war and militarization, utilization of natural resources, etc. On the other hand, it is in the subject-matter of psychology and the social sciences where they have the greater interest in restricting, cutting, hewing, shaping, and interpreting research results according to preconceived plan. Could the reverse have been true, the situation would have been entirely different so far as the conflict with accepted scientific routine and habits of mind are concerned.

But there lurks even here a general misconception regarding the scientist. He is, after all, a human being and not a superman. He cannot be expected under the best of circumstances to be a clear-eyed, matter-of-fact searcher for ' objective truth ' and an expert in dispassionate analysis beyond the fringes of his own special field. There seems to be relatively little of the so-called ' transfer of intelligence,' and not any too much of scientific habits of mind, as he passes beyond the boundaries of his own specific knowledge. Nowhere in all recent philosophical literature is there to be found more simple-minded and naïve acceptance of the myths of popular folklore than in the writings of Eddington, Jeans, Millikan, Planck, and other famous scientists. This was as true of German scientists even before the coming of Hitler as of all other scientists to-day. Scientists, in short, simply let themselves in for the charge that they have abandoned science when they become so careless as to assume that the *attempt to think rigorously in one field* automatically implies thinking rigorously whenever one thinks about anything at all. Here the scientist is no different from any man on the street. If he gives way to the temptation to generalize where he does not *know*, he is merely allowing himself to abandon *rational criteria* in favour of *uncritical belief*. Uncritical belief is never science ; it is always first cousin to bigotry itself.

The more narrow his field of research—a tendency to narrowing is more common with modern science than heretofore—the more apt he is to approach the bigot outside his own field. It is exactly in the natural sciences, which the Nazis leave the least disturbed, that this narrowing on intensive research is most pronounced. Hence arises the paradox that the physical scientist who would seem by training and disposition the least subject to emotional appeals is, perhaps, most susceptible of all his brethren to the blandishments of the fanatic and the bigot—most bigoted because he accepts uncritically what he can be made to believe is rigorously true.

The scientist, *per se*, is, hence, perhaps the most easily used and ' co-ordinated ' of all the especially trained people in modern society. The Nazis, to be true, fired a good many university professors, and dismissed a good many scientists from research laboratories. But the professors fired were primarily amongst the social sciences where there was a more common awareness and a more persistent criticism of the implications of Nazi programmes, and not amongst the natural sciences where thinking is supposed to be most rigorous. Those dismissed in this latter field were primarily Jewish or exceptions to the generalization made above—because of equally uncritical acceptance of beliefs running contrary to the Nazi philosophy.

Consequently the Nazis were able to ' co-ordinate ' scholars and scientists with relative ease, and hence to throw behind their elaborate propaganda the seeming weight of the bulk of German learned opinion and support. They have not even had much difficulty in filling the ranks of their ' race science ' institutes from regular university and similar circles—a success which they have registered by virtue of careful selection from amongst National Socialist university youth, and by forced transmutation of the relevant scientific criteria to meet their own specific ends."—Robert A. Brady in *The Spirit and Structure of German Fascism*, p. 76.

(12) The following table shows how the numbers of students at German universities have decreased :

Students taking :

Winter Term.	Total Number of Students.	Engineering.	Mathematics with Natural Sciences.	Chemistry only.	Medical Sciences.
1932–3	116,154	14,477	12,951	3,543	32,437
1933–4	106,764	13,452	10,852	3,504	33,482
1934–5	89,093	10,310	7,943	3,006	30,123
1935–6	81,438	9,293	6,493	2,696	28,383
1936–7	67,082	7,649	4,616	2,058	22,797
Per cent. change (1932–3=100)	57·8%	52·9%	35·6%	58·0%	70·2%

(Dr. E. Y. Hartshorne, *Nature*, Vol. 142, p. 175. See also his book *German Universities and National Socialism*.)

(13) " The teaching in school can give the young ' Bearer of Race ' (Rassenträger) something that will later be useful to him as Bearer of Arms. Tables can be learnt with horseshoe nails. Logarithms will find their most beautiful adjustment in the science of ballistics. In geography the world war can come into its own limitless rights. History is full to overflowing with examples of war-politics. Chemistry has equal application in the fight for daily bread as for the military struggle with gas. Physics problems can be explained equally well with a motor or a tank. Biological relationships do not only arise from the wanderings of peoples but also from the way states have been forcibly constituted in the past. The teaching of foreign languages is particularly bound up with military-political explanations. In German lessons, the great Moltke can be cited as well as Grimm." —*Wehrerziehung*, November 1935. Quoted in *Education in Nazi Germany*, p. 17.

(14) " The so-called revolutions of 1848 were but poor incidents, small fractures and fissures in the dry crust of European society. . . . The social revolution, it is true, was no novelty invented in 1848. Steam, electricity and the self-acting mule were revolutions

of a rather more dangerous character than even Citizens Barbès, Raspail, and Blanqui. . . . There is one great fact characteristic of this our nineteenth century, a fact which no party dares deny. On the one hand there have started into life industrial and scientific forces which no epoch of the former human history had even suspected. On the other hand there exist symptoms of decay, far surpassing the horrors recorded of the latter times of the Roman Empire. In our days, everything seems pregnant with its contrary. Machinery, gifted with the wonderful power of shortening and fructifying human labour, we behold starving and overworking it. . . . Even the pure life of science seems unable to shine but on the dark background of ignorance. All our invention and progress seem to result in endowing material forces with intellectual life, and in stultifying human life into a material force. This antagonism between modern industry and science on the one hand, and modern misery and dissolution on the other hand ; this antagonism between the productive forces and the social relations of our epoch is a fact palpable, overwhelming, and not to be controverted. Some may wail over it ; others may wish to get rid of modern arts, in order to get rid of modern conflicts. Or they may imagine that so signal a progress in industry wants to be completed by as signal a regress in politics. For our part, we do not mistake the shape of the shrewd spirit that continues to mark all these contradictions. We know that if the new-fangled forces of society are to work satisfactorily, they need only be mastered by newfangled men—and such are the working men. They are as much the invention of modern time as machinery itself."—From a speech made by Karl Marx at an anniversary supper of the *People's Paper* in 1856. Quoted in *The Correspondence of Karl Marx and Friedrich Engels*, p. 90.

(15) " With man we enter into the domain of history. Animals have their history too, the history of their descent, of their gradual evolution up to their present-day forms. But this history is made for them, and their participation in it is without their knowledge and will. Men, on the other hand, the further they get away from animals in the narrow sense, the more they control their own history, consciously, the smaller becomes the influence of unforeseen events and uncontrollable forces on this history, and the greater their success in shaping it to preconceived aims. If, however, human history—even that of the most developed peoples of to-day—is measured in this way, it is clear that an immense discrepancy still exists between planned aims and achieved results, that unanticipated influences predominate and that uncontrolled forces are far more powerful than those set in motion by planning. Nor can this be otherwise so long as the fundamental historical activity of man, which differentiates him from the animals and forms the material basis of all his other activities, that is, the production of the necessities of life—which means to-day social production—is exposed to the chance influences of uncontrolled forces and when the desired end is only attained exceptionally, and more often precisely the opposite. In the most advanced industrial countries the forces of nature have been tamed and pressed into the service of mankind and production has been infinitely increased, so that now a child can produce more than a hundred adults used to be able to. And what is the result ? An increase in overwork and an increase in the misery of the masses, and a conflagration every ten years. Darwin was unaware of how bitter a satire he was writing on mankind and particularly on his fellow countrymen, when he proved that free competition—the struggle for existence—which economists hail as the greatest historical achievement, was the normal state in the animal kingdom. It is only by a conscious organization of social production, in which production and distribution are planned, that man can be lifted, in the social sense, above the rest of the animal world ; just as it was by production as such that he was lifted from it in the specific sense. Historical evolution makes organization of this sort daily more inevitable and daily more possible. From it will arise a new epoch of history in which men themselves and all their activities, particularly the natural sciences, will undergo an unprecedented advance."—Introduction to *Dialectik der Natur* by Engels ; Marx and Engels, *Gesamtausgabe*, p. 494.

(16) " We know that Communist society cannot be built up unless we rebuild industry and agriculture, and these cannot be rebuilt in the old way. They must be rebuilt on a modern basis, according to the last word of science. You know that this basis is electricity, that only when the whole country, all branches of industry and agriculture have been electrified ; only when you have mastered this task will you be able to build up for yourselves the Communist society which the old generation cannot build. We are confronted with the task of economically regenerating the whole country, of reorganizing, restoring both agriculture and industry on a modern technical basis, which rests on modern science, on technique, on electricity. You understand perfectly well that illiterate people

are unsuitable for electrification, and even the mere ability to read and write is inadequate. It is not enough to understand what electricity is ; it is necessary to know how to apply it to industry and to agriculture, and to the various branches of industry and agriculture. We must learn this ourselves, and teach it to the whole of the younger generation of toilers. This is the task that confronts every class-conscious Communist."—From a speech by Lenin at the Third All-Russian Congress of the Russian Young Communist League, 1920. *Selected Works*, Vol. 9, p. 473.

(17) The situation in Physics, typical for the better developed sciences in Czarist Russia, is thus described by Prof. Joffe himself, one of the old guard of Russian science :

" Pre-revolutionary Russia could pride itself on a number of scholars, who left a notable trace in the history of physics. In addition to D. I. Mendeleyev, who was a remarkable physicist, as well as an outstanding chemist, P. N. Lebedev, A. G. Stoletov and B. B. Golitsin may be named. These three names are connected with such important successes in physics as the pressure of light, the photo-effect and seismology. However, pre-revolutionary Russian scholars were usually individuals, who left behind neither a scientific school nor a definite line. They themselves more often than not imported their themes from abroad, as a result of working with French or German scholars. Russian scholars would go to one of the Western European schools, and carry out there some research connected with the theme of this school, and then present their completed work in the form of a dissertation for a master's degree. Further development of this theme would be the subject of their doctor's dissertation, and it was quite natural to maintain the tendency of the foreign ideological centre. Independent Russian schools did not arise.

The single exception was the remarkable scientific school of Peter Nikolayevich Lebedev in Moscow University. However, in 1911 Kasso's policy drove it out from this refuge, and P. N. Lebedev himself died soon after. . . .

In Leningrad, until the Revolution, the position of Physics was considerably worse. The University remained fruitless. The absence of a vital creative line and the depressing system of master's examinations repelled from the University the most talented physicists (Gershun, Mitkevich, Lebedinsky). . . .

Until the Revolution, physics developed almost exclusively in Universities and in one or two higher technical schools. The number of doctors of physics did not exceed 15. The total number of working physicists was about 100, but for the great majority of these, scientific work was secondary to their main occupation of pedagogical work. . . .

The work of Lebedev's school and of several Leningrad physicists was of considerable scientific interest. The greater part of the scientific output, however, was not calculated to enrich the world of science. These works were partly ' provincial,' describing observations without giving any theoretical explanation, variants of foreign works, the measurements of various constants, and so on. In Leningrad University the ' scientific works ' of post-graduates were reduced to the reproduction of experiments, published in the latest issues of foreign journals.

Even the best works of Russian physicists were disconnected studies, forming no definite scientific line, setting themselves no profound problem or any kind of technological objective. It may be asserted that in pre-revolutionary Russia there was almost no technical physics, and the conditions for its formation were absent. Owing to the method of borrowing from abroad in a finished state, inclusive of working drawings, Russian technology had no need of its own scientific base, and did not have one. University physics counted itself as something apart from any practical applications. The Universities preserved the ' purity ' of science, and carefully protected it from technology.

Thus, in spite of the presence of great individual scholars, Russian physics was, until the Revolution, one of the most backward and weakest branches of world science."

(18) The Soviet Government has approved the distribution among the different commissariats and other bodies of the 12,520 young specialists graduated from the State universities and other higher educational institutions in the last term of 1937. The graduates include 7190 engineers of different specialities, 1049 agronomists, 1115 experts in zootechnics, 1274 doctors of medicine, 1087 physicists, chemists, biologists and other specialists, 342 veterinary surgeons, 298 economists and 165 other experts. Of the total number of young experts 2083 are being placed under the Commissariat of Heavy Industries, 2527 under the Commissariat of Agriculture, 1238 under the Commissariat of Public Health and 760 under the Commissariat of Education of the R.S.F.S.R.

(19) For example, *Soviet Science*, by J. G. Crowther ; *Science and Education in the U.S.S.R.*, by A. P. Pinkevitch.

(20) See *Britain without Capitalists*, p. 459.

(21) Further details as to how planning works are to be found in *Soviet Science*, p. 87 *et seq.*

(22) An admirable example is the work of V. Ilin, particularly *Man and Mountains*.

(23) For an account of the achievements of Soviet science in twenty years, see Priroda, October 1937 and Vestnik, January 1938.

(24) See *Soviet Science*, p. 29.

(25) The needs and the possibilities of Soviet science are movingly expressed in Pavlov's last testament to his students :

" What is it that I would wish the young men and women of my country who have dedicated themselves to science ?

First of all—consistency. Of this very important condition of fruitful scientific work I can never speak without emotion. Consistency, consistency and again consistency. From the very beginning of your work train yourself to strict consistency in the acquirement of knowledge.

Learn the ABC of science before you attempt to scale its peaks. Never embark on what comes after without having mastered what goes before. Never try to cover up the gaps in your knowledge, even by the boldest guesses and hypotheses. Such a bubble may delight your eye by its play of colours, but it will inevitably burst and you will be left with nothing but confusion.

Train yourself to reserve and patience. Learn to do the heavy work that science involves. Study, compare, accumulate facts. Be the wing of a bird never so perfect, it would never bear her aloft without the support of the air. Facts are the scientist's air, without which he would never be able to fly. Without facts, your theories are labour in vain.

But in studying, experimenting and observing—try not to remain at the surface of the facts. Do not turn yourself into a museum custodian of facts. Try to penetrate into the secret of their origin. Steadfastly seek the laws that govern them.

The second thing is—modesty. Never think that you already know everything. And however high the esteem in which you are held, always have the courage to say to yourself : ' I am ignorant.'

Do not allow pride to take possession of you. It will cause you to be obstinate when you should be conciliatory. It will cause you to reject useful advice and friendly help. It will prevent you from taking an objective view.

In the collective which I have to guide, everything depends on the atmosphere. We are all harnessed to a common cause and each of us helps it forward to the extent of his strength and possibility. With us it is often impossible to distinguish what is ' mine ' and what is ' yours.' But our common cause only gains thereby.

The third thing is—passion. Remember that science demands a man's whole life. And even if you had two lives, it would not be enough. Science demands from man great intensity and deep passion. Be passionate in your work and searchings.

Our fatherland is opening wide prospects before scientists and—it must be owned—science is being fostered in our country with the utmost lavishness.

What should I say of the position of the young scientist in our country ? Is not everything quite clear here ? Much is given him, but much is asked of him. For youth, as for us, it is a matter of honour to justify the great trust that our fatherland puts in science."—From *Pavlov and his School*, by Professor Y. P. Frolov, M.D.

(26) There has, for instance, in the last two years been the very important controversy on the subject of the foundations of genetics, in which Vavilov and Lysenko among others have been engaged. On account of the scanty notices that appeared outside the Soviet Union, this controversy has been magnified out of all proportion. It was claimed that the authorities were maintaining that genetics did not determine the evolution of species or the development of domestic plants and animals, and that it was a revival of the Weismann-Lamarck controversy on the relative importance of breeding and environment. In fact no such extreme views were put forward, but geneticists were criticized for attributing all inherited characters to specific unitary factors in the chromosomes, and neglecting cytoplastic and environmental factors, whose importance was probably exaggerated by their critics. For a full account see the article by Helix and Helianthus in the *Modern Quarterly*, Vol. 1, No. 4, p. 370.

Part II

WHAT SCIENCE COULD DO

Chapter IX

THE TRAINING OF THE SCIENTIST

The Reorganization of Science

A consideration of the present state of science in relation to society is enough to show that great changes are urgently necessary if science is to fulfil its functions or even maintain itself as a vital human activity. Some of the lines along which the reorganization of science should move emerge from the examination of its present defects. Their removal, however, would in itself not be enough. Piecemeal changes of this type might easily fail to achieve any useful object, partly because the different changes made would be uncoordinated and would not serve to assist one another, and partly because other consequences might result which would separately or in the aggregate tend to retard science and to reverse the intentions of the reformers. Any reorganization of science must be a comprehensive task and one which cannot be undertaken alone either by scientific workers themselves or by State or economic organizations outside science, but only by all working together in an agreed direction. The question, therefore, of whether science can be reorganized at all is not simply or even principally one for scientists. It is a social and political question. Every aspect of any reorganization of science concerns the economic and political structure of society. The recruitment and education of the scientist, the finance of research and the application of its results cannot be considered as simply scientific questions. If they are to be discussed at all profitably we must assume a certain attitude of society towards science. What that attitude is in existing society and how effectively it is crippling science has been shown in the first part of this book. To change this state of affairs, to allow science to grow freely for the benefit of humanity, presupposes therefore a change in society itself. For our immediate purpose it is not necessary to stipulate in detail what that change should be. It will be sufficient to assume that it would be a society that actively desired that science should be developed and used for human welfare and that it would be prepared to provide the means for that development and for the most effective social utilization of its results.

The Need for Expansion.—It is necessary to emphasize this because the primary overriding change which science needs is expansion, and that not a small but a very large expansion, up to a scale of operation something of the order of ten times what it is at present. In other words, the inadequacy of the scale of science is more immediately important than its inefficiency. On the social side this would appear in the crudest form as a simple increase of the annual budget of science to something like ten times the present figure. This may appear a somewhat extravagant claim, but, considering the actual size of the present budget, the increase would be completely imperceptible; it would be equivalent to a tax of less than 1 per cent. of the national income, and that only if the whole change were introduced all at once. In actual fact, with the greatest physically possible rate of increase, it is almost certain that, given an economic system that could utilize it, the net expenditure on science, *i.e.* its gross expenditure less the benefits directly attributable to this expenditure, would vanish in less than five years, becoming instead an ever-increasing surplus, and that it would never at any stage amount to more than one-half per cent. of the national income.

Organization and the Preservation of Freedom.—The problem for the scientists is, however, a much more difficult one. It is one of increasing the intensity and scope of scientific work while preserving and improving the efficiency and co-ordination of that work. Nor must this very increase of size and efficiency be allowed to lower the standards or to stifle the freedom and originality of scientific research. The whole framework of scientific activity, in recruiting, in education, in internal organization, and in intensity and utility of application, requires extension and improvement at the same time. This is a task the detailed accomplishment of which can only be undertaken by scientists themselves. They alone understand the difficulties of the problem and the dangers which may come from unwise changes. It is not surprising that many scientists, particularly of the older school, shrink altogether from the task and prefer science to remain inefficient and obscure so long as it is preserved as a free playground for the fortunate few to whom accidents of birth and temperament have made it accessible. To them the proposals contained in the present chapter will appear anathema. Only those will accept them who see that science is a gift that demands to be used to the full for the material and cultural benefit of humanity, and that if science is not so used it will itself be the first to suffer.

The Recruitment of Scientists.—If science is to develop it must first make the utmost use of the human material that is available. To-day this requires in most countries, and certainly in Britain, a complete recasting of the methods of recruiting the personnel of scientific research and teaching. This problem is intrinsically bound up with the more general one of the reform of education in the direction of giving full opportunity for the development of ability by the removal of all barriers based on economic class. We have already discussed how far the existing system falls short in these respects. Such a general change would not in itself be sufficient and needs to be accompanied by a qualitative change in the system of education in all its stages whereby science would permeate the whole educational structure and not appear as a late and ill-coordinated annex. Only when science permeates education, and through it the general outlook on life, can there be any hope of a rational choice of a scientific career. We do not want people to choose to be scientists merely because science is well paid or, if not well paid, gives an opportunity of a job free from many of the irritating restraints of commercial employment. The appeal of science should be partly that of intrinsic curiosity and partly the realization of the important and disinterested social contribution that can be made through a scientific career. By having far larger numbers to choose from and by developing a greater general understanding of science, the standard ability for entry into scientific professions could be raised at the same time as the numbers of the entrants increased.

Vocational Selection.—From the start, however, it would be necessary to realize that not one but many different types of abilities are required. In a well-ordered scientific movement capacities for administration and for teaching would be in demand as well as those of more purely research character. It would be a matter of developing the present rudimentary methods of vocational selection to see that the appropriate proportions of these different types of scientific ability were selected at any given time. It is clear that these proportions would vary markedly as science developed, partly because of the changing complexity of scientific organization which would probably demand, as time went on, a greater number of those with organizing talent, and partly because of the transitional need of building up the structure of science on a far larger scale than has yet been attempted, a process which would put great emphasis on the teaching of science.

It must be borne in mind that any marked development of science is only likely to take place simultaneously with other social and economic changes, all of which will make considerable demands on ability. To a large extent this will be met by a great release of hitherto unused ability, made possible by a really democratic educational system. But it is impossible to be sure, even in the absence of such negative factors as war and social struggle, that the rate of release of this ability will, in the first stages, be equal to the demand. Such excess demand will necessarily draw away from science, for a while, many that would in more normal circumstances be attracted to it. It is therefore all the more necessary to see that the fullest use is made of the available personnel.

A Wide Entry into Scientific Research.—For this purpose the net should be thrown wide. There is no reason at all why entry into a scientific career should only be through the conventional educational system of elementary school, secondary school, and university. Science should return to its earlier phase when, like literature, it was a liberal profession, one that could be entered from any other profession at any stage in life. In the greatest period of scientific development there was a particular emphasis on drawing into science men from active and practical life. This tendency has gradually disappeared; it requires to be revived. Effective facilities, both educational and economic, need to be offered and made widely known so as to make possible the entry, after a few years' training, of every kind of industrial, agricultural, or clerical worker into active and responsible scientific work.

The class of such recruits which could be made most immediately available for science are the laboratory assistants themselves, who already perform such a large and such a poorly recognized part of actual scientific work. This could be done both by a removal of the distinction between the research worker and the laboratory assistant and by an extension of their present utterly inadequate means of entry into official science.

We need to develop, and could easily do so even at present, amateur scientific societies in such a way that they should no longer be considered to be playing at science but to be taking an active, responsible and recognized part in its advancement. There are a large number of problems the solution of which could be found as well, if not better, by societies of amateurs capable of making co-ordinated observations than by individual research workers in institutes. This is already, of course, the case in astronomy and meteorology and could easily be extended to most other fields of science.

We have another untapped source of scientific ability, and one which will tend to increase, in the interest which might be taken in science by men and women retired from active life. There is in science an enormous amount of repeated and painstaking observations, of classifying and co-ordinating work which, though of the very highest importance, is of a nature particularly galling to young and active spirits, yet might nevertheless be an agreeable occupation to those who are more inclined to sum up a life's work than to wish to change it. In the fields of literature and bibliography a great deal of such work is done, but in science we have, up till now, lacked the organization to make use of such a fund of willing assistance. It should be possible at relatively little expense, not only to ensure to all such persons, showing a reasonable competence, such access to the laboratories and libraries and the use of apparatus in their own homes as is required for their work, but also to see that the work they do receives its due recognition.

A Directing Authority for Entrants.—Up till now the arrangements for recruitment into science have largely been left to chance or to uncoordinated bodies such as university appointment boards. We require as part of any rational organization of science some body responsible for recruitment into scientific research, one which would, of course, be in the closest co-ordination with the educational authorities. It is only in the text-books of economists that recruitment into any profession is supposed to be automatically determined by the requirements of that profession. Actually there is always a lag due to ignorance of prospects and, quite apart from cyclical fluctuations of employment, a chronic state of surplus in some sections and shortage of workers in others. The foresight which it is unreasonable to expect from students who have no experience of the world could be exercised by an authority which was able to survey not only the existing situation of science but also all its plans for future development. Such an authority would, of course, have a harder task in science than in almost any other profession because of the unpredictable character of scientific development, but this difficulty could be overcome by flexibility, particularly in the proper use of alternative occupations. In any rapid development of science shortage of personnel would probably be the limiting factor. Indeed, many, overlooking potential sources of ability, think that it has already become so. A recruiting authority would therefore perform an invaluable service by being able to indicate fairly accurately what personnel was likely to be available in different categories and in different subjects and thus prevent whatever plans were made from being held up by unexpected shortages of men.

CHANGING THE TEACHING OF SCIENCE

The importance of a change in the whole method of teaching science has already been stressed. At every stage in education we require not only an increased attention to be paid to science but also a complete change in the method of teaching it and of relating that teaching to the other parts of the curriculum. The aim of science teaching is twofold: to provide a background of the ordered knowledge already won from nature and to communicate effectively the means by which such knowledge has been and can be won and checked. But these two things are not independent. It is strictly impossible to convey an adequate picture of existing scientific knowledge if the learner is not aware of how that knowledge is obtained, and aware to the extent of being able himself to take part in some way in the process of discovery. It is in this latter aspect that present science teaching most signally fails. Scientific method is usually taught, even in practical laboratory work, as if it involved only measurement and simple logical deductions. The play of imagination and the building and the testing of hypotheses is hardly ever attempted, for reasons, partly traditional and partly economic, that we have already described. What we want to see is the inclusion of research as an integral part of the teaching of science, and this even more for those who will use their science knowledge in ordinary life or in teaching than for those who intend to carry out scientific research themselves.

SCIENCE IN SCHOOLS

At different stages in the educational process different changes are required. In schools the chief need is for a general change in the attitude towards science, which should be from the beginning an integral part and not a mere addition, often an optional addition, to the curriculum. Science should be taught not merely as a subject but should come into all subjects. Its importance in history and in modern life should be pointed out and illustrated. The old contrast, often amounting to hostility, between scientific and humane subjects needs to be broken down and replaced by a scientific humanism. At the same time, the teaching of science proper requires to be humanized. The dry and factual presentation requires to be transformed, not by any appeal to mystical theory, but by emphasizing the living and dramatic character of scientific advance itself. Here the teaching of the history of science, not isolated as at present, but in close relation to general history teaching, would serve to correct the existing atmosphere of scientific dogmatism. It would show at the same time how secure are the conquests of science in the control they give over natural processes and how insecure and provisional, however necessary, are the rational interpretations, the theories and hypotheses put forward at each stage. Past history by itself is not enough, the latest developments of science should not be excluded because they have not yet passed the test of time. It is absolutely necessary to emphasize the fact that science not only has changed but is continually changing, that it is an activity and not merely a body of facts. Throughout, the social implications of science, the powers that it puts into men's hands, the uses they could make of them and those which they in fact do, should be brought out and made real by a reference to immediate experience of ordinary life. (1)

As science advances it leaves the explanation of the more remote and obscure parts of life—the heavens or the mysteries of chemistry—

and becomes more and more able to cope with domestic activities which have been the first to be carried out but the last to be understood. It is along these lines that it should be possible to introduce the teaching of practical scientific methods by making students find out for themselves new relationships in things that already concern them and not in artificially simplified and unnecessarily abstract experiment (see p. 74). In such hobbies as photography and wireless, as well as in all the field of natural history, there are opportunities not only for observation but also for experiment and discovery. A whole new technique of experimental biology could easily be adapted for school use and developed in the direction of physiological, psychological, and social observation and analysis. The old ideas—that only exact science could be taught in schools and that the only exact sciences are physics and chemistry—must be abolished. But in the process of doing so, which is already under way, there is a danger of passing over from studies which provide criticism in a rigorous sense to those of vague and often sentimental description. The biological sciences could, however, be made as practical and, with the use of statistics, as exact as the other sciences.

A Living Curriculum.—The whole question of detailed curriculum or exact methods of teaching science is beyond the scope of this book. (2) The relative merits of formal and orderly, as against practical and discursive, teaching cannot be simply decided, if indeed there is only one answer. But, however that is determined, there is no question that in the developments of science in the last twenty years, or even more particularly in the last ten years, there has arisen, with such advances as the quantum theory in physics and chemistry and the gene and bio-chemical theories in biology, a general scheme of description that is a far more easily grasped basis for exposition than any previously existing. It is essential in any reconstruction of science teaching that this new knowledge should be so used and not relegated as heretofore for a probationary period of between fifty and a hundred years.

What we need is a permanent standing commission composed of active and young research scientists and of experienced science teachers to keep under constant review the teaching of science and to suggest and bring into practice a continual change and improvement. (3) Against such action there will always remain the enormous vested interest of the examination system and of the producers of text-books. It is gradually becoming recognized that examinations as they exist at present not only cramp the whole system of education and produce serious effects on students working for them but also are extremely unreliable in their one ostensible object of testing the relative ability of the candidates. The difficulty, of course, is that, in view of the monetary rewards for success in examination, far too much stress has to be laid on the prevention of all forms of fraud and spurious knowledge, rather than on giving opportunities for the expression of intelligence. Most school examiners, owing to the large number of candidates, are just hack-workers, and all attempts at reform are met by the objection of the extra expense and the impossibility of achieving uniform results on anything but the most stereotyped sort of examination paper. (4) The revision of the examination system is, however, being pressed for many other reasons. This simply adds to the plea for reform that we shall never have a rational teaching of science as long as the system remains as it is.

Science for All.—The aim of education as far as science is concerned is to see that everyone not only has a general picture of the world in terms of modern knowledge, but also appreciates and can use the type of argument on which that knowledge is based. The particular contribution of science to this is the creation of quantitative reasoning and the understanding of how phenomena can be brought about by different causes, each contributing to a definite degree. The schools should produce citizens who understand mathematics not, as now, simply as a means of reckoning pounds, shillings, and pence, but as a general way of thinking of all sorts of problems. The idea of graphs, correlations, and statistical distributions should be as familiar as the first four rules. (5) Only with this equipment is it possible to cope with the economic and social problems of our time. Further, they should be able to know where to turn when faced with any detailed problem that is beyond their immediate experience. For that it is not necessary to know all science, but to know where science is to be found and to understand enough to see its general bearing. Finally, a general appreciation of the importance of science needs to be widely spread partly because science can only develop adequately if supported by such an opinion and partly because this is our only effective safeguard against mystical enthusiasms and anti-rational tendencies which are otherwise at the command of all reactionary forces.

SCIENCE IN UNIVERSITIES

In its general aspect reform of teaching of science in universities should follow the same lines as already indicated for schools. But here, where the knowledge has to be far greater and better founded, we must examine the changes in greater detail. The first change should be in the methods of teaching. As has already been pointed out, university teaching, perhaps even more than school teaching, tends to become stereotyped into the lecture and practical work routine. The advance from this state of affairs in science would, of course, be only part of the general reform of university teaching methods. The lecture system must be cut down and transformed. All that need be left are a certain number of lectures, on new branches of science, or new aspects of old branches, which would mostly be given by the research workers themselves and should, at the same time, stimulate and give information not otherwise obtainable. A certain number of set lectures might remain for those who find it easier to listen than to read, but would, of course, be completely optional. (6) Instead of lectures there should be a much wider extension, even than that at present existing at Cambridge or Oxford, of individual or small group tuition and, even more important, of small discussion circles. The demonstrations which have sometimes to be used to justify science lectures could well be given at such discussions or placed in a working museum permanently accessible to students and representing only those parts of practical instruction which they cannot for reasons of expense or lack of experience perform for themselves.

Research as a Teaching Method.—At the same time practical teaching requires at least as drastic a modification. At present nearly all practical work is either preparation, measurement, or description, all operations essential to science but by themselves entirely insufficient. The use of intelligence in choosing the apparatus required to solve a particular problem and in facing the difficulties of interpretation of results is as important as handiness in manipulation and exactitude in measurement. The only effective way of dealing with this is to introduce research at an extremely early stage. For certain techniques, say, quantitative analysis and glass-blowing or the cutting of sections, a few formal lessons would still be required, but these could be taken at the same time as the earlier stages of research. There is something to be said for the return to the more primitive system of teaching by apprenticeship, of allowing students to attach themselves for a month or two to one research worker after another, so as to see at first hand real scientific problems being tackled. At any rate, no student should leave a university without having done at least one or two years of research, and this applies even more to those who are going to teach than those who are afterwards going into research proper. It is more important for a teacher to know how science is done than to have accumulated a mass of information which will always be available in written form in the school where he is going to teach. Much more attention should also be given to teaching the reading and writing of science as, for example, finding out all that is known on some particular subject and writing good accounts of original work or reports on work done by others. It is true that if, as is suggested later, scientific publications are drastically rationalized, the labour of the first of these will be largely unnecessary, but when that occurs there will still be ample opportunity for the individual student to collaborate actively in the day-to-day work of putting scientific publications into order. Above all, a student wants to acquire self-reliance and an ability to collaborate in pursuit of knowledge rather than to accumulate facts.

Science and Culture.—But it is not sufficient to turn out people who are just capable of being good scientific workers or at least of understanding what good scientific work is. It is equally important that at the university where they are acquiring a more detailed knowledge of science they should see all the more clearly the relation of their work to general social activities. Here again the history of science deserves to take a most important place. The whole structure of the industries or human activities connected with each branch of science should also be made clear, not only in formal teaching but also by the actual experience of seeing, and if possible working in, industrial or field laboratories. At the same time the effort must be made to recapture the ancient spirit of a university where the different disciplines of study are related to one another. To a large extent this can be done informally by general societies of scientists, historians, economists, etc., who are agreed to discuss current questions affecting them all in different ways.

All this would, of course, require greater expense to the university in the form of additional staff and, to a certain extent, of additional apparatus, but it might well be found that, if properly co-ordinated with research and carried out on a much larger scale, the expense would in fact be far less than might appear under present estimates.

Vocational Teaching ?—The question remains as to whether there should be one or many courses of science in universities according to the different intended careers of the students, that is, whether there should be different courses for those intending to continue in research or to enter teaching or business careers. Except for some differentiation based on intelligence, such as is at present represented by pass and honours degrees, themselves distinctions likely to disappear when entrance to the university is based more on intelligence than on wealth, there would seem little to recommend them. It would be very unfair to expect students on entering or even long before leaving a university to decide to which of these uses they would turn their scientific interests. Yet the requirements of teaching and research definitely do call for some special training. This would probably best be met, not by adapting the curriculum but by introducing in the latter years special teaching and research courses and by allowing a greater degree of specialization for those wishing to remain occupied in research.

Specialization.—The whole question of specialization is, of course, a very difficult one. As at present practised, specialization is peculiarly self-defeating. A certain number of set subjects—chemistry, biology, etc.—are taught so intensively as to prevent the acquisition of any general culture, but owing to their vast size not intensively enough for the student to acquire any detailed competence, which, if acquired at all, is acquired in post-graduate research. A better plan would seem to be a broader general course and what might be called a "sample"; more intensive specialization on some restricted field connected particularly with the practical research which the student is taking up. A somewhat similar scheme is now in force at Oxford with excellent results. Preferably, in the course of a university career, such "sample" courses should be taken not in one but in three or four of these fields as widely separated as possible. The total effect would be that the university would turn out students capable not only of doing good scientific work but also of understanding what their science is about and how in practice as well as in theory it could be used for human welfare.

Higher Universities.—The length of a modern university course has by now of itself become a serious problem. The growth of science in extent and in detail has so increased that the customary three years has become entirely inadequate. In other countries the course has already been lengthened to five or even seven years. The difficulty here is quite as much financial as academic. To lengthen the university course under present conditions is to postpone the entry of the student into earning life and to put him at a disadvantage as compared with less academically qualified competitors. Without an adequate system of maintenance grants this would simply penalize the poor student still further. In any case, the latter years of such longer courses must be considered as definitely research courses, and there is much to be said for the development of higher universities, corresponding to present post-graduate courses, but with a more definite status and organization. In them the workers would be at the same time students, collaborators, and teachers: attending certain advanced courses, doing their own research and lecturing on it or discussing it in colloquia with other research workers and in some cases with students in the university. A further difference from the ordinary universities would be that work there would be considered as a profession, or at least a probationary profession, and the post-graduate students would be paid, in return for which they would be doing useful research work. Incidentally, they would be permitted to marry, as most such students do in the U.S.S.R., which is far better for them than the state produced by the marriage prohibitions attached to Government grants in Britain. Naturally the arrangements of such institutions would be very flexible. They would not be so definitely located and would represent more a body of people at a certain stage of training than a school. They might be distributed not only in universities but also in technical institutes in other places.

Research and Teaching.—At present research work is not a fully recognized profession. The greater part of such work is done in universities by people already engaged in teaching. The proper relations of teaching and research have not been thought out. Undoubtedly the present division of research workers in the two categories of university teachers with a little spare time for research and of research workers who give an occasional lecture is a most unsatisfactory one. Teachers should be allowed much more time for research work and research workers be required to do more teaching. The two categories will always remain distinct on account of the fundamental differences in personality and temperament between them. Therefore there need be no fusing of the two in practice except that occasionally, for a term every few years, the research worker and the teacher might interchange.

Already this administrative separation of the teaching and research worker has been achieved in France, where equivalent grades in both are placed on an equal footing and there is full liberty of interchange between them at every stage (see Appendix VI).

Revising the Curriculum

So far the question of science teaching in the universities has been treated in perfectly general terms, but it is worth while giving in some greater detail the kinds of changes that might have to be made in the curriculum of the different subjects of university education. The chief criticisms of existing curricula are that they are over-loaded, confused, and out of date. What is required, therefore, is essentially a work of modernization and revision. We must reduce the time-lag between the incorporation of some new knowledge or new method and its teaching in the university. We must do this while emphasizing all the time the provisional and progressive nature of science in such a way as to avoid the criticism that no knowledge should be taught until it has stood the test of time. For this, teaching of the history of science should be of the greatest value. Further, the new knowledge does not require merely to be added to the old curricula but should be organically incorporated in them in a coherent and yet flexible way. It is clearly impossible for any one person to be able to make anything like a comprehensive plan for the modernization of science teaching in universities. What is called for, as in the case of schools, is a permanent revisionary committee which not only would have available to it the knowledge of the advances of science but also could draw on the best experience of university teaching. There is no reason at all to suppose that a uniform method of teaching would be desirable; on the contrary, variations within limits would allow for experiment and competition in the best methods. What follows is simply a rough sketch embodying a personal opinion of the most immediately necessary and indeed overdue alterations of the science curriculum in universities.

Physics.—In physics the general aim should be to combine an appreciation of the mathematical mechanical relations common to the most widely diverse phenomena with the description of the minute substructure of the actual world. The general concepts of motion, energy, equilibrium, inertia, oscillation, and waves could be brought out not exclusively, or even mainly, in relation to the now rather dull examples of classical mechanics, but rather to the whole range of modern application as, for instance, in quantum mechanics or radio engineering. The old historical divisions of heat, light, and sound, and electricity and magnetism require to be broken down and fused into a general picture of physical process. This has been done in popular books and even in some physical text-books. (7) On the other hand, it is necessary to emphasize the contingent as much as the formal aspects of physics. The student needs to acquire familiarity with fundamental structural units in the universe, with the primitive particles, photons, electrons, neutrons, etc., and their complexes in nuclei atoms and molecules. The whole great work of the present century should have a much more important place than heretofore in university physics teaching. These units are no longer doubtful or mysterious things, and can not only be spoken of but also be experimented with almost as easily as more familiar objects. Practical physics could afford to include much more research in this field. Very many pieces of electrical and optical apparatus are now really tools whose use can be taught far better by the practice of selection and assembly in solving some particular quasi-research problem than merely by using them to execute routine measurements. These problems may be graded, but each should be a real problem, not a mind-dulling exercise.

Chemistry.—In chemistry the changes required are more far-reaching than those in physics. From a formal and theoretical, though not from the historical or practical point of view, chemistry can now be regarded as a special branch of applied physics. The whole of the mechanisms of chemistry and the structural units— atoms, molecules, etc.—on which they operate are adequately described only in modern physical terms. Further, the new physical methods of investigation, such as spectroscopy or crystal analysis, give far more direct information than the older, more elaborate logic of chemical analysis. These conceptions are at present revolutionizing chemistry, but chemical teaching has still to be transformed. Though the transformation will need to be very thorough, so much so as to make the older method almost unrecognizable, it will prove to be well worth while, for in the modern view the processes of chemistry are not only better ordered, but even far simpler to understand than they were in the old. Chemistry can now cease to be a catalogue of properties and receipts that have to be remembered, and become a coherent and logical discipline. Without this discipline the chemist of to-day—and such chemists are being regularly turned out by universities—is obliged to grope with difficulty to the solution of problems to which direct answers can be found by means of the new methods. But the transition is difficult to effect largely because the chemical world, with its close connection with industry and its enormous personnel, is much more difficult to move than is that of the smaller, more professional sciences. There is no suggestion, of course, of abandoning the practice or even the teaching of the valuable methods of reactions and preparations that have been elaborated by centuries of independent chemical research, but such experience needs to find its place in the practical rather than in the theoretical teaching of the subject. Practical teaching in chemistry has also been somewhat stagnant, limiting itself to the parts which can most easily be taught on a large scale, qualitative and quantitative analysis and simple organic preparations. There is little relation between practical chemistry in the university and the most important chemical operations of industry. Practical chemistry requires to be extended in scope to include really modern analytic methods, such as the new physical methods of optics and crystallography and the most important sides of modern chemical practice, the use of catalysts, high-temperature and high-pressure chemistry as well as many of the simpler biochemical techniques. (8) Chemistry, which is of even greater importance in most aspects of life than physics, has heretofore remained far too much a closed science. Chemists are generally narrower in their interests than almost any other kind of scientist. This is largely the fault of chemical education. The role that chemistry plays in geology and biology, in industry and everyday life, should be part of every chemical course.

Astronomy and Geology.—The cosmic sciences—astronomy, geophysics, geology, and mineralogy—are only now, after a long relative eclipse, beginning to play their due part in university education. Largely because of the severity of its discipline, astronomy has been considered a subject unfit for undergraduate study, but most of the difficult parts of astronomy refer to the necessary, though now scientifically insignificant, operations of reduction of observations. Astro-physics itself is no more difficult and far more interesting than many other branches of physics, as shown by the immense success of popular books on the subject. It might accordingly be made one of the principal branches of applied physics, to be studied in universities or at any rate to be incorporated in all special spectroscopic studies.

Considering its growing economic importance, the general neglect of geology in university teaching is difficult to justify. The fact that it is not taught in schools is really an argument for teaching it in schools rather than for neglecting it in the university. But if it is to be effectively taught in the university it will need to change from its present almost purely descriptive and largely memorizing form to the status of a really logical science. Except in palaeontology, modern geology is on the way to becoming such a science. This we owe to the new methods of geo-physics, geo-chemistry, and crystal analysis. The processes for making and transforming the earth are beginning to form a coherent picture, and the method of reading them from evidence of the rocks is becoming more direct and certain. If more time could be spent in understanding these methods and the theories behind them and less on memorizing type fossils and geographical distributions, geology would become a subject not only more scientific, but also one which would attract a better class of mind than at present and would in consequence develop far more rapidly. It is in geology and mineralogy that we meet with the most clear connections with economic realities in the location and working of mineral resources. A really adequate teaching of geology implies not only some of this technical knowledge but the economic and political knowledge necessary to complete it.

Biology.—The present state of biological science is one of transition from an outlook primarily discursive, descriptive and classificatory to that of a unitary experimental science, drawing many of its basic ideas from recent developments in physics and chemistry. Because of the vast extent and intricacy of the field covered by biology this change is slower and less definite than in simpler sciences, and it is consequently much more difficult to suggest any scheme of teaching which is at the same time clear, comprehensive, and modern. Actually, however, the very fact that biology is being transformed, and in its transformation attracting the more intelligent minds among the younger scientists, means that in many places the teaching of biology is already much closer to the actual state of knowledge and practice than it is in the older and more established sciences of physics and chemistry. What is lacking, however, in biological teaching is any kind of coherence or uniformity; the theories of biology are still for the most part verbal rather than quantitative in form and contain an undifferentiated mixture of logical, or at least plausible, deductions from observations together with the remains of ethical and religious considerations carried over from primitive times. It is not to be expected that a really coherent or comprehensive theory can be presented. It may take decades or centuries before such a theory can be hammered out. The danger lies rather in the fact that the theories which are presented are given by implication the same weight as the more testable theories of other sciences, and their mystical and logical elements are not differentiated.

In biology more than in any other branch of science the corrective of teaching the history of science as an integral part of the presentation of current attitudes is an urgent necessity. The controversies between mechanists and vitalists, between Darwinians and anti-Darwinians, between preformationists and epigenicists are incomprehensible or misleading if not presented as part of the politico-religious controversies of the past and the present. It might be said that in the circumstances it is better to dispense with theories and stick to facts. This tendency, however, results in a completely unmanageable accumulation of observations and leads to the implicit adoption of even cruder theories than those explicitly stated. It is essential, moreover, that the provisional and tentative nature of biological theory be pointed out, not only as a caution but also as a spur to further work. In no other field is there such scope for the development of comprehensive theory.

In detailed biological teaching there is still much too much division into separate compartments. Biological forms are described separately from their physical or chemical functions and from the development of these forms in the individual animal. These studies are further separated from those of genetics and evolution which throw light on the significance of embryogeny. The whole complex of function, form, development, and genesis requires to be presented so that these relations are clearly seen, because only in this way can the full significance of each particular be grasped and the mystical theories used to fill in the gaps left by an artificial separation be avoided. Once the arrangements for greater co-ordination and different biological disciplines are made in the field of research, the problem of teaching will be very much easier. But we can before then at least break down the barriers between physiology, descriptive zoology, botany, bio-chemistry, and genetics sufficiently to avoid actual contradictory statements in the different sections and to provide some measure of correlation of presentation.

In biology, especially, the importance lies in the teaching of methods rather than results. To the old techniques of field observations and the microscope have been added a host of new methods, essentially adaptations of the experimental technique of other sciences to the much more complex and variable biological material. Biology is beginning to be a quantitative science partly on account of the impact of statistical methods and partly through the introduction of exact measurements of physical and chemical quantities. All this implies a need for the much wider training of the modern biologist, but one which, while it puts in his grasp these new techniques, does not encourage him to forget the especially complicated and variable material on which he is working.

The interdependence of different types of research is becoming increasingly important in biology. This is not only in the sense that each investigation requires reference to an ever larger number of previous observations in the same or different fields, but also in the growing necessity of consciously organized co-operative investigations. Individual research is becoming restricted to the elaboration of general concepts, the actual work becoming a collaboration. This implies the teaching, particularly in biology, but by no means restricted to it, of the importance of collaboration, and here by far the best and the simplest plan is to give more opportunity for students actually to take part in such collective researches.

Medicine.—At the present time the greatest confusion is caused in biological teaching by the nature of its connection with medicine. Organized teaching of biology arose primarily from medical schools, and it is only comparatively recently that other occupations, chiefly concerned with agriculture, have furnished opportunities for employment of non-medically trained biologists. It is becoming increasingly clear at the same time that the scope of biology is much wider than can be immediately related to medical practice. The result is to produce latent conflict and distortion of both subjects. Two opposite tendencies are apparent. From the side of the medical schools it appears to be desirable, in view of the long course, to get biological training cut down to a minimum and restrict it to those aspects of biology likely to be of immediate use to a doctor in hospital or in practice. (9) Others think that the primary requirement for biological students, whether they are going on to medicine, as most of them will be, or not, is to acquire a scientific and critical attitude towards biological problems. This plainly requires a longer or a less immediately useful course. The present scheme satisfies neither side (see p. 80).

It is unlikely that this difficulty will be resolved until there has been a complete change in the method of selection, training, and employment in the medical profession. So long as the doctor is considered to be primarily a professional man exercising his skill for money and not a member of a salaried health service, the objects of the entrants will be to get an adequate training for the least expenditure of time and money.   A medical education is considered simply as an investment, expensive enough to keep out all except the most brilliant of the entrants unprovided with means, but open at a price to every grade of intelligence.   Owing to this fantastic system of selection and training the medical student exhibits on the average a far lower degree of intelligence than that of other university students.   He lacks both the time and the ability to acquire an adequate grasp of scientific method.   The result is that the doctor who might be applying to his patients the best of existing knowledge in the most intelligent manner is generally dependent on tradition and experience, much of which has no more and no less validity than the practices of primitive medicine men (see p. 16).

Medical students should be chosen solely on the basis of ability and subsidized for a longer course of training than they now receive, repaying their debt to the community by their subsequent service, as is already done in the Soviet Union.   It should then be possible to plan a rational medical training which would be satisfactory both medically and scientifically.   There would be time and capacity for a real grasp of the principles underlying the human body in health and sickness, and, later, much fuller opportunity for dealing with actual patients in and out of hospital, and this not only on the clinical side but by participation in all the bacteriological, biochemical, and physiological research which would develop alongside medical practice.   As in biology so even more in medicine the collaboration of different disciplines is becoming increasingly necessary.   The general practitioner would still be needed, but his main functions would be more social and psychological, and his knowledge would be required more to direct the patient to a suitable polyclinic than to deal, as he is at present obliged to do, inadequately and incompetently with disease in all its forms. (10)

The Social Sciences.—Between scientific and humane subjects there has been growing up during the present century a group of subjects— psychology, sociology, and anthropology, archaeology, philology, and economics—which are beginning to count themselves as sciences, but which are as yet only in process of leaving the stage of purely verbal description and collection of facts, though already they are evolving their own particular disciplines and methods.   Apart from certain agreements on fact, there is no agreed theory in any of these subjects, but rather a number of theories in violent conflict with one another. Each school manages to achieve a certain internal coherence, but the whole picture is one of confusion.   The difficulties are not only in the extreme complexity involved in the existence and development of human societies, but in the fact that, by dealing with human societies at all, these sciences are brought into immediate contact with current moral, political, and economic conflicts, and their theories reflect more or less unconsciously the attitudes of different existing movements of opinion. In such circumstances it is not surprising that the teaching of these subjects should be in a very unsatisfactory state. Apart from the confusion of different opinions there is in their teaching in all countries, even the most apparently democratic, a definite bias in favour of certain orthodox views. This bias, which in Fascist states amounts to a distortion so gross that it removes these subjects from the bounds of scientific study altogether, in this country takes the subtler form of an apparently strictly scientific attitude. All views that might conceivably lead to some action in practice are thus excluded as tendencious, and studies in the social sciences are limited to pure analysis. As Professor Hogben remarks in his Moncure Conway lecture:

"The plain truth is that the academic value of social research in our universities is largely rated on a futility scale. A social inquiry which leads to the conclusion that something has to be done or might be done is said to be 'tendencious.' In daily hymns to the Idol of Purity this refrain recurs with soporific solemnity like Selah in the Psalms of David. If natural scientists prohibited all investigations when the research worker was suspected of wanting to find how to do something, science would come to a standstill. What distinguishes the scientific attitude from its opposite is not the absence of intention to get a particular result, but willingness to recognize when it cannot be obtained by one method and to try out other methods instead. The exaltation of 'pure' thought which bears no fruit in action exacts its own penalty in the growing disposition to regard reason and progress as exploded liberal superstitions. The younger generation have found us out. Their pitiable predilection for action without thought is the legitimate offspring of thought divorced from action."—*The Retreat from Reason*, by Lancelot Hogben (p. 9). Conway Memorial Lecture, 20th May 1936.

It is unlikely that, until we come to live in a state the basis of which can safely be exposed to rational investigation, these conditions will be much improved. Even now, however, it would be possible, at least in democratic countries, to achieve a certain amount in greater unification and coherence of the different subjects in the field of social science. Just as in biology the behaviour and the origin of animate existence is closely related, so in the general study of human society we cannot separate without loss of understanding the behaviour of individuals from their political and economic relations, or the structure of society from the development of that structure from earlier forms. What we need is a coherent and unified picture of human society in which the different disciplines of economic, psychological, and anthropological analysis and the reconstruction of history by the methods of scholarship and archaeology find a natural place. In any case such a step will be a necessary one in moving to the next stage of converting social science from an analytical and descriptive into an experimental and applied science.

It may be hoped that this cursory survey of the kind of changes which seem desirable in science teaching in universities should indicate in a broad way what is necessary before we can hope to turn out students adequately prepared for research, for the teaching of science, or for the application of scientific principles in other walks of life. The plea is not so much that precisely these changes should be made, but that the need for some change of an extensive character should be recognized, and that some organized provision should be made for bringing about that change as rapidly and smoothly as possible. All through the emphasis has been on the coherence of the different scientific disciplines and on their relation to the present structure and future development of society.

(1) How such a method of teaching could become an integral part of general education is sketched by H. G. Wells' British Association address, "The Informative Content of Education," reprinted in *World Brain* (Methuen, 1938). Hogben's *Science for the Citizen* would be an admirable text-book for such teaching.

(2) For this the work of the American Commission of the Progressive Education Association on the Secondary School Curriculum, as exemplified in their reports, is of the greatest interest.

(3) Such committees are in existence and doing good work, notably the Committee of the Science Masters Association in England and the Progressive Education Association, but they lack sufficiently authoritative standing and they are everywhere restricted by the exigences of the examination system.

(4) See *An Examination of Examinations*. Sir Philip Hartog and Dr. E. C. Rhodes.

(5) Hogben's *Mathematics for the Million* is the first simple text-book of mathematics which incorporates these ideas.

(6) This state of affairs has already been reached in certain science departments at Oxford.

(7) J. A. Prins' *Grondbeginselen van de Hedendaagse Natuurkunde*, also Pilley, *Electricity*, 1933.

(8) A beginning had been made in this direction in the University of Vienna. Professor Mark has entirely reorganized the chemical course, devoting the theoretical part largely to quantum mechanics and crystallography and including most of what is usually taught in chemistry in the practical course. Whether this course will survive Professor Mark's removal from his post is doubtful.

(9) This is the view so ably expressed by Professor Mottram in his contribution to *The Frustration of Science*. See also p. 92.

(10) An apparently opposite view of the functions of a G.P. is put forward in Cronin's novel, *The Citadel*. Here the G.P. would be responsible for the patient in health and sickness, but the difficulty of limited skill would be overcome by co-operative practice. Practical trial would be needed to decide which solution would be the best.

CHAPTER X

THE REORGANIZATION OF RESEARCH

FIRST PRINCIPLES

IT is far easier to criticize the existing methods and the organization of research than to suggest any effective means of remedying their deficiencies. The only sure test of any proposed changes is in practice, because we have no other way of knowing for certain that while they may remove a known evil they may not at the same time introduce other unsuspected ones. We already have, however, as a general guide, a certain amount of such practical experience in the application of new methods in different sciences and in different institutions. In each science there exist wide divergences of methods and performance. By selecting from each of them those features which seem to yield the most valuable results it is possible to form some picture, provisional and incomplete though it be, of desirable reform of research organization. The need for special caution in dealing with research is that, even more than teaching and far more than industry or administration, it is a novel and unpredictable form of human activity. Any measures aimed at giving greater assistance and scope to research must be balanced against the possible risks of restricting its freedom or limiting its imaginative possibilities.

We have always to keep in view two main considerations. The first is that research is carried on ultimately by individuals, and that therefore the conditions of the individual research worker require primary attention. The second is that, as research should be carried on for the benefit of humanity as a whole, it requires the most effective co-ordination of the work of the individuals. The ideal arrangement is one in which every individual is able to work at his best in an organization which makes the maximum social use of his work. The main problem is the reconciliation of the needs of organization for the whole and of freedom for the individual.

Science as an Occupation.—We must also bear in mind that science is not and is not likely to become a self-supporting occupation. It is true, as has already been pointed out, that science is profitable, but with very few exceptions that profitability is dependent on the supply of considerable funds and on the ability to wait for a number of years for tangible results. Consequently it is very rarely that scientists undertake work as a commercial speculation for their own profit and, indeed, there is a considerable feeling, both inside and outside science, that it would be wrong for them to do so. Science therefore differs from other occupations in that it requires a permanent subsidy, whether from individuals, institutions, or the State, to continue its operations. This would be true in a socialist as much as in a capitalist economy, but in the former case the peculiar position of science would disappear as every human occupation would be on the same footing. Under existing conditions in capitalist countries any plans for the organization of science must include the consideration not only of what funds are necessary for the proper maintenance and development of science, but also of how those funds are to be raised. In every case there is need for a specially close organizational connection between science and the administrative and economic arrangements of society.

But this cannot be easily achieved. Not only is science an occupation functionally different from other occupations, but by its very nature it is difficult to fit in with them. Under present conditions there is a general ignorance of scientific matters on the part of administrators and business men, and a corresponding ignorance on the part of scientists concerning the management of public affairs or business. We have to face the alternative dangers of science being run by efficient administrators, who assure its adequate maintenance at the cost of distorting and stifling its intrinsic development, or of its remaining in a semi-starved and disorganized state as a result of being left in the hands of uninfluential scientists not fitted for administrative tasks. The problem is not insoluble, but to solve it we need, as already indicated, in the first place a much more general knowledge of science diffused among the population, particularly among administrators and business men and, in the second, a much wider knowledge of public affairs included in the education of scientists. There then might grow up effective liaison officers in the form of administrative scientists and scientific administrators.

SPECIALIZATION

The difficulty of achieving this is closely bound up with the characteristically modern evil of science—excessive specialization. Specialization has grown up so imperceptibly that there is the greatest confusion both as to its merits and its evils. It would be impossible to disentangle, without the profoundest study, how far, in general or in any particular field, specialization has arisen from the inner necessities of the development of the scientific discipline and how far from the anarchy of scientific organization. For this anarchy, by preventing adequate co-operation between the sciences, would in any case force the individual scientist, if he is to be at all successful, to confine himself to a very narrow range of knowledge. Both factors have clearly played a part, but only one of them can be effectively controlled. Only that part of specialization which depends on social organization can be removed, though if it were it might well be found that with it the evils of specialization would have largely disappeared.

Specialization is by no means uniform in science. Certain sciences, such as chemistry, based on a relatively simple set of ideas and operations, underlie vast tracts of other sciences. Inside the field of chemistry considerable freedom of movement is possible. The great chemists have distinguished themselves by the wide range of chemical topics to which they have contributed. In chemistry, consequently, specialization is in general harmful or, at most, a chemical specialist is in the position of a useful but essentially minor auxiliary in the advance of the science, a convenient point of reference when some general investigation happens to demand something from his speciality.

On the other hand, in many of the branches of biology it is not so much general principles that are required—for these are largely imported from outside the subject and are of little use in practice—but concrete knowledge and experience of a vast number of connected facts which can only be acquired by experience in a more or less limited field. The mycologist, for instance, or even more so, the "drosophilologist," are efficient and valuable just because they are specialists and understand a mass of detailed facts with which it would be a waste of time, even for other biologists, to be acquainted, but from which there can be drawn new biological principles and new processes valuable both to biology and to practical life. As science progresses it may be that the spread of adequate theory will make much of such specialists' work unnecessary, but at the same time there is the probability that in new spheres, and in the expansion of existing spheres of knowledge, new specialities will arise. The problem is rather not how to abolish specialization but how to make the best use of the specialization intrinsically required at any period.

The Control of Specialization.—To a large extent this is simply a matter of organization. While unspecialized scientists should have their laboratories in every institution of a scientific or educational character, there should be no attempt to spread the specialized studies so extensively. One of the chief evils of present-day specialization is that in far too many universities or institutions there are only one or two of each particular kind of specialist, and this isolation leads to the development of that caricature of human knowledge, the scientific specialist who knows more and more about less and less. If this were recognized, then instead of scattering specialists, they would be grouped in institutions of ten or twenty workers situated at large centres of scientific work where they would have the advantage of co-operation among themselves and at the same time not be so cut off from their fellow scientists. There would be no necessity for each scientific centre to possess institutes of all the specialities; in many cases one in each country would suffice and in some cases only one or two centres in the world. If this were done there would still be the difficulty that those centres without any particular specialist institute might suffer from the lack of it. The remedy for this would be to provide, on a scale far greater than at present, travelling and hospitality facilities for scientists so that the life of a specialist might be divided between working in his own institute, working in the field if his speciality required it, and lecturing and giving technical advice in other centres.

While these changes would help, the intrinsic evils of specialization require more thoroughgoing treatment. The reform of scientific education suggested above, which would bring out far more clearly than heretofore the connections between the different scientific disciplines, is one step; another is the rationalization of scientific publications. To a large extent the specialist's isolation is due to the fact that he and he alone really knows the literature of the subject, not because the literature is particularly incomprehensible, but because it is presented in such a maze of papers without adequate summaries or critical reports that the outside scientist might spend months in finding his way through it. Consequently the specialist is needed as a kind of living encyclopaedia, or rather as one article in such an encyclopaedia, which, it should be realized, is a terrible waste of human personality. Deeper still lies the attitude of mind of the specialist. It has, of course, its valuable side—the consciousness of knowing and weighing knowledge about any particular point and being able to say that at the moment no one knows more about this than he does. But there is the corresponding evil of the restriction of that knowledge to such a narrow field that not only its implications but even its internal structure cannot properly be grasped, and there is the temptation, far too easily and unconsciously yielded to, of monopolizing a certain little corner of knowledge, not wishing to make it easy for others to understand, so as to enjoy that delicious sense of personal possession of knowledge which is the ultimate crime of the scientist. The attitude of the specialist is near akin to that of the adepts of esoteric mysteries of magic, religion, law and medicine, and is a reflection on the scientist's mind of the pervasive pressure of a society where the ideal is a striving for individual and private enjoyment. Hence it is clear that we shall never really have done with the evils of specialization until we achieve an integrated society based on human co-operation.

LABORATORY ORGANIZATION

The general problem of organization of scientific research can be simplified by dividing it into two problems, those of the inner and outer organization. The line of division is determined by what might be called the basic unit for scientific research—the laboratory or institute—characterized by the existence of a number of workers concerned with the solution of a group of interrelated problems. The first is the internal problem of how a laboratory should be run, and the second of how the work of the different laboratories should be co-ordinated into a coherent structure of scientific research. The first problem is concerned primarily with providing the best conditions for the effective work of the individual research worker, the second with the general conditions of science and its function in the service of humanity. These two problems, though conveniently separated, must not be thought of as independent. A great deal of the internal efficiency of a laboratory depends on how effectively it is co-ordinated with other laboratories and with State and economic services, while no scheme of extensive organization of science, however well thought out and administered, will be of the slightest value if the individual laboratories are run in any way inimical to the fullest and freest development of each individual scientist's work.

The Laboratory as Basic Unit.—It would be impossible and indeed ridiculous to attempt to give any standard definition of what should be the basic unit of scientific research. At present there exists an enormous range of such units, from the smallest one-man laboratory to a large multiple unit such as a Rockefeller Medical Institute with some hundreds of workers. In every different science there would be different requirements, depending largely on how self-contained any particular work is or how much it is dependent on laboratory, mechanical, or field experimentation. Nevertheless there are some limiting conditions that do suggest a natural unit of something between five and fifty qualified workers with anything between the same number to five times the number of technical assistants. The limit is roughly fixed by the number of individuals that can conveniently and over reasonable periods of time collaborate in any common work. When this number is too small it is impossible to maintain a sufficient amount of valuable internal discussion; each one knows too well what everybody has to say, and at the same time there is a very great danger of complete isolation from outside scientific work. It is a common experience to notice that a very large number of small laboratories, whilst they may possess distinctive individuality of approach to problems, are very apt to fall behind general development of knowledge and to waste their ingenuity on problems already solved elsewhere.

At the other extreme large institutions prove to be effectively unmanageable as such. It is impossible for everyone to have anything but the vaguest notion of what the others are doing. Discussions, when large numbers are present, result in only a few talking, and the remainder of slower witted, but not necessarily less intelligent, workers remaining silent and becoming separated from the general work of the institute. To counteract this there is a tendency to break up into cliques—a sure sign that the unit itself is too large. And, finally, administrative difficulties are multiplied. In the earlier days in the Soviet Union, when the distinctive characters of scientific research had not been fully realized, giant institutes of up to several hundred workers were formed, but it was soon found in practice that these were difficult to run and very inefficient, and they were broken up into smaller and more manageable units. Any successful laboratory tends to grow by attracting aspiring workers from outside, but this growth should not be allowed to increase indefinitely. At some stage new institutes should be formed by the more able of the earlier members of the school who will then be enabled to combine the value of the tradition they have learned with the development of their own bent, inevitably somewhat hampered by the parent institution. Otherwise there is not only the danger of unwieldy growth, but of ultimate and rapid decay which may set in long before the death or retirement of the original founder. This points to one of the most fundamental characters of scientific work—the necessity for growth, division, and dispersion. The function of science is not a maintaining function but a developing one, and unless science is allowed, and indeed actively helped, to expand, it will be choked by its own products. Each new generation of scientists must be larger than the last in order to cope with an ever-increasing accumulation of facts and operations.

Co-operative Enterprise.—Of crucial importance is the way in which the laboratory is regarded by the workers in it. In the early period of individual scientific research the freedom of the scientist, in respect to his work, was limited only by lack of material means. This freedom was one of the most important factors for the rapid advance of early science. The development of modern science has made such individual work in most cases not only inefficient but practically impossible. The individual cannot do without the assistance of his fellow scientists in active and daily collaboration, but this collaboration must be such as to preserve the essential characters of the earlier freedom. It must be a voluntary association of scientists for an object they all have in common. As we have already pointed out, this is only very partially so at present because of the over-riding importance of economic considerations. The necessity of earning a living must needs be, for the average scientist, more important than the mere desire to do some particular kind of work. Those laboratories which are conceived of as factories for knowledge, hiring servants at so much a year to do what they are told (and such exist unfortunately in only too large numbers), miss the essential character of scientific work and doom themselves to a relative and often an absolute futility. (1)

The Laboratory as a Training Centre.—Of course, it is only to the fully trained research workers that this conception of the laboratory as a voluntary association applies in its entirety. To a certain extent every laboratory is also the last stage of scientific education, and it would be absurd to expect of all students that before knowing the extent and difficulty of the field they should know precisely what they and others should be doing in it, although with better education such aspirations should be made far more easily available to the intelligent research student. To the majority of them the laboratory is the place to acquire technical ability and to get some idea of the direction which they afterwards wish to pursue. We have also to consider the position of the older workers, particularly of the founders of the laboratory. To them it must appear as a place where they can see carried out by many hands the fulfilment of the ideas they have worked on themselves in earlier and less influential days.

Laboratory Democracy.—These different aspects need not be, though they often are at present, in conflict with one another. There is no reason why the laboratory should not at the same time be to its younger members a school, to the majority a college or fellowship, and to the older members a regiment. What is needed is a more conscious appreciation of all these aspects and a refusal to let one dominate all the others. There are laboratories, particularly in universities, where the devotion to teaching prevents most serious research; others, where the dominating personality of the director reduces the rest of the staff to slaves. The key to these difficulties is the appropriate combination in the laboratory of intelligent and personal direction with democratic control. Up till now the official attitude towards laboratory work has emphasized only the former aspect. The management of a laboratory, because it has grown around the professor and his assistants instead of being a voluntary association of free research workers, has always been authoritarian in principle although wise professors have in practice allowed a considerable measure of internal self-government.

One way of approaching the problem of the internal management of laboratories is to consider in the light of experience the different functions that have to be fulfilled in the carrying on of laboratory work and the qualifications of the persons needed to carry out those functions. The description that follows applies to a more or less generalized laboratory in the physical or biological sciences. It would need modification to cover agricultural, medical or applied scientific laboratories. Of course in a small laboratory many of the different functions would be carried out by the same individual, but nevertheless each is a specific and distinct part of the general activity of the laboratory.

The Director.—In the first place, there is the general direction of the laboratory. It is usually taken for granted that every laboratory must have some kind of responsible director. In most cases this will probably be so, but it should not be accepted as a necessary principle. There is no reason why the council of the laboratory or some executive deputed by that council should not corporately fulfil the rôle of director and appoint a secretary for the more administrative side of the duties. (2) We have to balance, as in all political affairs, the dangers of arbitrary or incompetent action of a single individual against the possible lack of unity, inconsistency, and general obstructiveness of any corporate body. According to the temperament and abilities of the people available for the work at any particular time or place, one or the other method may be the more suitable. In a scientific laboratory an individual who, with his guiding ideas, markedly leads the way will be willingly chosen as a personal director; in other cases, it may be a small group who combine in a harmonious way a set of ideas which they can realize effectively only by working in close collaboration.

Up till now in the great majority of cases the functions of the director of a laboratory have been considered far too much as a kind of combination between those of professor and those of a business executive. It is melancholy to contemplate the number of important and promising scientists whose research work has been gradually but effectively sterilized by the entire absorption of their interest and time in administrative and teaching duties. (3) It is often maintained that the sterilization is only apparently due to this cause, that in fact after a certain age the scientific ability of many, if not most, men would fall off in any case, but because of their accumulated experience and prestige they still are ideal heads of laboratories. There is undoubtedly some truth in the first of these assertions, but the second by no means follows. A scientist who has lost his creative drive, although he may make an admini-strator, cannot really effectively lead research. The best he can do is to allow research to be done under his direction, but far more often he will, from motives of conservatism and personal jealousy, prevent rather than assist research. The real solution does not lie along the lines of giving the direction of research to those who have passed beyond active research themselves, but of an organization which makes the minimum demands, other than scientific, on the director of research, and consequently we may have as directors only those in their full scientific vigour. On the whole, directors of research should be far younger men than they are now, although there will always be notable exceptions. The great scientists are often men of supernormal vitality, which enables them to retain a freshness of outlook and enterprise into their very old age.

The true functions of a director should be limited to determining the general lines along which the work of the laboratory should go, and to selecting the younger men who will of their natural bent fit in and push forward this work. The director may or may not at the same time be a teacher, but this should be a matter of his real ability and inclination in that direction, not in any way a condition of office. In no case should entire absorption in research be pre-vented, as is so often the case in research departments of universities. It may be necessary, for reasons of prestige, to retain as director someone who is or has become primarily an expounder of science, but in that case the function of direction of research should be delegated to someone else. Apart from his scientific abilities the other main qualifications of the director should be psychological. He should possess not only the ability of getting on with men, but also that much more difficult one of making them get on with one another. Laboratories suffer from many of the defects of the monasteries of earlier times. There is the same possibility of inveterate internal feuds and jealousies, the same danger of that kind of loss of interest which the clerics called accidie. It falls to the director to maintain harmony and vitality in the laboratory, and he must be able to recognize when it is imperative to part from workers as well as to take them on. All this demands a somewhat exceptional character which may be, but by no means necessarily will be, associated with high scientific abilities.

We need to find some way of providing for the case of the brilliant research worker who is partially or totally unable to direct or even get on with his fellow workers. In extreme cases this means the setting up of private laboratories, but in the majority of cases it would be sufficient to have in the general laboratory a part set off for scientists of high attainments who prefer to work on their own or

are unsuccessful in the direction of other work.   Up till now much
damage has been done because direction of research is considered
a matter of prestige.   If it could be made clear that the status of the
scientist not directing research may be as high as or higher than that
of one who does direct it, this difficulty might vanish and unsuitable
persons might not be put in a position to stultify the work of others
besides their own.

The Administrator.—Every laboratory should have somebody
responsible for the whole of the administrative and financial arrangements.   This still may be the director of the laboratory, but only
in the rather exceptional cases where he is by inclination and ability
an administrator.   The function of the administrator is essentially
to look after the laboratory in its financial and material aspects, to
see that funds are provided and distributed, and to assure all the
necessary non-scientific services.   In a modern laboratory employing
numerous technical assistants and much complicated apparatus, and
having relations quite as much with industrial firms as with other
scientific bodies, the work of such administration is heavy and
demands a high degree of ability.   The administrator must possess
all the qualities of a business manager and many others beside.   He
has, in the first place, to deal not with a concern running along more
or less fixed lines, but with something which is always changing, and
changing rapidly; he has to translate into concrete terms the alteration
and direction imposed by the development of the purely scientific
part of the research.   This demands a much higher degree of flexibility than in ordinary business.   In the second place, he must really
be able to understand the work of the laboratory in its scientific
aspect, because otherwise there will be immense waste and friction
in the attempts of the scientific staff to explain their needs to the
administrator, or for the administrator to explain the material
possibilities and difficulties to the staff.   So far the position of laboratory administrator is not a recognized one.   People tend to drift
into it from a scientific career, picking up the business experience
as best they can, or alternatively, are first taken on in a purely
clerical way and pick up the science as best they can.   It is clear
we have here a profession that requires special training and, by the
training of a set of people equally versed in science and administration,
we could probably do more to increase the internal efficiency of
science than by any other means.

The Representative.—Besides these two main functionaries there
has been growing up in recent years, though in an unrecognized way,
a number of other specialized functionaries attached to all large
laboratories.   There is, first of all, what might be called the laboratory
representative.   More and more the work of co-ordinating the

activities of laboratories is coming to require an elaborate administrative mechanism. There are numerous higher bodies, committees, etc., with which the laboratory has to deal as well as less formal connections with other laboratories in the same field. In many cases the task of attending all these committees and boards, to which are generally added an equally large set of educational bodies, has, almost more than internal administration itself, diverted the work of the director from attention to research. The very overwhelming nature of these demands has, however, in other cases, forced the director to delegate this part of his work and to appoint a representative, officially or unofficially, to sit on many of the committees and councils. There has consequently grown up a number of persons who spend a great part of their time on such co-ordinative work, and these we may call laboratory representatives. If the directors of research are to be relieved of most outside work, the numbers and importance of such representatives are bound to grow, though they need not, and of course should not, be in all cases the same persons. Different aspects of the laboratory's work may require different representatives. The work of the representative will not be anything but part-time work; otherwise he would be effectively just a member of the general administrative staff of scientific research. His real value lies in the fact that he also works in the laboratory, that he can answer for it and put the case for it on other bodies. There is no need to create any special profession in this case, only to recognize that such liaison activities play an important and necessary part in the development of science and should be recognized in some titular and financial way.

The Raising of Money.—One task which at present devolves almost exclusively on the director of a laboratory and which might well be taken up by a laboratory representative is the raising of money. Under existing conditions this is a most exacting, unpleasant and, except to a few adepts, unsatisfactory business. It wastes a good scientist's time just at the period in his career when he can least afford it, not only in the actual negotiations and their social preliminaries, but by the worry and uncertainty that may last for years before any scientific venture can be considered financially secure. Much of this could be avoided by proper arrangements for the finance of science (see p. 310), but even then negotiations would still be needed over the amount allocated to a particular laboratory, and the director might well be spared most of this work. It is eminently one either for a laboratory representative or for the administrator. The reasons for preferring the former is that no one who is not closely associated with the actual work of the laboratory can effectually put the case for its current and future needs.

Librarian.—Other functionaries long attached to many laboratories are the librarian and curator. Up till now, however, it has not been realized how important their functions are and how much they need to be fostered. In what has been said earlier on the question of internal communication in science, it is clear that one of the major factors retarding scientific advance is the disorganized plethora of scientific publications themselves. Even if this confusion is remedied, as is suggested below, by a straightforward organization, the help of the librarian will still be necessary for the permanent maintenance of the new system of communication, a task which is not likely to grow lighter with time. The librarian in most laboratories is either a part-time research worker, who is supposed to look after the library in his spare time, or a salaried librarian with no particular scientific qualifications. His function is largely to see that the books and periodicals are not stolen, and that new ones which the laboratory can afford are regularly bought. To get full use of the library, however, much more is required. There should be someone deputed to watch the whole of current literature for items which might be relevant to the work of the laboratory, and to be able to indicate without loss of time where such items are likely to be found. It is to them that might be given the task of drawing up from time to time reports on current work from the particular angle of the laboratory. Further, the work of the laboratory itself requires to be made known in an effective way to outside bodies, and an adequate record of it over a number of years needs also to be available, because it is a strange but indubitable fact that it is extremely easy for scientific workers to forget the work they themselves have done in the past. All these tasks might reasonably fall to the librarian, who would have to be chosen partly for his comprehensive scientific interests, which need to be much greater than those of the other laboratory workers, and partly for his inclination to systematic thinking.

Curator.—The position of the curator is somewhat different. That is a matter of a transformation which is effecting itself automatically from a passive to an active attitude towards scientific collections. The extreme may be indicated by the attitude of a curator of a great museum who refused to let any of the specimens out of their cases for scientific examination, on the grounds that they might be useful to science at some later date. We are coming, however, better to realize that the mere existence of a collection is of itself of little value. The collection needs to be in continual use, and that not only in examination of individual items but even more so in the possibilities of significant arrangement which it offers. On one side there is, of course, the educative value of collections—the whole tendency that manifests itself in the creation of didactic museums.

" In the old days," a venerable Russian scientist once remarked to me, " they used to make museums for savants; now they make them for children." But it is not only children who benefit by the economy and clarity of the new museums. We have come to realize that the same material may have a number of radically different possibilities of arrangement, and that each arrangement will in itself bring out some new fact often unsuspected until that arrangement is made. The task of the curator will therefore be just as much to manipulate his collection as to guard it.

Mechanic and Storekeeper.—There remain two other functionaries who have always been put on a far lower plane of laboratory organization than they deserved, the chief mechanic and the storekeeper. It has, up till now, as elsewhere pointed out in this book, been very unfortunate for the development of laboratories that the class distinctions existing in ordinary life also hold sway there. The mechanic and the storekeeper are the non-commissioned officers of the laboratory, and consequently their contribution to science has neither been fully recognized nor fully made use of. So much in every laboratory depends on the mechanic that in fact he is generally respected and deferred to, but for lack of status he does not usually mix on equal terms with the research workers or take part in all their discussions. It does not seem to have occurred to scientific workers how much they lose by this. It is true that a mechanic of long experience has generally picked up as much science as a professor, and far more than most research workers, but he cannot make full use of this knowledge. He can, it is true, understand the needs of a particular research worker for apparatus often better than that worker can express them, but the initiative is never his. If an able mechanic took part in the regular life of the laboratory he would often be able to make suggestions for apparatus that only occur much later, if at all, to the research workers themselves. The proof of this is that one occasionally finds in laboratories research workers of mechanical training or peculiar mechanical ability, and this gift often proves of inestimable value not only to themselves but to all their colleagues. What we require is, first of all, that full opportunities for scientific advancement should be provided for all mechanics and laboratory attendants, and that those of them who have sufficient interest should take part on an absolutely equal footing in all laboratory meetings and functions. The same remarks apply to a less degree to the last functionary, the storekeeper, who will in general be in charge of all the material supplies of the laboratory. It could not but be useful if the storekeeper were in a position to understand much more clearly the uses to which his material is intended to be put, and were therefore in a position to suggest alternatives or additions.

Laboratory Council.—Finally, we come to what should be the most important regulating body of a laboratory, the laboratory council. In many laboratories (it is impossible to know how many) such councils exist, and it is easy to see what differences their existence does make to the whole life of the laboratory. Without a council in some form—it may be merely a tea club or a discussion circle—the work of the laboratory tends to be simply the sum of the work of a number of individual research workers. Each one may discuss his problems with the director or with some chosen friends, but essentially it is private work, and the laboratory simply consists of a number of research cells. With a council the results are effectively integrated or multiplied. Each worker sees his work and his needs in relation to others. He gets suggestions and directions; one worker is able to plan his work to help another, and the whole is infused with a greater spirit of fruitful activity.

Under present conditions there is in a large number of laboratories a great sense of personal frustration; each worker feels that he is not being given the opportunities he deserves. In an individually run laboratory this sense of frustration remains a private matter and drives the worker in many cases to abandon the struggle and relapse into mediocre and humdrum work. If the laboratory is an effective unit, however, the very frustration itself may become a drive. All that part of it which is due to internal lack of organization can be removed by the council in a much more open and satisfactory way than by private representations to the directors, which often result only in easing one person's burdens at the expense of another's. As for the remainder, once it is brought into the open it can be seen that it depends not so much on any private unfairness but is a general burden on all science for economic and social reasons. It then becomes something which can either be accepted as inevitable or fought against by common action, but it has lost its particularly thwarting character. These are all negative aspects. The great thing is that the workers of a laboratory should feel, and should have reasons for feeling, that they are taking part jointly in a co-operative enterprise which they themselves direct, so long as it fits into a wider general scheme, and not that they are either employees or individuals graciously permitted by higher but unseen powers to work out their own private curiosities.

Research Programmes.—If a laboratory council is to be of any positive use it must be a really responsible body capable of determining, in principle if not in detail, the course of work in the laboratory. Its main administrative function should be to discuss a programme of research at six-monthly or yearly intervals. A separate discussion on the finance of that programme would probably be needed to consider what claims can be made for finance and how the grants that are acquired can best be distributed among the different research workers. Its other function might be to discuss the proper relations between the work of the laboratory and that of other laboratories in the same or cognate fields. In all these cases the council will be functioning in a legislative capacity, the actual execution of the work being left to the director, the administrator, or the laboratory representatives. For the rest of the time the council need not meet as such, although it would in fact meet as a regular discussion circle for scientific problems affecting the laboratory.

Dangers of Organization.—So far I have spoken only of the advantages of the laboratory council, but naturally these carry with them corresponding dangers. The dangers have been, and will be, magnified by those opposed in principle to any council whatever, whether from belief in a scientific leader principle, or from a distrust of democratic methods brought too near home, or from a cynical disbelief in the ability of scientists to manage any kind of affairs whatever. The chief difficulty is one common to all corporate discussions, the danger that a clash of ideas reinforced by personal rivalries may effectively prevent any useful action being taken and actually lead to a worse state of affairs than the arbitrary action of a director.

It would be impossible to deny that such things might sometimes occur; but they also admit of easy remedy. In the first place, the scientists are in a better position for reaching unanimous decisions on policy than practically any other body of men. They may differ about facts, and even more on the interpretation of those facts, but they are all agreed that the phenomena must be examined and the facts well established. In practice, discussions of this sort can generally be carried out in a friendly atmosphere and lead to genuinely unanimous decisions, where no one perhaps gets all he wants but where there is sufficient feeling of give and take. The other two objections can be easily removed. The struggles between scientists on material questions are practically conditioned by the fact that there never has been really enough to go round. If science were adequately financed no research worker would mind anyone else getting a grant, because he would know that it would not affect in the slightest his own possibilities of getting one. As to the quarrels between scientists and the possibilities of the laboratory council splitting up into rival factions, the very existence of such a state of affairs is a proof that the laboratory is no longer a unit and that it is high time it was split into two, under independent direction and preferably in different places, each of which could maintain itself at any rate in internal harmony until a new split was necessary. This merely emphasizes what has already been said, that the very existence of scientific research is bound up with its possibilities of continuous expansion.

Even if the desirability of the existence of laboratory councils is granted, there is bound to be opposition to the idea that these should be authoritative and not merely advisory in function. This raises again the whole question of democracy or authoritarian direction of science. It is maintained here that a great deal of the internal inefficiency and external ineffectiveness of science is due to this very authoritarian principle, which places, in fact, the whole of the control of science in the hands of persons who, whatever their past qualifications may have been, are no longer in touch with the most living parts of it. Only a democratic organization can assure its full vitality, and that democracy must begin at the very bottom, in the laboratories where the essential work of science is being done. It is probably true that under existing conditions of selection and training of scientists a great number of research workers may not be fitted for or even desire internal democracy for science; this, however, is not an argument against democracy but against the system of education and selection. If it is allowed weight, then we may never expect better times, for it is quite clear that unless we have democracy we shall never get a better system of selection and training. All these remarks could be really paralleled by the discussion now raging about the extension of self-government to subject peoples, but for scientists the denial of self-government is even more ludicrous and self-defeating. In the first place, they are not less fitted for it than are the average citizens of Britain, let alone India, and, secondly, a delicate and growing organization such as science suffers far more from the restrictive checks of government by the old than does any form of civil administration.

Provision for Growth.—The nature of the tasks of science is continually changing. A laboratory in any particular field should not be considered as a permanent institution; the field may be exhausted, new methods may be worked out for which that laboratory cannot be adapted, or the subject itself may lose the importance that it had previously enjoyed in the history of science. At the same time, new subjects, new fields, and new methods are continuously being evolved and call for new institutions to cope with them. The laboratory then is, as it were, a more or less temporary camp of a scientific army permanently on the move. One of the abuses to be most guarded against in any organization of science would be the fossilization of laboratories and institutes. To counter this there should be some definite provision for the growth and development and also for the winding up of scientific institutions.

As an institution science is not adult; unless it grows, it decays. But the form that growth takes is in itself of considerable importance. The mere increase in numbers and equipment of any given institute may be, beyond a certain point, a hindrance rather than a help. The new ideas that appear in the course of any long-established research may be hampered by traditional modes of thinking and experimentation, which in science, as in everything else, attach themselves to any long-lived institution. It is necessary often to make a completely fresh start. Any study of the history of science shows how fruitful this method has been. The great laboratory of Liebig at Giessen was itself an offshoot of the Paris Chemical Laboratories of Dumas, which in later years it greatly surpassed. An incidental advantage is that the budding-off of new laboratories is one of the most convenient ways of avoiding those personal rivalries and jealousies that so often mar the whole progress of scientific research and make work in laboratories intolerable for all, and not merely the participants.

Initiative in Research.—No one has yet worked out any general principles which would govern the dividing up of scientific work, and probably it depends too much on particular scientific and personal considerations for such principles to be applicable. In ideal circumstances it would probably be best to leave it to individual initiative, that is, to allow the same freedom to the scientist of staking his claim as still belongs to the prospector. Anyone who has a clear enough idea of a programme of work involving the setting up of a laboratory, and who can find suitable and willing assistants, should be allowed and encouraged to set up that laboratory. The relation of that laboratory to others would be a matter for administrative and scientific co-ordination, but in every case the organization should exist to help the spontaneous growth of science and not to distort it into a fixed pattern. It might be in certain circumstances, however, necessary for the initiative to be taken from above if it appeared that any section of scientific work had been neglected through inadvertence or development of other fields. There should be positive encouragement for the setting up of such research, and in that case the men might be found for the job.

Organization and Freedom.—It is along these lines that the problem of attaining the most effective combination of organization and individual freedom and initiative should be sought. Many present-day scientists fight hard against organization because of the restriction they fear on individual freedom, but if we could achieve the double safeguard of democratic organization and the right to individual research, those fears would be found to be groundless. The primary condition is that any research for which there was a demand from inside or outside science should be not only permitted, but also aided. Though this might seem likely to lead to great wastage of time and money, that waste would be only apparent, for one or two really fruitful advances made in this way would more than compensate for the wasted work of a dozen others. Such individualism must plainly not be anarchy; it must fit into an ordered scheme. Indeed, the final solution may well be found in a kind of feudal system for science, in which each worker spends a determinate part of his time working in the field chosen for him by the higher organization of science, and at least as large if not a larger part working on his own problems, with full material and technical assistance. Naturally, the shares would vary from person to person, and science to science. Some might choose to be almost entirely regular workers, others free. Places would have to be found for those scientists who combine with genuine ability in science a complete lack of social competence, who are quarrelsome, unsocial, or helpless. For them the organization of science should offer a kind of right of asylum; they should be allowed either to work for themselves, to choose where they would prefer to work, or to wander indefinitely from laboratory to laboratory. Outside any regular organization there should be scope not only for such wandering scholars but for those who prefer not to make individual contributions to science but to stimulate the scientific work of others through conversations, discussions, and criticisms. At all costs science must be prevented from becoming a hierarchic orthodoxy; it must be able and willing to defend its theses against all comers, and it should not exclude but encourage critics of all kinds however unbalanced or irrational they appear to be.

The General Organization of Science

By itself the internal reorganization of laboratories and institutes would be of little value. An extensive organization of their mutual relations is even more necessary. The two are really correlative because the isolated laboratory, however well run, cannot contribute adequately towards either the internal development or the application of science unless it is linked up in some general scheme. The existing organization of science, with its extreme intricacy, confusion, and lack of communications already described in these pages, acts more as a brake than as a help to the advance of science. Yet from it we can see the type of organization which could be really helpful. Science is a growing and developing social activity; its organization must accordingly not be thought of in any fixed way but as flexible and adaptable. This degree of flexibility does not, however, preclude the permanent existence of a general framework or skeleton of organization which would remain substantially unchanged for a time longer than it is convenient to plan for.

Horizontal and Vertical Divisions in Research.—The general principles of organization of science derive directly from its function of interpreting and changing the world. As a body of knowledge it has different divisions such as physics, chemistry, and biology, and their finer sub-divisions, which have definite complex relations with one another. This is what might be called the horizontal classification of scientific activity. But science may be conceived of in quite a different way, as a circulation of information and activity, as the passing down of ideas from theoretical to experimental scientists, and further, through transformation by technicians into production and new human activity. Conversely, the difficulties of social life and technical production give rise to problems which in their turn stimulate the experimental and theoretical scientists to new discoveries. This double process has indeed been taking place throughout the whole history of science. What has happened now is that we are just beginning to be aware of it and could replace the clumsy and casual adaptation of the structure of science to this double flow by a more consciously thought-out scheme of what may be called the vertical organization of science. To a certain extent this has already been done in the Soviet Union. Indeed, the idea itself derives directly from Marxist thought and is so obvious and true that the difficulty is not to justify it but to explain why people never saw it before.

The Place of the Universities.—Besides these two main aspects there is the third, which formerly took almost the chief place in the organization of science, namely, the teaching of scientists. This has already been discussed and is only mentioned here to indicate that it needs always to be taken into account in planning any scheme for the reorganization of science. Its function, however, under such a scheme can never be as important as in the past. The universities of the last century maintained the research scientist in a socially recognized way and provided him with the means of working. The universities were to the scientists what royal courts had been at an earlier day, supporting them for reasons other than their principal function. Now that we recognize the technical and the social importance of scientific research sufficiently to admit its pursuit as a profession in its own right, the universities should return largely to their essential functions of teaching, although there is every reason to encourage the close association of autonomous research institutes with the universities.

The Complexity of Science.—Science may be considered as widely based in practice and reaching out into the unknown in discovery and theory. The length of communication between the base and the advance posts will vary in different sciences roughly according to their degree of development. The new sciences, like ecology and social psychology, are those that have arisen directly out of practice and have for a while been in direct touch with it. The old sciences, on the other hand, like astronomy or chemistry, have accumulated centuries of autonomous tradition; they have whole sections which are separate, both from technical theory and from technical practice, and develop to a considerable extent according to their own internal necessities limited only by the men and money available.

Schemes of Interconnection.—No uniform scheme can therefore be put forward for the whole of science, but only an intricate network in which the character of the science and its history are equally taken into account. A chart such as that given here (Chart I) brings out the connections more clearly, but the limitation to two dimensions makes it still a very imperfect representation. Such a chart must be taken not as an adequately considered scheme, which whole committees of experts would be needed to prepare, but as a sketch of the kind of organization that might be needed. It is based on the conception of vertical and horizontal divisions already discussed. These divisions are not absolute, but they afford a convenient basis for a rational organization of science. We can roughly distinguish three stages in the relation between theory and practice in science which may be considered to require three types of organization, which may be called for convenience, the academies, the institutes, and the technical laboratories. The first will be occupied mainly with what has been called pure, but should more accurately be called sophisticated science, the last only with practical problems, the link between being furnished by the institutes whose function is in a sense that of translating theory into practice.

ACADEMIES

The scientific academy would represent a natural development of existing bodies of two kinds: the old scientific societies such as the Royal Society, the Chemical Society, etc., in Britain, and general governmental advisory bodies such as the Science Committee of the Privy Council, the National Research Council, or the Conseil de Recherche Scientifique. Its functions, however, would be far wider than theirs. It would combine those of a general staff of scientific advance with the active pursuit of fundamental research under its immediate direction. This was, on a far smaller scale, the intention of the founders of the Royal Society, but in later years

CHART I

This table shows in general outline the scheme for the organization of scientific and industrial research. It follows closely the account in the text, except that it is impossible to indicate the third stage of scientific institutes, that of works' laboratories and field stations, which would be too numerous to include in any such comprehensive diagram. The stages of research are further subdivided, the idea being to put the more fundamental study of general methods at the top and the more systematic application to special parts of the field below. Thus, in fundamental research we have an analytic level referring to general modes of behaviour of matter and a descriptive level referring to those sciences concerned with the forms of the world as it is. The second stage—that of technical research—is similarly divided into that concerned mainly with production technique, and therefore with industry and production goods, and that concerned with consumption, living conditions and the practice of agriculture. These distinctions are not absolute and in many cases not even logical, but are necessitated by the difficulties of two dimensional presentation. The most important connections between research at different stages, *i.e.* between fundamental and applied research, are indicated by arrows. These do not imply, of course, administrative connections, but simply cases where close relations would be naturally maintained between workers in the academic and technical laboratories in question. The Physical Sector has been worked at greater detail than the rest, and the Sociological Sector least, corresponding roughly with the existing greater development of these sectors. In a fuller working out a number of new biological and physiological divisions would be necessary.

In general the sub-titles are self-explanatory, but the lack of space may produce a certain obscurity. The context must be taken as indicating the aspect of the subject under consideration. Thus " nutrition " appears in two places, under medical research and domestic engineering. In the first place it is the theory of nutrition in health and disease that is in question, and in the second of domestic supplies, marketing, and waste of food products.

Zoology " and " Botany " do not stand for the academic divisions of teaching of these names, but in the more restricted sense of descriptive and systematic sciences. Their first meaning is taken over by bio-chemistry and bio-physics. The five sectors of the lowest row are more closely inter-related than is indicated. In particular, social control and planning, which on account of their connections appear at opposite ends of the table, should really be considered as one unit.

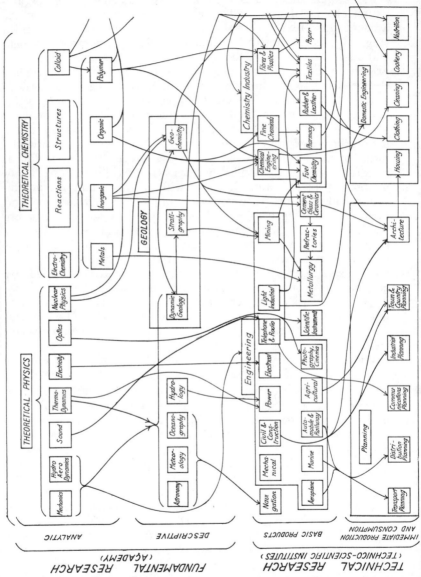

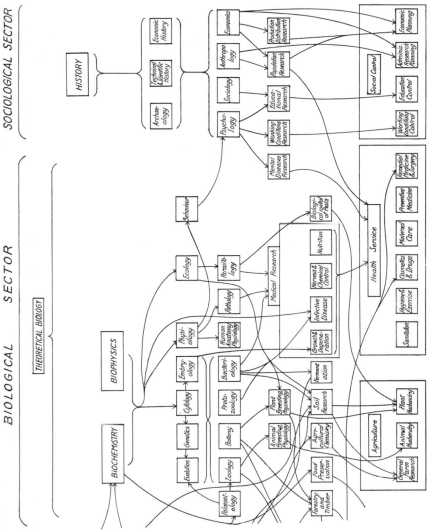

academies tended to lose such functions and become purely honorific in character, their only collective activity being publication. They had become the guardians and archivists of science rather than its leaders. The new academy would consist in each region of a body of co-ordinated research institutes, the academicians themselves being in general directors of such institutes, although there might be many academicians who preferred more individual methods of research and either worked by themselves or as ordinary members of an institute.

The relation of the academy to the universities would have to be carefully thought out. At present institutes for fundamental science are largely under university control, and this does not always conduce to their most efficient running or rapid development. There is something to be said for maintaining the contact with the university, but giving it a more informal character through some such device as making the head of an institute, responsible to and financed by the council of the academy, also a professor of the university. The divisions of the academy would follow for the moment the established divisions of science, though this would need periodical revision. Particularly in theoretical science it would be unnecessary and undesirable to have any actual institutes; the workers would be far better spread over a number of centres. But in other cases it might be well worth while to have central institutes for fundamental research of the type of the present National Physical Laboratory, but with a far wider scope and fewer technical and routine preoccupations.

Functions.—The academy would be responsible for carrying on the more fundamental aspects of scientific research and at the same time would act as the general directing body for scientific advance as a whole. In this latter capacity it would not, of course, be administrative or authoritative, but its functions would rather correspond to the legislative and advisory functions of government. For this purpose it would have to add to its numbers representatives of the more technical and practical sides of science, particularly in engineering and medicine. The academy would also have to be responsible for the archives of science and, to a certain extent also, current publications, and officially it would deal with the main part of the international relations of science. Such functions would require very considerable organization, but it would be waste of time at this stage, when we are so far from the realizing of any of these suggestions, to consider them in any detail. The general scheme of subdivision of the academy may also be seen from the chart. It would follow in the main existing divisions, but there would be a definite move towards bringing the different branches of science together in an integrated way, as indicated by the cross-connections.

Guarantees of Capacity.—The chief question we have to face, however, is whether any such body is likely to be capable of directing science. So far academies have shown themselves, though possessing the highest scientific distinction, generally extremely timid and lacking in initiative. This is of course largely a reflection of the politically and socially inferior position of the scientist, and where this has not been marked—in seventeenth-century England or in revolutionary France and Russia—academies have shown themselves capable and vigorous bodies. A good deal, on the other hand, depends on their position. For such a body to be effective it needs to contain a higher proportion of young men and of those experienced in practical affairs. (4)

When science is new or growing rapidly it is of course much easier for younger people and those attracted from other pursuits to attain high positions. Once it is well established, some special provisions would have to be made for their adequate representation. It might be best to reserve a certain fraction of the places in the academy for each age category, so that the really imaginative scientists of twenty to thirty years of age would be able to exert their driving force before waiting until age had dulled it. The difficulty of this course is that, if such members stayed on, the body would become an extremely unwieldy one. There might be something to be said for separating the organizing and directing functions of the academy from the carrying on of individual research by its members and even more from what might be called its honorary function. At present, possibly two-thirds of the members of scientific academies have no desire to do anything but continue their own work, and consider their membership more as an honour or as a recognition of their services to science than as an opportunity to direct its general advance. It is to be hoped that, when science and society have become more integrated, the proportion of such people will fall, but they will always exist, and for them it might be worth while founding a separate society or section of the academy, membership of which would be purely an honour and would not involve any responsibilities, while assuring to the members the fullest support in all their scientific work. In some such way the dullness and lack of initiative which besets official bodies, and which up till now has been considered almost as a law of nature, could be changed into an active drive for the advance of science and the welfare of society.

Mode of Election.—Whatever its precise functions, much will depend on the abilities of the members of the academy, and this will give added importance to the method of appointing them. Up till now membership of academies has been either by co-option by existing members—in the case of the Royal Society co-option by an inner council—or by Government appointment, as in the old French Royal Academy, but usually on the advice of the academicians. Either method assures a continuity of tradition and a certain standard of performance, but it also puts a premium on age and orthodoxy. As long as science plays a relatively unimportant part in national life such methods are good enough. The academy becomes a club, and if certain people dislike it or cannot get into it they have always the liberty to found a rival one. To a certain extent this liberty has been used in setting up the special scientific societies and the British Association, but in England at any rate the Royal Society, despite occasional periods of torpor, has never ceased to be considered as the representative organ of natural science.

Now that science has become a directing influence in social and economic life such parochial methods of election can no longer be accepted. Action and foresight will be needed as well as learning and reputation. The simplest alternative would be the democratic one of direct election of the academicians for life or for a fixed period of years by the body of all qualified scientists. It may be objected that this would expose science to the evils of vote-catching and political partisanship. Perhaps it would, but their effects are not likely to be worse than the toadying which is rife in science to-day. A more serious objection is that the main body of scientists would neither be competent nor interested enough to act as electors. This difficulty might be overcome by dividing the academy into sections based on subjects, but this would serve to perpetuate existing divisions. Alternatively the academy could be divided into age-groups of fixed relative numbers to which both candidates and voters should belong. Another method which has the advantage of democratic choice with the safeguard of academic competence is the one of reciprocal election suggested by Dr. Pirie. In this, election to the academy would be not by the scientists as a whole but by a body of some two thousand electors chosen for their general scientific competence by the academicians themselves. Thus the academy would tend to represent the active and responsible scientists of the day. Some such method combined with a limited time of service and the separation of the honorific from the functional aspects of the academy should serve to make it a suitable body for the general direction of scientific work.

TECHNICO-SCIENTIFIC INSTITUTES

The idea of technico-scientific institutes is a relatively recent one, and one which in Britain is in a very early stage, although for many years they have played an important part in European and American science. They are of multiple origin; in part arising from university departments and technical schools, in part from the scientific departments of the Government, and in part from the research laboratories of big industrial enterprises. While all these exist separately, it has been seen that there is a particular advantage in having some kind of intermediate liaison organization between fundamental sciences represented by academies and universities and practical applied science in industrial works and Government Departments. In this field the great Kaiser Wilhelm Institutes at Dahlem have been a model to the rest of the world, largely because they mark an appreciation of the necessity of intelligent and organized application of science to industry as a whole and not to the working of individual firms. In Britain the corresponding body, the group of institutes known as the National Physical Laboratory, performs a similar function, though up till now with far less internal initiative.

Two-way Communication between Science and Industry.—One function of the scientific institutes is to serve as a channel of communication working in two directions between fundamental science and its application. Problems arising in industry, agriculture, and medicine would be referred first to them. Such problems would be presented in the direct form of how to make a certain product or how to avoid a certain defect or disease. It would be the business of the institutes either to solve these problems by the application of known scientific principles or to reduce them to a form involving fundamental questions which can be referred to the academy. The reverse process to this would also be their concern. It would be their task to look for any practical applications that might result from fundamental advances in science and to develop these to the stage where they could be passed on to industrial laboratories, field stations, or medical centres.

The Institutes and New Production.—Until now, everywhere except in the U.S.S.R., this positive function of technical institutes has been held back because the actual initiating of developments, which may have profitable conclusions, has been a prerogative of industrial firms. An independent technical institute putting forward new productive methods would be obliged either to go into production on its own, to take out patents, or to hand over the operation of the new process to a firm or firms, a course which would practically amount to its becoming a section of their research laboratories. In England the Research Associations of the D.S.I.R., already discussed, largely fulfil this latter function. But for this very reason they are unable to take on the wider functions of technical institutes. The value of a technical institute would depend largely on how far it could maintain close contact with industry and a high standard of scientific excellence. It ought to be in a position to review a whole industry from a rational standpoint and to consider not only the improving of processes but also the question of whether any process is or is not necessary from the point of view of industry as a whole. Here again it is extremely difficult to reconcile the function of such an institute with a competitive industrial system because any recommendations which tended to change the structure of industry would mean shifting the balance of profit between some firms and others, and could not fail to be obstructed in practice.

Personnel.—The personnel of the technical institutes would have to be drawn fairly evenly from science and industry, with very considerable opportunities of mobility and interchange. The whole positive function of the institutes would depend on their ability to seize on and develop new ideas, and such new ideas generally come from fields outside the immediate scope of the industry itself. They should serve to break down the barrier that exists at present between the academic scientist and the practical engineer, and permit an interchange of attitude which should be to the benefit of both. A possible arrangement for such institutes is shown in Chart I. The value of any particular arrangement could only be discovered in practice, and it should further be emphasized that any arrangement must be extremely flexible and allow for the splitting of existing institutes and the creation of entirely new ones as well as for the winding up or absorption of those that have passed the time of their most effective utility. The general arrangement of the institutes would be in four sectors: physical, chemical, biological, and sociological.

Physical and Chemical Sectors.—In the physical and chemical sectors we should have two general types of institutes which might be called the methodic and the systematic, or, perhaps more simply, those concerned with processes and those with materials. The first would cover all the varieties of engineering, in so far as they deal with different arrangements of materials to achieve definite ends. The second would involve a study of the materials themselves; their occurrence, which would bring in the mining industry and industrial agriculture; their production and processing and the uses of their products. Up till now the approach to this subject has been entirely *ad hoc*. Each problem has been dealt with as it came up, and surveys of the industry as a whole with an attempt to put it on a rational basis have rarely been made. It cannot be doubted that if such an analysis were carried through, and its findings applied, this would result in what would practically be a new industrial revolution, with an immense increase in social effectiveness.

Biological Sector.—The biological sector, both in its agricultural and in its medical aspects, would also gain immensely from such rationalization. Indeed, it stands to gain more, on account of the particularly chaotic state of its present organization and the consequent waste of most of the relatively small funds at its disposal. Besides extension and rationalization of existing agricultural and medical research, a whole set of new institutes would need to be called into being, dealing with the hitherto neglected side of industrial research, namely, that of direct consumption. This could all be grouped around an institute of domestic engineering which would concern itself with the scientific study of nutrition and cookery, of clothing and furniture, and of housing and housework, all considered from the point of view, not of the profitable selling of consumption goods, but of designing a way of life not only healthy but also free from the waste and inefficiency of our present half-traditional, half-scientific domestic organization.

Sociological Institutes and Planning.—Sociological technical institutes would break entirely new ground; they would be concerned in effect with the whole problem of planning, the development of human society with the aim of producing general welfare and the most rapid and harmonious development, both material and cultural. The whole question of the planning of town and country, of the location of industry, of the control and distribution of population, of working conditions and education would come within their scope (see p. 378). They would, of course, be research bodies having neither legislative nor administrative functions. Central governments or municipalities would seek their advice and carry it out or not according to the political or economic situation. But it may be hoped that as time went on such advice would be increasingly easy to take and the institutes would become effectively the planning organization in its scientific aspect. This latter qualification should be specially noted because there is no suggestion here that science should usurp the place of popular choice in social development. All that such social institutes could do would be to indicate the means by which certain ends could be most effectively achieved. They would provide the basis for a number of alternative methods of social organization and it would be left to popular taste to decide between them.

INDUSTRIAL LABORATORIES AND FIELD STATIONS

The final link in the chain of scientific organization would be provided by the industrial laboratories and experimental factories, field stations and medical centres. The effective contact between science and productive life would be made here. To a certain extent such laboratories exist at present, but their scope is excessively narrow and in practice amounts to little more than routine testing. They should be made essential parts of the general scientific scheme, for it is in its relation to practice that science has most to give, and if such laboratories could be filled with workers eager to notice every unexpected event and to turn to useful purpose each new scientific advance, the result could not fail to be of equal benefit to science and production. To a certain extent this could be done by a much more frequent change of personnel than at present takes place. All scientists ought to have the opportunity of spending part of their time in such laboratories, while industrial and agricultural research staffs need to spend more of their time in universities and higher institutes.

Experimental Factories.—But more than that is needed. Science has, up to the present, been largely an addition to existing industrial processes. It must become an integral part of them, and this can only happen if it takes on a much more positive function. One of the chief difficulties in applied science is the translating of small-scale laboratory experience into industrial experience. Some intermediate form is needed. Already this has appeared in the laboratories of some of the biggest industries in the shape of the experimental factory where industrial processes are carried on on a semi-technical scale and in the charge of a scientifically trained personnel. This system needs to be immensely developed and extended. In the ordinary progress of production economic factors put a limit on variation of existing processes, and yet new processes of greater efficiency may often result from the development of processes themselves not economical. Some means of getting over this difficulty must be provided. Up till now this has been done very slowly and ineffectively by using the fluctuations of the trade cycle. In good times firms can afford to experiment and new methods can be tried out with reasonable chance of success on a rising market. In times of depression, on the other hand, every type of cost-cutting and labour-saving device is at a premium. The result is, of course, that when the new method really does become successful there is an immediate rush for developing it, leading to over-expansion and disastrous obsolescence for the older methods. All this could be avoided by a rational use of experimental factories in the operations of which economic costs and returns do not enter as a limiting factor, although, of course, they would always be carefully considered and used as a measure of the success achieved. In this way the earlier non-economic stages of development of a process could be passed so as to produce the new process at the right time, economically and technically. Rapid obsolescence would be avoided, for this occurs to the greatest degree when a process is being used commercially at a time when it is undergoing rapid technical development, whereas here such stages would be passed in the experimental factory.

Field Stations.—In agriculture the experimental factory would be represented by the field station. A network of field stations closely scattered over the whole country in touch with one another and with the higher agricultural institutes would fulfil the same double function of study and trial. Such networks do exist though in a very minor way in many countries, but they lack co-ordination in the service of a consciously planned and balanced agricultural programme. Even more do they lack the executive function which would enable the practical results of their work to be translated at once into general farming practice. It should be realized, moreover, that science has still almost as much to learn from agricultural practice and tradition as to teach it. Up till now this learning has been sporadic because of the small resources of agricultural science. The net of field laboratories could, however, gather this knowledge in, collate it, compare practice in one country with that in another, and discover in doing so the scientific phases of successful practice.

In medicine the primary units would be laboratories in hospitals and health centres. They would serve to break down by actual contact the misunderstanding between the laboratory, the clinic, and the experience of the general practitioner. One of their services would clearly be the collection of reliable and significant physiological medical statistics which, after analysis in the higher medical institutes, could be the basis of a really adequate knowledge of public health. It should be possible through them also to carry out tests of new remedies and treatments far more rapidly and safely than by the casual methods of to-day. The chief difference from the present state would, however, lie in the power which they would need to see that tested methods would effectively be used in practice, not only in the questions of remedies and treatments, but in the provision of living conditions favourable to health. The destruction of health by useless or dangerous patent medicines and food (see p. 154) would be stopped once and for all. It would, however, be idle to discuss their functions in detail because they depend so much on the general reorganization of medical practice in the service of general health and well-being instead of the mere cure of disease.

The Character of Applied Research.—Of course it would be necessary to recognize that development in technical as well as in fundamental science will still contain a very large element of chance. The older attitude towards research, of payment by results, is particularly vicious in relation to science because of this chance factor. Research pays not in the sense that every penny spent on a particular research leads to a corresponding profit, but that the total amount of money spent on a number of different researches, most of which comes to nothing at all, leads to a really economical development.

The Control of Obsolescence.—At present obsolescence is the curse of applied science. Only in countries in a state of rapid economic advance, as in the U.S.A. in the early part of the century, can it be faced in its crudest and most disorganized form. The alternatives before us are either to slacken the whole pace of industrial advance and technical application of science or to rationalize it along some such lines as are here suggested. The first course means not only losing the benefits which science can give to society but also a definite stifling of the advance of science itself. For in restricting applications we are not only cutting off sources of funds for scientific research but also the source of new ideas that comes from close connection with industrial advances. Only with an integrated and rational structure of scientific organization, reaching from the most abstract science to the most detailed application, can we ensure a simultaneous and harmonious development of both science and production.

THE APPLICATION OF SCIENCE UNDER CAPITALISM

It would be absurd to imagine, however, that a rationalization of scientific application to industry would be easy to adapt to the conditions of Monopoly Capitalism. Few of the factors (discussed in Chapter VI), which at present hamper the application of science, can be removed even by the intelligent action of the directors of industry, and such action is in any case extremely unlikely. Interindustrial and international competition and the advantages of monopoly restriction are not easily to be exorcised. With new inventions the temptation to hold back expensive changes when there seems no risk of competition, and to rush them forward once this risk appears, will add to the natural irregular onset of technical change. It has, however, been very cogently argued by Lord Stamp that the major difficulties of scientific application are intrinsic and independent of the type of economic system. In his *The Science of Social Adjustment* he maintains that normally technical innovation must be limited to the rate at which the working population in the trades affected reproduces itself or otherwise severe unemployment and capital loss would ensue. This in a condition of static or falling population would mean a very considerable slowing up of the present rate of application of science rather than the great increase which humanity needs and science could supply.

Socialism and the Condition of the Advance of Science.—The logic of the argument is excellent but the premises require examination.

Lord Stamp himself suggests that only the operation of agencies which have existed in the past but no longer do so would permit a far more rapid rate of increase. They are: (1) Elasticity of demand; (2) Rapid introduction of novelty; (3) Rise in population; (4) Overseas outlet. Now only the second of these, which in any case appears somewhat paradoxical, depends on the relations of science and industry. It is, however, almost certain it could be achieved by the type of organization here described. It would be possible, by short-circuiting the existing process of application, to produce capital and labour-saving devices at such a rate that the losses they produced in one direction were more than compensated by gains in another. Nevertheless we may agree that by itself this factor would be insufficient to induce rapid industrial transformation under capitalist conditions, since for one thing aggregate profits would hardly be affected. It is the variation of the other three conditions which Lord Stamp assumes fixed that would be decisive. Now no one denies that under capitalism the population is static or falling, that there is little elasticity of demand because the majority of the people simply have not the money to spend, and that overseas outlets are rapidly closing. Indeed, as Lord Stamp is at pains to point out elsewhere, all this talk of poverty in the midst of plenty is nonsense, because there is being produced all that it is possible to produce—within the framework of the present system. Only if the system is changed and production is made for public use instead of private profit, can his conditions be satisfied and the applications of science increase rapidly without the complications of unemployment and economic instability. Once a union of Socialist states is in being the effective demand would rise at once, first for producer and next for consumer goods, while the very economic backwardness and crushing poverty of the great majority in non-industrial countries would furnish a demand for production goods of all kinds, particularly agricultural machinery, that would far surpass that of the mercantile period of the nineteenth century. At present the natural demands of 95 per cent. of the world's population for the barest biological necessities of food, clothing, and shelter are being held up by the economic system. Once released their satisfaction will call for the most rapid possible development of production technique.

(1) The conception of a laboratory as a voluntary association is actually one of the earliest in science. The Accademia del Cimento in the seventeenth century was formed almost on the model of a religious order and carried its co-operation to such lengths that no account was taken of individual work, everything being published from the Academy as a whole.

(2) This is already common practice in the United States.

(3) One of the most tragic cases was that of Joseph Henry, a man of the same calibre as Faraday, who wasted most of his life as director of the Smithsonian Institution. See Crowther's *Famous American Men of Science*.

(4) This was realized at the founding of the Royal Society, as expressed in the words of Hooke :

" And the ends of all these Inquiries they intend to be the Pleasure of Contemplative minds, but above all, the ease and dispatch of the labours of men's hands. They do indeed neglect no opportunity to bring all the rare things of Remote Countries within the compass of their knowledge and practice. But they still acknowledge their most useful Informations to arise from common things, and from diversifying their most ordinary operations upon them. They do not wholly reject Experiments of meer light and theory ; but they principally aim at such, whose Applications will improve and facilitate the present way of Manual Arts. And though some men, who are perhaps taken up about less honourable Employments, are pleas'd to censure their proceedings, yet they can shew more fruits of their first three years, wherein they have assembled, then any other Society in Europe can for a much larger space of time. 'Tis true, such undertakings as theirs do commonly meet with small incouragement, because men are generally rather taken with the plausible and discursive, then the real and the solid part of Philosophy ; yet by the good fortune of their institution, in an Age of all others the most inquisitive, they have been assisted by the contribution and presence of very many of the chief Nobility and Gentry, and Others, who are some of the most considerable in their several Professions. But that that yet farther convinces me of the Real esteem that the more serious part of men have of this Society, is, that severa Merchants, men who act in earnest (whose Object is meum and tuum, that great Rudder of humane affairs) have adventur'd considerable sums of Money, to put in practice what some of our Members have contrived, and have continued stedfast in their good opinions of such Indeavours, when not one of a hundred of the vulgar have believed their undertakings feasable. And it is also fit to be added, that they have one advantage peculiar to themselves, that very many of their number are men of Converse and Traffick ; which is a good Omen, that their attempts will bring Philosophy from words to action, seeing the men of Business have had so great a share in their first foundation.

And of this kind I ought not to conceal one particular Generosity, which more nearly concerns my self. It is the munificence of Sir John Cutler, in endowing a Lecture for the promotion of Mechanick Arts, to be governed and directed by This Society. . . . This Gentleman has well observ'd, that the Arts of life have been too long imprison'd in the dark shops of Mechanicks themselves, and there hindred from growth, either by ignorance, or self-interest ; and he has bravely freed them from these inconveniences ; He hath not only obliged Tradesmen, but Trade it self : He has done a work that is worthy of London and has taught the chief City of Commerce in the world the right way how Commerce is to be improv'd."—From the Preface to *Micrographia.*

That was in an age when commerce was the rising force. To-day, though financial interests are in control, the place of merchants is taken by engineers and administrators. Once that control is removed, however, these as well as manual workers should take their place in the academies. To do so before is simply to tie the academy more firmly than ever to financial interests which represent at present the main force frustrating science.

CHAPTER XI

SCIENTIFIC COMMUNICATION

THE problem of the reorganization of science would not be solved by administrative or financial changes alone. It will also be necessary to reorganize in a most comprehensive way the whole apparatus of scientific communications. Indeed in science communications take much of the place of administration in other services. In the old ideal of science, communications were the only link between scientists. The scientific world consisted solely of individuals following their own bent of inquiry and needing only the bare knowledge of what their fellows were doing. In those days, however, the number of workers was so small that there was a reasonable possibility of acquiring this knowledge, but now as we have already seen (p. 117 *et seq.*), the very quantity of scientific information has made its diffusion an enormous problem, with which existing machinery has utterly failed to cope. Unless something is done we shall soon reach the position when knowledge is being lost as rapidly as it is gained. It is clearly no longer sufficient to see that every new observation and discovery is published. The problem has to be looked at from the other end; we need to be sure that every scientific worker, and for that matter every member of the general public, receives just that information that can be of the greatest use to him in his work and no more. This requires the most serious thinking out of the whole problem of scientific communications, not only between scientists but also to the public. It is by no means sufficient to remedy abuses that already exist. Improvements here and there may in fact by increasing anomalies do more harm than good. The problem can be divided into that of providing special and general information; the first is the function of scientific publications proper and other means of personal contact between scientists, the second is that of scientific education and popular science.

THE FUNCTION OF SCIENTIFIC PUBLICATIONS

The present mode of scientific publication is predominantly through the 33,000 odd scientific journals. It is, as we have already shown, incredibly cumbersome and wasteful, and is in danger of breaking down on account of expense. What can we put in its place? The prime function of scientific publications is to convey information about acquired knowledge, but it is clear that whereas certain information is needed by certain workers in full detail, the great bulk of it is only needed by any given worker in outline, if at all. An adequate system of communication would consist in principle of a limited distribution of detailed accounts, a wider distribution of summaries or abstracts, and the frequent production of reports or monographs covering the sum of recent advances in any given field. Behind this must be a body of readily accessible archives in which reference can be made to the work of the past. The problem is essentially a technical one of selecting units and arranging for their proper distribution and storage, a problem which is every day solved in large business houses or mail order stores. To see how it could be solved it is necessary to consider the units and their possible mode of distribution in greater detail.

Categories of Publication Units.—The first is the note, representing perhaps a week's or a month's work of one research worker. It may be the making of some new measurement, the correcting of some old one, or the establishing of a point which, though it may have occurred during the course of some other research, deserves remark on its own merits and may easily be lost sight of if incorporated in a larger communication. Such a note must of course be distinguished from the notice of a recently established discovery of considerable importance or the putting forward of some speculative point of view or argument in controversy. These are not strictly finished work but part of work in progress and require a different treatment. After the note comes the "paper," dealing with the individual or small joint research, which has been up till now far the commonest basic unit of scientific communication, and represents anything between a quarter and two worker years. Next follows a category which has become increasingly common, but for which there is no proper name ; the account of a connected inquiry undertaken by anything from three to twenty workers and going on for a period of up to ten years. The contributions of the individual workers are here so closely related that a coherent common account is clearly the most desirable form of publication. According to the time spent, this may take the form of a long series of papers or, alternatively, where material requires working over, of one long paper or monograph.

The next category is the report on the advance of any particular field of science which may, though compiled by one man or a small number of persons, represent anything up to a thousand worker years. When they are short such reports may be original scientific works in the form of monographs, in contrast to text-books intended for teaching or popular exposition. These latter differ from reports mainly in the fact that they are written by fewer people, and because the opinions contained in them are necessarily more individual and less judicial. Besides these forms of publication, which from their permanent nature require to find a place in the archives of science, there are the notices which, though ephemeral, are equally important for the immediate carrying on of science. These include the announcement of discoveries, accounts of new techniques both practical and theoretical, reports of meetings and discussions, and the more personal side of scientific news.

Most of the types of publication hitherto mentioned are intended for use inside a branch of science, that is, a region wide enough for everyone to understand the terminology and arguments of everyone else in it. Besides this, and of growing importance, are those publications intended to explain the current advances and techniques of one science for the benefit of another, and the syntheses which can be made between a number of sciences, serving to bind them together into a unity such as was achieved by the great synthesis of physics in the last century.

The Problem of Distribution.—The problem of seeing that these various kinds of scientific intelligence are published and distributed to those who would benefit most by reading them would seem, on the face of it, to be such an obvious technical problem as not to be worth discussing, but, since it has not been solved or even been felt to exist, it is necessary to do so. The most important intrinsic difficulties, apart from mere conservatism and vested interest, arise from the very vastness of the field of science, the number of workers involved, and the rate at which they publish results. Mere publication in such circumstances will not be enough; far too much is published at present for workers to be able to read even those parts which are relevant to their immediate researches. Yet this is largely because, owing to lack of organization, they are actually obliged to read a great deal of useless material on the chance of coming across something which may be useful to them. The kind of organization we wish to aim at is one in which all relevant information should be available to each research worker and in amplitude proportional to its degree of relevance. Further, that not only should the information be available, but also that it should be to a large extent put at the disposal of the research worker without his having to take any special steps to get hold of it. This implies a system, or rather a service, of recording, filing, co-ordinating and distributing scientific information. Such schemes have in fact already occupied the minds of scientists in different countries. (1) The most elaborate study has been made by the documentation division of Science Service, Washington, where a complete science service for the U.S.A., and ultimately for the rest of the world, has been planned in some detail (see Appendix VIII). The suggestions contained here are partly based on this work, but differ from it in a number of respects.

Distribution Service to supersede Periodicals.—All schemes have in common the remodelling, and to a large extent the abolition, of all existing scientific periodicals, at any rate those which contain, for the most part, separate scientific papers or monographs. The publication of such periodicals, quite apart from the question of overlapping and lack of co-ordination already discussed, is obviously an inefficient way of distributing a large amount of scientific information, although they were invaluable in an earlier age when every scientist could read all the scientific publications there were, and ask for more. At present scientific publications, when taken by individuals, are rarely read to an extent greater than ten per cent., whereas if taken by libraries they are almost invariably wanted by a dozen people at once. The obvious solution is to make the separate paper itself the unit of communication between scientists.

This is in fact a practice which, in a very clumsy and expensive form, is growing up spontaneously through the distribution of reprints of such papers privately among scientists themselves, a reversion in fact to the old system of scientific letter-writing. The present arrangement is costly because the printing is expensive for the small numbers involved, and inefficient, partly because only a limited number of scientists practise it, and partly because those who do so cannot know exactly who will be interested in their papers. They consequently fail to send them to many who would be interested, and actually send them to many who only throw the reprints away. In any case, as the cost of reprints and their postage usually falls on the private income of the scientists, the practice could never be operated on anything like the scale which is required. The rational proposal would be to make the sending out of papers—no longer reprints—the main method of scientific communication and to organize an editorial and distributing service to carry this out in the place of the multiple editorial boards of existing periodicals. For the most part these papers would be sent to actual scientific workers, but a certain number of copies would, of course, be sent to laboratories where they could be bound up according to some rational and pre-arranged system, and a number preserved in archives.

Photostat Reproduction.—Here a technical point arises. If the papers were printed as at present the saving would only be in editorial office expenses, but there is no reason why they should be printed, and many reasons for using newer processes which are gradually coming into use for other purposes, in particular the micro-photography of original typescript of a special kind (see p. 377) and its reproduction on normal scale. It is estimated that printing is more expensive than photography for all editions of less than 2000, and most scientific papers are not read by anything like that number of people, even when the edition of the scientific journal reaches these figures. But photography has two other advantages particularly brought out in the American investigation. In the first place, the micro plates or films from which papers are reproduced occupy far less space than an ordinary paper; they consequently can be kept far more easily and filed very much more conveniently. Thus they afford the best kind of archives both from the point of view of ease of preservation and ease of reference. By applying modern business filing methods to scientific papers it would be possible, for instance, to provide by automatic machinery complete bibliographies with the actual papers relevant to any inquiry and thus save months and years of scholarly research which is pure waste from the scientific point of view.

How the System would Work.—The way the system would work would be more or less as follows: the research worker, whatever his subject, sends his paper in to the publication office; it is then submitted to an editorial board of referees as at present and, if passed, amended or unamended, is reproduced photographically. A certain number of copies are sent immediately to all libraries and to all workers who have indicated on cards sent in at some previous date that they wish to receive copies of papers in such and such fields. A further number are sent out to others who, having seen a notice of the paper, in a way to be described below, have asked for copies. The original master copy or film is then stored and a copy can be run off it on application at any subsequent date, even if years have elapsed, thus producing an immediate reprint with no more trouble than is required for the first copies. Such a system, though it may appear at first sight more complicated than the present one, would be in effect both more businesslike and more economical. A great deal of purely technical editorial work which now hampers many scientists would be dealt with efficiently by a small central staff, and for the same expenditure of money it would be possible to publish, if desired, far more papers than at present. In particular, papers which from their length or other expensive features cannot be published nowadays, would on this system not offer any extra difficulty.

Abstracts.—The arrangement for publishing and distributing scientific papers is, however, only one part of fundamental importance in the general scheme of scientific publication. Although, with the system outlined above, papers would go largely to those and only to those who were interested in them, it would still be possible, if this were all, for a number of important papers to be lost altogether, with the consequence, already described, of holding up science for lack of available information. This difficulty, which exists of course to a far larger extent under the present system, is there met by the preparation of abstracts. The present abstract system, however, suffers from many defects. In the first place, in spite of efforts to rationalize it, there are still, both nationally and internationally, far too many separate abstracting journals, and these in general work so badly that, whereas one paper may be abstracted many times over, others may slip through the net completely, at any rate for two or three years.

It would, of course, be an over-simplication to have only one set of abstracts, because the users of abstracts may want to read the papers from a number of different points of view. For instance, the chemist's attitude towards the abstract of a bio-chemical paper would be different from that of the physiologist. Nevertheless with suitable provision for differences of outlook, the abstract system could be unified. The preparation of the main abstract of a paper could be made in general by the author himself (2), though it might need to be amended for the sake of uniformity, and further abstracts need only be employed for papers of an interest in more than one subject. Instead of furnishing abstracts in the form of books, which themselves require indexes, and where the abstracts are arranged partly according to subject and partly as they come in, it would be better to go straight to a card system, to arrange for complete sets of abstract cards to be sent to libraries and institutions and for selections according to subject to be sent to research workers who asked for them. This would, of course, include far more abstracts than would be found in the selection of papers sent to the same workers. If the abstracting were done by the same authority responsible for the papers postage costs would be reduced and the total additional cost need be very small.

Reports.—There remains the question of the grouping together of the units out of which scientific communication is built, in other words, the syntheses of various kinds, in particular the monograph and the report. Here it might not be necessary to do more than extend the present practice. Many scientific societies issue annual reports. All that would be required would be to extend this over the whole of science and to co-ordinate different reports of the same or allied sciences. The importance of such reports is great and will certainly grow. It will be necessary to depend more and more on them for guidance in following the progress of science. Reports would be needed, however, not only for scientists, but for technicians and administrators, and their preparation would probably require a special service. This might well take the form of the excellent suggestion of Lord Stamp in *The Science of Social Adjustment*:

> "The third general action is the development of a practice, by the responsible body in each branch of science, of reviewing periodically the immediate hinterland of their subject. They should set out, for each period, what they deem to be the chief discoveries and improvements in their own field. These should be analysed into those which have received practical application in the social or economic field, either directly or through the medium of another branch of science. An estimate should be attempted of the effect of each in creating unemployment and embodying new capital, together with another estimate of any employment or capital displaced, and of changes brought about in the location of industry. It would probably be found that a common service of statistical technique would facilitate these *ad hoc* inquiries, and certainly one would be wanted for collating them and bringing them into a general picture. In some sciences, such as astronomy and mathematics, the 'products' would all be only indirectly used, through physics. But the effort to work to a common schedule or questionnaire which would have to be reconciled in a common result, would develop a social awareness in the specialist, of greatest value in his later work. The earliest efforts would be crude and sketchy, but the point is that the right kind of specialists can contribute in an indispensable way, and might themselves gain greatly in so doing."—*The Science of Social Adjustment*, by Lord Stamp, chap. iv., p. 149.

With regard to monographs and original scientific works still less change would be needed. Here it is more a question of a unified policy of editorship and of seeing that qualified authors are persuaded to write up their subject at suitable intervals, than any more technical change. There ought also to be a similar provision for text-books, because only in such a way can the standards of text-books, and consequently of scientific education as a whole, be kept up to date. To a certain extent this function has been filled in the past by the monumental series of German Handbücher, which conscientiously followed the details of the advance of science in every field. It ought to be possible even under the present system, by agreement between different publishers, to see that science in the English language was covered as adequately, though it may be hoped at shorter length. Only one section of scientific publication in the journal form need remain, namely, that of the type of *Nature*. This would give in the form of notes the latest scientific news, not only of discoveries but also of new laboratories and administrative changes, and at the same time reflect the relation of science to wider social problems.

Control of Abuses.—In proposing a rational organization of scientific publication we must, at the same time, face the danger that such a change might entail. Scientific publication is exposed to two main types of abuse: one of laxity, allowing to be printed quantities of material which is either inaccurate or of doubtful value, and the opposite danger of strictness, preventing the publication of material which may be of the greatest scientific value, but which at the time of its first production is not in line with orthodox views. It may be feared that any attempt at centralizing science might lead to an increase of either of these two evils. Actually if it were properly done it should have the effect of removing them.

It is not proposed, for instance, to put the editorial functions of the publication in the hands of a permanent administrative staff. These would merely act as a link between the writers of papers and the persons who, under the present system, are editors of scientific journals. How properly these people fulfil their functions will be a matter of how they are chosen, and consequently will depend largely on the organization of scientists themselves. In particular, young men should have a far greater say in the question than they have at present. On the whole the tendency would be elasticity in practice, on the ground that the publication of a foolish scientific paper would do less harm than suppression of an eccentric but possibly valuable one. Under the new system useless papers would not be in demand; they would not clog up scientific periodicals, and would not impose any undue expense on the system, while their ultimate value would be judged in periodical critical reports. It might be left as an axiom that a paper of which any one member of a board of editors approved should be published.

The existence of an enormous number of scientific journals has often been justified by the claim that a new branch of science, or a new attitude towards an older established branch, cannot expect, in present circumstances, to receive due recognition in existing journals, and consequently a number of its devotees get together and found yet another new journal. Here the same end could be reached in a much more economical way by securing the representation of the new branch on an editorial board adhering to such rules. To check the mere mass of scientific publications it might well be possible to substitute for the present abuse of publishing papers in several different periodicals at once, a double publication for certain papers. Papers, for instance, that contain a large amount of valuable material most of which, however, is of interest to only few persons, might be published *in extenso* in a very small number of copies and in a shortened form for general consumption. Only certain central archives would need to contain all the full-length papers. All of them could be duplicated in micro film and so stored that it would be unlikely that war or earthquake could destroy them, or at least that there would be a chance that some complete sets should survive.

The essential check against either type of abuse of publication would be furnished by the closest linking of active scientific work and publication. The publication service would come to be more and more a kind of convenient post office between scientific workers doing for them what can be done by direct personal contact and interchange of data between individual scientists in the same institute.

One possibility it would offer is that of keeping scientists informed within limited fields of what work was in progress. This would eliminate unnecessary overlapping and provide short cuts to much information. At present jealousy and the thirst for priority would probably wreck such a system, but once science were well organized and supplied with funds much of this attitude would disappear. The publications organization would in no sense dominate science but only serve it.

Immediate Possibilities.—The rationalization of publication differs from most of the other suggestions contained here in that it is far more close to actual attainment. This is partly because it would not involve any serious initial expenditure, and after a little time would prove far more economical, and partly because it implies no change in the relations between science, state, and industry. The difficulties that would hinder its introduction are rather those of winding-up the old system and starting anew. There is a certain amount of vested interest in scientific publications on the part of publishers, but the profits got from science publication, apart from text-books, are very small, and under the new system it might be possible to compensate the publishers by promising them their share of the increased production of semi-technical and popular books that would certainly follow the rationalization of internal scientific publication. At the same time use might be made of their services in the building up of the administrative part of the new system.

A more serious difficulty would have to be met in the opposition of the existing scientific societies that undertake the bulk of scientific publication. Although in most cases this publication is a serious financial burden to the societies, it gives them in many cases their main *raison d'être*, and the abolition of scientific journals might also be resented for purely sentimental reasons. Once it was realized, however, that the present system has already strangled scientific advance and may altogether stifle it in the not too distant future, and that the new one would lead almost immediately to a great increase in the ease and efficiency of every scientific worker, these objections would cease to carry weight. After all, periodicals exist for science and not science for periodicals. It might be possible, if it was so desired, to effect a compromise which would save the tradition by binding together certain groups of papers, of particular value in a certain field, and constituting them a continuation of the original journals in the charge of a scientific society and appearing as such in special libraries and ceremonial archives.

THE INTERNATIONAL PROBLEM

So far the question of scientific communication has been considered as one effecting a homogeneous body of scientists and the difficult question of nationality has been left out. The degree to which science is international, and its narrowing down to four or five large supernational spheres, has already been discussed. It is, of course, for scientific publications that this division becomes of the greatest importance. Any system of rationalizing publication, of the type just sketched out, could hardly be effective unless applied on a scale much larger than that of most national units, though it might possibly work with such large countries as the U.S.A. or the U.S.S.R. It would gain its full effectiveness, however, only if it were entirely international, because having a rational national organization, in one country only, would mean that all the labour and confusion of following foreign work would still remain, with the additional difficulty of having to adopt one system at home and another for abroad. This would certainly result in even further cutting off of national science and the break-up of its international unity. Unfortunately the present state of the world is not one to encourage any considerable belief in an immediate internationalization of science. The most that could be hoped for is some measure of co-ordination. Even if science is to be used increasingly for national ends there will still remain what might be called an export surplus, consisting of material which is not considered of immediate military importance and which may, by its quality, enhance the prestige of the exporting country. This might mean that the most valuable parts of science would be international and they alone might be presented in an organized and rational way.

Decentralization.—Present national considerations apart, however, it may well be that although science has an international unity, its organization and particularly the organization of its publications can, in most cases, best be carried on in a decentralized way. Geographical considerations make it certain that, in general, there will be closer communication between people working in the same country than between those in different countries, and that only a certain amount of the advance in any particular country can profitably cross its frontiers. Under an ideal system there would not be just one central clearing-house for scientific publication but a number of such centres, which would be in close communication with one another.   Each centre would act as a point of collection and distribution for scientific workers in its own country or district.   They would send those scientific papers that were needed for distribution in other countries in bulk to the corresponding centres.   In this way the maximum degree of local autonomy and international co-ordination could be secured.   The different sciences, of course, differ very markedly in the degree of international co-ordination which they require.   Certain of them can only function at all if internationally co-ordinated.   Astronomy, meteorology, geo-physics, soil science, and epidemiology have all already efficient and rational international organization and there such organization could immediately take control of publication.   In other sciences this may be neither possible nor desirable.

A Secondary Scientific Language?—The question of language is still a difficult one.   A certain degree of rationalization has already been effected in this field.   English, French, and German are the three scientific languages *par excellence*.   Other national languages are, however, used for all scientific papers circulating inside national boundaries.   An ideal system would be one in which, apart from all the national languages, there was one accepted international scientific language which played the part that Latin did in the first great period of scientific advance.   There is some hope that, in spite of nationalist difficulties, this might be attained through the use either of English or of a simplified variety of it such as Basic English. (3) There is no doubt that such a change would have a most immediate and beneficial effect on science.   The barrier of language is still a very real one.   It is only necessary to read any text-book on a scientific subject to realize how very much more familiar the author, who is presumably a trained scientist, is with the works published in his own language than with those in foreign languages.

It would, however, be a mistake to hold up the rationalization of scientific publication until such a universal secondary language was adopted.   It should not be difficult to adapt the new system of publication to the existing situation in respect to language.   Each distributing centre in a national area would deal with papers written in the national language.   The editorial board would arrange that all papers adjudged of sufficient importance, together with those for which there was a special demand abroad, should be translated into one or all of the three scientific languages.   On the other hand, they would, in respect to any papers for which there was a special demand in their own particular country, arrange for its translation into the native language.   The abstracts of all papers would appear in the three scientific languages and also in the languages of those countries which had important enough scientific work to justify this, and the same practice might be followed for reports. There would be national journals for scientific news in the national language, but they would all carry the same service of notes of discoveries of international importance. It will be seen that such a system, while allowing for the maximum of interchange of information, neither does violence to existing national feelings nor would it involve rigid control from one international centre. Three or four co-ordinating centres, however, say one in Geneva, one in the United States, and one in the Far East, would certainly help to link up the activities of the national centres.

The Importance of Personal Contacts

Not all, and hardly even the larger part, of scientific communication is carried on by published papers. To an extent much larger than is realized, the transference of scientific ideas from one set of scientific workers to another is effected by means of visits, personal contacts, and letters. In many cases new ideas do not spread beyond the laboratory of their origin until that laboratory has become so famous as to attract to it important workers from other centres. Some of the greatest developments in modern science, which depend on the interplay of ideas from different sources, have occurred only when workers, who had absorbed both ideas in different centres, happened to come together. The appearance of the Bohr theory of the atom, which is the basis of all our modern physics, occurred because Bohr, who had absorbed in Germany the quantum theory of Planck, came to work in Rutherford's laboratory and there came in contact with the nuclear theory of the atom. The value of such interchanges can hardly be exaggerated, and it is quite certain that they do not play anything like the part they could in the development of science. Almost every visit of a scientist from one laboratory to his colleagues in another results in the introduction of a new piece of information or point of view that no amount of reading had managed to effect. Partly, of course, this is due to the existing plethora and confusion of publication. But, even if this were removed, there would remain techniques which are impossible to transmit without visual demonstration, and ideas too intangible to be put into writing, yet capable of communication by personal contact.

Facilitation of Travel.—Up till now the chief factors that have hindered such visits is lack of money. Except for a certain number of invitations to congresses, the scientist travels at his own expense and his salary is rarely sufficient for him to do so nearly enough, particularly in those years when he is most impressionable and active. We require a much greater provision for travel and residence in other centres of work. The institution of the sabbatical years is a step in this direction, although seven-year intervals are too far apart. The needs of different kinds of scientists vary widely, but on the average it would be fair to say that it would pay scientists to spend two months every year in laboratories other than their own, quite apart from their normal recreative holidays. The expense of this, though large for the individual scientist, would appear small for science as a whole. It would be easy to extend present funds for travelling in such a way as to make these visits at very little cost, particularly in countries where the railways are under the control of the State. As to hospitality, where the collegiate system exists there should be no extra expense, on the average, because the number of guests would always be equal to the number of hosts who were away, while private hospitality could be charged on a central fund and would not be a burdensome expense. The value of such interchanges should not be confined to the higher scientific staff. Not only should they be freely available to younger scientists but they might also very profitably be extended to mechanics and laboratory assistants, for whom at present practically no opportunity for travel exists. It is particularly to them that the value of interchange of practical techniques would apply, and if such visits could be arranged the standard of laboratory technique would become more uniform and develop with increasing rapidity.

The general effect of the reorganization of scientific communication would be a rapid improvement in the efficiency of scientific research. Not only this, but science understanding itself would also come to be understood far more easily by the general public. Intelligent co-operation would take the place of admiration of the incomprehensible. There is hardly any change from which such considerable effects could be secured by so small an effort.

POPULAR SCIENCE

It is no use improving the knowledge that scientists have about each other's work if we do not at the same time see that a real understanding of science becomes a part of the common life of our times. Lack of knowledge of science and, even more, partial and distorted knowledge, is largely responsible for the mental attitude that has permitted and indeed encouraged the return to barbarism which is so evident to-day. The basis of an understanding of science lies in the reform of education, but it is almost as important to see that adult minds have the opportunity of appreciating what science is doing and how it is likely to affect human life. The media through which such dissemination can naturally be carried out are the press, wireless and the cinema. Besides these, more solid relations can be established through books and through the actual participation in scientific work.

Science and the Press.—Press science of to-day is for the most part sensational and superficial. In a sense this is the general attitude of modern journalism to all aspects of life, but there is a special reason why the controllers of the press do not wish science to receive the interest which its importance deserves. If the possibilities of science for human welfare were being drummed into people every day there would be an irresistible demand for the realization of these benefits which would not be to the liking of the vested interests of owners and advertisers. Nevertheless for popular commercial reasons, which the American press has already grasped (4), the press in Britain could do with a great deal more science news. What is required here is an adequate science news service, prepared by competent scientists and circulated to the press, and the appointment to all daily and weekly papers of science editors, primarily journalists, but with a background of scientific training. It is only occasionally that working scientists can be successful in scientific journalism, and there should be no attempt to restrict these fields to scientists. The development of the system of reports suggested above should make it far easier for journalists to get an accurate and interesting picture of science.

Science through Radio and Cinema.—A good start has been made by the B.B.C. with talks on scientific subjects, and indeed some of the discussions, such as those by Julian Huxley and Professor Levy, have exhibited far more social understanding than any other presentations of science. Since these have been given there has been a notable reaction, but with any liberal control it should be possible to lead the public through the spoken word, or now through television, into the actual working of science. The public could listen in and see experiments in progress. The cinema offers even greater possibilities, which are beginning to be understood and used. Instructional films of the highest quality already exist. The cinema can show aspects of science, for example, the growth of plants, far more vividly than can in many cases direct observation, and many of these films are exciting and beautiful. Recently we have seen the beginning of a more comprehensive production of such films by the creation of the Scientists' Film Group (5), which will ensure the collaboration of a number of scientists in production. In any reorganization of science the production of films would form a necessary part, as such films with small modification can be used as research tools, for education and for popular science.

Books on Science.—The enormous success of recent popular scientific works has shown that there is an immense demand for science. Up to now, however, the production of these books has been through isolated efforts by enthusiastic scientists or enterprising publishers. They have been produced either on no scheme at all, or on one based on personal acquaintance. Science as a whole has been most unevenly covered by them, such topics as astronomy and other mysteries of the universe, for instance, taking altogether a disproportionately large place. There is scope for a connected series of popular works on science, preferably by young working scientists and not by elders of the profession who have lost touch with what is being done. Science can be presented in popular form without losing any of its accuracy and indeed gaining importance by being related to common human needs and aspirations. Professor Hogben's two pioneer works, *Mathematics for the Million* and *Science for the Citizen*, show how effective and successful such attempts may be.

World Encyclopaedia.—Behind these lies another prospect of greater and more permanent importance; that of an attempt at a comprehensive and continually revised presentation of the whole of science in its social context, an idea most persuasively put forward by H. G. Wells in his appeal for a World Encyclopaedia of which he has already given us a foretaste in his celebrated outlines. The encyclopaedic movement was a great rallying point of the liberal revolution of the eighteenth and nineteenth centuries. The real encyclopaedia should not be what the *Encyclopaedia Britannica* has degenerated into, a mere mass of unrelated knowledge sold by high-pressure salesmanship, but a coherent expression of the living and changing body of thought; it should sum up what is for the moment the spirit of the age:

"We have been gradually brought to the pitch of imagining and framing our preliminary ideas of a federal world control of such things as communications, health, money, economic adjustments, and the suppression of crime. In all these material things we have begun to foresee the possibility of a world-wide network being woven between all men about the earth. So much of the World Peace has been brought into the range of—what shall I call it?—the general imagination. But I do not think we have yet given sufficient attention to the prior necessity, of linking together its mental organizations into a much closer accord than obtains at the present time. All these ideas of unifying mankind's affairs depend ultimately for their realization on mankind having a unified mind for the job. The want of such effective mental unification is the key to most of our present frustrations. While men's minds are still confused, their social and political relations will remain in confusion, however great the forces that are grinding them against each other and however tragic and monstrous the consequences."—H. G. Wells' *World Brain*, pp. 39-40.

"This World Encyclopaedia would be the mental background of every intelligent man in the world. It would be alive and growing and changing continually under revision, extension and replacement from the original thinkers in the world everywhere. Every university and research institution should be feeding it. Every fresh mind should be brought into contact with its standing editorial organization. And on the other hand, its contents would be the standard source of material for the instructional side of school and college work, for the verification of facts and the testing of statements —everywhere in the world. Even journalists would deign to use it; even newspaper proprietors might be made to respect it " (p. 14).

The original French Encyclopaedia which did attempt these things was, however, made in the period of relative quiet when the forces of liberation were gathering ready to break their bonds. We have already entered the second period of revolutionary struggle and the quiet thought necessary to make such an effort will not be easy to find, but some effort is worth making because the combined assault on science and humanity by the forces of barbarism has against it, as yet, no general and coherent statement on the part of those who believe in democracy and the need for the people of the world to take over the active control of production and administration for their own safety and welfare.

Popular Participation in Science.—All these means of making science an intimate part of our life and culture have this defect in common, they are all passive. They are presentations of science which can either be listened to or rejected by a public which has no part in them. Science will never really be popular unless all citizens at some part of their lives and many citizens throughout their lives play an active part in scientific research themselves. One of the chief reasons why a scientifically educated population can accept the tragic nonsense of racial theory or the ancient superstitions of astrology and spiritualism is that they are presented under the guise of science, and as long as science appears as a set of statements, which for the majority of people have to be accepted on faith, there will be nothing intrinsically to distinguish true science from these base imitations. The factual content of science is essential but it is not sufficient. The method of science can for most people only be grasped in its application. How this can be done is a problem as much of social as it is of scientific organization. At present participation in science is rendered difficult by prejudices which exist against it. On one side we have the cultured contempt for scientific knowledge and even more for scientific practice, a prejudice inherited from the classical contempt for the manual worker. (6) On the other hand, we have the deep distrust of the working-class for science as it is practised to-day, for whom it is a danger to their employment and a means of increasing the monotony and severity of their work. Popular participation in scientific work can only be realized where, as in the U.S.S.R., social changes have made this attitude untenable (see p. 228). Nevertheless, much can be done even now. The beginning, of course, needs to be made in the schools as already indicated, but there is much scope for adult interest in science. We have up and down the country hundreds of scientific societies, but they are small, largely isolated and not nearly well enough in touch with the central scientific institutes. A beginning has been made in organizing visits to laboratories (7), the next step is to organize actual scientific work in connection with research centres. This work, in the first place, would largely be concerned with leisure interests, particularly in relation to natural history. It should be possible, however, to bring a whole new set of interests into play by concentration of scientific research on industrial conditions and enlisting the help of the trade unions, not only as has been done by the setting up of the Trades Union Congress Scientific Advisory Committee (see p. 407), but by getting the workers themselves to engage in research on both the technical and the human factors in their own conditions. Intelligent employers would see at once the advantages this would bring to production as well as to the improvement of conditions. Where employers are not so intelligent, the position of the workers would be immensely strengthened in pressing demands for better conditions by exact knowledge of the effects of existing ones and the technical and administrative means for removing them. Any such development calls for a joint movement on the part of workers and scientists. There are signs that such a movement is beginning ; we already have in this country such bodies as the Workers' Educational Association, though its interests are largely literary and sociological and its attitude towards science is still too passive. In France there is the Université Ouvrière where scientists of every degree of eminence join hands with organized workers. This beginning can be developed, and it is important that it should be, because it is largely on such a popular base that the advance and even the continuance of science depends.

(1) Federovsky in Russia and van Iterson in Holland have interested themselves in this problem.

(2) It is often maintained that the author is the worst person to abstract his own paper. Nevertheless, the growing practice of demanding extensive summaries shows that he can provide some assistance in condensing his work.

(3) *Basic English Applied Science.* C. K. Ogden.

(4) Several American newspapers have scientific editors of repute and maintain a high standard of scientific reporting. Besides this, there is the organization " Science Service " which collects and distributes to the rest of the press far more reliable and less sensational news than is available in this country.

(5) See *Sunday Times*, 15th May 1938 ; *Scientific Worker*, November 1937 and April 1938.

(6) See Professor Farrington's essay, " Vesalius on the Ruin of Ancient Medicine," *Modern Quarterly*, Vol. 1, p. 23.

(7) Visits to the Cambridge Biochemical Laboratory, for instance, have been arranged for groups from the Cambridge branches of the National Union of Railwaymen, Amalgamated Society of Locomotive Engineers and Firemen, Railway Clerks Association, and the National Council of Labour Colleges.

CHAPTER XII

THE FINANCE OF SCIENCE

Science and Economic Systems

An integral part of any reorganization of science would be the provision of a satisfactory system of finance. It is, however, far more difficult to discuss such a system than the administration of science, because the finance of science is not something lying within the scope of science itself but depends even more on the economic structure of the society in which it is working. In a later chapter we shall discuss the kind of economic structure that would seem to be demanded by any adequate utilization of science for human welfare. For the moment, however, it will be sufficient to consider arrangements for the financing of science in respect to two types of social organization: one in which the whole economy is consciously controlled and can be directed to any desired end, and one in which, as in present society outside the Soviet Union, the effective control of economic factors is in the hands of the owners of monopoly enterprises and of the State which represents their joint interests. It is hardly worth considering the third alternative—that of pure small-scale competitive capitalism—as this has now only an historic interest.

Financial Needs of Science: Elasticity and Security.—The requirements of an organized and integrated science service are flexibility, continuity, and a steady or increasing rate of growth. The unpredictable elements in science and the complexity of the interrelations between different sciences make any scheme of a rigid character extremely wasteful. Not only the total financial needs of science but also their distribution among the various sciences are apt to vary over relatively short periods by considerable amounts. Any scheme which gave a rigidly fixed income to science as a whole or to any separate branch of it would lead to hardship and waste. Either money would not be available for following up new and important lines, or there would be a temporary surplus which, considering the ineradicable desire of all departments not to return money to its source, would be wastefully spent. It is this variable quality of the needs of science that makes the type of financial administration suitable in other parts of civil service so disastrous, and that has led many scientists themselves to reject the whole idea of an organized science because they cannot conceive any forms of administration other than those they see at present existing.

After this, it may seem paradoxical to claim that the chief abuse in the present financing of science is not its rigid character but its extreme variability. There is, however, a fundamental difference between variable funds due to varying needs of science and variable funds due to the exigencies of the national finances and the accidental incidence of large bequests. At present, science suffers both ways. No fresh funds are available for new developments when they are urgently needed while at the same time large sums may accrue when there is no particular need for them and when, in fact, no men are available to carry out the requisite work. On the other hand, those scientific enterprises that require to work for long periods with a steady income are subjected to sudden cuts, with resulting wastage of a great deal of the work already done.

SCIENCE IN A PLANNED ECONOMY

Determination of the Budget.—The ideal arrangement would be one in which the budget of science was fixed jointly by consultation between the financial side of the scientific organization itself and the representatives of the national economy, including industrial, agricultural, and social services. The amount of money and its distribution would then be determined on the balance between the need of the internal development of science, according to its own estimates, and the need for particular developments of one or the other sciences on account of some urgently required application in the interests of the community. Thus the scientists might put in a claim for increased funds for chemical embryology, pointing out that its development was needed to clear up problems which were holding up other sciences, while the national economic council might wish for intensive research on the efficiency of furnace linings. These claims need not conflict. The actual line of development of science would be the result of a due appreciation of the total integral trends of science with their assumed probabilities of successful results, and at the same time the total estimated needs of the community with consideration of the possibilities of a scientific satisfaction of these needs within a measurable time.

Internal Distribution.—It might be claimed that the distribution of funds inside scientific research, given a total amount available, might be left to the scientists themselves. It is, however, doubtful whether scientists are at present the best judges of the optimum development of science, and it is certain that if they had to consider the developments of science in relation to social needs of the time

the funds would be much better placed than if the internal development of science alone was considered. The opposite contention—
that science is something which should not be bought in such qualities
and quantities as social needs require—is, of course, equally false.
One of the largest sources of waste in present-day science is precisely
this idea of science as a commodity, or payment by results, a natural
consequence of a commercial age. It is indeed this attitude which
has engendered, almost from the birth of science, that peculiar form
of dishonesty by which the scientist acquires money for research
which he thinks fundamentally important by pretending that he is
going to spend it on something that will bring profit to his backers.
As Kepler said, "God has provided every animal with the appropriate
nourishment, to astronomers he has given astrology."

At first, joint consultations between the representatives of science
and national economy would be difficult, because some time would
be needed for each to learn the other's language, but before long,
as is already occurring in the Soviet Union, such consultation would
begin to appear as both natural and essential in the interest of both.
The consultation would necessarily include not only the representatives of scientific research through the academies but also those of
the universities, because any plan for the development of science
necessarily implies the provision of suitable men and the apportioning
of them to different fields. The great development of the biological
and sociological sciences, which any rational financing of science
would lead to, would in itself require considerable changes both in
the number of students in the different fields and in the organization
of the teaching.

The Financing of Laboratories.—The unit for financial as well as
for administrative purposes in science would be the institute or
laboratory. It would be the business of the financial council to ensure
the continuity or expansion of funds demanded by each laboratory
if they were satisfied that a good case had been made out. They
would also be in a position to assure to any laboratory with a long-
term programme that the work could be carried out without
interruption for lack of funds. Such continuity would give a basic
budget for science which would increase in a slow but perfectly
regular way. Besides this, there would be a demand for extraordinary
expenditure. A new discovery, for instance, might open up a field
for which a new institute was required, or alternatively, a new social
need might demand an institute to inquire into the means for satisfying
it. Such developments, although they would balance out over a long
period of years, would lead, since they also include capital expenditure,
to a short-term irregularity which might amount to anything up to
one-third of the whole budget of science. According to the character

of the national economy such sums might be voted as the demand for them occurred, or a special fund be set aside into which a regular amount was paid, but out of which irregular payments might be made.

Building up Science.—So far we have considered the finance of science as a going concern, allowing, however, for a certain regular increase which need be no more than proportional to the increased real income per head brought about by the applications of the science itself. But the immediate and much more actual problem is to bring the development of science and its applications up to a level at which it is able to give the best return to the community. Now it is clear that in no country in the world at present has this level even been approached. In countries where science has been established for many years the scale of its operations is altogether inadequate, while in the Soviet Union, where the budget of science is approaching some measure of adequacy, the tradition of science and its cultural background will need time to build up, and its absence has as yet prevented the results of this expenditure from yielding anything like its potential returns. The first task of the finance of science would be building up science rather than merely preserving it in running order.

The Utilization of Ability.—Unfortunately, unlike material techniques which can be multiplied by the mere application of economic resources, that is, ultimately, of crude man power, the building up of science is necessarily a slower process because it depends on the existence of persons above the average in intelligence and experience. The growth of science has therefore an upper limit which is fixed by the men rather than by the funds available. That is not to say, however, that the growth could not be incomparably more rapid than it is to-day, and that the rate of growth itself could not be progressively increased. It would be impossible to start off in science as in industry with anything like 25 per cent. or 50 per cent. growth increase per annum, but the 10 per cent. growth could be reached now and, once the system got into swing, it could rise to 20 per cent. or more if that were necessary. The reasons for this have already been stated. They lie essentially in the extreme wastefulness of the present system of recruiting and organization of science. The intelligence is there; it only requires to be used. The serious advance of science must begin in the educational system, but this means practically that a period of eight to ten years must elapse before any palpable benefit is felt on this score, even supposing that sufficient men of ability were available for the tasks of education itself.

For more immediate results, dependence would have to be placed on using to the full the existing trained scientists of ability. There can be no question that merely to put into operation the schemes of research, already existing in fairly detailed plans, which are held up for lack of funds, would, in practically every country outside the Soviet Union where this restriction does not operate, result in a sharp increase in the value of effective scientific production. There would, of course, be difficulties that would follow necessarily from the increased demand of science, shortage, for instance, of instruments or trained assistants. These would hold up the work a little, but they are mainly mechanical obstacles and would themselves yield to a mere increase in available funds. It is clear that any sudden liberation of scientific initiative would be wasteful, but only in the sense that all new constructive enterprises are so. Compared with the alternative of the present stagnation that waste would represent a social gain.

The Status of the Scientific Worker.—In any schemes for the finance of science the actual conditions of the scientific workers themselves are a prime consideration. We have already discussed the disabilities they suffer at present (see Chapters IV, V), these must clearly be remedied, but merely removing them is not enough; the scientific worker requires special consideration if he is to be able to do his best for science. His chief requirements are security of employment, adequate leisure and appropriate status. The profession of scientific research needs to be recognized as such. This does not mean that the research worker would never do anything else, for example, teaching or administrative work, but that if he was effective at research he would not be obliged to occupy himself in any other way which would be injurious to the carrying out of his research, as is only too often the case at present. The policy adopted in France (see p. 201 and Appendix VI) of a definite graded profession with possibilities of exchange into teaching or administration offers an ideal solution. In the matter of pay, at present, in accordance with the general inequality of the social system, there is much too great disparity between the pay of the few at the top and the many at the bottom of the scale. The younger years of the research worker when his ideas are most free and productive are often clouded by financial anxiety. It should be possible to arrange a more gently graded system which would be apportioned to the real needs of the scientific worker. The high pay of professors at the present time is justified on two grounds; their need to be able to assist in support of scientific societies and entertainment of foreign scientists, etc., and the more potent one of requiring to maintain themselves at a rank in society which would permit them to move among people of sufficient wealth to be able to collect money for the carrying out of their work. The first of these needs should be met, as has already been suggested, by the reform of scientific societies which, as they would no longer have to bear the cost of publication, would not be a burden on their members, and by the provision of entertainment funds. The second and more serious one implies a change in the economic system, where the importance of the scientist would be recognized directly and would not need to be marked by money payments.

Their conditions of work should be relaxed to allow the scientists to have long and irregular holidays, which, as they habitually are in the Soviet Union and to an increasing extent elsewhere, could be combined with scientific expeditionary work. The essential point is that the scientist should be able to withdraw into himself to think out his problems without detriment to his position. This should apply as much to industrial as to academic scientists; indeed one of the most essential reforms is the blurring of the distinction between these two groups by allowing for frequent interchange and regular meetings. Once science has been recognized as an essential part of the mechanism of modern life the status of the scientist will automatically change. He will no longer meet with a mixture of practical contempt and superstitious admiration, but be recognized as a common worker with the fortune and ability to deal with new instead of established things.

No External Limitation of Funds.—It should be realized that the expenditure on science is of a different character from that of normal productive enterprise. Any given sum of money in science may be wasted but, in the aggregate, the return from science as a whole repays that expenditure in a proportion much larger than corresponds to expenditure in any other form. To put it in another way, the actual sums expended on scientific research are of the order of a fraction of 1 per cent. of total social expenditure, but they are capable of increasing social income by anything up to 10 per cent. per annum. It would therefore probably be economical in the long run to allow unlimited sums for scientific research, that is, sums limited only by the ability of existing scientists to spend them. The extravagance of such a proposal will not seem reckless when it is recollected that expenditure on scientific research would be subject to very definite intrinsic limitations. First of all, those engaged on it would have to possess qualifications which involve both high ability and hard work on their part. Secondly, the extra money spent would not go to their personal expenditure, except that an increase of pay in the junior ranks of scientists would be desirable, and thirdly, the expenditure on apparatus would be limited by the amount of apparatus a man could use, which, though possibly twice or three times as great as that at present available, is not indefinite.

Optimum Expenditure.—It is held of course, particularly in scientific circles in Britain, on a kind of sour-grapes principle, that much money is actually bad for scientists. They point to the U.S.A. as an example, where the existence of a much larger endowment of science has not produced proportional results and has produced a number of abuses. It is quite true that up to a point the ability to buy expensive apparatus of a more or less standardized type may prevent the construction of apparatus which, though inferior and laborious to work, may open up new possibilities. But this is an abuse which has to be balanced against the total inability to get results in the absence of certain apparatus. Similarly, it is argued that if science seems to be a well-endowed profession it will attract to it a number of undesirable characters who are there for what they can get out of it. But this has to be weighed against the fact that underpaid, insecure, and restricted employment in science deters many men of ability from entering the profession at all. Some balance must be struck between these conflicting arguments. There must be a certain expenditure on science which gets the greatest returns for the money expended, but this is by no means necessarily the optimum expenditure on science. From the social point of view it may well be worth while to spend twice as much money to get half again as much scientific return. It is by no means certain that, though American science may be more wasteful than British, it is not of greater value to the community. It has already been indicated, however, that the present wastefulness of science is largely due to defects in its organization. This source of waste far exceeds what might occur from expenditure on possibly fruitless experiments in a well-planned science. Besides this, many of the abuses associated with increased expenditure on science have really nothing to do with science but are merely special cases of abuses in the economic system. As long as profit-making is considered a desirable end, no profession, even the profession of science, will be safe from it. But it by no means follows that, in a society where such activities are deplored, increased expenditure on science would lead to the disadvantages at present associated with it.

The ideal financing of science would provide, first, for a rapid increase limited only by the possibility of securing sufficiently able recruits and, later, for an increase which might still be as rapid if not more so, but which would correspond to the consciously realized social need for advancing science. If we consider for a moment the possibility of a well-ordered society, free from the present anxieties of economic insecurity and war and able to develop science for human welfare, we can see that in such a society there would be a double drive for the development of science. This would be partly for its utility to society and partly because, owing to the very activities of science, the necessity for other occupations would be less and science might be studied, for the first time with full social legitimacy, for its own sake.

Financing Science in a Capitalist Economy

If we turn from this picture of how science would be financed simply for its value to the community, to consider the more immediate problems of how science could best be financed under existing conditions, we are faced at the outset by a number of difficulties and contradictions. In the first place, as has already been pointed out, the finance of a scientific research for private profit suffers from one crucial disadvantage. In general, expenditure on scientific research, however profitable in the long run, does not bring the profits to those who originally put up the money. The existence of competition and the necessary secrecy which it entails offer another obstacle, and these between them have made it necessary to build up the extremely complex and inefficient system by which science in capitalist countries is financed, partly by industries and partly by the State. Even more serious than these difficulties is the increasing tendency to national monopoly of science in the interest of State power, economic and military. It need not follow, however, that within these limitations the finance of science could not be placed on a better footing than it is to-day in most countries.

Need for greater Understanding between Science and Industry.— Besides the hindrances already mentioned, others exist which should not be irremovable and which are mainly due to mutual lack of understanding between the academic directors of scientific work, the business executives, and the Government administrators. The present system of financing research is not one that has been deliberately conceived, it has grown up as an accumulation of expedients for dealing with different developments as they arose. Its complexity and inefficiency is due largely to the fact that it has never been reviewed as a whole. If this were done it should be possible both to raise more money than can at present be found for science, and to see that that money is expended more wisely. Before the first end can be achieved, science in a capitalist state must make its value known, and this can only be done effectively by the methods already developed for commercial enterprise, namely, advertisement and publicity. Professional ethics have so far, in Britain at any rate, largely prevented the use of such methods. There is not even an adequate service of scientific journalism. In Britain no big paper has a science editor and very few have even regular scientific correspondents. Things are certainly better in the U.S.A., but even there discoveries and applications of vital importance are rarely front-page news, as they are, for instance, in all the papers of the U.S.S.R. As science is not known it is not appreciated and money has to be raised for it by devious and *ad hoc* methods, resulting, as has already been pointed out, in an unedifying struggle between scientists for the little money there is available instead of a united demand from all of them for an adequate budget for science.

The Endowment of Science.—The solution which is still technically possible, though it may well be doubted whether it can be achieved, is some form of centralized endowment for science which would bring together all existing sources of scientific income and be in a position to implement them by increased grants from individuals, industries, and Government. The distribution of this fund would be in the hands of a scientific and industrial council similar to that described in the previous section. The most difficult problem to solve is not so much the distribution of the fund as the means taken to raise it and the relative proportion of the money which should come from different sources. It is clear from the outset that in a capitalist society we cannot expect to have a unified science service because a certain portion of scientific work will still be needed by individual firms for their own benefit. Nevertheless, we can reach a much closer approximation to it than exists at present if firms could contribute at any rate part of the sum they set aside for research, to researches affecting the whole of their particular industry. This is the principle used in Britain in building up the Research Associations, but it could be expanded there to cover the whole and not, as at present, only half of existing industry. On the other hand, for research of a more fundamental character which may be of assistance to many industries and also for the research of value to society as a whole, it would be Utopian under present conditions to expect industries to subscribe. The cost of such research must fall under present conditions on the Government, that is, on the direct or indirect taxpayer. A proposal for an Endowment Fund for science along these lines has, in fact, been put forward to the Government by the Parliamentary Science Committee. The main recommendations are shown in the Appendix. Its central thesis was that in applied science a time of the order of ten years was needed to reach a practically useful stage. The needs of science were consequently not related to production conditions now but ten years hence. Continuity was a prime requisite, the sums available for research varied with the trade cycle with the deplorable results already described (pp. 45, 60). An Endowment Fund into which large sums could be paid in prosperous times and little or nothing in depressions would iron out the fluctuation and permit a steady and slowly increasing income to research. Together with this went the proposal for an extension of the scope of applied science to cover all British industry instead of about a half as at present.

Official Objections.—As might have been expected, the official reply to the suggestions of the Parliamentary Science Committee was unfavourable. (See Appendix V.) The Advisory Council based their objections on two grounds: first, that it was inadvisable to subsidize research from Government funds to a greater extent than industrialists were themselves willing to contribute, and, secondly, that the principle of endowment was inherently unsound. They pointed out that while the industrialist's appreciation of the benefits of science might be slow, it was growing. They referred to their own report to explain why this is so:

" The application and development of scientific ideas in industry depend upon a complete understanding of the way in which industry can make use of science and scientific method. The application and development can be fully attained only if the problem of this co-operation is studied by the man of science as well as by the industrialist. Between men of scientific education and most of those engaged in productive industry there are differences of training, experience and outlook which are not always present to the mind of those who are anxious to secure the potential benefits which science, wisely used, can bring to the community. The scientist has to meet the industrialist half way. For that reason one of our most important tasks is so to organize the conduct of research as to promote contact with industry. . . .

There are those who would urge us forthwith to recommend greatly increased State expenditure on research for the solution of industrial difficulties. In our view, such a development, without qualification, could not be defended. The expenditure which is defensible in the national interest depends on the degree to which industry generally is prepared to apply scientific method and advances in scientific knowledge. So long as we are convinced, as we are to-day, that industry is showing itself increasingly ready to make effective use of science, so long shall we be able to justify to the nation the policy of steady development to meet new needs as they arise which has guided our predecessors and ourselves since the appointment of the first Advisory Council in 1915."— Report for 1930-1.

Their second point is that the Government contribution has steadily increased, although from their own figures the rate of increase was only $1\frac{1}{2}$ per cent. per annum between 1928 and 1933, and for the next five years $7\frac{1}{2}$ per cent., showing very clearly the effect of the trade cycle. It was apparently assumed that the latter rate of increase would continue indefinitely. The mere possibility of a slump which has since then become a pressing reality is not even considered. The objection to endowment was on the basis that it would remove control from Parliament. This parliamentary control seems to be of rather theoretical importance, as the estimates for the scientific departments have occupied one half-hour in the debates on the last fifteen budgets. This reply in itself is a complete admission of the incapacity of our present economic and industrial system to utilize science adequately, even in its own interests. The official view, under the circumstances, may well be right, the present system of research finance may be the best available under the existing economic dispensation.

Private Benevolence.—There is still a third source of revenue for science—that of private benevolence; but this is necessarily extremely difficult to bring into any ordered scheme. Under modern conditions it is probably the worst method of financing research. It is necessarily highly irregular in its incidence and largely unpredictable in amount, but its worst feature is the general direction in which such funds are allocated and spent. The reasons for which large sums are now given to science are, with a few honourable exceptions, those of advertisement or conscience money. A large donation to science by a firm or an individual may be very useful in enhancing or safeguarding the reputation of the donors. In Britain it may be a path to honours, in the United States to general respect. But, from whatever motive the sums are given, the existence of large donors or potential donors is a standing temptation to individual scientists or groups of scientists to intrigue for a share of these gifts. The money does not go in general where it is most needed, but to those scientists who are most skilled in the art of extracting money from the wealthy. The result is enormous bequests which are wasted on bricks and mortar or on inferior or time-serving scientists. Even worse is the general attitude of servility towards the wealthy and their institution that the possibilities of such donations induce in the world of science. Most professors with a radical turn of mind hesitate to express their views when they feel that such expression may prevent funds coming for the benefit of the work which they have most at heart. Experience has shown that these evils can be modified only when the sums involved are large enough to admit of gradual spending and where they can be controlled by an impartial and independent board. No fund, even the Rockefeller Foundation, is, however, large enough fully to satisfy these conditions. If there were a general science endowment fund to which industries, Government, and individuals all contributed, many of the present evils would be removed, though even then the general class subservience would necessarily remain.

Could Science pay its Way?—The problem of raising money would be solved at one stroke if it were possible for the scientists them-selves to get some measurable fraction of the return from the applica-tion of their discoveries. Attempts of this sort have been made through the taking out of patents on scientific discoveries for the direct benefit of research. The most notable of these are the patents taken out by the University of Wisconsin for the manufacture of vitamin D. On the whole, however, such practices are not looked on favourably by scientists themselves, because they see clearly that in most cases the result of patenting processes is to hold up the application of the beneficial results of science. This is particularly true in the field of medicine, where remedies which would be of value to the whole of humanity are kept, through patent restriction, at such prices that only the wealthiest are able to use them. For scientists themselves to be a party to such transactions, as they must needs be owing to the close ring of existing firms, is felt to be a denial of their essential principles.

Apart from such ethical considerations, however, there are serious practical difficulties in any plan of financing science through patents. There are few patents now of any importance that can be operated successfully except by big industrial monopolies. It may be sometimes worth while for such monopolies to buy up patents, but it is generally much easier to evade their provisions, and in any litigation the longest purse always tells. It is, on the whole, a salutary instinct on the part of scientists to have kept out of business. Given the particular nature of their abilities, it is probable that losses would be as frequent as gains. Such losses might involve the closing down of whole branches of scientific research for indefinite periods and widespread personal suffering. Even where scientists do succeed in business they can generally only do so at the expense of their scientific qualities and by accepting the standards of secrecy and exaggerated advertisement which are necessary for success there, but which are so foreign to the spirit of science.

Economic Nationalism and Planned Science.—Of increasing im-portance in the finance of science in modern States is its national economic aspect. Indeed, it is almost to this alone that we owe the preservation, in certain States, of any science at all. In Germany, for instance, the whole atmosphere of public life is antagonistic to the spirit of science. Blood and soil are considered more important than intelligence, and yet it is reluctantly admitted in a modern world that blood and soil are not enough to secure national honour and national freedom. Science is required for two things: the perfection of the war machine, and, what is merely another aspect of the same thing, the perfection of the national economy in the direction of making it self-supporting. Yet, though this is the most extreme example, the same tendency is plainly present in all other capitalist countries. It has stimulated in Britain, for example, the formation and continuance of the Department of Scientific and Industrial Research (see p. 30). The effect of national economic pressure on science is largely to drive applied research in two directions: one, into the heavy industries mainly concerned with armaments, particularly the metal and the chemical industries; and the second, to a lesser degree, into the problems of food production and preservation, thus exaggerating the disproportion that already exists between the physical and the biological sciences. This would, of course, not be so marked if the food research were of a more biological character, but here we come across one of the contradictions inherent in modern politics, namely, the political concern for primitive methods of agriculture which always runs parallel to economic nationalism. It is necessary to keep agriculture primitive because the conservatism of landlord and peasant must not be disturbed, as it is on them that depend the strength of civil reaction and military man-power. As a result, enormous chemical ingenuity will be expended on producing synthetic foods to save the relatively small administrative and political changes necessary to introduce a rational agriculture. The researches on food preservation turn out in practice to result in advantages far more to the middle men, organized in large distributing trusts, than either to the direct producer or to the consumer. Yet in an indirect way the development of science in the interests of economic nationalism can be advantageous because it indicates, for the first time, some conception of an organized scientific attack on problems of interest to the community, and suggests that in better times such organized research might be turned from its present purposes of preparing for war to those of benefiting the community.

THE FREEDOM OF SCIENCE

This sketch of the possibilities of science in two different types of social and economic environment may serve to show what are the requirements of a social organization in which science can play its full part. It is essentially a question of a wider aspect of the freedom of science. The freedom of science is not merely the absence of prohibitions or restrictions on this or that research or theory, though in certain countries to-day science has not this elementary freedom. The full freedom of science goes much further. It is useless to permit a research if at the same time the funds to carry on that research are unprocurable. Lack of means fetters science as effectively as police supervision. But even if means are provided, and provided in some measure according to the inner requirements of scientific advance, science is yet not fully free. The complete circle of scientific activity is not closed with the making of a discovery; it is only closed when that discovery is fully incorporated, both as an idea and as a practicable application, in contemporary society.

Frustration.—The full development of science is only possible if it can play a positive and not merely a contemplative part in social life. This is certainly what science was doing in the great days of its advance, in the seventeenth and in the early nineteenth centuries, when capitalism provided for the first effective utilization of natural forces. But more and more to-day the utilization of science is being cramped and devoted to base ends. The lack of freedom and distortion of science in turn reacts on its internal development. Where a great tradition has been built up it is still possible for science to follow out the lines of that tradition, but elsewhere, as in the biological and sociological sciences, advance has been definitely held up. Science divorced from the effective life of its time is bound to degenerate into pedantry.

The general problem of the finance of science is thus seen to be far more social-economic than purely scientific in character. Once science plays a recognized part in social advance the problem of raising money for it adequately under a rational plan should not be difficult. The total amounts required are so small that, except in times of acutest crisis or in reconstruction after destructive wars, there should be no difficulty in finding ample and more than ample funds for scientific research. Once science is so organized that its benefits can flow rapidly and directly to the public at large, its value will be so obvious that there will be no difficulty in setting aside the 1 or 2 per cent. of the national income which will represent as much as it is likely to absorb for the next two decades and from five to twenty times the amount it absorbs to-day in most capitalistic countries. There is so much to be done that the limiting factor will not be the amount of money available but the number of men who can use that money. Science has the prospect of being fully employed until human needs are met in a way of which we at present can form no picture.

Science needs Organization.—We have now considered in its different aspects the general problems of science organization. The discussion has necessarily been somewhat academic because we have been concerned with forms which, because they exist only in a possible future, do not lend themselves to concrete examples. In such a treatment only measurable factors can be taken into account, but it is the unmeasurable factors that are far the most important. No organization, however well thought out and however integrated with the general social scheme, can be of any use if it does not represent the effective desires of the people who are to work the organization. It is largely then from the attitude of the scientists themselves and of the public towards science that we can gauge the possibility of the success of any reorganization of science. It would be idle to deny that there has existed in science up to the present a distrust of any organization whatever. But this distrust is founded partly on the old tradition of the freedom of science from the obscurantist restrictions imposed by the Church and by scholastic universities and partly on the more immediate experience of state-regulated science. As to the first, this dwelling on past struggles of science has too often served to obscure the real danger of the present: no longer the suppression of science as a whole but its exploitation in detail. The freedom of science needs to be considered in its modern aspect as freedom to act and not merely to think. For this organization is necessary, but organization of science does not and cannot mean, if it is to be effective, the type of organization that has been taken over in unthinking fashion from business or civil administration. To submit science to such discipline and routine is certainly to kill it. The great section of science that suffers from it at the moment is in fact effectively dead. But organization need not mean such discipline and routine. It can be, as we have tried to show, free and flexible at the same time as remaining ordered. If it retains as its central core democratic spirit expressed in democratic forms, no organization of science will be able to lose touch with the corporate feeling and the desire for knowledge and human betterment that is inherent in the effective progress of science. If we are to have an organization of science it must be largely built up by the efforts of the scientists themselves. How they can do so will be discussed in a subsequent chapter.

Scientists and the People.—The setting up of a scientific organization, however, cannot rest with scientists alone. The scientists cannot force their services on society; they must form part of a willing and conscious partnership between science and society. But this implies far more than an adequate appreciation on the part of the non-scientific public of the achievements and possibilities of science. For its full effectiveness it requires also a society economically organized so that general human welfare, and not private profit and national aggrandizement, is the basis of economic action. With such economy the scientists, possibly more than any other of the relatively wealthy sections of present society, will find themselves in agreement. For science has been at all times a commune of workers, helping one another, sharing their knowledge, not seeking corporately or individually more money or power than is needed for the pursuit of their work. They have been at all times rational and international in outlook and thus fundamentally in harmony with the movements that seek to extend that community of effort and enjoyment to social and economic as well as intellectual fields. Why this fundamental identity is not as yet fully realized by the scientists or by society will be discussed in a later chapter.

CHAPTER XIII

THE STRATEGY OF SCIENTIFIC ADVANCE

CAN SCIENCE BE PLANNED?

ONCE we have solved the problems of adequate finance and organization of science we are faced with the more concrete one of how that organization should be directed in research and in its application. We have, in fact, to draw up a plan for science. At first sight the problem of the strategy of scientific advance seems insoluble. Science is a discovery of the unknown, is in its very essence unforeseeable, and a plan for its advance might seem, and has seemed to many, a contradiction in terms. But this is to take far too absolute a view; in fact, science could not advance at all unless it were to a certain extent planned. Although it is true that we do not know what we may find, we must, in the first place, know where to look. Some amount of short-range planning has always been inherent in scientific research, and long-range planning is contained implicitly in the training of scientific workers. Chemists, for instance, would not be trained unless it were considered that for another fifty years chemistry would be studied. A plan of advance does then implicitly exist, but it is a mixture of tradition and opportunism. Our task is to put in its place a more consciously thought-out scheme which will, at the same time, take into account the unpredictable nature of scientific discovery.

Flexibility.—It is clear that to make such a scheme requires the collaboration of workers in all fields of science. What follows here is not so much an actual plan as a sketch of the kind of plan that such a body might evolve. It does not pretend to be a definite plan; the emphasis might be found to have entirely shifted when all the prospects open to the different sciences were brought together and worked into one general programme for science. It is nevertheless worth while to attempt a plan if only to provoke a move towards such a common enterprise. The first requirement of any such plan would be flexibility. Nothing could be more fatal to science than rigid adherence to a plan laid down beforehand as, for instance, the now almost forgotten scheme of Herbert Spencer in the realm of sociology. Periodical, and in fact permanent, revision would be required. Perhaps a five- or ten-year scheme for the whole of science and shorter schemes for individual sciences would be workable and provision would have to be made for changes, as at any moment the importance of new integrating discoveries might be such as to demand a complete recasting of pre-existing schemes. Here conscious direction should prove far more flexible than the existing planless development of science. For lack of organized prevision the effect of any new discovery often takes years before it is felt even in its own field, and decades before it penetrates into other fields of science.

Advance along the Line.—The advance on the front of scientific knowledge has never been, and should never be, uniform. It will always contain salients where advance is easy and rapid, where, so to speak, the line of ignorance has been definitely broken through. Such salients at the moment are nuclear physics, quantum chemistry, the structures of solids and liquids, immunology, embryology, and genetics. Up to the present the tendency has been for most of the able workers to rush to these points and to drag after them a horde of less gifted workers, much as in a gold rush, where experienced prospectors are followed by men merely eager to get rich quick. The result is that the other fields of science, where spectacular advances are not being made, become sadly neglected and may even retrogress through the loss of knowledge of earlier promising work. Thus chemistry has, relatively to its great advance of the nineteenth century, made little progress in the present one. These forgotten regions of scientific advance become in time, once attention has been drawn to them, the most easy to develop with the assistance of new principles and new methods drawn from the more developed sciences. With better organization this ultimate advance could have been maintained all the time, and knowledge not allowed to lapse and have to be caught up again.

Sticking Points.—There are also on the front of science regions where an impasse has been reached, where a certain line of development either seems to peter out or come up against insuperable theoretical or practical difficulties. Electricity was in this state towards the latter half of the eighteenth century, from which it was rescued by the discoveries of Galvani and Volta. Biology was held up in the nineteenth century until the development of the achromatic microscope. Genetics was held up till 1900 for reasons difficult to analyse. Theoretical cosmic physics is held up to-day. The very existence of these hold-ups of scientific advance implies the need for a general organization of science. A problem which may appear insoluble to workers in one field may have a solution already available in another. If this is not so, and the difficulty is quite beyond the reach of contemporary science, it is clearly one which calls for concentration at these points of the best brains in its own and neighbouring fields. Because it is just in those regions where scientific observations appear to fail, or lead to contradictory results, that we have the strongest reason for suspecting some inherent defect in theory and therefore for a new break-through into unknown regions. Such was the position of physics at the end of the nineteenth century, from which it escaped through a series of lucky accidents. It is not difficult to see how the present position might have been reached much earlier if a more general view had been taken of physics and the persistent anomalous phenomena had been properly attended to. In the history of science it is often far more difficult to explain the reason why a certain discovery was not made than why it was. One of the definite advantages to which an organized planning of science would lead is the reduction of the number of such cases.

Widening the Front.—There are, besides, regions of ignorance on which there is no scientific attack whatever. The fro'.t of science is still too narrow. It can be extended with profit to itself and to humanity at large. We still regulate a great part of our lives by traditions which have been found more or less useful but which have no scientific basis. Until the last twenty years we did not even know, or bother to inquire scientifically, how we ate and slept, or brought up our children, and even now our whole domestic arrangements—eating, washing, cooking, etc.—are untouched by science except of the most short range and mercenary variety. In the purely scientific world there are still large regions between the sciences practically unexplored. The great successes of physical chemistry and biological chemistry are examples of the filling up of such gaps. But the gap between physiology and psychology, and those between psychology, sociology, and economics are still largely unfilled. Any adequate planning would take special account of these and would direct on to them some of the best available forces.

The rapid multiplication of sciences in the last two centuries has shown into how many new fields scientific intelligence can enter. At the same time this development has been a partial loss to science because what was once a single field has now been split into departments having at first little connection with one another. Physics and chemistry were once indistinguishable; at the end of the eighteenth century they definitely split apart. In the middle of the nineteenth century it was found necessary to create a new subject, physical chemistry, to connect them. It will be the business of organized science to see that such connections are permanently kept up and not created as afterthoughts. The advance in any science should be immediately made available to all others. This clearly cannot be done by demanding that the results in one science should be assimilated *in toto* by workers in all others. It should be the function of scientific publications to see that these advances are handed on in a condensed but intelligible form, adapted for use in each of the fields where they may be needed rather than only in that from which they emanated. New workers should be encouraged to enter the intermediate regions so as to preserve an unbroken continuity of work along the front of science.

Consolidating Advances.—But it is not only the front of scientific advance that is to be considered. Advances, once made, require to be consolidated. One of the advantages which we now gain by studying the life and work of past scientists is the number of unworked-out suggestions which they contain, pregnant for future development. This means a large part of their work was wasted in their own time, not because they could not have developed any of these points taken one by one, but because it was not physically possible to develop them all themselves, and they lacked sufficient schools of co-workers capable of taking them up. It would be an important part of the scheme of scientific organization to see that the most rapid advances of science were adequately followed up by large-scale co-operative research and that no promising opening was allowed to lapse into oblivion.

Finally, it will be always worth while to conduct mopping-up operations after the main outlines of a new branch of knowledge have been made clear. There are always to be found careful and systematic workers who prefer routine to pioneer work. To them can be given the task of working out in detail implications of general theories. The necessity for this is not a mere pedantic desire for all-inclusiveness but the knowledge that it is often by such patient search that examples of the failure of theories are discovered, which may in turn prove a starting-point for new and significant revisions.

The Importance of Theory.—The advance of science is of little value unless the ground gained by new discoveries is secured by the building up of adequate and inclusive theories. We have seen in the past alternations in many subjects, and particularly in biology, between multiple and uncoordinated experimentation and the building of general theories insufficiently related to facts. The connections between the experimenter and the theorist in science, when these are not the same man, require to be strengthened. Not that theories can be made to order. The building of new theories will still remain one of the most unpredictable prerogatives of individual minds. What we can do is to present to anyone wishing to integrate a given field, the results of all previous work in that field in a form that can be taken in at once, rather than leave them to be found piecemeal after much inquiry and scholarly research. Any ordered advance of science should make the present position once and for all impossible. It is now often easier to investigate a field anew than to find out what reliable work has been done on it before, and that, not from the lack but from the very multiplicity of the work done previously. What we must aim at is to have theories fitting as closely as possible the results of experiments, and pointing out the direction of future experimentation.

Permanent Revision.—It is not, however, only the absence of theory which is a retarding factor; quite as important is the drag on new developments exerted by obsolete theories. The weight of a dead past obscures and discourages active thought. As long as the control and direction of science is exclusively in the hands of older men this is bound to occur. The remedy already suggested—of supplementing individual direction of research by laboratory councils containing younger men—is one way out of this difficulty. Another is to see that directors are relieved periodically and given time to get up to date, as long as they have the elasticity of mind to do so. In planning the advance of science it would be necessary to go further than this and say that the moment a new theory has invalidated older views in any region of science, a thorough revision of that region should be carried out with the minimum of delay. Naturally, older theories, in so far as they have proved satisfactory in their time, must have valued elements, and these are not necessarily only the ones which are found in the new theory. Sometimes, as was the case in the wave and particle theories of light, some aspects of the old theory are found again in the next theory but one. The revision of any field of science in the light of new theories would have to take these factors into account, but their existence is no justification for the perpetuation of that self-contradictory jumble of new and old knowledge which is at present taught as science. With the full development of theory and the existence, where theory is lacking, of ordered summaries of experimental knowledge, it should be possible to have at any given moment a general conspectus of existing knowledge, and one capable of furnishing, in lesser or greater detail according to the nature of inquiries, an integrated sum of facts and techniques which could serve as a basis for work in any field whatever of science or practice (see p. 297).

Balance of Fundamental and Applied Research.—Throughout any plan of scientific advance it would be necessary to keep a just proportion between fundamental and applied research and to maintain at all times the closest contact between them. We have discussed elsewhere the detailed organization which would make this possible, the sequences of institutes through which field and workshop problems would be reduced to their fundamental origins and the solutions from them worked down again to their practical application. But in this organization it will be necessary to secure a proper balance between the number and the quality of men and the funds available to the different sections, a balance which will necessarily differ in different subjects and at different times. In fields where the general basic theories are understood, in so far as they affect actual practice, as in chemistry or physics, for instance, great weight can be given to the applied aspects; in biology far more fundamental work is needed, but it is of course artificial to separate fundamental and applied work in any field and particularly in fields where our exact knowledge is just beginning. The sterility of studies of sociology, economics, and political theory is largely due to their not being integrated with practical action in these fields. Even more than the study of the physical world, social studies require to be compounded with social activities.

The First Stage: A Survey of Science

The first stage in planning the general direction of scientific advance is a survey, in the sense already indicated, of existing knowledge and techniques in all departments of human life. The very making of such a survey could not fail to lead to further investigations in all branches of science. This idea is not a new one; it has preceded other great periods of scientific advance. Several surveys were initiated by the founders of the Royal Society in the seventeenth century and by the French Encyclopaedists in the eighteenth century, but we can start on a much higher level than they did. (1)

The World of Nature and the World of Man.—Two main regions of inquiry and action have to be considered. In one, the world of nature, we face the problem of how to find and make the best environment for man as a physiological unit. This involves at once the whole of material techniques and the physical sciences behind them, and biological techniques based on a far deeper knowledge of biology than we at present possess. We must understand the full workings of pre-human nature before we can secure the best biological background for human enterprise. No part of natural science, however remote or abstract, such as astronomy or the theory of groups, is irrelevant to this purpose. In the second, the social world, the problems are already more urgent than those of biological existence. The whole economic and political interplay of societies, races, and classes requires far more understanding and integrating than we have at present the means to attain. Moreover, it is clear that in the future the social aspect of mankind will become relatively still more important. Not only will man's biological needs be more easily satisfied but he will be creating a social world of greater complexity than the natural world in which he first found himself. Until now the social world has been created unconsciously though, by conscious agents. In future the consciousness of society must be the decisive agent in its change, and this knowledge must affect the immediate future direction of scientific advance.

Need for Effective Social Science.—It is becoming increasingly apparent that we need to bring up what may be called the left wing of science—biology, and still more, sociology and economics—to the level of the earlier development of physics and chemistry. This is not merely a matter of providing more funds for the study of these subjects or of attracting into them workers of great ability. The great trouble about biological and, still more, sociological sciences, and the basis of the feeling that they are not real but pseudo-sciences, is that they have no adequate positive relation to practical life. The physicist or the chemist is discovering techniques which, if they are internally efficient, have every prospect of finding their way into direct application for human welfare. There are, it is true, increasing abuses which have already been discussed, but they are not sufficient to make the whole work seem ultimately futile. For the biologist there is still considerable possibility of application in medicine. The agriculturist, however, is now faced with a world where restriction, and not development, is the order of the day, and the enormous potentialities of biological discovery have no prospect of being realized in practice. With sociology it is far worse. Not only are all sociologists removed from any executive power, so that sociology cannot become an experimental science, but the very inquiries which are made into social forms are blocked when it appears that they would lead to a criticism of the existing order of society and diverted on to a sterile and merely descriptive academic plane. If biology and sociology are to be brought into line they must be combined closely with actual forces which are changing both biological environment and society itself (see p. 341).

The Prospects of Science

After considering these more general aspects of scientific advance we can pass to its immediate concrete prospects. These can be looked at in two ways, from the point of view of the development of scientific technique and theory and from the point of view of the satisfaction of human needs. The former most clearly determines the immediate intrinsic possibilities of scientific development, the latter its long-range trend. It would, of course, be better if it were possible to present a picture of scientific advance exhibiting at the same time both of these aspects. But such a picture would almost necessarily lose in clarity what it gained in comprehensiveness. Consequently in this and the next chapter the two aspects will be presented here in succession with indications in the first case of how scientific development might be used to assist human needs, and in the second how human needs may lead to the development of science.

Tasks left Undone.—The picture of the natural world has been already sufficiently blocked out for us to see which are so far the most significant tasks left undone. These are the search for ultimate, or rather ulterior, mechanisms beyond the reach of present knowledge on the physical frontiers of science and the search for the connecting links between the hierarchies of organization, such as those between physics and chemistry, between chemistry and biology, between biology and sociology, and finally, between sociology and psychology. It is really immaterial whether these ranges of phenomena can or cannot be made to fit into one coherent whole. What does matter is that we know that there is far more to find out about these intermediate links, and that our present ignorance of them still effectively prevents us acquiring a full understanding of the significance of the regions themselves. In one of the cases mentioned, that between physics and chemistry, the gap has already largely been filled. Through the development of the quantum theory the phenomena of chemical combination and affinity can receive the same type of explanation that holds for the physical phenomena of electricity and light. We have acquired in the process a far deeper knowledge of classical chemistry. In the same way it cannot be doubted that any further knowledge acquired of the chemical basis of biology will serve to throw light on what have been previously considered to be purely biological questions. Indeed, one of the most striking results of recent trends has been the light thrown on physiological and even psychological behaviour by the study of the effects of relatively simple chemicals such as the vitamins and hormones. It is not suggested that the central subjects should be neglected in favour of the intermediate subjects, but that they may expect to gain from them new impulses for experiment and new bases for theory. What follows is a sketch, necessarily a very generalized one, of the immediate prospects of research, particularly in these intermediate regions from physics to sociology.

Physics

In physics the search into the ulterior nature of the physical world is proceeding naturally as an inquiry into the smallest, the quickest, the most energetic, and the most distant and ancient parts of the universe. The study of the nuclei of atoms is at the same time the study of the interior of stars and of the origin and development of galactic systems.

More than that, by going beyond our ordinary human experience, it puts the most severe test on those practical rules of conduct which we call the laws of nature and serves to distinguish how far these are in any sense ultimate and how far they are simply practical approximations for creatures of our size and rates of living. The principle of the conservation of energy, for instance, essential in biological and industrial applications, may or may not be found to hold in the interaction between individual particles and rays of light. Yet whatever the answer may be, the inquiry is bound to tell us more about the significance of the conservation of energy in the macroscopic world. Marking as it does the outer boundary of our knowledge, theoretical physics necessarily attracts not only the most ingenious but also the most speculative minds. Almost inevitably many of its most general conclusions partake as much of mystical and metaphysical intuitions drawn consciously or unconsciously from pre-scientific beliefs as of reasonable induction from observation and experiment. Much of the work of the future will be concerned with removing these obstructive elements, but to do this it will be necessary to base our approach to the problems of physics on a much broader foundation of general knowledge of the universe and its development.

But it is not only on the theoretical side that modern physics has much to give. The techniques involved in it, that of high-tension electricity, of vacuum tubes, and of oscillating circuits, can be used to transform many other branches of science and in themselves furnish a direct link of utility between physics and the electrical industries. There is already here a very intricate give and take by which science produces ideas of technical value and receives in return the money and the new tools with which to make still further advance. The further development of electron tubes and oscillating circuits will have important implications inside and outside of science. The electron microscope is already an accomplished fact, its performance has already exceeded by several times that of the optical microscope; with it is linked the development of television. Everything that can affect any kind of radiation is now within reach of human observation, an infra-red telescope capable of seeing through cloud and fog has already been perfected. It remains to apply these methods to the problem of the other sciences and to effect a revolution similar to that brought about by the telescope and microscope.

The possibilities of new combinations of oscillating circuits are infinite. With a proper collaboration of mathematical and electrical ingenuity they can be made, to a larger and larger extent, to substitute for the operations of calculation. Already with such applications mathematics is becoming mechanized, but at the same time there is opened a new era of mathematical mechanism. These new mathematical physical methods can be used to control apparatus and machinery, not, as heretofore, in the mere transmissions of human will to machinery, but in actual substitutions for human observation and control. Already processes can be watched by an infra-red eye, and errors humanly unobservable can be picked out. We have before us the possibilities of a new mechanics in which human intelligence will be used primarily in the designing of the machine, whose operations will be completely automatic, self-regulating, and self-repairing, with the ultimate elimination of the necessity for machine minders.

Nuclear physics has now begun to offer greater and unforeseen possibilities. The transmutation of elements is an accomplished fact, still of course on a sub-microscopic scale, but already sufficiently developed to be of enormous value to chemistry and biology. Through the new radio elements, such as radio sodium or radio phosphorus, we now have a means of following the movements of single atoms and thus unravelling in a direct way the problems of assimilation and metabolism. Biology must be ready to make use to the full of the immense spate of work which these methods will provide.

The Structure of Matter.—The older and rather neglected branches of physics, which dealt mainly with the properties of materials, are now in process of rapid transformation. Up till recently physics was concerned with the intimate structure of matter only in the consideration of electrical fields and collisions between particles; otherwise its generalizations were based on elementary acceptances of properties of matter—rigidity, elasticity, plasticity, etc.—which could be used but not in any sense explained. Recent developments in optics and in the X-ray and electron study of matter have completely altered this state of affairs. A large new branch of physics is appearing, linking up with chemistry and dealing with the structure of solid or liquid matter. The first stage of this is an examination of the atomic structure of existing forms of matter, which has already led to the understanding of the properties of technical materials— metals, ceramics, fibres, etc. The need for development along these lines lies in the possibility of creating new materials, not by blind experimentation, which will never produce anything radically new, but by the full use of structural theory with the aim of producing materials having any desired properties.

Our knowledge of solid matter is already passing beyond a knowledge of structure towards an understanding of how structures are changed. The development, simultaneously in the U.S.S.R. and England, of the knowledge that friction and plastic deformation are alike accompanied by a local heating and even melting of the material, is bound to have a profound effect on engineering practice both in relation to the working of metals and to problems of bearings, lubrication, frictional electricity, and even the detonation of explosives. Another direction of the greatest promise is that of the study of the boundaries and surfaces of matter. This has the theoretical advantage of exhibiting two- and not three-dimensional properties, but is also of the greatest practical importance in corrosion, absorption, the flotation of minerals, catalysis, and other processes on the boundaries of physics and chemistry.

Geophysics.—One effect of the greater range of modern physics is the possibility of explaining rather than merely describing the development of our own earth. This is a particular aspect of the cosmic problem involving nuclear physics, for it is in nuclear physics that we must look for the reason for the abundance or scarcity of elements which go to build up the earth. But the sorting of these elements from one another and their distribution in the different parts of the crust or the interior is a matter for the new crystal physics to determine, and in the process we may expect some answer to the historical question of the origin of continents and mountain ranges and the more immediate practical question of the causes and prediction of earthquakes. Here the rapidly developing geophysical methods— gravity, magnetic, electrical, and vibration—offer the greatest promise both in their theoretical aspects and in their contribution to a rational prospecting for mineral deposits. Most particularly, of course, are we interested in the developments of the earth's surface, the problems of the atmosphere and the hydrosphere. Not only have these enormously increased in practical importance in relation to flying, water power, fisheries, and navigation, but it has now begun to be realized that they are significant for science as throwing an essential light on the apparently arbitrary chemical make-up of life, and consequently on its origin. Geology by itself can only give us half the answer to this question: the other half must be furnished by chemistry.

CHEMISTRY

All the advances in chemical science in the last hundred and fifty years have been due to the applications in practice of the great revolution in chemistry instituted by Lavoisier. What has not been sufficiently realized is that a far greater revolution has been effected within the last ten years by the application of the new quantum mechanics and of the new methods of spectroscopic and X-ray analysis. We can now link up the behaviour of mechanical systems of electrons and nuclei with the long familiar reactions of chemistry. At first, of course, this leads only to a re-interpretation of chemistry, but clearly it must go beyond it and lead to a new chemistry far more rational than nineteenth-century chemistry, just as much as that was more rational than the empirical chemistry of earlier times. It is now clear that much of the apparent simplicity of early chemistry was due to almost exclusive concentration on simple salts and gaseous molecules. The regions where it failed to account for the most elementary observations, such as those of the rock-forming silicates or of the metals and their ores, were simply left on one side. The new methods have already changed all that and are likely to bring still greater changes. Silicate chemistry is now sufficiently understood to show that it is simply an extension to the complex conditions of the crystalline state of the electrochemistry of simple salts. That understanding is bound, however, to have a profound importance for geology and for the ceramic, glass, and cement industries.

Metals.—Metal chemistry, on the other hand, has proved to be something of a totally different character from the rest of chemistry, determined by the presence of the free electrons which give metals their peculiar lustre. Although our modern civilization is based almost entirely on the use of metals and alloys, all we knew of them up till ten years ago was purely empirical knowledge achieved by methods of trial and error of the same character as those of the metal workers of the early civilizations. Now we have through X-rays a way of analysing metal structures and through electron theory a way of connecting these structures with the properties— mechanical, electrical, etc.—of the metal. This means the birth of rational metallurgy with untold possibilities in the way of technical applications, though their development has been and is being held up by our present irrational chaos of scientific and industrial organization.

Reactions.—In other parts of chemistry developments less fundamental but no less important may be expected. In a sense the statical problem of molecular chemistry is already solved. We know, or we have the means of finding out in most cases, what are the chemical structures of molecules. It is now the dynamical aspect that is most interesting; the problem of how certain molecules change into others. The solution of this problem will give us new means of synthesis, but more important, it will help to bridge the gap between the chemistry of the laboratory and that of life. Except for the proteins, we now know the structure of most of the molecules that take part in living processes. We can even in certain cases synthesize them, but we are still for the most part completely ignorant as to how those substances are made in the living animal or plant.

The Reconstruction of Chemistry.—To solve this problem it will not be sufficient to consider classical chemistry; the whole range of modern physics will also have to be invoked. In the present state of science this process is hindered by lack of understanding between the sciences and by what may be called the vested interest of classical chemistry. The great nineteenth-century development of chemical industry left the chemists as the largest and most homogeneous body of scientists. There are still more chemists than all other kinds of scientists put together. Chemical technique has tended to become a closed system which can be worked only by its adepts. New methods from outside find tardy acceptance. The methods of X-ray crystallography, for instance, which are capable of shortening the work of both the research and works chemist by very large factors have already waited fifteen years and may well wait in the present dispensation for another fifty before they come into general practice.

Colloids and Proteins.—We are coming to realize more and more that the underlying characteristics of life are of a colloid chemical nature, that the structure that matters for most vital processes is not the relatively gross structure of cells, nuclei, chromosomes, etc., but the fine structure of protein molecules, protein or polysaccharide chains or membranes. So far we have accepted colloids as given by nature. Now we are beginning to see that the colloid particle owes its existence to a certain degree of the same polymerization (or joining together of many molecules) that gives rise to fibrous substances such as cellulose and rubber. By far the most important of colloid substances are the proteins, whether in the form of globular molecules, fibres, or membranes. When we have solved the problem of proteins, including the explanation of their chemical activity as enzymes, such as yeast in fermentation or pepsin in digestion, we shall have gone far towards bridging the gap between living and non-living systems. It was Engels who said, "Life is the mode of existence of albumen." We may soon be in a position to put his assertion to the test. (2) Practically, of course, the knowledge of colloid and biochemistry is of enormous importance to the principal industries that affect human life. The production, the storing, and the preparation of food; the textile, leather, and rubber industries, all depend for their improvement on the development of these sciences.

BIOLOGY

The two great perennial problems of biology are those of function and origin. How do living beings work and how do they get to be like that? The biology of the last century was mainly concerned with the forms of living things. These forms are now seen as inseparable from the functions they fulfil in the life of the animal. Morphology and physiology are being fused into one. But an organism is not a given thing, it is a process repeated, over and over again, in the course of individual lives, and once and for all in the course of the evolution of life. Embryology, genetics, and evolution are together part of another problem, that of origin, without which the problem of function cannot be unravelled. In recent years both these have taken on a new aspect. What we crudely observe of living beings— their appearances, microscopically and macroscopically, their movements, their patent growth, development, and similarities or differences —are seen to be only superficial signs of hidden chemical changes in a physico-chemical structure, itself extremely complex and ancient. One of the great problems for the immediate future is the understanding of the chemical basis of the functioning and development of life. Biochemistry is bound to develop in the future on a scale dwarfing many other sciences. For what we know now is only the beginning of the knowledge of the existence of problems for which as yet we have no solutions. The processes of the chemical equilibrium of organisms, the detailed interaction of food substances, oxidative agents, and specific chemicals such as hormones and vitamins have all to be unravelled. In doing so we shall find many new means of controlling life to an extent hitherto undreamt of.

Biochemistry.—It is in such analysis that lies the chief hope of the development of effective medicine. The transition of medicine from a half-empirical, half-magical practice to an applied science began with the discoveries of bacteriology towards the end of the last century—but it has only begun. Bacterial and virus disease is an attack on the body from outside; in all other disease, and in many bacterial diseases as well, the chief factor is the faulty functioning of the body itself with respect to the balance of natural chemical substances. The knowledge of what these substances do in health and disease is the first step to rational control. The analysis of the conditions of diabetes and pernicious anaemia leading to the discovery of a specific substance and a cure requires to be extended to all other diseases. On the two major unsolved problems of disease, chronic sclerosis and cancer, which between them account for most of the deaths of old people, the attack is only beginning. It is held back by the unintelligent planning of biochemical research in relation to medicine, with over-insistence on the chemical aspect and by the vested interest of the profession and of the manufacturers of medical supplies. Advance would be rapid once these were removed and an organized collaboration secured between colloid- and bio-chemists, physiologists, and pathologists.

Biophysics.—At the same time the physical aspect of life will not be neglected. Modern physics has already entered biology in an attempt to explain the fundamental mechanisms of motion and sensation. Muscular contraction, the transmission of nervous impulses, digestion and secretion are as much physical as chemical phenomena. But the biophysicists' task is only just beginning. All the new methods of examination of the structure and changes of matter—electron microscopes, X-ray analysis, ultra violet and polarizing microscopes, thermal, electric, and acoustic detectors—require to be put in the service of biology and used by men who understand the significance of their finds both physically and biologically. The great value of this approach as against that of either the older histologists or of the biochemists is that with refinement of technique it is easier to approximate to the detailed study of the mechanism of an intact animal or plant. The higher animals exhibit, from the point of view of efficiency and co-ordination, extraordinarily efficient mechanisms, and their study must throw light on many other mechanical and organizational problems, particularly those of social co-ordination. One of the major problems of science is that of the complex mechanism of nervous control leading up to the interpretation of the action of the human brain. Here biophysics must take the leading place together with biochemistry and behaviour studies.

Embryology.—The development of our knowledge of function would be completely lop-sided if it were not combined intimately with the study of origin and development. The critics of the mechanists are right in so far as a mere explanation, however complete, of how an organism works is no explanation of the organism. Two further great problems remain: the problem of embryology, how from an apparently formless egg an elaborate organism develops conforming to a pre-existing model, and he problem of genetics, of how that model is determined immediately by similar and further back by dissimilar parentage. Embryology itself is becoming and will become far more chemical. (3) Here again the visible structures appear as the result of invisible, but probably very complicated, chemical changes. The scope of embryology stretches far beyond the study of the growth of a young animal. It applies to all tissue regeneration and degeneration, to the problems of senescence, of the healing of wounds and of malignant disease. The new techniques of tissue and organ culture make us feel that at last we are beginning to understand, and at some time may be able to mould, the development of living matter. What such control could mean to mankind cannot yet be imagined. At the least it would mark an enormous step towards the conquest of disease.

The Nucleus and Genetics.—Yet the core of life lies still deeper. All physiology and embryology lead up to the study of the cell nucleus which contains in itself the specific and inheritable characters of the organism. The discovery of the connection between the genes in the chromosomes and the unitary factors of inheritance will rank with the quantum theory as the major discovery of the early twentieth century, but it is still a Keplerian and not a Newtonian discovery. We know that certain spots of matter in a chromosome have a definite connection with certain groups of changes in a developing organism and ultimately with certain characters in the adult organism, but the nature of the connection between the two is completely obscure. Its solution invites the best minds not only in biology but in physics and chemistry, because with the genes we are reaching dimensions of the same order as those of large chemical molecules. Beyond that problem there still remains that of the origin of genetic structures. This is one that leads from evolution to that of the origin of life itself. Here biology links again with geological and cosmological problems. With our new knowledge of genetics it is now possible to go back to the problem that Darwin stated but did not solve, the origin of species and their distribution in time and space. It is no longer the fact of evolution that needs to be established, but its mode of operation that needs to be analysed in detail. Long before these problems are solved, however, genetics furnishes us with another quite independent means of modifying life through selective breeding and even by the creation of mutations. Since the invention of agriculture and the domestication of animals man has never acquired such control of organic development as the science of genetics now offers.

Ecology.—With the object of understanding as well as of controlling life the study of the relations between organisms is as important as that of the organism in artificial isolation. The animal and plant world form between them a beautifully balanced system of chemical and physical interchanges, but this system is not invariant; it changes both in place and time, and particularly it has been altered by human interference. Agriculture implies the imposition of a new ecology and produces, besides its immediate objects of humanly valued goods, many other results, some of them highly undesirable from the human point of view. Already biology has gained immensely from the studies, which the economic interests of farmers have forced them to make, concerning the relations between crops and domestic animals, soil bacteria and insect pests; with a rationally organized agriculture a far greater extension of knowledge might be expected.

The whole problem of parasitism is a special side of the study of the relations between organisms, and here again science and medicine can gain enormously from one another. Infective disease in its cruder forms has been effectively dealt with in the past few years, but we are still far from having an adequate understanding of the mechanisms of infection and immunity. We may expect from such knowledge an ability not only to prevent the evil effects of infection but actually to use the reactions of the body and bacteria in certain cases for the promotion of health. Already it is becoming apparent that the reactions involved in infection and immunity are of an extreme chemical delicacy, and this study of a complex biological process may in turn provide a new means of understanding many problems of laboratory chemistry.

Animal Behaviour.—Great developments may be expected from the study of the behaviour of animals in relation to their environment. It is only recently that we have begun to see that by placing animals in certain clearly defined situations we can, through a study of their behaviour, discover logically something of the mechanism which in man we call thought and memory. We can in this way realize the wish of the magician, of learning the language of birds and beasts. Intuitively, of course, this was done by the hunters of palaeolithic times and animal-tamers of early neolithic times as it is done by animal lovers to this day. But this knowledge requires to be freed from the mixture of superstition and emotion which has characterized men's relations with animals from the earliest times. Such knowledge will not only enable us to establish new understanding and relationship with animals but also will give us much insight into our own behaviour.

Animal Societies.—The study of animal societies, whether temporary or permanent, must throw light on the problem which, for us, and probably cosmically, is highly significant—the origin of humanity. We recognize now that man is not merely a superior mammal, but differs in kind from all other mammals in being self-made, a product of the society of which he himself is the unit. To unravel the initial tendencies, whether of sexual association or of primitive economic grouping, which made this change possible twenty million or so years ago, is a study which brings together the biologist, the geologist, and the historian. Just as human society must carry in itself the marks of its origin, so a knowledge of that origin is of crucial importance in the understanding and control of existing society, the problem which transcends all others in urgency.

SOCIAL SCIENCE AND PSYCHOLOGY

It is clear that to solve the problems of social structure and control we shall need a far greater concentration of ability in the field of animal and human psychology than we yet have. The danger is, of course, that the society in which we now live has no adequate motive for such studies, and indeed they cannot be honestly undertaken without undermining the forms of that society. On the other hand, by not undertaking them we retain the extraordinary paradox—the most elaborate crudity and the self-defeating stupidity of greed that distinguish our present civilization. It is here, of course, that the contrast between theory and practice is most glaringly apparent. Discoveries in physics and even in biology are generally destined in spite of delays to achieve sooner or later their counterpart in application, but discoveries in sociology or economics are not conceived of as anything but academic studies, and may even be banned as tendencious if they would seem to imply that the world would be better run in a different way. It is consequently impossible to forecast the development of the social sciences, anthropology, psychology, and economics independently of that of the society in which they are studied. As long as the present economic system lasts, they are destined to remain descriptive, clinical, and academic; where Fascism takes its place they are the first to submit to grotesque distortions. Only in a socialized economy effectively concerned with providing maximal welfare can the full development of the social sciences be expected, for there they needs must become in practice and theory an integral part of the machinery of communal life. Social sciences differ in kind from the physical sciences in that they deal not with repetitive states obeying laws and consequently capable of exact experimentation, but with an internally conditioned and unique development. Human psychology cannot be reduced to a study of the reactions of an organism to its environment because a human individual carries inside him, in a way that no other organism does, the results of the social influences that have been working on him since birth. We have seen in the work of Freud the beginning of a study of the effects of some of these social influences, namely, the influence of the family, but it is a very partial analysis, as the family itself is closely bound up with economic and social influences that also have their own direct effects. Psychology is still very much of a pseudo-science; it contains embedded in it many metaphysical and religious ideas which the history of science shows must be removed before an effective objectivity can be reached.

Sociology is even more of a pseudo-science, the units with which it deals are indeterminate and shifting. But it can develop in relation to concrete objective, economic and anthropological studies, not only of savage races but also of civilized communities. Social, economic, and psychological forms can be adequately studied only in relation to the origin of those forms. This approach we owe primarily to Marx. For the lack of it we have had the fatal split between highly abstract and conventional sciences assuming fixed categories—human nature, the psychic or the economic man—and a history that is either literary or didactic or merely pedantic chronicling. The line of development of the social sciences must be one which integrates them with history, and this in itself requires a general reorganization of science and the humanities.

There is no doubt that we need the development of the social sciences to an even greater extent than the physical sciences, but it is no accident that these are at present so poorly supported. It is not so much their intrinsic difficulty as the fact that their mere study is a damning criticism of present social institutions. They are never likely to be developed in our form of society. The struggle for the development of social sciences is at the same time the struggle for the transformation of society. (4)

THE FUTURE OF SCIENCE

In any survey of the possibilities of scientific research general lines of advance can be seen and fairly probable conclusions drawn from them. What cannot be seen are the possibilities of fundamentally new discoveries and their effect in revolutionizing the whole progress of science. We have had such discoveries in the past, those of X-rays and radio-activity being the most startling of recent times. It has been argued that because such things cannot be predicted, for indeed to predict them would be to make the discovery itself, there is no sense in examining the future of science. This is only partially true; the larger and more important discoveries are not made *in vacuo*. They are the fruit of intensive study of a particular field, but that field must be extensively studied for some other reason before the discovery is made. It would have been impossible to predict in the early nineteenth century the mechanism of cell reproduction, but reasonable to say that unless cells were studied carefully with a microscope nothing about their reproduction was likely to be discovered. In the same way unless electric discharges through gases had been the object of study, X-rays and radio-activity and all that followed from them would never have emerged. The practical problem, therefore, is to see that science advances on the widest and most comprehensive front, being prepared to accept and to use as welcome gifts the radical discoveries that come in its way.

Interactions.—In the rough sketch of the front of science and ignorance which has just been given it is possible to see in many places the interactions among the different sciences and between them and human activities, but by arranging the sciences in sections cross-connections are largely lost. To some extent the chart given on p. 280 helps to remedy this defect. The internal connections between sciences are there shown as well as those between science and the more immediately practical sides of life. The importance of ultimate and bridge sciences, such as nuclear physics and bio-

chemistry, is brought out by the exhibition of the number of connections which these sciences have over the whole field.   It would, of
course, be possible to make a far more complete picture, but its
complexity would probably obscure the main relationships.

So far we have spoken of the kind of development along which
science is being urged through its own inner necessities.   Sufficient
has been said to indicate, however, that science is not an isolated
activity and that there exists a possibility of practical external application which in turn furnishes material justification for the carrying
out of that branch of science.   Science until now has been mainly
concerned with the analysis of the world as it existed prior to man
and not with man's own work.   The whole artificial armoury of
science in instruments and apparatus exists not to create a new nature
but to enable man to make those material and logical separations
necessary to understand nature as it is.   But this is only the beginning;
the world as made by man requires also to be studied and controlled.
As time goes on the part of the universe determined by man will
become relatively more and more important, but as this part will
have been more rapidly constructed it will necessarily be less stable
and will require a more thorough and careful understanding to
prevent the crushing of man by his own creations.

(1) Three schemes for such surveys are being made at the present moment.
(2) Since this sentence was written, viruses, which have been considered as the simplest
forms of existing life, have been shown to consist largely if not entirely of specific
nucleoproteins.
(3) See J. Needham, *Chemical Embryology*.
(4) Engels expresses this idea in *Anti-Duhring* :
" The conditions of existence forming man's environment, which up to now have
dominated man, at this point pass under the dominion and control of man, who now for the
first time becomes the real conscious master of Nature, because and insofar as he has become
master of his own social organization.   The laws of his own social activity, which have
hitherto confronted him as external, dominating laws of Nature, will then be applied by
man with complete understanding, and hence will be dominated by man."

CHAPTER XIV

SCIENCE IN THE SERVICE OF MAN

Human Needs

If we take human life and its development as the centre of our study, the activities of science assume a different aspect and appear related to each other in ways different from those described in the last chapter. Human needs and aspirations furnish a continuous motive power for inquiry as well as for action, and science can be regarded as one of the ways in which we can get the knowledge necessary for the satisfaction of any particular need. We can divide the needs of human beings in society into four grades of urgency to each of which science has a definite relation. There are, first of all, the primary biological needs of food, shelter, health, and enjoyment. After these comes the need for the means of providing these requirements in the form of productive industry, transport, and communication, as well as the whole administrative, economic, and political mechanism of civilized society. But society not only lives; it grows. Old needs require to be better satisfied and new ones arise. These dynamic needs of human society find their motive force in political movements, but the form in which they are ultimately embodied is determined by science, which thus tends to become the chief agent of social and economic change. Finally, society takes cognizance of itself and at the same time expresses itself in what may be called its culture: in manners, art, and in the general attitude towards life. Here again not only operative science, but also the world picture which science presents, are essential factors.

Primary Needs: Physiological and Social.—It is beginning to be recognized, for the first time, that society is at last in a position to satisfy adequately primary human needs. It is only recently, and through science, that this has been made possible, but we know also that this has not been done to anything approaching the measure of its possibility, not from any lack of science but from defects in the social and economic system. Starting out from known primary needs it would now be possible to construct a technical system of production and distribution in which those needs would find satisfaction. The advantage of doing this is that, once definite and quantitative statements of requirements are made, the problem of supplying them becomes also something definite, and the degree of practicability of each demand can be measured in terms of existing technique. Recent work on food, for instance, has shown that once it became possible to establish scientifically both minimal and optimal standards of nutrition, far more effective political and economic action in favour of realizing them could be taken than when equally real hunger was expressed in unassessable terms. Once a need can be defined in more or less quantitative terms its satisfaction becomes a definite technical and economic problem. If organized society determines that the need should be satisfied and is prepared to meet the cost it becomes a purely technical one. Technology could advance to meet such problems much faster than it has up till now, and it is possible to forecast what technical changes will be necessary for this purpose with a fair degree of accuracy. (1) In what follows an attempt will be made to make such a forecast, one which goes slightly beyond the existing technical trends but which is in no sense Utopian, that is, does not suggest any changes which we cannot see a way to realize.

We may divide primary human needs into physiological and social. Man is, however, so much a social animal that this division is necessarily an artificial one. Social needs control action no less than do physiological. Hunger and discomfort will be endured in many cases rather than the transgression of social codes and, in fact, the possibility of the maintenance of the gross inequalities of our present system depends far more on the compulsion of social custom than on the possibilities of physical force. The physiological needs have, however, one degree of greater urgency. For the lack of them, beyond a certain point, man cannot live at all. It is probable that an overwhelming majority of diseases that occur throughout the world are due directly or indirectly to the lack of primary necessities, generally food, and many of the remainder are attributable to bad working conditions. (2) In other words, men are really murdered by the system they live under, or to put it in a more positive form, the adequate supply of primary necessities would give some twenty to thirty years of added life on the average to each person in the world. This may sound extreme, but it merely reflects the fact that no one draws plain inferences from the difference between the Englishman's expectation of life of fifty-five years and the Indian's of twenty-six.

FOOD

The first and principal necessity is food. It is now easy to assess the food needs of the present population or any given world population, but more difficult to estimate the total agricultural production necessary to give this population an optimal food consumption. All estimates, however, that have been made agree that if the available good agricultural land of the world were worked by the best modern methods it would provide a food supply between two and twenty times the amount required for the optimal standard. We can arrive at this in another way. Sir John Orr, in his report on nutrition in Britain, a relatively favoured country in this respect, not only showed that half the population suffered from deficient feeding but that one-fifth of them were below even minimal fitness and state of health. From these figures we can calculate the amount of food required to bring the whole population up to a sufficient standard. The value of this is 20 per cent. more than that of present consumption, and roughly three times more than that of the agricultural production of Great Britain. If we take the population of Britain as 44,000,000 and the cultivated area as 12,000,000 acres, this would give a requirement of just under 1 acre per head of population on a British standard or of 2,000,000,000 acres for the world as a whole, which is less than half of the present cultivated area of 4,200,000,000 acres, itself hardly 12 per cent. of the land surface of the earth.

New Agriculture.—Sketchy though these figures are, there can be no question that a minimal application of science could increase the rate of agricultural production manifold. (3) The scientific study of soil and of plant and animal breeding, together with the production of a certain amount of artificial manure and mechanical agricultural implements, could certainly, in the course of twenty years or so, develop the food productivity of the world not only by producing greater yields per acre but also by widening the area of cultivable land. (4) The development in the case of commercial crops where there is a greater inducement to improve production emphasizes this conclusion. Thus, in Louisiana, sugar-cane production was improved from 6·8 to 18·8 tons per acre in the course of 3 years. (5) Actually under the present system such improvements were disastrous and they have been, in fact, replaced by elaborate devices for retarding improvement and even for destroying crops. What can be done even in an extremely backward country is shown by the results already achieved in the Soviet Union where, besides those already quoted on p. 227 *et seq.*, great improvements have been produced by the large-scale introduction of new scientific techniques such as artificial insemination, which has revolutionized stock breeding, and vernalization, which enables the advantages of winter wheat to be achieved artificially. (6)

Advances in gland physiology and genetics may produce even greater changes in animal husbandry. Up till now these changes have been almost purely commercial in incentive and, though they have resulted in much greater yields of such products as eggs and milk, it has been at the expense of increasing the incidence of disease which, in the case of tuberculosis in milk, is passed on to human beings. The conditions of forcing animals are not only unnatural and cruel but inefficient. (7) There is no reason why in a well ordered economy the well-being of animal populations should not be a primary consideration of husbandry.

All this, however, merely represents the first stage of the application of science to the production of food, a simple rationalization of existing traditional methods. Beyond lie vistas of methods for food production, the importance of which is not so much to provide an existing population with food, for that, in principle, is a problem already solved, as to provide it with food with the least expenditure of monotonous or unhealthy labour, and to open a possibility of progressive increase of population. An enormously increased extension of the cultivated area could be attained by fairly simple physical means through effective irrigation of desert lands and ultimately by the covering over of deserts and turning them into vast greenhouses. Another method is the agrotechnical method of Dr. Wilcox and Professor Gerike, by which, by growing plants in water troughs containing chemicals, the yield is enormously increased. As much as 75 tons of potatoes or 217 tons of tomatoes have been produced per water acre. (8)

Bacterial and Chemical Food Production.—It is, however, probable that before these methods pass into general practice the use of the higher plants, however intensively cultivated, as primary food supplies would be replaced by methods of using lower plants such as algae and fungi. The primary sources of food in the sea are the algae of the plankton; hitherto we have used this source only indirectly through the fishes who eat it. It should be possible to convert this indirect use of three-quarters of the world's surface into a direct one by deliberately growing plankton in the sea and harvesting it, although probably it would be more economical to produce food by a number of factories working in sunny districts for the continuous growing of algae. At one further remove food products might be synthesized by bacteria or even by the enzymes of bacteria. Ultimately all our food is contained in the materials of the air, water, and rocks, and if we used our reserves of coal, or even limestone, as basic food materials we should have enough for a population thousands or millions of times that which exists at present on our globe.

Distribution.—The mere production of food is, however, only part of the story. It is essential that the food should be distributed in a nutritious and palatable form. An enormous amount of waste occurs to-day in food distribution and preparation. Although in recent years great progress has been made in food transport and pre-servation, there are still very heavy losses on this score. Most of them, it is true, are due to economic and not technical faults. The total retail sales of food in England would provide for every man, woman, and child, if properly divided and consumed, slightly more than the British Medical Association nutrition standard (see pp. 65, 375). Yet it is quite clear that a substantial portion of the population has a far lower standard than this and, consequently, that a corresponding proportion of food sold is wasted either from over-eating on the part of certain sections of the population, or, probably to a much greater extent, by domestic waste inherent in the small-scale manipulation of food.

Cookery.—While other arts have been improved and regulated by science, cookery has not changed in its essential processes since palaeolithic times and is almost entirely untouched by science. This, of course, reflects the fact that cookery as a domestic occupation has not the same profit motive which leads other industries to adopt scientific technique. With a fairly small application of biochemical knowledge to cookery, coupled with a further reduction of unnecessary domestic operations, it should be possible not only to eliminate waste, but to produce for the table, far more easily and economically than at present, a great variety of old as well as of new dishes. There is no more reason to suppose that science would injure the art of cookery than to imagine that such a practical example of the application of science as the piano would ruin the art of music.

CLOTHING

Supersession of Textiles.—The provision of clothing has not any of the same urgency as that of food. On a purely physical basis the population of the world is probably more over-clothed than under-clothed, though most of this clothing is of excessively poor quality. The value of clothing is now rather social than utilitarian; its main object is to enable people to enjoy or, at any rate, not to be ashamed of, their appearance. For that reason what we need in clothing is more variety and beauty at a price available to all rather than mere warmth and comfort. The new development in the study of fibres will make almost indefinite improvements in clothing possible. Already artificial silk has shown that in this respect nature could be very adequately imitated. But more radical improvements could come not so much from attempts to produce new types of fibres as by short-circuiting the whole method of clothes production through making clothes directly from porous plastic material rather than from spun and woven fibre. In this or in some other way the permanence of clothes and the necessity for repeated washing could be dispensed with, which would immensely simplify living conditions. New clothes could be worn for a few days and then discarded. As things stand at present the complete elimination of textile industries

would, however, be a social disaster, provoking only unemployment
and want.　In any rational system of production men would not be
so attached to industries that these had to be maintained even when
they had lost any productive justification.　Changes of this type
would, on the contrary, be welcomed as releasing workers from
monotonous toil for more interesting occupations and increased
leisure.

HOUSING

The question of housing still remains an important and difficult
one.　Houses tend to outlast the habits and possibilities of those who
live in them, and this is further emphasized by the almost universal
tendency of allowing the poor to live in the discarded houses of the
rich.　We are just beginning to see that it is possible to build a house
or a city round the requirements of the inhabitants.　These requirements are only partly physical; sociological factors actually play a
predominating part in the planning of houses.　To a large extent the
quality of the demand for houses depends on social tradition far more
than on physical needs.　The house is not only a shelter from the
weather and a place for preparing food and sleeping; it is also a
centre of a complicated social ritual.　These two aspects interact with
one another.　Social habits and the uses to which houses are put
themselves depend on what kind of houses are available.　We can
discern at the moment two general tendencies: one towards large
integrated housing units with common services, situated in urban
concentrations, and the other, a peripheral grouping of small,
practically identical, self-contained houses.　Both tendencies may
continue or some compromise may be found between them.　In
either case science has much to offer in transforming conditions in
the direction of convenience and beauty.　The main principles of
architecture are just beginning to feel the effect of the revolution
introduced by new materials and new processes.　It will soon be
possible to break altogether with conventional architecture, with its
tradition of putting stone on stone or brick on brick unchanged
since the time of the Pharaohs, and move in the direction of rational
fabrication.　The physical functions of architecture are principally
insulation and support, but these are perfectly separable factors.
Thick walls and heavy girders are a most inconvenient way of
providing both together.

New Materials.—Of the new materials, some, such as the light
metals, can be used exclusively for support, others, as yet but imperfectly developed, for insulation.　What we require at the moment
is a material as light as, if not lighter than, cork, strong enough to
withstand wind-pressure, fireproof, and offering good insulation

against heat and sound.   These are not impossible requirements. Indeed, materials satisfying nearly all of them have been already prepared (9) and it is almost certain that, with the development of aerogels, the problem can be satisfactorily solved.   As such material will not be built up but furnished in large slabs attached to the framework, building will come to resemble more and more the assembly stage of machine production, the preparation of the materials corresponding to the fabrication stage. (10)

Internal Climate.—The services attached to buildings have in the past only too often been afterthoughts; in rational architecture they will become essential parts.   Given good insulating walls, the problem of heating houses entirely disappears.   Indeed, even in winter, the heat generated by the inhabitants of the houses would require some method of cooling to get rid of it.   To secure this degree of self-sufficiency, however, it would be necessary to devise a rational ventilation system which did not, as at present, take in air cold and send it out hot, but arranged for the outgoing hot air to warm the incoming cold air in winter-time and vice versa in summer.   The domestic fire would then become of purely ritual importance.   If such complete segregation from outside air was not required, and it would not be for many country houses, both heating and cooling would still be necessary, but this could be achieved without the expensive means used to-day.   Already reversible heat engines which would pump heat into a house in winter or out in summer have been run on one-third to one-fifth of the cost of direct heating methods. (11) Almost as economical is the practice of heating cities as in America and Russia by waste steam from power stations.

Considerable developments may be expected in the application to buildings of aerodynamic principles, the least of which would be the abolition of draughts.   But it is beginning to be realized that with the appropriate use of properly shaped channels it is possible to maintain an opening secure against wind without the interposition of any material.   Thus the front windows of French express loco-motives, which are particularly apt to become choked with oil and soot, have been replaced by baffle-guarded clear openings.   A similar device may soon replace the automobile wind shield.   In this way it might be possible to be able to have open windows summer and winter alike, guarded either by the wind itself or by jets of air forming part of the general ventilating system.   The ultimate development would be the weather-proof room without walls or roof.

Domestic Convenience.—It might be thought that in the question of domestic convenience everything possible had already been done in the United States, but it is almost certain that the results of planned sociological research into human needs would reveal the possibility of linking up different domestic functions so as to increase general convenience in unsuspected ways. As in many other cases, the solution to domestic problems may well be found where the conditions which have to be fulfilled are rigorously limited, as for instance, in the motor-house or caravan-trailer, and we may expect from these developments a much greater flexibility and compactness in internal arrangements and a complete breakaway from the restriction of traditional methods.

The City of the Future.—Great as are the changes which science can introduce in the details of dwelling accommodation, far more could be done in the construction of large dwellings or houses. With the use of strong and light materials it should be possible to enclose spaces much larger than those dreamt of by past or present architects. The totally enclosed spacious air-conditioned town is rapidly becoming a practical proposition. It would be undesirable to attempt to concentrate all human activities in one such enclosure; probably several would be needed for different kinds of productive work and for recreation, each with its appropriate climate. Good construction with a plentiful use of sound-proof walls and a rational development of engineering should eliminate noise, a major affliction of modern city life. Most industrial noise in any case is an indication of waste.

Town and Country.—A well-designed ventilating system, together with the proscription of the liberation of all forms of dust, smoke, gases or vapours, should make such city air indistinguishable from that of the country and by appropriate control of temperature, humidity, and air movement, the most stimulating, enjoyable, and varied climates could be produced. Such a city would, of course, only furnish a definite part of a background of life; the essential values of the country are not merely its atmosphere but its very negation of city life. But the adequate concentration of urban construction would, in fact, even without a considerable restriction of necessary agriculture, leave far more space to wild nature. Unless the population of the world increases to some hundreds of times its present number, there will still be enormous tracts of wild country to which access will be easy and rapid, and it should be possible to grade this in such a way that every degree from mild suburbanism to absolute isolation could be provided according to taste.

Planning.—The problem of housing, however, is far more an organizational than a technical one. Urban and regional planning are as necessary as the building of the houses themselves, and planning requires the development of applied human geography which is only beginning. The various degrees of centralized or decentralized building, the position of factories and of means of transport all require to be thought out in relation to the development of economic life with the aim of providing for the well-being of the whole community rather than producing the biggest private profit. The difference between the position of town planning in Britain and in the Soviet Union shows effectively enough the disadvantages of private ownership, particularly in exaggerated ground values amounting to obstructive blackmail.

HEALTH

Essentially health is a necessity which might well come before any of the others but for the fact that it is dependent on satisfactory food and shelter. Moreover, we have not yet gone very far towards improving the health which we derive from nature unaided. Up till about fifty years ago the enormous amount of human ingenuity which had gone into the profession of medicine had, in fact, produced little more than a superficial knowledge of the phenomena of disease and death and a very comforting but totally unfounded claim of being able to control them. Since then bacteriology has made a successful attack on infective disease, but chronic infections and degenerative and constitutional diseases are still effectively untouched by science. Here again, however, the problem is mainly one of social organization rather than direct application of science. Mortality and illness rates show that in Britain at any rate the greater part of disease is avoidable in that it is avoided by the wealthiest sections of the population. The first stage in the conquest of health is to give those conditions of food and surroundings to the whole population to enable them to reach the standard of health enjoyed at present only by the rich, without, of course, encouraging the excesses by which the very rich ruin their lives.

Control of Disease.—The scientific approach to medicine is only now beginning to make itself felt. Already the problem has been seen to be that of preserving the health of the members of the community rather than the securing of fees by doctors administering to their diseases. Medicine needs to become in all its branches a public service in which research and practice are developed side by side. Immense improvements may be expected, for instance, from as careful a study of healthy people to see why they are healthy as of diseased ones to see why they are diseased. Periodical inspections of health, together with an adequate service of medical statistics on a world scale, could not fail to point to the origin of many troubles. The problem of disease, however, must not be underestimated. A human body is of a totally different order of complexity from that of any mechanical or chemical system which man has constructed or worked. This does not mean the problem is insoluble, but that it is necessary to devote to physiological research far more time and money than has yet been made available. Infective diseases can now be to a certain extent guarded against or even cured. With proper world co-ordination of health services they could be totally abolished. This in itself, as Professor J. B. S. Haldane has pointed out, is enough to make a world Socialist State an imperative need. Far more attention needs to be given to the natural processes of recovery from disease. Once they are understood it should be possible to hasten recovery or at least to see that everyone can make use of the curative faculty of the most disease-resisting persons. It should not be an unattainable idea within a generation of rational health administration to see that disease should play a negligible part in the great majority of lives.

Diseases of Old Age and Death.—The fatal diseases of old age are in a different category and offer the most immediate and serious challenge to science. Here success must go beyond nature, and this requires a very deep understanding of the processes of development and decay. Without that understanding we cannot even tell what is physically possible (see p. 338). It may be, or it may not be, possible to arrest that general hardening and drying of tissues which marks old age in all higher animals. It may be that rejuvenation or even regeneration of the body or of parts of it may be possible by means of the appropriate growth-promoting substances. The development of organ and tissue substitutes may serve to prolong life where only one part of the body is threatened. There is certainly hope that the problem of cancer, that most dreaded of diseases, is reaching a solution. What progress has been made, moreover, has been due to the collaboration of scientists in many different fields, but any really rapid and effective advance requires a far greater degree of co-ordination. It is idle to guess now how far death can be postponed for the majority by such measures, though it can hardly be to an age less than that of the oldest men now living. But it is a question which science can legitimately frame and attempt to answer. We do not even know in what sense death is an inevitable biological necessity or how far it is the shortest term of a series of pathological accidents, each one of which can be separately eluded. When we have found the answer to this we shall know whether the age of Methuselah is a fable or a legitimate aim.

Population Control.—Closely allied to the question of health is that of the biological control of populations as a whole. At present man attempts to control every part of the universe other than himself. Man has not become in that sense a domestic animal. He breeds at haphazard, and the resulting changes in quantity and quality of men have the most violent social repercussions. At the moment, to those who accept social events as fatalistically determined, it appears as if the population of Western Europe and most of America will soon reach a maximum and then decline even faster than it first arose. (12) As the Western Europeans not only maintain an elaborate civilization largely based on their dense population, but also control and exploit the greater part of the world, diminution of their numbers would be likely first of all to increase the severity of their exploitation, but sooner or later to lead to its complete breakdown. As this decrease would also be accompanied by an increasing average age and, therefore, an increased conservatism, these effects would be likely to be exaggerated.

But why is the decrease in reproduction taking place? Simply because for most women under existing conditions there is insufficient incentive to bear a number of children adequate to maintain the population. Fascist tyrannies attempt to overcome this by patriotic appeals and forceful suppression of birth control without much visible result. (13) It is fairly obvious from the development of nineteenth-century England and modern Russia that it is only necessary to make the having of children desirable, and to provide for them a secure and hopeful future, to attain any degree of population growth required. It is ludicrous, however, that this process should be left to pure chance. The inducement to parenthood should be adjusted exactly to the optimal requirements of population growth.

A great Increase under good Social Conditions.—What these requirements are it is much more difficult to say. Optimum population is usually defined as that population which is such that either increase or decrease of numbers would lower the standard of living. But this assumes a fixed economic system. Once the possibility of greatly increased consumption is admitted, the optimum measured in this way becomes indefinitely large. There is in the world food enough and room enough for centuries of increase at the maximal biological rate, say, doubling every forty years. Of course, under the present economic system these possibilities cannot be used, but here we are discussing optimal and not actual conditions. Why, it may be asked, should we have such a large population apart from intuitive or metaphysical appreciations of the value of the largest possible number of souls? One argument is that an important factor in human progress is the presence of sufficient numbers of men of exceptional capacity. At present we do not know, nor are we likely to for some time, any way of producing such persons at will, and consequently the only way to get them is to increase the population. A population much larger than the present one is often objected to because of overcrowding. This would be valid only if the present conditions of crowding in uncomfortable and noisy towns were allowed to remain.   At present 30 per cent. of the world's population is crowded into $\frac{1}{20}$ per cent. of the land area and another 30 per cent. is scattered over 75 per cent. of the land area.   Under modern productive conditions there should be no need for this concentration. Improved transport communications and housing would make most of the world habitable and the more beautiful parts could be saved for enjoyment and solitude.

This is a long-range view; at the moment what we want is not so much to breed more ability as to use more of the ability which we already possess.   In such a highly civilized country as England only one-quarter of the most intelligent children get an opportunity of higher schooling, and probably not more than one in fifty of university education.   With a really democratic government education could increase the number of able and trained men anything up to fifty times.   Even that might prove insufficient for the complex problems of a new and growing civilization.   The population policy this would demand is bound to be different from that envisaged for a world where opportunity has to be severely restricted.   Those who wish to control population at the moment do so mainly with the view that, by encouraging the wealthy to breed and discouraging the poor, or, as they would say, by encouraging superior and discouraging inferior stocks, they will enable the former to maintain effective dominance.   The fact is that no genetic differences among human beings can acquire any real significance as long as they are masked by socially maintained economic differences. (14)   Once social equality of opportunity is maintained, however, qualitative population problems will obtain a great importance.

WORK

One of the chief differences between an economy based directly on human needs and one in which they appear only indirectly through their profit value is a complete change in working conditions.   We are apt to think of work as one of the necessary disadvantages of life and to avoid it if we have the wit or money to do so.   Actually the unpleasantness of work is itself the product of social conditions. Ever since the discovery of agriculture made work necessary it has been forced on subjected people—women, slaves, or labourers—while those who controlled it had no interest in making it pleasant.   The industrial revolution actually made things far worse.   It abolished the traditional alleviations, the songs, dancing, and drinking which encouraged work.   At the same time it replaced the multiple variation of the farmers' work around the year by the regular drudgery of the factory, and made a lesser effort far more wearisome in its monotony and in the grimness and squalor of its surroundings. All this with modern technical possibilities is wholly unnecessary, and is only maintained on account of the imagined comfort and security of the few in our out-of-date economic system.

The Worker, not Profit, as a Prime Consideration.—Assuming that the larger part of active human time is still spent on work, a change in the conditions of work would mean enormously increased possibilities for enjoyable life. Up till now the chief research on working conditions has been from the point of view of efficiency alone. Such improvements as rest pauses and shorter hours have been introduced only in so far as they have been shown to result in increased production. Now it is even questionable whether factories designed for the convenience of workers would be less efficient than those where men are treated as part of the machinery, but any loss of efficiency there might be from this source would be more than covered by the corresponding increase in absolute labour-saving machinery, that is, in machinery designed to remove completely from human operation such processes as were found too strenuous or too monotonous. The conveyer belt, for instance, has helped to exaggerate the monotony of work and has created an inhuman and compulsive tension. Most jobs which are simple enough to be done in series can be done entirely mechanically, but where labour is cheap and conditions need not be considered, it is not thought worth making the machines.

Machinery to Remove, not Create, Drudgery.—The demands for machinery in which the worker was the first consideration would raise entirely fresh problems and would act as a powerful stimulus to invention and research. Up till now machinery has been used mainly to substitute for the motions of the human body, and has multiplied the force and speed of these motions. Already, however, the process is beginning of substituting recording and detecting devices for human sense organs. Electrical devices, and particularly the photo-electric cell, can be substituted for sight, hearing, and touch in many repetitive processes. Concern for the worker would press these developments far further and would lead to a third stage, that of finding mechanical substitutes for judgment, linking the detector elements to the moving parts so that variable material could be dealt with as accurately as uniform material in the older machines (see p. 366).

Work as Pleasure.—Meanwhile science could be used to remove the bad features of the work which still needed to be done, by development and application of industrial psychology. Of course, it would be ludicrous at present to expect a development of industrial psychology aimed at making work comfortable, easy, and interesting. What industrial psychology does exist, as it were on sufferance, can only be justified by its value to employers and not to workers, and the essential co-operation which would be necessary from workers in such research is consequently conspicuously lacking. Once it became clear that applied industrial psychology was intended to improve conditions of work and not to speed up production, it would be possible through co-operation with workers to remove altogether the implications of compulsion and unpleasantness which have been attached to the idea of work in all past ages.

PLAY

After work comes play. It is gradually becoming recognized what an important function recreation and amusement have in any community, above all in one where economic and material changes have broken up a balanced traditional order of life, and provided far more widespread leisure. Any rational development must provide more leisure still, but the new leisure should no longer present any problem. Leisure can be used either creatively or recreatively or it can be wasted in boredom. Our present system obstructs in every way the creative use of leisure, for everything creative has a value and therefore it either interferes with the present competitive system and cannot be allowed, or is part of it, in which case it immediately qualifies as work. Only domestic and trivial occupations—fretwork or rabbit breeding—remain as stunted samples of what people could and would do if they had training, equipment, co-operation, and encouragement. Recreative leisure, on the other hand, has been almost completely commercialized. The pace is set by the rich whose indefinite leisure is filled by sport and entertainment, while its enjoyment by the majority of the population is limited by lack of money. Short of sheer boredom the cheapest form of recreation is also the most passive—wireless, cinema, and the watching of sports. Up till now the application of science to leisure has been practically confined to the diffusion of these passive forms of enjoyment, it has diminished boredom only to put phantasy in its place.

In any other form of society the contribution of science would be quite different. It would be absurd, however, to attempt to predict its form, for the characteristic of enjoyment is its spontaneity. All we can say is that science, free from profit-making, will be found as useful in extending our capacities for enjoyment as it is of our methods of material production. Recreation can be made more intense, more individual, and more varied. The new techniques of cinema, wireless, and television have other possibilities than providing fantasy escapes from life or aesthetic appreciation of new forms. (15) Both are a means for enormously increasing the range of human experience, not only in making available to all what may be experienced by some, but also by opening new spheres of experience through the exploration of unknown regions of nature. Creative leisure, too, can be developed through science. Spontaneous individual or co-operative efforts will find new possibilities and, what is perhaps even more important, the sense of fitting in, of being real and important. Science itself may become for many an absorbing recreation.

Remaking the World.—But it is possible to see beyond this. There is the world of nature to enjoy, and by the increased facilities of travel, in fact and in thought, which science could bring, that world should be available to far more people than it has been in the past. But there is also a new world which man himself is constructing, and this new world will offer opportunities for enjoyment and interest as great as the actual utility and safety that it will bring to humanity. No one can now be in a position to specify what these possibilities will be. This inability is pathetically illustrated in the unsatisfactoriness, from the human point of view, of all Utopias. But we are fairly safe in assuming that the tendencies which made man extract enjoyment from every phase of his material cultural life up to the present will continue in the future. All these tendencies can be seen even at present in a spontaneous interest in motors, aeroplanes, and wireless, although they are held back by commercialized entertainment and by a snobbish imitation of obsolete aristocratic traditions. When free from this, as the example of the Soviet Union shows, there is an immense stock of popular interest and enthusiasm in the building up of a new and more extended culture.

Production

So far we have considered social ends rather than means. The satisfaction of direct human needs in a modern society implies, however, a complex and scientifically inspired system of production. The building up of the system has been the great monument to the individualist capitalism of the eighteenth and nineteenth centuries, but the final mechanism is so social in form that for its maintenance and development a far more conscious social system will be required. In this science will have to play a double part, in providing firstly the technical means, and secondly the organizational forms through which these technical means can be effectively co-ordinated. Up to the present the first of these functions has been the only one to be adequately developed. We are in a position to see fairly clearly the immediate prospects of the application of science to the technical means of production. Their development has not been nearly as rapid or effective as it would be in any rational economic system. The reasons for this have already been indicated; it remains only to give a brief sketch of realizable possibilities and of directions in which future advance may be expected.

Some general tendencies of productive industry are already evident. Predicting their future course for a short way is reasonably safe. (16) Common trends of all production processes are the following:— (1) Automatic working; (2) Increased control of processes; (3) Automatic registration of conditions and products ; (4) Continuity of processes; (5) Increased speed of operation; (6) Diminution of amount of goods at intermediate stages of production; (7) Simplification of processes; (8) Diminution of bulk and weight of machinery; (9) Rational and functional design; (10) Flexibility. (17) All of these are called for for economic reasons, all are work-saving and some, notably nos. 5-9, save working and fixed capital. All are made possible by recent technical and scientific advances. They are closely interrelated, though some, such as 5 and 7, may, but need not, be alternatives. All of them are hindered by other economic factors discussed in Chapter VI, and can only be fully co-ordinated and used in a rationally planned state. Their partial adoption under present conditions leads to speed-up, unemployment and economic insecurity. The general effect of their adoption in a rational state would be greatly to reduce the time taken in production, to shorten hours of work, to reduce the amount of necessary machinery and even more the space it occupies. One has only to think of an eighteenth-century eight-horse-power steam-engine occupying a two-storey engine-house and a thousa: 1 horse-power aeroplane engine which would fit inside its cylinder. The free development of machinery would paradoxically enough lead to its playing a far less conspicuous part in everyday life.

Integration of Industries in a Rational Society.—For practical purposes it is convenient to divide industrial production and distribution under the headings of: extractive industries; power production; the manufacture of forms, or mechanical and electrical engineering; the manufacture of substances, or chemical engineering; transport distribution, communication, and administration. These must no longer, however, be looked on, as we have so long been in the habit of doing, as separate trades run for profit, but interrelated parts of one organic whole. The purpose of the whole is to maintain social human life and to expand its possibilities. The relative developments of the different industries and their mutual relations must be considered only from this point of view. In the theory of the apologetic economists this must needs happen already, through the increased profitability of industries which are insufficiently developed and the ruin of superfluous industry. In fact, this does not happen. Production is held up where it is most needed by restriction schemes

CHART 2

This chart is an attempt to picture the technical side of the production and consumption process. It does not deal with the financial and economic aspects, *i.e.* it neglects activities concerned with banking, government, business administration, war, and also those of entertainment and religion. It attempts to represent, though in a merely qualitative way, the flow of commodities and services in an industrial society. It is divided into three levels. The top level is that of extractive industry, the obtaining of the primary raw materials, agricultural and mineral. The second level is that of intermediate production or heavy industry, the preparation of agricultural products, the manufacture of machinery and means of transport and electric power. The third level is that of final production of consumption goods, it includes light industry, transport and other services. Finally through distribution the stage of consumption is reached. The arrows are of three kinds. ⎯⎯⎯⟩ represents actual transport of materials. ⎯ ⎯ ⎯ ⎯⟩ represents the transfer of services such as transport. ⎯⎯⎯⎯⎯⟩ is restricted to the transfer of electrical power. Only the main transports of material or services are indicated, otherwise the diagram would become too complicated. It could be made quantitative by indicating by thickness of line or otherwise the quantity or value of the products passing in any given time between different parts of the system, but that is a task for the economist.

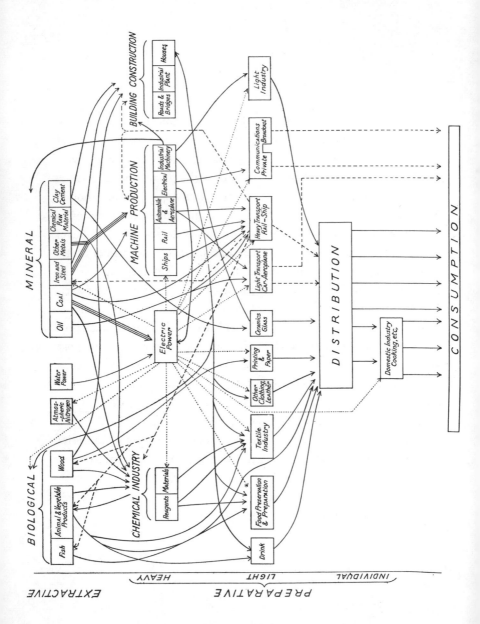

to keep up prices, and maintained where it is not needed by vested interests through Government subsidies. The structure of industry in a rational and humane society would be very different from the present one, and it would have a much greater flexibility and potentiality of development. The extractive and heavy industries would be relatively, and perhaps after some time absolutely, less important than they are at present. The chemical industry would increase and cover much of the fields at present occupied by agriculture and metallurgy; so would the light electric industry, wireless, television and automatic devices, etc. The structure of industry as it would be if rationalized on the basis of existing scientific and technical knowledge is shown in Chart II. What follows is an attempt to forecast the lines of immediate development in each industry.

MINING

The material basis of industrial production lies in the extractive industries, mining and quarrying. Here techniques are rapidly changing, and we may expect even greater changes in the future. The great days of coal, and possibly also of iron, have passed, but there will be no slackening in mining as a whole because of the increased demands for a far wider range of metals and minerals than earlier centuries were content with. Mining will increasingly tend to become mainly concerned with producing raw materials for a more generalized chemical industry. There is no lack of available supplies; the main difficulty about the extraction of mineral raw materials at the moment is not a technical one but a by-product of economic and national anarchy. A rational system of surveying the world for mineral resources, such as that practised over the smaller but comparable area of the Soviet Union, would certainly reveal vast quantities of unsuspected mineral resources; while a full exploitation of these with increasing chemical and physico-chemical methods of extraction would make it possible to provide metals, cements, and chemical raw materials at a cost far lower than those prevailing at present.

Supersession of Underground Work.—The whole technique of mining, however, is likely to undergo a fundamental revolution under the impetus of advances in chemistry and concern for human life and work. Up till now nearly all mining has consisted of cutting out rock and ore by hand or machinery from far below the ground, bringing it up and there processing it and extracting the valuable materials. The miner's work underground is harder and more dangerous than any other occupation; it is also extremely costly and cumbrous. (18) Now quite apart from improvements in mining machinery, which need not, as they do at present, increase the arduousness of the miner's work, there are a number of developments which would reduce the necessity for underground work and ultimately remove it altogether. There is first the possibility of bringing the needed material to the surface in liquid form, thus reducing mining operations to drilling and pumping as is already the case with oil, salt, and sulphur. By the use of suitable solvents injected into the veins it may be possible to extend this principle to metalliferous mining. As to coal, the idea of converting the seams by controlled fires underground into oil and gas has already been tried with some success in the Soviet Union. Refined methods of chemical extraction, flotation and dielectric separation, will make low-grade surface deposits more economic to work than deep mines. Open-cut mining is increasing very rapidly in the United States, thanks to the development of improved blasting and gigantic shovels. (19) This tendency will be further reinforced by the increasing utilization of the light metals, aluminium and magnesium, which are found near the surface or in liquid form. Finally, there is the more remote possibility that, by the use of specific chemicals made surface-active or attached to plastic filters, almost all elements can be extracted from sea-water at least as efficiently as is already done by those sea-animals which have copper or vanadium in their blood.

Smelting: the New Metals.—On the whole, the demand for mineral substances is bound to increase, though changes in utilization may lead to a diminished demand for some of them. That demand can be adjusted to the cost of production in the more favoured localities and thus avoid the ruinous uncertainties of alternate over-production and restriction of output. Up till very recently the older tradition of the mining and smelting industries has remained on an essentially pre-scientific basis, and the processes implied have been merely variations of those of the primitive miners and smelters of 4000 B.C. The application of science will tend to alter all this, to introduce in general lower temperature and consequently processes less wasteful of heat. The most important of these processes would be the low temperature production of iron, using methane or hydrogen instead of coke as a reducing agent. (20) Similar processes might short-circuit the cumbrous methods at present used for smelting sulphide ores. Electrical methods are also bound to be increasingly used. Already the manufacture of magnesium, the base for a whole series of light alloys, is an almost automatic sequence of chemical and electro-chemical operations in which the raw material, brine, enters the system at one end and the magnesium metal comes out at the other. The most important problem which still remains to be solved is the economic production of aluminium from clay or possibly from the scarcely less common laterite. It is often thought that the abundance of aluminium in nature should ensure its being the commonest and most useful metal, but even if the difficulties about its source were removed, the determining factor in cost would be the energy needed to separate it from its oxide. If this is supplied electrically it means that it cannot be less than three times the cost of separating iron by the use of coal directly, as the equivalent of this coal has to be turned into electric power. Unless some means of direct reduction is found, the price of aluminium is hardly likely to be less than five times that of iron, but as it is now about twenty times as much there is a good way to make up. (21)

At least as important as the extraction of metals is their rational use. Now that we are beginning to understand the structure of metals (see p. 336), the possibility is open to develop new metals or to combinations of metals with far more useful properties than any we now have. One great development is towards corrosion-proof metals ; if these could be perfected the great wastage of metals that now goes on could be checked and the danger of exhausting natural reserves of metals reduced. (22)

POWER PRODUCTION

Capital Saving.—The problem of power production has a large-scale and a small-scale aspect. There is the production and distribution of power in the undifferentiated form of electricity on a large scale, and that of the production of power by a large number of small-scale independent units, particularly for transport, *i.e.* motor-cars and aeroplanes, but also for hundreds of other detail uses. In the first case the main problem is that of working cost efficiency, and much scientific research has already been spent on improving this. For instance, in England in 1910, 1·8 tons of coal were used per thousand units of electricity, in 1934 only 0·7 tons. In the United States the average figure in 1937 was 1·43 tons, for the best plant it was 0·79 tons. The theoretical minimum for a 40 per cent. efficient heat engine would be 0·65 tons, so that nothing much more can be expected in the way of decreased working cost. The essential problem is far more one of social organization than of technical improvement. Even where, as in Britain, the evils of multiple and competitive electrical producers have been largely eliminated, the range of utilization of electricity is so variable that the average production only employs some 50 per cent. of the machinery which must be kept in existence to cope with peak demand. If electricity were internationalized these irregularities would largely be smoothed out, and if this were combined with lowered costs of transmission, which scientific research would probably provide if it were paid to do so, the working cost of electricity would be reduced to a figure so low that it might, almost without economic dislocation, be distributed free.

New Generators.—The capital cost of power production requires to be drastically reduced. An electrical power station is extremely economical in labour costs, being almost entirely automatic, but it does involve heavy capital expenditure. Science offers the possibility, through the development of modern vacuum techniques, of producing a small high-voltage, static-electrical machine to replace the cumbersome and heavy electromagnetic dynamo. This improvement would, however, be far more useful if at the same time the primary power producers could be replaced by others of a much smaller size working at higher speeds. The immediate problem for power engineers is the production of the gas turbine, held up largely through the difficulty of producing a material which would stand up to the stresses and temperatures involved. Beyond that lies the possibility of working at speeds sufficient to utilize the actual momentum and not the energies of the heated gas, and thus gaining a still further increase in efficiency and diminution of size. These considerations also apply to the problem of the detached small power unit where capital saving and effectiveness per pound weight both go together. The importance of capital saving is crucial because the accumulation of large and expensive machinery as a necessary adjunct to the production either of goods or other machinery is a limiting factor in economic development. On the whole, capitalist economy rather discourages than favours capital saving, though in doing so it brings its own nemesis in the shape of decreased returns on capital. A rational economy would strive to eliminate every unnecessary piece of material machinery as well as every unnecessary operation. We need to develop electric machinery that can work at full efficiency for all loads.

Power Storage.—Of greater importance is the need for some method of storing electrical energy as efficient as, but far less costly, heavy, bulky and inconvenient than our present accumulators. The solution of this may come from the study of dielectrics with extremely high dielectric constants such as some of the new plastics possess. Alternatively, an isothermal reversible chemical reaction with large energy charge may be discovered. There is a further possibility of developing thermal insulation in such a way as to preserve large masses of matter more or less indefinitely, either well above or well below ordinary temperatures, as available energy stores. Widespread use for various industrial purposes of liquid oxygen and liquid methane might make it possible to combine the storage of energy with the processes of production of important industrial products. The efficient storage of electricity would not only mean an enormous saving of capital in power production, but also serve to replace the small and very inefficient power units of cars and aeroplanes. (23)

The Application of Power.—Another aspect of the problem of power is the qualitative one. The form in which power is applied is obviously as important as the amount of power itself. So far we are still at the stage where rotary motion, whether of a prime mover or an electrical motor, has to be translated into whatever kinds of motion is required of cranks or screws. It would be much better if, for such operations as striking blows, producing sudden pulls, or setting in motion streams of liquid or gas, we had a means of quick production of pressure or tension, and could dispense with mechanical moving parts where fluid motion is concerned. The first problem involves either some electrical or fluid counterpart of the action of animal muscle. Existing methods, such as that of the pneumatic drill, are mechanically extremely inefficient. New developments of rational design of hydraulic machinery may overcome this difficulty (24), and there is reason to believe that the possibilities of working with variable frequency electrical currents would be another way of solving the problem of efficient reciprocal motion. This line has not been developed on account of the vested interest in older methods. A further possibility is even more fascinating, that of constructing some colloid system which could vary its tension with the application of electrical currents, but to do this we shall need to know a great deal more about the physico-chemical properties of muscle.

Hydrodynamics: Rocket Flight.—The solution of the second problem, that of fluid motion without moving parts, is in line with the whole trend towards a greater utilization of the possibilities of hydro-dynamics. We have already rumours of effective aeroplanes in which air, driven by an injector system without engines or propellers, is blown over the wings in order to produce the necessary air circulation for lift. Along similar lines is the modern development of rockets, first for the exploration of the upper atmosphere, but later with the view to space navigation. The difficulties are formidable at present, indeed almost insuperable, because we know no source of energy sufficiently concentrated to lift its own weight clear of the earth's gravitation field, and the only solution which has been suggested, but not tried, is a rather clumsy one of a series of step rockets of decreasing size. Nevertheless there are a number of serious engineers in many countries of the world who are attacking the problem, and there is no more reason to say it will not be solved than there would have been, at the beginning of the eighteenth century, to say man would never fly. (25) Ultimate developments in this direction may have to invoke new principles, and this is, of course, one of the main reasons why such apparently hopeless enterprises are always worth undertaking whether they succeed in their first object or not. If we find a practical way of producing directed molecular beams, or even better, beams of neutrons, the problem would be completely solved and we should have gained at the same time a generalized source of concentrated energy.

ENGINEERING

The profession of engineering has always been intimately connected with science. Many great scientists in the past, and in our days Dirac and Einstein, started as engineers, and the converse has been almost as frequent. Nevertheless, in many ways engineering remains a traditional rather than a scientific profession, and the possibilities of a wholesale application of science to engineering have not been seriously thought out or applied. There are signs, however, both in the U.S.A. and the Soviet Union, that this state of affairs is changing. The earlier engineering problems on the civil side were largely those of translating ancient techniques, such as road and bridge building, to new large-scale needs with new materials, and on the mechanical side those of imitating as closely as possible human operations which could be multiplied and speeded up by mechanical methods. As in the case of nearly all human traditions, old models were used long after they became rationally entirely unnecessary.

Rational Mechanism.—It is now possible to see that we have in engineering, particularly in machine construction, an independent set of possibilities which might be used scientifically instead of traditionally. Once the problem of what particular operation needs to be carried out is given, it should be possible to find that arrangement of moving parts which will be most economical to set up and work. A key to this may be offered by recent developments in the field of mathematics, particularly in calculating machines. The kind of equations which a calculating machine attempts to solve are essentially similar to those which occur in manufacturing processes. Such rationally designed machinery would actually turn out to be far less cumbersome and complicated than existing machinery. In practice these developments are forced on engineering whenever the necessity arises for the large-scale production of machines.

Intelligent Machinery.—But science has more to offer than this. The chief characteristic of older machinery was the rigidity of its action, which not only limited the availability of machines to deal with anything but stock products of more or less the same size and shape, but also necessitated the employment of a disproportionately large number of simple hand processes. Modern machinery should be able to deal not only with exactly repetitive processes but with roughly repetitive processes. This can be achieved by far greater use of the new sense organs and controls which science can offer, particularly the use of electrical devices such as the photo-electric cell to replace the eye of the machine minder. (26) A machine whose operation is both sensitive and flexible would be approaching perfect automatism. A further step would be made when the machine was arranged to be to a certain extent self-repairing, that is to say, able to detect, eject, and replace its own outworn parts. It would be wrong to suppose that such machinery would necessarily be so complicated as never to be economically operable. In the first place, if properly designed, the result would actually be greater simplicity; in the second, we must remember the present efficiency of machines has always to be balanced against cheap and monotonous hand labour, and that it is always wasteful to employ men and women at tasks which do not use their full potentialities; in the third place, planned development of industry would eliminate the danger of obsolescence which, under the present system, leads either to hasty construction and ruthless scrapping or to a conservatism completely failing to make use of existing potentialities.

Civil Engineering.—In civil engineering we may expect a large increase of scale of operations necessitated by the greater problems which will need to be tackled, and make possible the development of powerful machinery and new materials. With comprehensive planning of cities and the countryside, civil engineering and architecture will tend to merge again to the great advantage of both. We have as yet no rationally planned city, thought out from the very beginning in terms of the functions for which people will want to live and work there. Leonardo da Vinci planned such a city four hundred and fifty years ago, but till now we have had to get along with piecemeal alterations and additions to older centres. Buildings, roads, bridges and tunnels need to be worked together into one complete and co-ordinated circulation system (see also p. 350 *et seq.*). There are larger tasks for the civil engineer in moulding the earth's surface, in reclaiming land, in extending irrigation and water-power production, and in changing climate (see p. 379).

CHEMICAL INDUSTRY

In the course of time those industries devoted to the production of substances and materials have come to occupy a more and more important position in economy. At first, materials such as wood or clay were taken as found; later came those produced by simple and rough methods, such as metals or glass. Now we are beginning to see that those substances which are required for direct or biological consumption or as sources of energy, such as food, artificial manure, or coke, and those which are required for various mechanical properties, such as textiles, rubber, and paper, are both essentially the products of a chemical industry. In the future we may come to depend also for biological and industrial materials almost entirely on the chemical industry, which will then occupy a central position in economy. (27)

There is no need to insist on the close relation between the developments of science and those of chemical industry, but it is not sufficiently realized that the chemical industry is based on the science of the nineteenth century and that we have not yet begun to make use of the far greater theoretical and practical possibilities which the great quantum revolution of the twentieth century has brought to chemistry. Much of our heavy chemical industry is obsolete, but to bring it up to date would require a very different attitude towards the functions of the industry. What holds the chemical industry back is that it is only one part of a group of industries—textiles, paper, rubber, etc.—using chemical processes. If all chemical processes in all such industries as well as the chemical industry itself were under one control, and if, instead of supplying goods at intermediate stages for markets which exist by virtue of certain traditions, the system were considered as an organic whole, a larger number of intermediate processes and substances would be cut out with great economies of material and labour. For instance in 1932, out of a production of 800,000 tons of sulphuric acid, 163,000 tons were used for the production of ammonium sulphate which could be produced directly without the intermediate production of any sulphuric acid. (28) Unfortunately, the chemical industry in the world at present suffers under the uncomfortable handicap of maintaining an uneconomic structure in peace in order that it can be rapidly converted to the production of explosives and poison gas in war. It is consequently necessary to keep up a potential production of sulphuric acid for such purposes. As things are, waste of chemicals in industrial processes is encouraged rather than checked in order to keep up profits for the chemical industry.

Planning Substances for Needs.—With the chemical industry forming an integral part of a general industrial complex, it would be possible to depart from tradition and plan rationally for ultimate needs. Changes would come both in the materials used and the processes used for producing them. The final products of chemical industry are of two kinds: those required for their chemical properties, such as food, fuel, solvents, soap, and chemicals in the narrow sense; and materials required for their mechanical or thermal properties, such as glass and rubber. Of the first we can say that the future holds a possibility both of far greater variety and of increased availability or lower price. In the past the heavy chemical industry has concentrated on a few general chemicals produced in bulk, such as sulphuric acid or soda; the tendency is now to choose chemicals more suited for the particular tasks they have to fulfil, and this tendency would gain impetus both from new developments inside chemistry and from any more integrated chemical production.

Food Production.—The most striking developments may be expected in the catalytic production of complex substances, starting from the simplest raw materials of coal and air. In the future coal may become far more important as a raw material for the chemical industry than as a source of power or domestic heating. The use of high pressures in chemistry is only just beginning; it will enormously extend the range of possible products. The chemical production of food has already been touched on. Though technically possible it is unlikely that, except for war purposes, it will for a long time prove more economic or convenient than biological food production. Chemistry is, however, bound to come more and more into the food industry. Different stages of food preparation, storage, and cooking will be controlled chemically. This will mean an increasing trend in the chemical industry towards biochemical methods, which is bound to react on the rest of the industry and lead to an approximation under controlled conditions to the enzyme syntheses of living systems. Thus it may ultimately be possible to produce complex substances with flavours and nutritional properties superior to any nature provides.

Drugs.—Of particular importance is the synthetic production of drugs with high and specific biological activity, such as hormones, vitamins, and specific bactericides, to replace and extend the scope of those already drawn from plants and animals. These substances will be wanted in small quantities, it is true, but at a price sufficiently low to make them generally available. This will demand a very considerable reorganization of the fine chemical industry and a bringing it into closer relation with scientific developments both in chemistry and physiology. Our present pharmacopoeia is based essentially on traditional experience and magical theories of medicine. It needs to be replaced by a radically new one containing substances whose activities are thoroughly understood as the result of co-operative work of clinical and biochemical research. The use of the new drugs would, however, not only be medical in the strict sense, but also for the more deliberate control of physical and psychological states. Mankind has been too long tied to the universal drug alcohol; we could do with a range of non-habit-forming drugs for different emergencies or enjoyments.

Cosmetics.—The production of cosmetics and cleaning agents is a large and growing part of the chemical industry. At the moment it is a particularly unpleasant racket playing on vanity and snobbery with the least regard for the underlying physiology. It is certain that if chemical industry were adequately organized in the service of the consumer and not of profit, it would be possible to make people look clean and attractive at far less cost and trouble to themselves. In most cases it would be much more to the point to study and control the conditions of life leading to good complexions than to try to alter them from outside. To the degree that this is necessary it would be worth looking for and making substances more akin to natural skin products than the meagre and crude chemicals which are used at present. Soap is a typical example of a chemical which has been used substantially unchanged since the barbarian Germans reddened their hair with it to frighten their enemies. It cleans moderately well, but it mixes badly with most water, and it is much too rough in its action on the skin. We need instead some neutral, soluble, surface active substance, possibly of a sterol or bile acid type, which will do all that soap does without its disadvantages.

Wastes.—The chemical industry needs to concern itself with the disposal of waste as well as the production of new substances. This problem is becoming, with the increase of industry and the concentration of populations, one of increasing urgency. At present we are throwing away an appreciable proportion of consumable materials and doing so in a way which destroys the amenities of country and town alike. To a large extent this is a problem of social organization and control, but the chemical industry can provide the means of making the control effective and valuable. Smokes and noxious dusts and gases are some of the major sources of depression and ill-health in all urban districts. Most of them could be stopped at the source by the use of suitable fuels and preparative processes, and the rest could be collected electrically or otherwise. Such processes, though always from the point of view of the community, are productively efficient only for large units, and consequently the effect of prohibition of smoke and dust and gas emission would be to concentrate plants liable to produce them into large units. This would lead to further economies in the recovery of useful by-products. Almost as much corrosive sulphuric acid goes into the air with smoke as that produced by the whole of the chemical industry. The domestic fire is in England the chief offender. Only an extension of the use of smokeless fuel, pending a reorganization of housing and domestic heating, can remedy this nuisance. Other domestic waste is more important as loss than nuisance. The extension of the use of containers, metal tins, glass, and paper has added an almost intolerable burden to the already difficult service of disposal of animal and vegetable refuse. With good urban organization involving a certain amount of sorting, all these could be recovered or turned to good use in the chemical industry. Industrial waste and sewage presents an even more urgent problem. We are throwing away, and polluting rivers and sea in the process, essential elements such as phosphorus and complex and valuable chemicals. It would be possible by bio-chemical and bacterial control not only to make all of these innocuous as is done with some even now, but to recover the major portion in a utilizable form. It should be clear that the whole budget of in- and outgoing of industry, agriculture and human life requires to be subjected to an active chemical control. If this were done the result would be a manifold multiplication of goods without a comparable increase in primary production.

New Materials.—It is in the manufacture of new materials, however, that modern chemical industry can most strikingly show its effectiveness. Already we have, in artificial silk and plastics such as bakelite, materials which are successfully displacing natural pro-ducts; and this tendency may become more general. The advance in theoretical chemistry, particularly in structural and colloidal chemistry, will make it possible to plan the structures of materials according to desired properties, as direct a process as the planning of buildings or machinery. Materials can indeed be constructed, but the units are atoms and molecules and not blocks of already formed material. For any given purpose, either of direct human utility or for some process of industrial production, materials are needed with a certain combination of specific properties—lightness, strength, elasticity, toughness, hardness, thermal or electrical resistance or refractoriness. For one purpose one set of qualities will be required; for another purpose, another.

For the building of walls of houses, for instance, a material is wanted which combines a certain degree of strength, lightness, and thermal resistance. Up till now the combinations of natural or semi-manufactured products have been used for this—wood, cork, cellular bricks and cement, asbestos, etc. But none of these possesses all the desired properties at once. Already, however, on the laboratory scale materials having all these properties have been prepared. The aerogels, first made out of silica gel by removing the water without shrinking the gel and replacing it by air, are materials of lightness one-fiftieth of that of water, and of thermal **resistance** several times better than wool. (29) The problem of extending this manufacture economically on a large scale may yet take some years, but it is clear that in some such way the ideal materials for the walls and roofs of dwellings will be made (see also p. 351).

In a similar way the needs of modern horticulture and future agriculture require a material transparent both to visible and infrared rays and strong light, and cheap enough to enable large areas to be covered over. Such materials have already appeared in reinforced cellophane sheet and artificial rubber, still, however, too heavy and expensive to satisfy all these needs; but, again, research may lead to the overcoming of these difficulties, and the result would be to transform agriculture to the extent of making it practically independent of climatic conditions.

Up till now, for hard and refractory materials we have depended almost entirely on those provided by nature, such as the diamond and emery, but it is beginning to be clear from modern chemistry that there is a whole range of combinations of elements which have hardnesses and melting points far beyond any that the chance combinations of elements in the history of the earth have given us. Already we have in the tungsten-carbide-cobalt alloy (carboloy), a material which will work glass almost as easily as metal. The further extension of such materials would lead to a complete revolution in the practice of mechanical engineering.

New Processes.—These examples should be enough to show the beginnings of the possibilities that chemistry has to offer us in the way of new substances and new materials. Equally, if not more, important are the prospects of radically new processes in the chemical industry. So far chemical industry has mainly concerned itself with economy of material; it considers the yield of a product as a proportion of the raw materials which can be converted into the material required. It has paid a certain attention to the time of production as this represents waste of expensive plant, but relatively little to the energy economy. The earlier processes of chemistry, except where animal or plant products are concerned, as in tanning or brewing, were mostly carried out in furnaces, and even now a far greater number of chemical reactions than are necessary are carried out at high temperatures. The application of science to chemistry will lead to the replacement of these by low-temperature electro-chemical, catalytic, or enzyme reactions.

Chemical industry is more than almost any other dependent on the close interrelation of many processes, and thus the tendency towards monopoly has in this industry a more natural basis than in many others. But the combination of processes occurring in any chemical works is still left far too much to chance. A really scientific co-ordination of all chemical processes with the necessary flexibility to allow for new uses would result in still further economies of material and energy and consequently in the greater cheapness and availability of chemical reagents and materials.

TRANSPORT

The problems of transport are essentially more of a sociological and economic than of a purely scientific nature. Apart from travelling for pleasure, the total amount of transport required either of persons or goods is in part due to the localized nature of certain natural resources or opportunities for using them, but in a far larger degree to the sheer unplanned confusion of the economic system. An improvement of this would probably do more for transport than any technical improvements in vehicles and ships. Two factors enter into the economics of transport: the value of the waste of time while goods and persons are in transit, and the expenditure of energy required to move them from place to place.

So far the first of these has received the most attention. Speed has been developed regardless of economy of fuel and, indeed, to paradoxical lengths, so that motors are designed to be at their maximum efficiency at speeds which can practically never be attained on account of the poor construction of roads and the presence of other vehicles. It is not generally realized that the mechanical efficiency of a good motor-car is only 8 per cent. and that at least two-thirds of its price is taken up with inessentials such as fashionable, but useless, streamlining and advertising expenses. (30) Actually, if driving or being driven in cars were not felt to be a pleasure in itself, we should have to reckon the millions of man-hours spent in this occupation as pure waste.

Air Transport.—It should be possible from the passenger point of view to get rid of the disutility of transport either by making it extremely rapid or by arranging that the normal occupations of life could be carried on with perfect convenience while travelling, or both. The first method points to the further development of the aeroplane, but it is unlikely to be effective except for long distances. The possibilities of really high-speed travelling, *i.e.* at 300 m.p.h. or more, are difficult to realize lower than the stratosphere because of air resistance, and the stratosphere would, under good conditions, take at least an hour to reach. In any case the business of getting started and landing takes up time, so much so that a fast flight occupying less than half an hour would not be worth the saving of time. Matters would be changed, of course, once an effective, small and cheap autogyro or helicopter was invented, for here the greater flexibility and the possibility of starting and landing near the desired spot would make up for the very considerable loss of speed.

Comfort in Travel.—Turning to the second alternative, we find that the ship or the passenger train most nearly fulfils the requirement of enabling time to be spent usefully or pleasantly according to inclination. It should not be impossible to design motor-cars to make it equally so for the passengers. One of the greatest disadvantages of the motor-car is, however, that it is predominantly the machine for individual or small party transport, and that therefore the number of drivers is almost as large as the number of passengers. The distinction would vanish if motor-driving could be made automatic or semi-automatic. This might well be done for long distances, and indeed the tendency of providing two-track roads and signalling systems is already pointing in this direction. It would not be difficult to devise an electro-magnetic control for all cars using such roads, ensuring that they keep an adequate distance apart and draw out of line when passing, stopping, or turning. Such a device, if it could be made fool-proof, would eliminate the necessity of any driving except for pleasure, and might indeed, enable goods to be despatched from place to place without any drivers at all, the appropriate turning-points on the road being indicated on a punched card.

The most irritating form of travel at the moment is, however, not so much between towns as in them, and in particular the unavoidable business of the daily suburban migration. Here the anarchic development of a modern town and the occupations inside it have made the necessity of such a congestion that the speed of travel is reduced below the riding and, even in some cases, the walking rate of past times. With proper design of cities the necessity for a great part of urban and suburban transport would disappear, and it would be possible greatly to simplify the remainder by an orderly and methodically conceived plan. The solution to urban traffic problems lies probably in the direction of the increasing use of escalators and conveyors in the more congested central areas, and of non-stop trains with accelerating and decelerating platforms for the outer districts.

Goods Transport.—For goods transport, economy rather than speed is the major requirement, but the economy can be achieved as much or even more by the arrangement of production units to make transport unnecessary as by economies in the transport itself. With sufficient decentralization of industry the amount of goods required to be transported for long distances would only be such as could not be conveniently produced locally, that is, certain minerals or, more properly speaking, the finished objects made from them, and certain kinds of food products, *e.g.* tropical fruits. It will be a long time before, in these matters, land transport reaches anything like the efficiency of present-day ocean transport. This itself could be further improved by scientific design of ships and engines.

Further Possibilities.—All these transport possibilities are within immediate reach, but we may expect, if science is allowed to develop, far more revolutionary changes. Rocket propulsion may become the fastest and most efficient method of long-distance travel, that is for distances of two thousand miles or over, while any possibilities of wireless transmission of power would completely revolutionize air transport. At the same time, air transport would meet a serious rival if ground friction could be eliminated from land transport by supporting and propelling vehicles maintained just above but not in contact with the ground by such devices as alternating electro-magnetic fields. This was, in fact, done on a small scale more than twenty years ago, but the development of the aeroplane distracted attention from it and no attempts have been made to develop it further.

DISTRIBUTION

The nineteenth century saw the growth of manufacturing production beyond all previous bounds; the twentieth has seen the consequent development of distribution. It is not that actually very much more is consumed by individuals than in previous times, but as production has become localized or canalized by new methods of transport, everyone depends for most of his consumable goods on the system of distribution. In June 1937 2,700,000 insured workers were employed in distribution in Great Britain as against 7,700,000 in production. Yet this vast modern system of distribution has grown up in the most haphazard manner. Only in the case of fluid commodities such as water, gas, and electricity has it acquired any degree of rationality. The economies which science could bring into distribution would be far more on the economic than on the technical side, and could only be effective in a society where the whole of production and distribution were socially organized. Such economies would be very well worth while. At present there is very considerable waste of consumable commodities owing to failures in effective distribution.

Food.—Thus the value of food consumed per annum per family of population as estimated by a study of retail sales is £304·8, reasonably close to the desirable estimate of expenditure on food, £317; (31) and yet we know, from Sir John Orr's study among others, that half the population suffers from actual deficiency of food, and one-fifth is suffering from all-round malnutrition. A certain amount of food must be consumed by sheer overeating by the wealthy, as the prevalence of a number of diseases peculiar to them attests, but as there are not very many who can afford to do so and human appetites have limits, this cannot amount to very much. More is probably consumed advantageously by the middle class, since an optimum diet is certainly more than the minimum figures given. The greater part, however, of the food is almost certainly simply wasted and thrown away on account of our bad system of distribution and the lack of provision for buying food in sufficient quantities and of storing it. The distribution of food requires to be rationalized; as it is a primal necessity, this should clearly be done on a purely biological basis, each person receiving by legal right enough food of different kinds, with reasonable freedom of choice, to provide an optimum diet. On the more technical side the chief problems are those of biological engineering with respect to food, combining suitable means of production and rapid transport with methods of improving storage which do not damage the biological value of the food.

Commodities.—For other commodities where necessity plays a smaller part and choice a larger, we have to work out a system by which people can receive the most of what they want in a form that pleases them at the least cost to the community. In theory, this is what the system of private enterprise was supposed to do, but in fact it has palpably failed to do so and private enterprise is plainly leading to its own destruction in monopoly. It needs to be replaced by a conscious planning of needs, resources, and means. But this problem is a far larger one than that of distribution; it is merely an aspect of the foundation of a new civilization.

COMMUNICATION

As with transport, the problems of communication are far more social than technical. It is difficult to estimate the social utility of such inventions as the telegraph because it has been used, in fact, far more for the transmission of speculative business information and sensational news than for any socially constructive purpose. But whatever the origin and justification of these means of communication, we are clearly moving towards a state when the ability of every individual to communicate freely and immediately with any other in as complete a manner as possible is a definite and realizable goal. (32) We already have the institution of a television telephone service, and the immediate future development will be plainly towards cheapening this service and making it more accessible. At present communications are far too much tied up with governmental and monopoly interests to be able to render their full quota of convenience. The chief technical difficulty at the moment is at the transmitting end.

It should ideally be possible for everyone to carry his own portable transmitting set for private communications. If this were generally possible, it would seriously increase the liberty of individuals in disseminating information which might be considered undesirable by governments, and we are consequently likely to have to wait a considerable time before this side of communications is adequately organized.

The development of the more public forms of communications, cinema, radio and television, is bound to exert an increasing influence. Although their use for entertainment is not likely to diminish (see p. 358), they are likely to acquire, as they are perfected and become more common, other useful functions. Human co-operation in all fields will become independent of place and the possibility of forming groups with special interests scattered throughout the world become practicable, as has, indeed, been the case already for many years with radio amateurs.

Elimination of Drudgery.—Radically new methods of communication and recording will need to be developed to abolish the senseless drudgery of the shorthand writer, the typist, and the printer. Already we have photographically operating printing machines working from an ordinary typewriter keyboard, eliminating at once both the casting and setting of type. (33) Such machines can operate by wire or wireless and might, if combined with microfilm, enable material typed anywhere to be printed immediately, eliminating the compositor. A further stage which would eliminate the typist would be a vocally operated typewriter or some more direct vocal recording which may be easily read. Ultimately this may be simply ideography, which may be further developed to take the place of language and writing together. Communication from mind to mind may become possible, not through the mystic futilities of telepathy, but through an understanding and application of the electro-neurology of the brain. The communication of the future will mean far more than that between individuals. Even now the great bulk of communications are official rather than personal. Much of this official communication—advertisement, touting circulars—is parasitic, much is simply a reflection of an ill-organized economy. From the standpoint of a well-organized society practically all the money and business transactions of the present day come under this category. Even if these were removed, the increasing complexities of civilization would very soon raise the need for communication to the original level or above it. This would tend to become an intolerable burden on administrative workers, which can be eased only by an increase in automatism of working.

Automatism.—So far automatism has been limited to the mechanism of communication, such as the automatic telephone; it will need to be extended to the communications themselves. Machine must talk to machine without human intervention. Already something of the sort has been achieved in power production networks; it could be extended to all forms of productive industry. Thus with the production of a complex unit, such as a motor-car or a house, the total output would be communally determined, but once this was done the rate of output of each part, whether in the same or in a different factory, would be adjusted to that output. This is in line with the development of nervous control in the higher animals and man, where consciousness is reserved for the most difficult actions, while even such complicated ones as walking and digestion are dealt with by the lower centres of the brain.

Administration and Control

As the general framework of civilization becomes more complex, the importance of adequate administration and control becomes crucial. Anarchic private interests on the one hand or stupid bureaucracy on the other can destroy most of the potential value that might accrue from technical advances. We need to apply science to the field of administration or civilization will choke itself with its own products. Development is needed in two opposite senses, towards the simplification and automatism of routine and towards a much deeper understanding of direction and planning. The new devices already used in distribution and communications will be of immediate use in administration. Particularly valuable will be the handling of statistical material by card, film and electrical means which will make practicable the collection and use of the vast mass of facts without which any accurate forecasting and planning are impossible. Special care would, however, have to be taken to prevent this leading to a dangerous inflexibility and the domination of the machine. This danger can be avoided only by building up a school of practical sociologists able to understand the internal mechanisms that control the development of a complex society and at the same time by a general social education and training by which everyone in a greater or less degree understood and took active part in that development. One important problem that has to be faced by administrators under modern conditions is the choice of the best possible areas for different functions. (34) The development of transport and communications has made existing administrative areas entirely inadequate and indeed meaningless for such vital services as power distribution. On the one hand, this would indicate the necessity for centralized control of such services on a continental if not on a world basis. On the other, the producing of an increased number of commodities economically in all parts of the world and the waste at present occurring owing to unnecessary cross-transit of goods would indicate the need for considerable decentralization. There is no reason why these two should be incompatible, but the type of organization which would result from their combination would obviously be far more intricate than anything we have at present. If rationally planned, however, it need not be very complex. The existing complexity has arisen largely because a society has grown up, as has that of Western Europe and America, through a great revolution in technique without any radical changes of administration. It should be possible to have a flexible and rational system of administration which would secure economic efficiency and at the same time preserve and encourage the characteristics of national and local cultures.

GENERAL EFFECTS OF SCIENCE

Any general picture of the effects which science could have on the conditions of human life is necessarily difficult to make or to grasp. We see the possibilities of the future too much in the light of the present. If they merely follow existing trends, nothing appears to be changed; if they go much beyond them they produce an atmosphere of unreality. Yet detailed objections and apparent limitations should not blind us to the scope and importance of the function of science. It has two main directions, the removal of preventable human ills and the possibility of new activity of a socially satisfying kind. Of the first, this brief survey has given some picture. Lack of food, drudgery, much ill-health, science can remove; it can give opportunity for individual and social development. The second is more difficult to specify. For what positive things the men of the new society will use science, is for them to find and not for us. These things will be done both for their own sake and for the good which may come out of them.

Man's Major Tasks.—There are large tasks still for mankind to undertake—the ultimate conquest of space, of disease, and death, most of all of their own ways of living together. We get a kind of foretaste of this activity by the work of the Soviet Union in the conquest of the Arctic. With a fully organized world society such tasks could be pushed far further. It will no longer be a question of adapting man to the world but the world to man. For instance, the present Arctic with its wastes of tundra, glacier, and sea-ice is a legacy of the geological accident of the Ice Age. It will disappear in time, leaving the world a much pleasanter place, but there is no reason why man should not hasten the process. By an intelligent diversion of warm ocean-currents together with some means of colouring snow so that the sun could melt it, it might be possible to keep the Arctic ice-free for one summer, and that one year might tip the balance and permanently change the climate of the northern hemisphere. Similar major tasks are the utilization of the oceans, the deserts, and the internal heat of the earth. Beyond them stretch other tasks. If human society, or whatever emerges from it, is to escape complete destruction by inevitable geological or cosmological cataclysms, some means of escape from the earth must be found. The development of space navigation, however fanciful it may seem at present, is a necessary one for human survival, even though that necessity may lie a few million years ahead. Other necessary tasks which we cannot now imagine must lie before a developing humanity, and science will have its part to play in carrying them out.

The Fulfilment of Science or its Frustration.—The prospect of the new life and the new possibilities for action which science offers do not, however, any longer evoke the same enthusiasm as they did from the days of Friar Bacon to those of the early H. G. Wells. This reserve, common in literary and even in some scientific circles, arises in part from a disillusionment in the results of science up to now, in part from a failure to recognize the human and poetic elements in science, and in part from sheer inability to conceive of life lived much otherwise than it is to-day.

Given the present political and economic system, this reserve is completely justified. It is the very success of the industrial application of science in the past which has led us to the state where war and economic crises, far from being remote contingencies, are permanently with us. A further development of science in this direction, in the present economic structure, will make this conclusion more certain and more destructive. It is consequently not surprising that scientists themselves as well as the general public find it difficult to raise any enthusiasm for the industrial possibilities of science taken as a whole, though they do not object to some of the minor conveniences it brings. The possible application of science to industry serves only to emphasize the supreme illogicality of the present state of affairs. It shows that it is possible technically to arrange for life without most of the dangers and many of the inconveniences which now beset it, a life which would set men free to undertake new and unforeseen tasks. But in the light of these greater possibilities the present chaos and decadence of economic, social, and intellectual life stand out even more markedly than they do to those who only see the present in the light of the past. If once, however, we admit the possibility and indeed the necessity of an economic and political system capable of realizing these possibilities, this type of objection to the development and application of science no longer holds. Instead we must, in the interests not only of humanity but of science itself, strive to secure such a system.

The Rejection of Utopias.—There remains the other ground of objection based on the refusal to see a scientifically directed world as anything to strive for. At bottom this attitude is one of sentimental reaction, a longing for a simpler life without a realization of the miseries and hardships which that life entailed, and an idealization based on the condition of the more fortunate classes. Not unexpectedly it is a prevalent attitude in literary circles, expressed in such works as E. M. Forster's *The Machine Stops* or Aldous Huxley's *Brave New World*. It finds its justification, however, largely in the failure of the Utopian writers to present a humanly convincing or attractive picture. The Utopian writers, H. G. Wells not least of them, are as much the victims of present-day conditions as are their reactionary critics. Their pictures fail largely because they have no understanding of the social forces and merely project material and biological advance along present lines. Except for poetic visions innocent of anything but emotional detail, such as William Morris's *News from Nowhere*, all Utopias present two repulsive features: a lack of freedom consequent on perfect organization, and a corresponding lack of effort. To be a citizen of a modern Utopia, the critics feel, is to be well-cared for, regulated from birth to death, and never needing to do anything difficult or painful. The Utopian seems, notwithstanding his health, beauty, and affability, to partake too much of the robot and the prig. Fairly envisaged, it seems hardly worth while sacrificing much in the present if this is all the future has to offer.

A New Civilization: Freedom and Struggle.—It would, in any case, be difficult for anyone living in the present to accept personalities of a new civilization, but this is made more difficult by their essentially false presentation. The great change, of which we are now witnessing the first stages, between a social life based on traditional techniques and one based on science will certainly be reflected in an entirely different attitude towards freedom. The freedom of the nineteenth century was a seeming thing. It was an absence of a knowledge of necessity. Its basis lay in social relations through a market. In liberal theory every man should be free to do what he liked with his own, buy or sell, work or idle. In fact he was tied by the iron laws of economics: laws socially produced but taken as laws of nature because they were not understood (see p. 344). In an integrated and conscious society this conception of freedom is bound to be replaced by another—*freedom as the understanding of necessity*. Each man will be free in so far as he realizes that he is taking a conscious and determinate part in a common enterprise. This kind of freedom is most difficult for us to understand and appreciate ; indeed, it can only be appreciated to the full by living it. The terrible struggles and miseries of our time are largely due to the difficulty of man's learning his new powers. These are no less individual powers than before, but the individual will then express himself consciously with society, and not as at present unconsciously through it. Considering the magnitude of the tasks which humanity has before it, not least that of fitting human desires into such a new framework, it seems absurd to imagine Utopias in which men lead effortless and easy lives. Difficulties and strivings will be there as much as ever, but they will be of a different kind. At present men waste themselves in efforts against trivial and preventable evils. They struggle for primary necessities at a time when, technically speaking, these can be had for the asking. They are pulled down by preventable diseases and totally unnecessary social and family troubles. If these were removed it does not follow that life would be passed in easy and contented idleness. The energy liberated would be needed for the far more significant and difficult task of welding a really organic society.

Faith in Man.—The reason why people believe that a scientific world order is impossible, or that even if it were possible it would not be worth while, lies in a deep-seated lack of faith in humanity. The sceptics see the present state of the world and observe the apathy with which its sordid misery is accepted. What they do not realize is that this is the result of a systematic though unconscious degradation carried out by those who profit by it, to preserve an economic system which is of itself anachronistic and unstable. Nor do they appreciate the significance of the apparently hopeless yet undying struggle which is being waged against that system. The new world is not something imposed on humanity from without, it will be made by men, and the men who have made it and those who follow them will know what to do with it. The freedom and achievement which comes from action based on understanding is always growing though never complete. A Utopia is not a happy ecstatic state but the basis for further struggles and further conquests.

SCIENCE AND SOCIETY

We have spoken of science in its application both to the satisfaction of human needs and to the processes of productive industry through which in modern society those needs can be satisfied. These are not the only, though they are the most immediate, uses of science in society. So far science comes in them only as a means of satisfying desires in which science itself takes no part. Science appears as a slave to social forces foreign to itself; it appears as an external and uncomprehended force, useful but dangerous, holding a position in society like that of a captive workman at the court of some savage monarch. To a large extent this does represent the position of science in modern capitalist society, but if this were all we should have little to hope for either from science or from society. Fortunately science has a third and more important function. It is the chief agent of change in society; at first, unconsciously as technical change, paving the way to economic and social changes, and, latterly, as a more conscious and direct motive for social change itself. Up till now there has been little appreciation of this further rôle of science; the needs which people have sought to satisfy were either primary physiological demands for food and shelter or more indirect social satisfactions of power and prestige which could be obtained through the accumulation of wealth. It was in the process of satisfying these needs that science grew up, but with its growing up has come a wider realization of its function. It is no longer a question of finding means to satisfy the already formulated desires of those who are in a position to command science. We have now a wider picture of human society engaged in one task of which the outlines are already beginning to appear. How can all mankind best be maintained at a level of bodily efficiency and well-being, and how can we, once that minimum has been reached, secure the greatest possibilities for social and intellectual development? These are the crucial problems of our time. To solve them requires, in the first place, a wide extension of the field of science. No amount of physical or biological knowledge will suffice. The obstacles to the solution of the problem are not any longer mainly physical or biological obstacles; they are social obstacles. To cope with social obstacles it is first necessary to understand society. But society cannot be understood scientifically without at the same time changing it. The academic social sciences of the present day are useless for such a purpose; they need expansion and transformation. The science of society must grow up in contact with the social forces which are moulding it.

(1) See S. C. Gilfillan's article in *Technological Trends*, pp. 15 *et seq.*

(2) See Orr, *Food, Health—Income.* See also article in *What Science Stands For*; G. C. M. McGonigle and J. Kirby, *Poverty and Public Health*, 1936 ; League of Nations report on Nutrition ; and McNally, *Public Ill Health.*

(3) The changes that have occurred already are startling enough. It is estimated in *Technological Trends*, p. 99, that in 1787, 19 people on the land were needed to support one city dweller ; at present 19 people could support 66 city dwellers, although a certain number of these, probably about 6, are co-operating in production indirectly by making agricultural implements.

(4) The work of Professor Stapleton in turning heath and mountain into good pasture shows what research can do in this field.

(5) See *Technological Trends*, p. 111.

(6) See Crowther, *Soviet Science*.

(7) See *Technological Trends*, p. 114.

(8) Professor W. F. Gerike, " Crop Production without Soil," *Nature*, Vol. 141, p. 536.

(9) Microporite, a calcium hydrosilicate made by heating a mixture of lime and silica with steam, is a fine-pored material of apparent specific gravity between $0\cdot2—0\cdot5$. It can be made up in slabs and has already been used for houses. See *Industrial and Engineering Chemistry*, Vol. 27, p. 1019. Also *Architectural Record*, October 1936, p. 277.

(10) For the immediate prospects of prefabricated houses see *Technological Trends*, pp. 370 *et seq.*

(11) See *Technological Trends*, p. 371.

(12) Enid Charles, *Twilight of Parenthood* ; Hogben, *Political Arithmetic*.

(13) The gross reproduction rate for Italy in 1931 was $1\cdot57$, in 1936 it had dropped to $1\cdot40$. For Germany, the figures for the net reproduction rate are as follows : 1924, $0\cdot924$; 1929, $0\cdot818$; 1931, $0\cdot748$; 1934, $0\cdot86$; 1935, $0\cdot91$; 1936, $0\cdot93$.

(14) J. B. S. Haldane, *Heredity and Politics* ; Hogben, *Nature and Nurture*.

(15) Some of these are commented on by S. C. Gilfillan, *Technological Trends*, p. 25.

(16) *Technological Trends*, p. 15.

(17) *Technological Trends*, p. 24.

(18) It is estimated that in hand coal cutting in the U.S.A., the cost amounts to $7·50 per kilowatt hour of energy used, or 150 times its cost as electric current. *Technological Trends*, p. 152.

(19) *Technological Trends*, p. 151.

(20) See, however, *Technological Trends*, p. 358.

(21) See *Technological Trends*, p. 356.

(22) See *Technological Trends*, p. 346, for developments.

(23) It is not usually recognized that in a modern industrial country the aggregate available horse-power in small transport units is many times larger than that used for power production. In *Technological Trends*, p. 249, the following facts are given : If we make arbitrary and plausible assumptions about the utilization of this power by introducing load factors, we still find the actual power generated in car engines is far the greatest, as this power is generated at an average efficiency of not more than 5 per cent., this means that the overall average for efficiency of power production in the United States is only 9 per cent., which is a significant index of the enormous wastage of natural oil resources.

(24) A new type of pump (the Keelavite pump) has just been perfected, so well designed geometrically that it can work reversibly and so transmit power with an efficiency greater than 95 per cent. Owing to its small size and the possibility of using it for variable speeds it is already replacing electrical machinery in aeroplanes and ships. (See article in *The Engineer*, 17th December 1937.)

(25) It has been stated that Colonel Lindbergh is one of those who considers the development of rocket flight as something worth trying for.

(26) A list of 142 applications of the photoelectric cell are given in *Technological Trends*, p. 321 ; see also pp. 24 *et seq.*

(27) For the immediate prospects of the chemical industry see H. E. Howe's article in *Technological Trends*, p. 289.

(28) See *Britain without Capitalists*, pp. 303 *et seq.*

(29) S. S. Kistler, *J. Phys. Chem.*, 39, pp. 78-85, 1935.

(30) See *Tools of To-morrow*, Norton Leonard.

(31) Engineers' Study Group on Economics, *Interim Report on Food*.

(32) See *Technological Trends*, pp. 210 *et seq.*

(33) Already we have photographically operated printing machines working from an ordinary typewriter keyboard.

(34) See *Technological Trends*, p. 36.

CHAPTER XV

SCIENCE AND SOCIAL TRANSFORMATION

Social Conditions and Science

WE have now considered in turn the present structure of science, its possible modification, and the results which would flow from such a modification. It should be clear that if science is to be free adequately to serve society, changes are needed, and changes of a fairly drastic character. But to say that the changes are necessary is only a small, though essential, step in bringing those changes about. In this chapter we shall consider what the prospects of these changes are and what are the forces retarding them or driving them on. The problem is not one for science alone, or even primarily for science at all. As has already been shown, the proper functioning of an organization of science requires appropriate modifications made in the economic and political organization of society. Without such modifications, though small improvements in science can be introduced and certain abuses remedied, there can be no fundamental change in the present inefficient, wasteful and frustrating system.

How Science changes Society

The change of the system is therefore a necessity for science just as much as it is for society. In bringing it about the scientists have to play their part with other forces tending in the same direction. Science is predominantly a transforming and not a conserving influence, but the full effect of its action has yet to be seen. Science reacts on society unconsciously and indirectly through the technical changes it brings about, and directly and consciously through the force of its ideas. The acceptance of the ideas of science carries with it an implicit criticism of the present state of man and opens the possibility of its indefinite improvement. The developing and spreading of these ideas must be the work of the scientists themselves. But the carrying of them into action depends on social forces outside science. This process has been going on ever since the beginning of modern science but in a sporadic and uncoordinated way. The task of the future is to make the work of the scientist more conscious, more organized, and more effective; to create a proper appreciation of that work by the mass of the people and to link both together in a common effort to realize, in practice, the possibilities that science offers.

Influence on Productive Methods.—The indirect effect of science through its inexorable influence on productive methods is now, and is likely for long to remain, its most important form of influence. In this sense the difficulties with which the present world is faced are due to science and to science alone. Science does not create these difficulties directly, rather does it bring about a growth of technical possibilities in relation to which old economic and political institutions come more and more to act as cramping and distorting restrictions. The possibilities which science does offer can only be realized by creating a new ordered and integrated political and economic system on a world scale. For science to effect social change in this way it is not necessary that there should be any conscious intention on the part of scientists. It is through their work and not through their economic position, social knowledge, or political convictions that they prove so effective, and the force they exert is all the more inexorable because of its blindness. Only by stopping science altogether can its activity for social change be blocked. We are witnessing to-day a half-hearted and confused attempt at such a suppression of science. It is necessarily half-hearted because in our present society, although science is considered by those in power in most countries as an element creating social and economic disturbances which endanger their position, it remains a necessity in the pursuit of wealth and power in peace and victory in war. Attempts are made to discriminate between these two aspects, to suppress or to fail to encourage science except in so far as it ministers to these ends. It is the effect of these attempts, carried out without conscious purpose, that we recognize as the frustration of science.

Consciousness of Frustration.—In becoming conscious of this frustration the scientist is forced to inquire into the factors which control the development of science itself and to ask why it should be hampered and distorted in this way. For a long time individual scientists in many different fields have felt this in relation to their work. But it is not till now that this feeling is overstepping the boundaries of the particular sciences and is seen to reflect a universal state of affairs. The demand of the scientists that science should be allowed to develop and to be used for the benefit and not for the destruction of mankind is a force which, though not so powerful as the direct result of the scientists' work, is yet one to be reckoned with. For, unless it is met, the willing collaboration of the scientist in the present economic system will gradually be replaced by a grudging acquiescence, and finally by a blank refusal to co-operate, or a tacit sabotage. Meanwhile, on the other side, the popular forces will come to learn from the scientists how the benefits which science could bring are being denied to them by social forces over which neither scientists nor the people have as yet any control.

THE SCIENTIFIC WORKER OF TO-DAY

The success of this parallel development depends, however, not only on the circumstances of the time but on the position, the character, and the aims of scientists themselves. The growth of science in the last and the present centuries has, while multiplying the number of scientists, led at the same time to the production of a very different type from that of the founders of modern science. As science becomes a recognized part of human institutions, so the scientist tends to lose much of his originality and uniqueness, and to become more assimilated to the general group of professional men. Any examination of the possible part which science may play in social change must take this fact into account.

The scientist is no longer, if he ever was, a free agent. Almost universally he is now a salaried employee of the State, of an industrial firm, or of some semi-independent institution such as a university which itself depends directly or indirectly on the State or industry. Consequently the real liberty of the scientist is effectively limited, by his needs of livelihood, to actions which are tolerated by his paymasters. This is most clearly seen in relation to war and to the war preparations which are now taking a more and more important part in the work of science. Although many, if not most, scientists are opposed to the use of science for war, it is extremely rarely that a scientist refuses to do this kind of work. He knows too well if he does he stands to lose his position, and someone else will be only too willing to take it.

Economic Dependence.—The scientist is held economically in a double way. It is not only, possibly not even mainly, that his personal livelihood depends in the long run on his pleasing his employers, but that, as a scientist, he must have scope for the work which is often the mainspring of his life. To get that scope—the opportunities for research, the funds for apparatus and assistants—it is not enough not to displease the authorities who have money to dispose of; he must contrive positively to please them. The situation of the teaching scientist is just as bad; he himself may be secure from economic pressure, but he has to consider the livelihood of his students, and he does not wish to see them discriminated against for coming from a school or institute where advanced views are prevalent. To the effects of this economic pressure must be added those of a more or less consciously operated selection which gives a definite differential advantage, particularly for senior positions, to those of generally conforming views.

The Tendency to Conform.—At least as important as these direct economic factors are the unconscious all-pervasive effects of social environment. The selection and upbringing of scientists do, as we have seen, help very materially to modify the scientist's character in a direction of general conformity. The predominating selection from middle-class families in itself leads to acceptance of the present state of affairs and sets a tone which inevitably influences in the same direction those coming from working-class families. The scientist, outside his work, is generally no different from his fellows. Whatever his social origin, his work will bring him among professional men of the middle classes, and he will tend in the main to conform with their attitude and point of view. This was not so in the earlier stages of science when the scientist was a rare bird and was expected to be eccentric in his opinions and general behaviour. The mass development of science has brought into its field large numbers of people whose main concern is to appear as much like business men or gentlemen as they can. This applies particularly to scientists of working-class origin, who, in the present educational system, have had a very hard struggle and consequently cannot afford, as can scientists of independent means, to appear different from the people they work among and have to get on with. There is no conscious pressure, only a general atmosphere of conformity to accepted standards.

" The typical member of the Association of Scientific Workers to my mind is a very ordinary individual who works in some great concern and finds grains of truth such as the best percentage of nickel to put in steel for motor-bus springs, or a better way of getting an uncontaminated culture from a throat suspected of diphtheria. He has a science degree which cost him a lot of money and hard work, a wife and children at Balham, and a salary of £5 a week terminable at a month's notice. He sees other men in the same organization with no other qualifications but a glib tongue and a natty suiting getting twice his salary as salesmen. He isn't allowed to publish the results of his work, but if he does happen to light on a real nugget of truth it is quite probable that the head of his department will contrive to get all the credit for it—and the money that goes with it.

This man is typical of the 'multitude' that ought to be in the A.S.W. I know lots of them personally. Their main object in life is the same as yours and mine. They want to earn enough to live in comfort, to put by a little against old age or illness, to have a little spare time and cash to cultivate their minds by travel and pursuing uncommercial knowledge, to educate their children so that they will be at least as well equipped to do the same in their turn, and above all they want to get rid of the constantly haunting fear of getting a month's notice and being out of a job for a year.

These men are in a scientific job because they like scientific work. Their work is a pleasure in itself, but the reason they are in a job at all, doing what they are told to do and not what they want to do, keeping to a specified road and not turning up by-ways where they think they might make great discoveries which would put them in the Royal Society—the reason why they are working in such a job is that it is their means of livelihood.

They don't want to participate in the Councils of State. If they want to promulgate scientific facts, it is because they observe that those who do so obtain benefits of one sort or another thereby. If they want to inculcate reverence for science it is because it would lead to increased respect and better jobs for themselves."

Letter from "London Member," in *Scientific Worker*, Vol. ix, No. 5, January, 1937.

The Scientific Bent.—This attitude of general conformity is actually reinforced by many of the characteristic qualities which determine people to enter the scientific career. The scientist is still, though less often and less markedly than in previous times, a person of definite psychological abnormality. He is driven to satisfy his curiosity for its own sake, and, in order to be free to do this, he is willing to fit into any kind of life which will offer the least mental and material disturbance to what is his main concern. Besides this science itself is an eminently satisfactory occupation; its pursuit withdraws interest from external things, and offers as well a means of solace and escape for those who find the events of the outside world distressing. The great bulk of scientists are therefore, as long as their science is not threatened, likely to be the most docile and amenable of citizens. If the capitalist system could manage without war or Fascism it could safely count on the continued support of the rank and file of scientific workers, and even on many of the greatest scientists of the time.

Science and Religion.—The conformist tendencies of scientists in recent times are well exemplified by the development of the relations between science and religion. It is not a hundred years since the struggle between science and religion was the central conflict of the intellectual world. A scientist was practically synonymous with an atheist, or at least an agnostic. Now we are assured, on both sides, that the struggle between religion and science has been resolved by discovering there is nothing incompatible between the two, while eminent scientists vie with bishops in supporting mystical views of the universe and of human life. The difference is not in the least due to the invalidation of the arguments used in the earlier controversies, but rather to the fact that in the middle of the nineteenth century religion was really trying to interfere with the growing sciences of biology and geology. The scientist did not wish to be thought irreligious, but he was then faced with the awkward choice of appearing so or denying the plain meaning of his work. The moment that denial was no longer formally demanded of him the scientist of the later period was only too willing to return to religion and, with it, to general social conformity. The change was particularly marked after the Russian Revolution because it was then that the importance of religion as a counter-revolutionary force was again fully appreciated. The same state of affairs had occurred at an earlier period, at the end of the eighteenth century. At that time science and deism of the Voltairian type were closely, and it seemed inevitably, associated. When, however, the French Revolution showed that deism was definitely dangerous for the existing order of things, science for a while fell under the same ban, which was not lifted until it was found possible in the early part of the nineteenth century to combine a science which knew its place with proper attachment to Church and King.

Narrowness of Vision.—The relations between science and religion show most conclusively how overriding are the effects of the social environment on the direct intellectual results of the scientist's own work. The social environment is emotional, whereas science has been carefully purged of emotional factors. The social environment has been all-pervasive, whereas science is highly specialized. These advantages were enhanced by the development of the idea of pure science in the nineteenth century. Scientific education and tradition, by insisting on technical competence through specialization and repudiating any organic connection between science and society, made science itself appear to the scientist as a narrow doctrine quite incapable of satisfying his general human needs. For this he had recourse to every form of contemporary influence unconnected with science: religion, mysticism, idealistic philosophy, or aesthetics. None of these could easily be reconciled with their science, and the habit grew up of dividing the mind into water-tight compartments. This attitude, exemplified extremely clearly in the lives of the great nineteenth-century scientists, stands in striking contrast to the seventeenth-century habit of extending science into the political, philosophical, and religious spheres. Galileo's theological and Dr. Priestley's political interests stand in sharp contrast to the Sandemanian religiosity of Faraday or the spiritualism of Crookes. Its effect was not only to break the links between the scientist and social movements but also to react on science, impoverishing it through specialization and the lack of philosophic breadth.

The Gerontocracy of Science.—The influences we have already mentioned are those operating on individual scientists, but in considering the social influence of science as a whole that of its organization must be taken into account. Here there exists a factor which militates strongly against any positive reaction of scientists to social forces. As science has grown in numbers and influence its control has increasingly fallen into the hands of groups of older scientists. This gerontocracy is, at the present moment, the greatest factor in holding up the advance of science. The way in which it works has been discussed in previous chapters. It is at present a self-perpetuating and indeed a self-intensifying system, and is becoming more and more closely linked with government and high finance. The very fact that science is growing rapidly both in numbers of workers and in increasing intrinsic complexity makes the hold of the older men more complete, and at the same time makes them necessarily less competent to understand the workings of the machine they control. The positive factors pushing science forward have so far overcome these retarding influences. If, however, the pressure is not maintained and intensified, it is certain that, sooner or later, the effects of gerontocracy, in our civilization as in that of Greece and Rome, will be to turn science into pedantry with an undue respect for authority and for the greatness of the past. The democratization and the rejuvenation of the control of science is an essential condition for its survival.

THE SCIENTIST AS CITIZEN

Fortunately the influences retarding the development of the social consciousness of scientists are not the only ones ; nor are they increasing as rapidly as counteracting influences. The increasing assimilation of science as a part of the normal administration of a modern state has, as we have pointed out, decreased the independent, critical attitude of the scientist. But it has, at the same time, brought him into much closer contact with the problems which affect the ordinary citizen. This applies particularly to what might be called the rank and file of scientists and to that very important section of them, the junior scientists. Most of the advantages which a commercial civilization gives to science accrue to the senior scientists and not to very many of them. It is true that the hope of becoming one of the fortunate few exerts a powerful influence on the remainder. (1) But with increasing numbers it is becoming plainer and plainer to the majority that their expectations in this respect are very poor, and they are tending, in common with the great mass of administrative and clerical workers, to concentrate more on the improvement of their actual conditions.

The Impact of Events.—These direct considerations of conditions and status would by themselves lead only to a very slow development of scientific professional consciousness, but they are reinforced by others derived from the changes and instabilities in political and economic spheres. Left to himself the scientist would probably prove a more docile and conforming individual than a member of almost any other profession—but he is not left to himself. Violent events from the outside world come to disturb his serenity and force him to consider more seriously than ever before his position and function in society. Of these events the four most important of recent years have been the economic crisis, the building up of the Soviet Union, the advent of Fascism in Germany, and the universal intensification of preparations for war.

The Crisis.—It is beginning to be realized that the rate of modern industrialization has now become great enough to warrant our considering this present age as a second industrial revolution, and that in this industrial revolution science is playing a much larger and more conscious part than in the first. The possibilities of applied science are now much more directly visible. Further, it is becoming obvious, to scientists at least, that a world of plenty and leisure is technically possible now and not merely in a rather indefinite future. It was the example of the U.S.A. in the first place that led to the recognition of the importance of technical change, and it is appropriate that there the recognition achieved its most typical though brief embodiment in the doctrine of Technocracy. Actually, however, it was not until the slump that the real significance of this potentiality was brought home by the violent contrast of economic regression and technical advance. The older prophets of science down to H. G. Wells had taken economic and technical advance altogether for granted. Now it appeared that violent economic oscillations could interfere drastically with the human value of technical advance and not only threaten to check that advance but even turn its achievements to anti-social ends, particularly in mass unemployment and war. It was clear that the march of invention was not enough; something had to be done with the economic system.

The Five-Year Plan.—While these questions were being asked answers to them were in process of being set out in the Soviet Union. The putting forward of the first Five-Year Plan in its full comprehensiveness attracted many minds disappointed with the muddled competitiveness of economic development in other countries. But it was its practical success at the very depth of the world slump that began to convince the more practical-minded. It was clear that the obstacles which Russian planning had to face and which it successfully overcame were mainly technical, due to lack of material and trained workers rather than economic, as in all other countries.

At once the idea of planned production began to appeal, and .the planners were added to the technocrats in one of the hopeful though brief-lived movements of the depression. Theirs was an attempt to imitate the success of the Soviet Union without facing the implications of the economic changes which made that success possible. But it had an appeal, particularly to scientists, because it pointed to a way in which the incredible muddle and confusion of present-day application of science could be overcome.

Marxism and the History of Science.—Soviet influence also worked in other ways. The organization of science in the Soviet Union and the relatively vast sums of money spent for its development and for scientific education showed the world that at last there was one State where the proper function of science was being realized, a fact which was admitted even by those who were most conscious of the actual shortcomings and backwardness of Soviet science. At the same time, curious minds in other countries wished to know more about the ideas which led to this rational use of science, and discovered, effectively for the first time, the theoretical groundwork of the dialectic materialism of Marx which had lain unrecognized in Western Europe for half a century. In England, interest in dialectical materialism dates effectively from the world congress on the history of science in 1931, which was attended by a strong Russian delegation, who showed what a wealth of new ideas and points of view for understanding the history, the social function, and the working of science could be and were being produced by the application to science of Marxist theory. (2) About the same time similar interests revived in the U.S.A. and France and in many other countries, particularly in Japan.

The Coming of Fascism.—The third, and in some ways the most decisive, factor in widening the outlook of the scientist was the advent of Fascism. Until Fascism appeared, or more strictly until it appeared at the very centre of scientific thought in Germany, the social functions of science were considered rather as ideals than necessities. Many scientists thought that it would be nice if science were used for human welfare and were properly organized and endowed, but the majority doubted whether this desirable end was worth taking any serious trouble about. It might be just as well to carry on and make the best of the present state of affairs; after all, even if science was not very well treated, it was at least left alone. Hitler's advent changed all that. The expulsion of Jewish and liberal scientists abruptly reminded even the most complacent and well-placed scientists in other countries that they could no longer count on personal immunity, and that science itself was endangered, while it was quite clear that the Nazi transformation of the State implied the transformation of science into something quite un-recognizable. Biological and sociological sciences were being distorted to fit the race theories which were the basis of the party's propaganda, and the rest of science was being ruthlessly controlled in the interest of war preparations and war economy (see pp. 212 *et seq.*).

The Scientists' Reaction.—The reaction to Fascism on the part of scientists in England was unexpectedly varied. Only a very few found themselves in sympathy with Nazi theory, and these were the people who had already very definite views on race and on the value of war as a biological pruning-hook. Others, while they deprecated the Nazis' attack on science, and particularly their anti-semitic policy, felt that the reaction to it should be limited to the assistance of its victims. Far from realizing that the situation required a positive action on the part of scientists against Fascism, they considered that the lesson of Germany was that scientists should meddle even less than before in political and social matters. The immunity of the scientist to political persecution depended, they thought, on his political neutrality. As Professor A. V. Hill stated in a letter to *Nature*:

"If scientific people are to be accorded the privilege of immunity and tolerance by civilized societies, however, they must observe the rules. These rules could not be better summarized than they were 270 years ago by Robert Hooke. Among Hooke's papers in the British Museum, Weld records a statement, dated 1663, which was probably drawn up after the passing of the Second Charter of the Royal Society. It begins as follows:

'The business and design of the Royal Society is—To improve the knowledge of naturall things, and all useful Arts, Manufactures, Mechanick practises, Engynes and Inventions by Experiments—(not meddling with Divinity, Metaphysics, Moralls, Politicks, Grammar, Rhetorick or Logick),' and continues:

'All to advance the glory of God, the honour of the King . . ., the benefit of his Kingdom, and the generall good of mankind.'

Not meddling with morals or politics: such, I would urge, is the normal condition of tolerance and immunity for scientific pursuits in a civilized State. I speak not with contempt of these—indeed the scorn with which some superior people talk of such necessities of social existence as morals and politics seems to me intolerably childish and stupid. The best intel-lects and characters, not the worst, are wanted for the moral teachers and political governors of mankind: but science should remain aloof and de-tached, not from any sense of superiority, not from any indifference to the common welfare, but as a condition of complete intellectual honesty. Emotion, entirely necessary in ordinary life, is utterly out of place in making scientific decisions. If science loses its intellectual honesty and its political independence, if—under Communism or Fascism—it becomes tied to emotion, to propaganda, to advertisement, to particular social or economic theories, it will cease altogether to have its general appeal, and its political immunity will be lost. If science is to continue to make progress, it must insist on keeping its traditional position of independence, it must refuse to meddle with, or to be dominated by, divinity, morals, politics or rhetoric."—*Nature*, pp. 132, 952 [1933]. (3)

In xtreme cases this led to an even more definite withdrawal from any socio-political activity. One world-famous scientist remarked, when asked to join in some form of political protest, "I do not know anything about politics and I do not want to know anything about politics, because if I keep out of it I do not see how they can do anything to me." With others, however, including many of the most active as well as the younger scientists, the effect has been very different. It has led to a far greater interest in political questions and to the insistence that the scientists must take up a position for or against Fascism. As Professor Blackett says in his broadcast, afterwards reprinted in *The Frustration of Science*:

"Unless society can use science, it must turn anti-scientific, and that means giving up the hope of the progress that is possible. This is the way that Capitalism is now taking, and it leads to Fascism. The other way is complete Socialist planning on a large scale; this would be a planning for the maximum possible output and not a planned restriction of output. I believe that there are only these two ways. You are now being told—and in the next few years you will be told again a thousand times—that there is a third way, neither Socialism nor Capitalism, but something called a planned economy, which will benefit everyone equally. You will be told, for instance, that unemployment insurance and housing policy should be taken out of politics and treated objectively, scientifically. As if such questions are not the very essence of politics! If sacrifices are to be made, there will be 'equality of sacrifice.' The divergent interests of rich and poor will be obscured by an appeal to emotional nationalism and an emphasis on service and national discipline. All these trends are clear enough in this country, though their full expression is to be found in Italy and Germany. I do not think, therefore, that Fascism is something peculiar to the Italian or the German temperament, nor even that it is the peculiar creation of two vivid personalities; but I do think it is the logical end of a policy which meets the world crises of Capitalism by restriction of output, by economic nationalism, and by lowering the standard of life of the working-class. And we in this country seem to be meeting the world crises by the same methods.

Can this way succeed? I believe not. I believe that this retrograde movement will provide no solution. Consider, for instance, what happens when, in the interest of the small man, a large concern is split up into smaller concerns, and machinery is displaced by hand labour. Then all the economic forces inherent in Capitalism that have caused combination and the introduction of machinery in the past will act so as to do so again.

Capitalism cannot save itself by going back to the conditions out of which it is just emerging.   I do not think, as a matter of fact, that the industrial leaders in Germany and Italy for a moment believe it can.   They may tolerate or even encourage a popular campaign against machinery and in favour of the small workshop against the factory.   For they need desperately the political support of the middle classes, and they must pay a price for this support.   But big business knows perfectly well that machinery is necessary to them.   Much more will be said against machinery than actually done.   Whatever the actual measures against science and machines, the atmosphere created is certain to be disastrous not only to science but to all attempts at objective intellectual activity.   The hopes of the middle classes from Fascism are bound to be disappointed.   Some day they will find they have been duped.   They think they are getting something new, neither Capitalism nor Socialism, but in fact it is Capitalism that they are getting.   For Fascism is certainly Capitalism in the two Fascist countries to-day.   When I wrote this first there were only two openly Fascist countries.   Now I am losing count.   And it is odd, and also very significant, that behind the facade of help for the small man set up by Fascism is apparently going on a particularly rapid elimination of the small man.   This is occurring, in Fascist states as elsewhere, by the inherent force of Capitalism.   The huge bankruptcy statistics of Italy in 1932 do not suggest that Fascism can really save the small business. . . .

I believe that there are only two ways to go, and the way we now seem to be starting leads to Fascism; with it comes restriction of output, a lowering of the standard of life of the working-classes, and a renunciation of scientific progress.   I believe that the only other way is complete Socialism.   Socialism will want all the science it can get to produce the greatest possible wealth.   Scientists have not perhaps very long to make up their minds on which side they stand " (pp. 139-144).

Nor has this attitude limited itself to words.   Robert Merriman, a distinguished American scientist, has already given his life for the defence of democracy in Spain, and scientists and medical men of all nations are in their professional capacities doing what they can to help.

Preparation for War.—The final influence which is more and more impressing on the scientists the necessity for a social orientation is the increasing preparation for war.   The difference between the very depressed state of scientific research in 1932 and its present relatively flourishing condition cannot fail to appear to be associated with the increased rapidity of war preparations.   The scientists are being brought more and more into such preparations, either indirectly in the assisting of industries such as the steel and chemical industries, largely concerned in the production of armaments, or directly in the Government Departments concerned with defence.   This is most notably the case in the seeking of scientific collaboration for air-raid precautions which is going on at a rapidly increasing rate in Britain.   Chemists and doctors, particularly, are being recruited and allotted to important functions in local defence schemes. Already the first stage of the conscription of science has been reached with the setting up in the universities of a technical officers reserve. (4)

It becomes no longer possible for the scientist to remain outside; he has to decide whether or not to collaborate with such schemes and, if he is to collaborate, on what terms. Here again a large number are inclined to take the path of least resistance, to accept official pronouncements, and to volunteer their assistance. A determined minority, however, and a much greater one than in the late War, has already taken a completely pacifist attitude and refuses to have anything to do with these war preparations. The remainder are in the process of making up their minds, and inclined to be critical both of the politics and of the nature of the technical preparation of their Governments. There is undoubtedly a strong and growing feeling that war represents a definite perversion of science; but there is also the greatest diversity of opinion on how war can be prevented and what part the scientists must play in this task. In this connection the activities of the Science Commission of the International Peace Campaign (already referred to, p. 186) are significant of the desire of scientists to connect themselves as such with wider popular peace movements.

Social Consciousness

The cumulative effect of these influences is to make all scientists to a certain extent, and many of them acutely, aware of the relation between their work and livelihood and political and economic factors they had hitherto considered to be altogether outside the sphere of science. It has led to the realization among a large and growing number of scientists that the work of science does not end in the laboratory; that the scientist needs to be concerned immediately with the conditions under which he and his fellow scientists are working and ultimately with the state of society which will permit science to continue to exist. It is only on an extremely short-range view that any scientist can at present be completely satisfied in carrying out his work. Even if he has no desire to see that work developed and turned to a beneficent end, he must at least realize that the possibility of continuing it or passing it on in the tradition of science depends on the continued existence of that tradition, and hence on the development of society and not on its degradation by Fascism or war. To some it may seem that the needs of social preservation are at the moment even greater than those of discovery. To the majority, however, scientific work will be, and must needs be, the chief concern until the laboratories are blown up or shut down and the workers drafted off to war service or to prison. However, it does

not follow that the contribution towards the greater social problem
need be a negligible one.

The Scientist as Ruler?—The issue between the progressive and
retarding forces in the development of science and in its relation to
society is only part of the issue of the major social struggle of our
times, but in so far as it does depend on scientists it wil require an
activity among them both greater than and of a different character from
that which has hitherto existed. The solution that is most often and
most persuasively put forward, from Plato to H. G. Wells, has been
the ideal one of placing the management of affairs, in general, in the
hands of the philosophers or scientists. Unfortunately, it suffers from
two radical objections: first, that no one can think of any way of
transferring control into their hands; and, second, that most existing
scientists are manifestly totally unfitted to exercise such control. The
reluctance of democracies to choose people who appear, at least to
themselves, so eminently suitable for controlling the community
has led most of the proposers of these schemes to turn to authoritarian
or, in modern language, Fascist solutions. But in Fascist states it
happens that the scientists are used merely as tools for war preparation
and propaganda. Nevertheless, though we may dismiss as fantasy
the prospect of the scientist ruler, the scientist will certainly have a
large and critically important part to play in the formation and
development of the social organization of the future.

THE ORGANIZATION OF SCIENTISTS

The first and most immediate problem is to find the way in which
the scientist can act now so as to contribute most effectively to the
preservation of science against the forces which threaten it. As an
individual he has no less but no greater influence than any other
citizen; only by combination among scientists can the social importance of science make itself felt. But mere combination in itself is
not enough. The technical importance of science, great as it is, is
not sufficient to give even united scientists any serious political
influence, as long as they stand alone. This can only be achieved
if scientists, through their organizations, can combine with other
groups having the same goal of social progress.

The history of the development of associations among scientists
is a long one, and these associations in different periods have had very
different characters. The early associations, such as the Royal
Society in the seventeenth and the Lunar Society of the late eighteenth
century, existed for the double purpose of collecting together previously
isolated scientists for mutual assistance in the pursuit of science and of

impressing on the powers, whether governmental or commercial, the practical importance of science. Since then these functions have been split, the first remaining the *raison d'être* of the innumerable learned societies, the second becoming the function of semi-popular bodies such as the British or the American Association for the Advancement of Science. To these has since been added a third type of association of a professional character similar to that already existing among lawyers and doctors, such as the Institutes of Chemistry and Physics.

The Recognition of Social Responsibility.—Until recently, none of these bodies occupied themselves with the social effects of science. In the last few years, however, a marked change has taken place. "Science and Social Welfare" was the theme of the British Association at Blackpool in 1936. A suggestion was put forward by Mr. Ritchie Calder of a world union of scientists for the defence of peace and intellectual liberty, and for the most effective utilization of science for human welfare. (5) This suggestion was not taken up at once, but next year it received important support in the United States. The council of the American Association for the Advancement of Science at its meeting in 1937 passed the following resolution:

" Whereas, Science and its applications are not only transforming the physical and mental environment of men, but are adding greatly to the complexities of the social, economic and political relations among them; and

Whereas, Science is wholly independent of national boundaries and races and creeds and can flourish permanently only where there is peace and intellectual freedom; now, therefore be it

Resolved by the council on this thirtieth day of December, 1937, that the American Association for the Advancement of Science makes as one of its objectives an examination of the profound effects of science upon society; and that the Association extends to its prototype, the British Association for the Advancement of Science, and to all other scientific organizations with similar aims throughout the world, an invitation to co-operate, not only in advancing the interests of science, but also in promoting peace among nations and intellectual freedom in order that science may continue to advance and spread more abundantly its benefits to all mankind."

Meanwhile similar developments were taking place in another quarter. The International Council of Scientific Unions at its meeting in 1937 at the instance of the Academy of Sciences of Amsterdam arranged for the formation of an international Committee on Science and its Social Relations (C.S.S.R.). This was to be essentially a fact-finding body under the auspices of such bodies as the Royal Society and other scientific academies. It was felt that without a wider interest among scientists this work would proceed slowly, consequently the proposal was put forward in *Nature* (6) that a society for the study of the social relations of science should be founded.   This proposal was supported by many representative scientists in Britain. It resulted in the foundation, not of a separate organization, but of a special division of the British Association for the study of the Social and International Relations of Science, which was definitely incorporated at the Cambridge meeting of 1938.

Associations of Scientific Workers.—All these bodies are, however, essentially limited to research and discussion.   They represent the widest possible agreement among scientists, but are not in any sense propagandist or executive bodies.   What is needed is a body of more conscious scientists whose main function will be, not to assist in the pursuit of science or to establish the rights and dignities of the scientific profession, but rather to spread among scientists a clearer consciousness of the social implications of their work, and of the need for changing the organization and status of science if it is to continue as the main driving force for transforming civilization.   Such associations already exist in several countries: in Britain the Association of Scientific Workers, in France the Syndicat de l'Enseignement Supérieur, and now in the United States the newly formed American Association of Scientific Workers (see Appendix X).

The origin of the Association of Scientific Workers in Britain, or rather of the National Union of Scientific Workers as it was then called, was the same consciousness of the importance of science which gave rise at the end of the War to the Department of Scientific and Industrial Research.   Here it was the scientists themselves, however, and not the Government, who thought something ought to be done.   At the beginning the National Union's aims were definitely industrial and political.   In the words of one of its first pronouncements :

" The National Union of Scientific Workers marks the beginning of a new era in the history of professional organization in this country.   Hitherto the bodies formed by professional men in combining to further their interests have either had no legal standing or been Chartered Associations or Limited Liability Companies; but these types of organization have been proved inadequate by several recent events.

The objects of the Union are twofold; they are concerned with the part to be played by science in the national life and with the conditions of employment of scientific workers.   In the opinion of the Union, the attainment of the second group of objects is a necessary condition for the attainment of the first.   What has been wrong with British Science in the past is not its quality, but its quantity; not its position in the world of pure learning, but its position in the world of politics and industry.   Its defects can be cured only by attracting to the pursuit of science a much larger fraction of the best ability of the country, and obtaining for the profession a social standing comparable with its national importance.   Those—and there are still such—who think that the pursuit of science should be its own reward and that it would be debased by an attempt to improve greatly the pay and prospect of scientific workers forget three things; first, that few men are so free from family ties as to be able to take up ill-paid work without inflicting hardship on others; second, that any man not so fortunately placed would be adopting the most selfish course in sacrificing the physical comfort of his dependents to his personal taste; and third, that much of the spade work essential to the progress of science and its application to industry is not of a nature to excite the passionate devotion of the artist and will always be done by persons who, while interested in their profession, are no more and no less indifferent to its material rewards than are lawyers, medical men and manufacturers. . . .

If, therefore, the professional workers in industry wish to have a share in looking after their own interests, it is necessary that they organize them-- selves into Trade Unions as quickly as possible. . . .

The foregoing remarks concern mostly the industrial side of scientific work, and the need that scientific opinion should be adequately considered in questions of industrial development, which is as much a national need as a professional one. The more academic side is, however, regarded as at least as important by the promoters of the Union, for on it industrial success and the progress of pure science alike depend. This fact is at last realized by the governing classes in this country, and the Department of Scientific and Industrial Research has been formed for the purpose of increasing the output of research, both pure and applied, and co-ordinating science and industry so that new discoveries of economic value may be utilized as early as possible."—Preamble to Draft Rules, 1919.

The ferment of reconstruction which followed the War was of short duration; by 1926 there had settled down in England a general uncomfortable apathy which was subsequently to be recognized as the period of pre-slump prosperity. The National Union of Scientific Workers, in a kind of panic after the General Strike, changed its name to the Association of Scientific Workers and in doing so lost many of its members without attracting those who were presumed to have been frightened by the earlier title. For a while it fell on very bad days, then, after 1931, similar external causes—first, the effects of the slump, and then those of insecurity and rearmament which followed, and under which we are now living—forced the attention of scientists more than ever to problems outside their own fields. This was reflected in the renewed activity of the Association, particularly among the younger scientists and the students of science. The new orientation, though similar, actually differs in many ways from that of the original foundation; much has since then been learned and unlearned.

The basis of the Association is now recognized to be twofold: one, professional and individual concern with preserving and im- proving the conditions of employment of its members, and establishing the status of "scientific worker" as in some way similar to that of the doctor or the lawyer; the other concern is with the whole position of science in society. The two are closely linked, for it is only if science plays its appropriate part in the social structure and is permitted to develop its latent possibilities that the condition of the individual scientific worker can be appreciably improved. These two sides are illustrated on the one hand by the efforts which the Association is making to improve the conditions of young research workers (7), and on the other, by its work in conjunction with the Parliamentary Science Committee to secure adequate endowment of science on a national scale (see p. 317). Whether or not it succeeds in either of these aims, it cannot be doubted that there is coming into existence a powerful drive for professional organization among scientists with wider social aims in Britain and throughout the world. This shows itself not only in bodies similar to the Association, but in the renewed activity of some of the purely learned societies and the general concern with social matters which appears in scientific journals.

SCIENCE AND POLITICS

The activity we have been discussing so far is one inside the structure of science itself, but clearly it cannot remain limited in this way. In so far as the scientist, individually or corporately, is attempting to influence society, he is acting politically, and though up to a point this action could be exercised without the consciousness of its nature, we have now reached a stage where this is no longer the case. Unless the scientist is conscious both of the internal structure of science and its relation to society, much of his efforts to improve the status of science and to see that its gifts are given to humanity will be doomed to frustration. On the other hand, neither politicians nor the forces behind them can by themselves either fully realize or know how to release the latent possibilities of science. They must be assisted by some of the scientists who know enough of both the scientific and the political field to be able to establish the fusion of the two.

Although necessary, direct political action by scientists has, it must be admitted, serious dangers. Up till now, from the point of view of both economic and political rulers, scientists have been, and have been considered to be, neutral. They were supposed not to concern themselves with the results of their work as long as their pay for continuing it was forthcoming. They were even afforded a little of that indulgence which in less sophisticated communities is given to lunatics. It is not easy to get away from the attitude of neutrality to one of responsibility without endangering these advantages. Even the slightest attempts to do so are invariably labelled as tendencious, and the tradition has grown up that science on no account must be tendencious. The result, as we have already pointed out (see p. 341), has been to sterilize those branches of science where every result of value must of necessity be tendencious and to isolate the other branches of science from society.

Neutrality impossible.—Any attempt on the part of the scientist to think for himself outside his own field exposes him to severe "sanctions," as the example of Germany has well shown us. It is therefore argued that in the interests of science it would be far better for him not to do so. Nevertheless, things can arrive at such a state that neutrality can compromise the very existence of science itself as a living force, for even if science is not suppressed it will cease to attract all active and adventurous minds. The association of scientists in times of crisis with other positive and progressive forces is not a new phenomenon; it occurred in the age of Bruno and Galileo and again in the French Revolution. It is certain that science would have lost far more if Dr. Priestley had been persuaded to remain in cautious orthodoxy than it did by the burning of his house and the destroying of his apparatus. Lavoisier might be cited as a counter-instance, but it is clear that he suffered not as a martyr to science, but as a symbol of a hated tax system of the old régime with which he had allowed himself to be associated. This Radical tendency has been, as Hogben has shown, a special feature of Anglo-American science. (8) The movement in this direction at the present time is due not only to the feeling that science requires an ampler and more equitable economic system in which to function, but even more to the reaction against the definitely anti-scientific drive which is characteristic of Fascism. No scientist can afford to remain neutral in this conflict.

The Popular Opinion of Science.—The political reactions of the scientist represent one aspect of the tendency to bring together science and society; the other is represented by the greater realization outside the ranks of science that its safeguarding and growth are necessary for the progress and even for the existence of civilization. This realization as yet has no organized expression. It is shown by an increasing public interest in such subjects as the frustration of science and more crudely by the short vogue of Technocracy. It marks a third stage in the lay appreciation of science which began by a simple appreciation of the economic benefits of science. This gave place after the War to the opposite tendency of blaming science for all current evils and calling for a return to the good old times, as presaged by Butler in *Erewhon.* The reaction to this begins by taking into account the fact that science is not a free agent. Its power is used for good or ill where it is profitable for the rulers to use it, though like the blinded Samson it may strike back at its masters. Set science free, and it will work for the good of humanity far more effectively than it does now for the gains of a few.

Science and Democracy.—Science must appear as an ally and not as an enemy of all those who are striving to achieve social justice, peace, and liberty. Indeed, the aid of science may prove decisive in the struggle which is only just beginning between the progressive and reactionary forces in the world. It appears likely that for some years to come the world may be divided into democratic and Fascist states, relentlessly struggling for supremacy. In that struggle the weapons will be the internal and external force of ideas, material production and war potential. Fascism necessarily sets itself against the ideal of international science, though it needs science to provide it with material strength. The attempt to stifle the spirit of science while preserving its benefits leads to a conflict in which science and ultimately the State itself will suffer. Technique may be maintained or even improve, but in the long run the lack of ingenuity and flexibility is sure to manifest itself. If at the same time science is not only left free but fostered in the democratic countries their rapid economic and cultural development may prove so overwhelming that by their example Fascism may break down from within, without the need for a long and destructive war, or, if the war must come, the rapid success of democracy would be assured. But can we be sure science will be fostered in the democratic countries? As we have shown, there is little evidence of this up to the present. If it is to happen it can only be through the collaboration of politically conscious scientists, individually and through their association with progressive political forces. To achieve this will be difficult, for it requires real understanding, on the part of both leaders and rank and file of the political movement, of the importance of science and its needs. (9)

The Popular Front.—The scientist may, and indeed must, become a politician, but he will never become a party politician. He sees the social, economic and political situation as a problem to which a solution must first be found and then applied not as a battle-ground of personalities, careers, and vested interests. As long as the progressive forces in the democratic countries are divided into parties by such considerations, he cannot see his way to collaborating with any of them. Only when the parties can get together on a broad programme of social justice, civil liberty and peace, can the full help of the scientist be expected. Once they do so, however, as the example of France has shown, there are possibilities for fruitful collaboration. Many scientists helped, through the "Comité de Vigilance des Intellectuels Antifascistes," in the formation of the

Popular Front, and this work has been continued under the new Government in setting up a really effective Ministry of Science. At the same time, the spread of popular science in the best sense is being helped forward in France through the workers' university, in which eminent scientists discuss their problems with working-class audiences and help to dissipate the misunderstandings and prejudice which very naturally has grown up against science. What we need is the extension of such collaboration between the forces of Science and Democracy throughout the world. By coming together the two will grow to understand one another. Science will find its full liberty and development, and the democratic forces will come to learn its powers and possibilities.

How the Scientist can Help.—How this can be done will vary from country to country. At present, in the world at large, it resembles a tendency rather than a concrete programme. In countries like Britain, where the progressive forces are kept divided by rigid party loyalties, hardly as yet affected by the movements in the rest of the world, the scientist individually and through his organizations can best help by making no exclusive commitments and assisting all progressive parties without favour. The kind of help the scientist can bring is in exact surveys of social and economic conditions, in preparing plans on technical questions, and in criticizing current civil and military programmes. Inevitably this will of itself help to show the concrete necessities of the situation—the abolition of restrictive private control of the competitive, wasteful and dangerous elements in national sovereignty, and of the exploitation of depressed classes or races—and emphasize the necessity for unity to achieve these ends rather than separate activities which fail as often as they succeed and gain at most partial and ephemeral ends. The effort will not be easy, but must succeed if pursued with all the energy, devotion, and intelligence which the scientist could once expend on his own subject alone. If he does so, and only if he does so, can the safety of science be secured and its possibilities begin to be realized.

(1) In the report of the University Grants Commission, 1935, it is stated that the salaries of professors have been increased while those of junior lecturers and demonstrators have been diminished. Commenting on this, the Commissioners remark :

" The rise in professorial salaries is particularly gratifying, proving, as it does, that the Universities are fully alive to the necessity of making reasonable financial provision for the Professoriate, if the services of the best men are to be secured. Any weakness here must affect adversely the reputation of the University, and the continuous improvement of these salaries, which has been noticeable since the War, has been of prime importance."

". . . For the recruitment of apprentices for the profession of University teaching the actual salary during the first few years is much less important than the prospects of the future. A University which cannot afford to do both would accordingly get better results by raising the salaries attainable at the age of, say, 40 to an attractive figure, than by adding small sums to the salaries which it offers to young graduates on the threshold of their careers."

The figures also published in the report (see Appendix I) unfortunately also show that, taking the average tenure of a junior lecturer's post as twelve years and a professor's as twenty-four, the probability of his becoming a professor is only one in two and in reality probably far less. The "attraction" is therefore somewhat of a carrot.

(2) See *Science at the Cross Roads*, Kniga, 1931. Hessen's article on Newton, which it contains, was for England the starting point of a new evaluation of the history of science.

(3) See also the subsequent correspondence, particularly the reply of J. B. S. Haldane, and the article by Joseph Needham in *Christianity and Social Revolution*, Gollancz.

(4) Cf. *The Times*, 25th April 1938.

(5) See *Nature*, Vol. 141, p. 150 ; Vol. 142, pp. 310-11 and pp. 380-1.

(6) *Nature*, Vol. 141, p. 723.

(7) For example, in 1937 a delegation from the Association of Scientific Workers interviewed Sir Frank Smith, Secretary of the Department of Scientific and Industrial Research, urging among others the following points with regard to junior maintenance grants :

1. That the maximum for Junior maintenance grants be raised to £150 per annum (instead of £120 as at present).

2. That where the holder of a grant undertakes teaching work, his grant should be reduced by not more than half the amount he earns by teaching. (At present Oxford and Cambridge students are allowed to keep one-sixth of what they earn, and students in other universities one-third.)

3. That the word "loans" be deleted from paragraph 21 of the regulations drawn up by the D.S.I.R. Advisory Committee. In the later issue of the regulations revised in January, 1937 this has been done. (Provision by which applicants are obliged to apply for loans from local authorities before being eligible should be rescinded.)

Unfortunately, only in the last of these was the Department willing to make any concession. As far as the first complaint of the miserable scale of maintenance grant, the spokesman of the D.S.I.R. stated " that the amount of £120 had been fixed by the Advisory Council of the D.S.I.R., which consists not of Government officials but of University professors, as being perfectly adequate to keep a student in London or one of the provincial universities, who had no other means of support at all. He stated further that the Council was always ready to consider exceptional circumstances and to increase the grant on the recommendation of the University authorities. Prior to 1931 the maximum had been £140, but had been reduced when the cost of living fell. (Though it was not raised when the cost of living rose again.) When asked whether he did not think that the smallness of the grant did not tend to drive the best men into other lines of employment than scientific research, leaving second class students as applicants for D.S.I.R. grants, he stated that this did not concern the department, as second class students often proved the most valuable research workers." (*Scientific Worker*, Vol. ix, No. 8, November, 1937.)

The letter quoted on page 388 goes on to explain why the average scientific worker should join the association :

" The reason why I belong to the A.S.W. is because I think it wrong that a man of scientific attainments should be exploited at road sweepers' wages, and with less than road sweepers' security by commercial concerns who make large profits by his work. It is wrong that Colossus Ltd. should be making large profits out of the Colossus Patent Switch when the patent was granted to John Smith, B.Sc., who assigned it to Colossus Ltd. for £1 under the terms of his agreement with them. It is wrong that a director of Colossus Ltd. should embody without acknowledgement in a paper he reads before a learned society facts and formulæ discovered first by the said John Smith and that Smith should connive for fear of losing his job. It is wrong that the facts regarding the commercial exploitation of their work should be jealously kept from the knowledge of the scientific staff of a technical business and that consequently when administrative posts have to be filled they should be given to accountants and salesmen ; and it is wrong that these non-technical people, not appreciating the scientific work they depend on, should hamper, starve and obstruct their technical men and then sack them for not producing results.

All these things are happening almost daily, and I could find concrete examples of every case mentioned. The Association of Scientific Workers has done a good deal by supporting members in their demands for proper treatment by their employers and investigating posts advertised at low salaries, and I regard the rapid development of this side of our activities as the most important object for us to pursue. In dealing with such matters, particularly

NOTES

when a Government department is concerned, political influence is of great use, and to that extent ' Participation in the Councils of the State ' is a proper object of the Association."

(8) *Science for the Citizen*, pp. 582 *et seq.* ; *Science and Society*, Vol. I.

(9) The recent decision of the Trades Union Congress to set up a Scientific Advisory Committee is a welcome sign that this process has begun in Britain. This committee, first announced at the British Association meeting in 1937, has now been definitely constituted, half of scientists nominated by the British Association and half of representatives of the Trades Union Congress. It will be strictly non-political and will concern itself with the following problems : Foods and Agriculture ; Coal Technology ; Occupational Diseases, Disabilities and Industrial Welfare ; Synthetic Plastics and Cellulose ; Heavy Metals ; Light Metals ; Power Production and Transport ; Mineral Resources in relation to Potential Developments ; Defence and Aviation ; Technical Education and Administration; Population and Vital Statistics ; etc.

CHAPTER XVI

THE SOCIAL FUNCTION OF SCIENCE

At the end of our inquiry we come closer to being able to define what is the contemporary, and what may be the future, function of science in society. We have seen science as an integral part both of the material and economic life of our times and of the ideas which guide and inspire it. Science puts into our hands the means of satisfying our material needs. It gives us also the ideas which will enable us to understand, to co-ordinate, and to satisfy our needs in the social sphere. Beyond this science has something as important though less definite to offer: a reasonable hope in the unexplored possibilities of the future, an inspiration which is slowly but surely becoming the dominant driving force of modern thought and action.

The Major Transformations of History

To see the function of science as a whole it is necessary to look at it against the widest possible background of history. Our attention to immediate historical events has, up till very recently, blinded us to the understanding of its major transformations. Mankind is, after all, a late emergence on the scene of terrestrial evolution, and the earth itself is a late by-product of cosmic forces. Up till now human life has only undergone three major changes: the foundation first of society and then of civilization, both of which occurred before the dawn of recorded history, and that scientific transformation of society which is now taking place and for which we have as yet no name.

Society and Civilization.—The first revolution was the foundation of society, by which man became different from the animals and found, through the new habit of transmission of experience from generation to generation, a means of advance altogether faster and more sure than the haphazard evolutionary struggle. The second revolution was the discovery of civilization, based on agriculture, and bringing with it a manifold development of specialized techniques, but above all, the social forms of the city and trade. Through these mankind as a whole was removed from parasitic dependence on nature and a certain section of mankind liberated altogether from the task of food production. The discovery of civilization was a local event. It had acquired nearly all its essential features by the sixth

millennium B.C., but only at its centre, somewhere between Meso-
potamia and India. We cannot trace in the succeeding thousands
of years right up to the Renaissance and the beginning of our own
times any substantial change in the quality of civilization. The
whole of this period of recorded history marks only relatively small
cultural and technical changes, and these, for the most part, of a
cyclic character. Culture after culture rises and decays, but each one,
though different, is not essentially in advance of the one before. The
real imperceptible advance is only in area. Every breakdown of the
civilization internally and through barbarian invasions meant in the
long run, after a period of confusion, the spread of that civilization to
the barbarians. By the end of the period all the easily cultivated lands
of the world were civilized.

   The Scientific Revolution: The Rôle of Capitalism.—It is apparent
to us now, though it was certainly not then, that by the middle of the
fifteenth century something new was beginning. We have come to
look on the Renaissance as presaging the rise of capitalism, but it was
not until the eighteenth century that any fundamental change was
generally recognized. By then, through the application of science
and invention, new possibilities were available to mankind which
were likely to have an even larger effect on its future than those of
agriculture and the techniques of early civilization. It is only recently
that we have been able to separate in our minds the development of
capitalist enterprise from that of science and the general liberation of
human thought. Both seemed to be inextricably connected parts of
Progress, but at the same time, paradoxically, their appearance was
greeted as evidence that man was returning to his natural state, freed
from the arbitrary restrictions of religion or feudal authority. We
now see that though capitalism was essential to the early development
of science, giving it, for the first time, a practical value, the human
importance of science transcends in every way that of capitalism, and,
indeed, the full development of science in the service of humanity is
incompatible with the continuance of capitalism.

   The Social Implications of Science.—Science implies a unified and
co-ordinated and, above all, conscious control of the whole of social
life; it abolishes, or provides the possibility of abolishing, the dependence of man on the material world. Henceforth society is subject
only to the limitations it imposes on itself. There is no reason to
doubt that this possibility will be grasped. The mere knowledge of
its existence is enough to drive man on until he has achieved it. The
socialized, integrated, scientific world organization is coming. It
would be absurd, however, to pretend that it had nearly arrived or
that it will come without the most severe struggles and confusion.
We must realize that we are in the middle of one of the major transi-

tion periods of human history. Our most immediate problem is to ensure that the transition is accomplished as rapidly as possible, with the minimum of material, human and cultural destruction.

The Tasks of Science in the Transition Period.—Although science will clearly be the characteristic feature of the third stage of humanity, its importance will not be fully felt until this stage has been definitely established. Belonging to an age of transition we are primarily concerned with its tasks, and here science is but one factor in a complex of economic and political forces. Our business is with what science, here and now, has to do. The importance of science in the struggle, moreover, depends largely on the consciousness of this importance. Science, conscious of its purpose, can in the long run become a major force in social change. Because of the powers which it holds in reserve it can ultimately dominate the other forces. But science, unaware of its social significance, becomes a helpless tool in the hands of forces driving it away from the directions of social advance, and, in the process, destroying its very essence, the spirit of free inquiry. To make science conscious of itself and its powers it must be seen in the light of the problems of the present and of a realizable future. It is in relation to these that we have to determine the immediate functions of science.

Preventible Evils.—We have in the world to-day a number of palpable material evils—starvation, disease, slavery, and war—evils which in previous times were accepted as part of nature or as the actions of stern or malevolent gods, but which now continue solely because we are tied to out-of-date political and economic systems. There is no longer any technical reason why everyone should not have enough to eat. There is no reason why anyone should do more than three or four hours of disagreeable or monotonous work a day, or why they should be forced, by economic pressure, to do even that. War, in a period of potential plenty and ease for all, is sheer folly and cruelty. The greater part of disease in the world to-day is due directly or indirectly to lack of food and good living conditions. All these are plainly remediable evils, and no one can feel that science has been properly applied to human life until they are swept off the face of the earth.

But that is only the beginning. There are a number of apparently irremediable evils, such as disease or the necessity for any kind of unpleasant work at all, which we have very good reason for believing could be dealt with if a serious and economically well-supported scientific drive were made to discover their causes and eliminate them. The starving of research of potential human value is but one step removed from the starving of man.

Discovery and Satisfaction of Needs.—These are all, however, but negative aspects of the application of science. It is plainly not enough to remove as much of present evil as lies in our power. We must look to producing new good things, better, more active and more harmonious ways of living, individually and socially. So far science has hardly touched these fields. It has accepted the crude desires of a pre-scientific age without attempting to analyse and refine them. It is the function of science to study man as much as nature, to discover the significance and direction of social movements and social needs. The tragedy of man has too often lain in his very success in achieving what he imagined to be his objects. Science, through its capacity for looking ahead and comprehending at the same time many aspects of a problem, should be able to determine far more clearly which are the real and which the phantastic elements of personal and social desires. Science brings power and liberation, just as much by showing the falsity and impossibility of certain human aims, as by satisfying others. In so far as science becomes the conscious guiding force of material civilization, it must increasingly permeate all other spheres of culture.

SCIENCE AND CULTURE

The present situation, where a highly developed science stands almost isolated from a traditional literary culture, is altogether anomalous and cannot last. No culture can stand indefinitely apart from the dominating practical ideas of the time, without degenerating into pedantic futility. It need not be imagined, however, that the assimilation of science and culture is likely to take place without very serious modifications in the structure of science itself. Science of the present day owes its origin and much of its character to the precise needs of material construction. Its method is essentially a critical one, the ultimate criterion being experimental, that is, practical verification. The really positive part of science, the making of discoveries, lies outside scientific method proper, which is concerned with preparing the ground for them and with establishing their reliability. Discoveries are usually unthinkingly attributed to the operations of human genius which it would be impious to attempt to explain. We have no science of science. Another aspect of the same defect of present-day science is its inability adequately to deal with phenomena in which novelty occurs and which are not readily reduced to any quantitative mathematical description. The enlargement of science to cover this defect is needed for its extension to social problems, and will be more so the more science becomes assimilated with general culture. The dryness and austerity of science, which had led to its widespread rejection by those of literary culture and, among scientists themselves, to every kind of irrational and mystical addition, is something which must be removed before science can fully take its place as a common framework of life and thought.

To a certain extent this transformation will represent a fusion of existing tendencies inside and outside of science. Particular scientific disciplines; the dispassionate assembling of evidence; the means of dealing with multiple causation, each factor having a definite quantitative part to play in the final result; the general understanding of the elements of chance and statistical probability, will tend to become the background of every kind of human action. At the same time, history, tradition, literary form, and visual presentation will come more and more to belong to science. The world picture presented by science which, though continually changing, grows with each change more definite and complete, is bound to become in the new age the background of every form of culture. But this change by itself is not sufficient, the transformation of science and not the mere assimilation of other disciplines is required for the new tasks which science will have to face.

THE TRANSFORMATION OF SCIENCE

The stages of scientific advance have marked a progress from the large and simple to the small and complex. The first stage of science, that of the description and ordering of the available universe, is already essentially completed. The second stage, understanding the mechanics of this universe, is on its way to completion, for already we can see in principle the general scheme of this explanation. There remain unknown, and indeed in part necessarily unknowable, possibilities beyond this, though we can already glimpse a little of this future development. It is quite clear that, if humanity does not in the near future destroy that elaborate co-operative effort, which distinguishes civilization from the previous purely biological existence of man, it will have to tackle a universe which will itself become more and more a human creation. Already the chief difficulties both in the theory and practice of science lie in the problems that human society has created for itself in economics, sociology, and psychology. In the future, as the simpler conquest of non-human forces is brought to its completion, these problems will become increasingly important.

The Problem of the Origin of New Things.—This process will bring new aspects into evidence. The more thought deals with the problems of a rapidly developing society, in part consciously motivated, and in part moving by the indiscernible interaction of the different forces working within it, the more the methods of coping with problems will need to be modified in order to deal with the novel and the unexpected. The first sciences to emerge into rationality were those of the simplest operations—mechanics, physics, and chemistry. Our pattern of rationality is founded on the study of systems where everything is uniform and nothing really new happens. In biology already this mode of thought is beginning to break down. The theory of evolution not only marks an advance in our understanding of nature but is also a critical step in our method of thinking, because it involves the recognition of novelty and history in science. Men have, it is true, studied history already for millennia, but in a very different spirit from that of science. Indeed, they have gone so far as to deny that history could be a science at all because of the very possibility of novelty in it. But there is no intrinsic reason why science should not learn to deal with the novel elements in the universe, which, after all, are as characteristic of it as the repetitive and regular ones. Science has not done so up till now because it has not had to. Now for the first time the problem is fairly presented. If we are to master and direct our world we must learn how to cope not only with the orderly but also with the novel aspects of the universe, even when their novelty is of our own making.

Dialectical Materialism.—Karl Marx was the first to realize this problem and to suggest how it might be solved. He was able to draw from the study of economics, in the place of the superficial regularities that sufficed for the orthodox school, a profound realization of the developments of new forms and of the struggles and equilibria from which still newer forms derived. We have here the beginning of a rational study of development as such, but it is one in which it is no longer possible rigidly to separate the observer from the observed, and which consequently identifies the student with the forces he is studying. In the turmoil and struggle which our social and political world is passing through, these ideas are rapidly winning their way even into the camp of their most violent enemies. They have found their justification, not only in predicting but also in moulding human development, a task which would have been impossible within the limits of a science based on the conception of an ordered and invariable world.

Now as science itself has proceeded almost entirely by the method of isolation, the Marxist method of thinking has often appeared to scientists as loose and unscientific, or, as they would put it, metaphysical. Isolation in science, however, can only be achieved by a rigorous control of the circumstances of the experiment or application. Only when all the factors are known is scientific prediction, in the full sense, possible. Now it is quite clear that where new things are coming into the universe all the factors cannot be known, and that therefore the method of scientific isolation fails to deal with these new things. But from the human point of view it is as necessary to be able to deal with new things as with the regular order of nature. Science is perfectly right in restricting itself to the latter. It is wrong only if it implies that outside this regular order the human mind is helpless, that if something cannot be dealt with "scientifically," it cannot be dealt with rationally.

The Extension of Rationality.—The great contribution of Marxism is to extend the possibility of rationality in human problems to include those in which radically new things are happening. It can only do so, however, subject to certain necessary limitations. In the first place, the degree of prediction where new things are concerned can never be of the same order of exactitude as in the regular and isolated operations of science. Exact knowledge, which has been looked on as an ideal, is, however, not the only alternative to no knowledge at all. There are even very large regions inside science itself where exact knowledge is impossible. The whole trend of modern physics has, for instance, shown that it is hopeless to expect it in atomic phenomena. But there the difficulty is circumvented by relying on the exactness of the statistical knowledge of a large number of events. In a similar way, the exact dates and localities of the critical changes, the wars and revolutions which affect human society, are unpredictable, but here statistical methods are not fully applicable, there being only one human society. Nevertheless, the intrinsic instability of certain economic and technical systems is something which can be generally established, and their breakdown becomes, within a wide range of years, inevitable.

The Trend of the Future.—There can be no question, even to those completely unaware of the methods by which the Marxist predictions are reached, that the Marxists have some way of analysing the development of affairs which enables them to judge far in advance of scientific thinkers what the trend of social and economic development is to be. The uncritical acceptance of this, however, leads many into believing that Marxism is simply another providential teleology, that Marx had mapped the necessary lines of social and economic development which men willy-nilly must follow. This is a complete misunderstanding. Marxist predictions are not the result of working out such a scheme of development. On the contrary, they emphasize the impossibility of doing this. What can be seen at any given moment is the composition of the economic and political forces of the times, their necessary struggle and the new conditions which will be the result. But beyond that we can only foresee a process which has not ended and will necessarily take on new and strictly unpredictable forms. The value of Marxism is as a method and a guide to action, not as a creed and a cosmogony. The relevance of Marxism to science is that it removes it from its imagined position of complete detachment and shows it as a part, but a critically important part, of economic and social development. In doing so it can serve to separate off the metaphysical elements which throughout the whole course of its history have penetrated scientific thought. It is to Marxism that we owe the consciousness of the hitherto unanalysed driving force of scientific advance, and it will be through the practical achievements of Marxism that this consciousness can become embodied in the organization of science for the benefit of humanity.

Science will come to be recognized as the chief factor in fundamental social change. The economic and industrial system keeps, or should keep, civilization going. The steady process of technical improvement provides for a regular increase in the extent and commodity of life. Science should provide a continuous series of unpredictable radical changes in the techniques themselves. Whether these changes fit in or fail to fit in with human and social needs is the measure of how far science has been adjusted to its social function.

For the full value of these seminal ideas we must wait until the ending of the struggle, which, though it may seem to us interminably drawn out, will appear in history as an episode, though a great and critical one. Then mankind will come into its material heritage, and, far from needing science less, will make even greater demands on it to solve the greater human and social problems which have to be faced. To meet this task science itself will change and develop, and in doing so will cease to be a special discipline of a selected few and become the common heritage of mankind.

Science as Communism.—Already we have in the practice of science the prototype for all human common action. The task which the scientists have undertaken—the understanding and control of nature and of man himself—is merely the conscious expression of the task of human society. The methods by which this task is attempted, however imperfectly they are realized, are the methods by which humanity is most likely to secure its own future. In its endeavour, science is communism. In science men have learned consciously to subordinate themselves to a common purpose without losing the individuality of their achievements. Each one knows that his work depends on that of his predecessors and colleagues, and that it can only reach its fruition through the work of his successors. In science men collaborate not because they are forced to by superior authority or because they blindly follow some chosen leader, but because they realize that only in this willing collaboration can each man find his goal.   Not orders, but advice, determines action.   Each man knows that only by advice, honestly and disinterestedly given, can his work succeed, because such advice expresses as near as may be the inexorable logic of the material world, stubborn fact.   Facts cannot be forced to our desires, and freedom comes by admitting this necessity and not by pretending to ignore it.

These are things that have been learned painfully and incompletely in the pursuit of science.   Only in the wider tasks of humanity will their full use be found.

APPENDIX I

FIGURES CONCERNING UNIVERSITIES AND SCIENTIFIC SOCIETIES

(*A*) NUMBER AND DISTRIBUTION OF POSTS BETWEEN—ARTS, SCIENCE, MEDICINE, AND TECHNOLOGY

(*a*) Professors and other heads of departments ; (*b*) Other teaching staff.

University.	Arts.		Science.		Medicine.		Technology.	
	(*a*)	(*b*)	(*a*)	(*b*)	(*a*)	(*b*)	(*a*)	(*b*)
English								
Birmingham . . .	23	42	6	35	5	18	7	31
Bristol	10	28	9	52	6	21	3	8
Cambridge . . .	46	187	23	119	2	13	5	39
Durham	20	51	16	38	9	11	5	14
Exeter	6	26	5	13	—	—	—	—
Leeds	19	39	9	47	7	37	9	77
Liverpool . . .	22	3	10	29	13	24	10	29
London	100	244	68	236	78	197	18	106
Manchester . . .	25	75	9	42	8	32	15	110
Nottingham . . .	9	28	10	28	—	—	6	26
Oxford	79	378	27	82	12	23	2	8
Reading	15	31	7	16	—	—	14	21
Sheffield	14	17	7	24	7	10	10	42
Southampton . . .	9	24	6	21	—	—	1	7
Total English Universities .	397	1173	212	782	147	386	105	518
Welsh								
Aberystwyth . . .	15	30	8	15	—	—	—	—
Bangor	13	22	5	12	—	—	2	2
Cardiff	13	32	6	19	2	9	3	7
Swansea	8	19	5	15	—	—	1	8
Welsh National School of Medicine . . .	—	—	—	—	6	9	—	—
Total Welsh Universities .	49	103	24	61	8	18	6	17
Scottish								
Aberdeen . . .	24	27	5	17	10	15	3	4
Edinburgh . . .	40	42	5	27	12	36	7	12
Glasgow . . .	22	69	5	38	9	41	3	14
Glasgow Royal Technical College . . .	—	—	—	—	—	—	15	80
St. Andrews . . .	23	18	11	30	7	11	4	4
Total Scottish Universities .	109	156	26	112	38	103	32	114
Total for Universities of Great Britain . . .	555	1432	262	955	193	507	143	649

This table was calculated from figures provided by the Universities Bureau of the British Empire.

(*B*) Number of Full-time Teaching Staff in Different Grades and Average Income

	Professors.	Readers, Assistant Professors and Independent Lecturers.	Lecturers.	Assistant Lecturers and Demonstrators.	Others.
Total for Great Britain, 1934–1935	855	374	1391	856	259
Average Salary, 1934–1935	£1095	£664	£471	£308	£384

From the Universities Grants Committee Report.

(*C*) Number and Distribution of Advanced Students in Science, Medicine, Technology, and Agriculture

Branches of Study.	Full-time Students.		Part-time Students.	
	Men.	Women.	Men.	Women.
Mathematics	86	3	38	6
Astronomy	4	—	—	—
Biology	1	—	—	1
Botany	91	24	17	20
Chemistry	472	30	78	7
,, Applied . . .	46	—	25	1
,, Bio-Chemistry . . .	40	11	6	4
Colloid Science	8	—	—	—
Entomology	23	2	7	—
Eugenics	5	—	2	1
Genetics	6	3	2	1
Geology	34	5	6	1
Geo-Physics	1	—	—	—
Mineralogy	5	—	—	—
Mycology	—	—	1	—
Oceanography	1	—	—	—
Physics	200	12	39	5
Zoology	80	21	17	15
Principles, History and Method of Science	4	—	30	2
Total Natural Sciences . . .	1107	111	268	64
Medicine	33	1	190	8
Surgery	22	—	222	8
Obstetrics and Gynaecology . . .	2	1	11	3
Anaesthetics	3	—	1	—
Anatomy	2	—	5	1
Bacteriology	19	4	3	1
Cancer Research	5	—	—	—
Dental Surgery	—	—	1	—
Dermatology	2	—	—	—
Embryology	1	—	—	—
Carry forward	89	7	433	21

(C) Number and Distribution of Advanced Students in Science, Medicine, Technology, and Agriculture.—*continued*

Branches of Study.	Full-time Students.		Part-time Students.	
	Men.	Women.	Men.	Women.
Brought forward . . .	89	7	433	21
Epidemiology and Vital Statistics . .	2	—	—	—
Helminthology	1	2	—	—
Histology	1	—	—	—
Materia Medica	—	—	1	—
Orthopaedics	—	—	12	1
Parasitology	4	—	—	—
Pathology	4	—	21	—
„ and Medicine . . .	—	—	1	—
Pharmacology	9	1	5	—
Physiology	40	5	12	5
Public Health	1	—	—	—
Radiology	—	—	6	—
Therapeutics	1	—	—	—
Tuberculosis	2	—	—	—
Total Medical Subjects . .	154	14	491	27
Aeronautics	22	—	1	—
Architecture	5	—	12	—
Building	2	—	—	—
Dyeing	7	—	—	—
Engineering, General	24	—	2	—
„ Chemical . . .	42	—	1	—
„ Civil . . .	43	—	7	—
„ Electrical . . .	61	1	10	—
„ Mechanical . . .	35	—	15	—
Fuel Technology	17	—	4	—
Glass Technology	1	—	—	—
Leather Manufacture . . .	1	—	1	—
Metallurgy	39	—	12	—
Military Studies	1	—	—	—
Mining	3	—	3	—
Naval Architecture	4	—	1	—
Oil Technology	6	—	1	—
Textiles	25	—	4	—
Town Planning	—	—	6	—
Total Technology . . .	338	1	80	—
Agriculture	32	3	2	—
Agricultural Bacteriology . . .	2	1	—	—
„ Botany . . .	8	—	—	—
„ Chemistry . . .	1	—	—	—
„ Economics . . .	7	—	—	—
„ Entomology . . .	1	—	—	—
Dairy Bacteriology	4	1	3	1
Forestry	2	1	—	—
Horticulture	2	1	—	—
Total Agricultural Subjects . .	59	7	5	1
Total	1658	133	844	92

From University Grants Committee Returns, 1935–1936.

(D) INCOME OF

Institution.	Endowments.		Donations and Subscriptions.		Grants from Local Authorities.	
	Total.	Per Cent. of Total Income.	Amount.	Per Cent. of Total Income.	Amount.	Per Cent. of Total Income.
	£		£		£	
University of London . .	155,184	8·9	72,306	4·2	129,625	7·4
Birmingham University .	34,043	15·8	3,977	1·8	29,855	13·8
Bristol University . .	25,326	12·9	5,406	2·8	22,908	11·7
Cambridge University . .	157,053	24·3	8,414	1·3	703	·1
Durham University . .	22,166	9·6	4,011	1·7	26,606	11·6
Exeter University College .	2,124	4·5	810	1·7	15,262	32·5
Leeds University . .	12,558	4·9	13,508	5·3	50,395	19·7
Liverpool University . .	35,037	14·1	7,663	3·1	26,758	10·8
Manchester University .	48,780	18·2	4,947	1·9	19,105	7·1
Manchester College of Technology	—	—	115	·1	104,700	71·2
Nottingham University College	6,957	7·6	1,590	1·8	22,665	24·9
Oxford University . .	147,109	32·6	3,139	·7	—	—
Reading University . .	13,857	11·7	100	·1	5,623	4·7
Sheffield University .	8,206	5·5	9,977	6·7	32,101	21·6
Southampton University College	995	2·0	700	1·4	15,795	32·0
Total, England . .	669,395	13·8	136,663	2·8	502,101	10·3
University of Wales . .	22,134	6·1	4,305	1·2	58,113	16·0
Aberdeen University . .	22,487	18·4	1,000	·8	6,000	4·9
Edinburgh University . .	52,713	18·5	8,958	3·1	10,800	3·8
Glasgow University . .	44,491	17·2	4,433	1·7	8,700	3·4
Glasgow Royal Technical College	9,702	13·3	5,165	7·1	8,179	11·2
St. Andrews University .	24,983	22·0	1,675	1·5	4,500	4·0
Total, Scotland . .	154,376	18·1	21,231	2·5	38,179	4·5
Grand Total, Great Britain	845,905	13·9	162,199	2·7	598,393	9·9

Taken from the University

UNIVERSITIES, 1934–35

Parliamentary Grants.		Tuition Fees.		Examination, Graduation, Matriculation and Registration Fees.		Other Income.		Total Income.
Total.	Per Cent. of Total Income.	Total.	Per Cent. of Total Income.	Amount.	Per Cent. of Total Income.	Total.	Per Cent. of Total Income.	
£		£		£		£		£
579,710	33·3	521,799	29·9	146,180	8·4	137,926	7·9	1,742,730
76,506	35·5	50,729	23·5	10,785	5·0	9,836	4·6	215,731
84,882	43·4	32,251	16·5	6,962	3·6	17,871	9·1	195,606
161,115	25·0	173,212	26·8	78,641	12·2	66,582	10·3	645,720
78,183	34·0	58,298	25·2	14,065	6·0	27,448	11·9	230,777
14,500	30·9	12,973	27·7	1,251	2·7	—	—	46,920
78,164	30·6	60,728	23·7	7,635	3·0	32,841	12·8	255,829
90,426	36·4	70,597	28·4	11,165	4·5	6,715	2·7	248,361
85,152	31·7	71,916	26·8	13,005	4·8	25,497	9·5	268,402
14,500	9·8	22,471	15·3	552	·4	4,687	3·2	147,025
31,100	34·1	24,173	26·5	1,867	2·1	2,734	3·0	91,086
125,294	27·7	46,337	10·2	82,539	18·3	47,339	10·5	451,757
64,301	54·2	22,223	18·7	3,379	2·9	9,086	7·7	118,569
50,573	34·0	29,240	19·7	6,019	4·0	12,630	8·5	148,746
17,950	36·3	12,963	26·2	585	1·2	446	·9	49,434
1,552,356	32·0	1,209,910	24·9	384,630	7·9	401,638	8·3	4,856,693
177,197	48·6	74,796	20·5	16,494	4·5	11,241	3·1	364,280
55,728	45·6	23,779	19·4	8,983	7·4	4,312	3·5	122,289
100,159	35·2	73,497	25·8	28,152	9·9	10,473	3·7	284,752
88,023	34·0	77,991	30·2	33,234	12·9	1,597	·6	258,469
32,951	45·3	16,330	22·5	68	·1	341	·5	72,736
52,500	46·3	19,520	17·2	7,309	6·4	2,945	2·6	113,432
329,361	38·7	211,117	24·8	77,746	9·1	19,668	2·3	851,678
2,058,914	33·9	1,495,823	24·6	478,870	7·9	432,547	7·1	6,072,651

Grants Committee Report.

(E) Number of Scientists belonging to the Chief Scientific Societies

Society.	Membership.
Institute of Chemistry	7100
Chemical Society	3775
Physical	1100
Geological Society	1180
Astronomical	918 (including 48 foreign associates)
Biochemical Society	940
Mineralogical	260

These figures only cover some of the largest scientific societies. It is difficult to get from them any idea of the total number of scientific workers. For one thing, not all members of the societies are active scientifically, and conversely by no means all scientific workers belong to scientific societies. Also there is a large degree of overlap. Some idea of the total may be had by adding the figures for the Institute of Chemistry, the Physical, the Geological, and half the Biochemical Societies. To this should be added another 1500 for zoological and biological, giving a total of 11,250, representing the non-medical sciences. It is extremely difficult to find the number of working scientific research workers, but it is probably not more than another 3000, making 14,250 in all.

APPENDIX II

GOVERNMENT AIDED RESEARCH

(A) Government Scientific Research Expenditure, 1937

Fighting Services (see page 427)		£1,536,000
Department of Scientific and Industrial Research		583,000
Ministry of Agriculture and Fisheries (including £63,000 for Scotland)	£469,000	
Agricultural Research Council	61,000	
Forestry Commission	15,000	
		545,000
Medical Research Council	£195,000	
Ministry of Health	4,000	
		199,000
Development Commission	£121,000	
Mines Department	2,000	
Ministry of Transport	70,000	
Post Office	88,000	
Office of Works	180,000	
		361,000
Colonies Services	43,000	
Dominion Services	13,000	
		56,000
		£3,280,000

THE DEPARTMENT OF SCIENTIFIC AND INDUSTRIAL RESEARCH

(B) SUMMARY OF THE EXPENDITURE OF THE DEPARTMENT DURING THE YEAR ENDED 31ST MARCH 1937

Organization.	Gross.	Receipts.	Net.
Headquarters' Administration .	£29,685	£1,209	£28,476
National Physical Laboratory . .	244,081	138,492	105,589
Building and Road Research . .	87,957	55,693	32,264
Chemical Research Laboratory . .	26,420	5,274	21,146
Food Investigation . . .	54,926	15,928	38,998
Forest Products Research . .	41,281	1,899	39,382
Fuel Research	105,660	12,851	92,809
Water Pollution Research . .	10,613	9,215	1,398
Miscellaneous Programmes . .	7,521	4,519	3,002
Geological Survey and Museum .	70,241	1,792	68,449
Grants for Research:			
Research Associations, etc. . .	126,510		126,510
Grants to Students, etc. . .	25,285	78	25,207
	£830,180	£246,950	£583,230

Taken from the Report of the Department of Scientific and Industrial Research for the year 1936–37, p. 168.

(C) INCOME OF RESEARCH ASSOCIATIONS 1936-37

Research Association.	Income.	As per cent. of Net Product of Industry.
British Colliery Owners . . .	£5,030	0·003
British Cast Iron	14,865 ⎱ £66,681	0·07
British Iron and Steel Federation .	51,816 ⎰	
British Non-Ferrous Metals . .	28,521	0·12
Institution of Automobile Engineers .	16,763	0·03
British Electrical and Allied Industries	81,073	0·18
British Refractories	9,909	0·06†
British Food Manufacturers . .	4,668 ⎫	
Cocoa, Chocolate, Sugar Confectionery and Jam Trades	6,891 ⎬ £24,368	0·03
British Flour Millers . . .	12,809 ⎭	
British Paint, Colour and Varnish Manufacturers	15,998	0·18
British Rubber Manufacturers . .	11,360	0·06
Carry forward . . .	£259,703	

Income figures taken from the Report of the Department of Scientific and Industrial Research for the year 1936–37.

† Of all the pottery industry.

Research Association.	Income.	As per cent. of Net Product of Industry.
Brought forward . . .	£259,703	
British Leather Manufacturers . .	19,387 }	
British Boot, Shoe and Allied Trades .	5,037 } £24,424	0·09
British Cotton Industry . . .	80,239 }	
Wool Industries	19,913 } £119,440	0·08
Linen Industry	19,288 }	
British Launderers . . .	10,818	0·015*
Printing and Allied Trades . .	10,130	0·014
British Scientific Instrument . .	9,257	0·15
	£433,772	

Income figures taken from the Report of the Department of Scientific and Industrial Research for the year 1936–37.

* Of all the clothing industry.

(D) Total Government Grant and Industrial Contribution to the Research Associations

Year.	No. of Associations.	Income from Industry £000.	Income from Government £000.	Total £000.	Per cent. Increase or Decrease on previous year.
1920	17	£96	£65	£161	
1921	21	108	84	192	+19
1922	21	111	93	204	+6
1923	21	121	103	224	+10
1924	21	113	100	213	−5
1925	20	118	88	206	−3
1926	21	111	78	189	−9
1927	19	115	60	175	−8
1928	19	124	54	178	+2
1929	20	153	79	232	+25
1930	20	158	82	240	+3
1931	20	160	88	248	+3
1932	20	167	68	235	−5
1933	19	174	59	233	−1
1934	19	191	86	277	+19
1935	19	232	109	341	+23
1936	18	250	127	377	+11

Figures from the Department of Scientific and Industrial Research.

APPENDIX III

INDUSTRIAL RESEARCH

(*A*) Number of Large and Small Factories in Great Britain

(Figures for 1933, from the Home Office)

Number of factories employing up to 1000 workers . . 159,850
Number of factories employing more than 1000 workers . 335
Number of operatives employed in factories . . . 4,990,421

See also for United States the article by V. D. Kazahevitch in *Science and Society*, Vol. 2, p. 195.

(*B*) Number of Scientific Papers coming from Academic, Government, and Industrial Sources appearing in various Scientific Periodicals

Paper.	Year.	Academic.		Government.		Industry.		Total.
		No.	Per Cent.	No.	Per Cent.	No.	Per Cent.	
Proceedings of the Royal Society (A)	1924	63	96	3	4	—	—	66
	1929	117	92	7	6	2	2	126
	1932	127	93	7	5	3	2	137
	1936	130	90	6	4	8	6	144
Proceedings of the Royal Society (B)	1924	52	96	2	4	—	—	54
	1929	53	95	3	5	—	—	56
	1932	74	93	3	4	2	3	80
	1936	64	89	7	9	1	2	72
Journal of the Chemical Society	1929	150	90	6	4	9	6	165
Philosophical Magazine (10 months only)	1932	187	92	14	7	2	1	203
	1936	127	95	5	4	1	1	133
		1144	93	63	5	28	2	1235
Four Technical Journals	1924	25	39	16	25	23	36	64
	1929	30	30	27	27	42	42	99
	1932	26	28	34	37	32	35	92
	1936	30	28	45	42	32	30	107
		111	31	122	33	129	36	362

The four technical journals were:—Proceedings of Institute of Civil Engineers, Proceedings of the Institute of Mechanical Engineers, Proceedings of the Institute of Electrical Engineers and Proceedings of the Institute of Structural Engineers.

(These figures were collected by M. H. F. Wilkins and D. R. Newth.)

(C) Expenditure of Firms on Industrial Research

Name of Firm.	No. of Staff.	Expenditure.
W. H. Allen, Bedford	6	4,000
Armstrong Whitworth, Gateshead .	6	1,200
Audley Engineering, Newport, Shropshire	2	550
Automotive Engineering, Twickenham .	4	1,500
Arthur Balfour, London, E.C. 2 . .	9	4,000
British Engine Boiler, Manchester .	3	3,000
Bruntons, Musselburgh . . .	3	2,000
William Butler, Brewery, Wolverhampton	1	Under 1,000
C. H. Champion, London, W. 1 . .	4	12,000
C. M. D. Engineering, Warwick . .	2	1,000
Co-operative Wholesale Society . .	9	10,000
J. Dampney, Newcastle-on-Tyne . .	9	2,000
D. R. Duncan, Wimbledon . . .	3	30
Edison Swan, Enfield	1	3,000
Glenfield & Kennedy, Kilmarnock .	6	3,800
Glaxo, London, N.W. 1 . . .	11	8,000 to 10,000
Ioco Rubber, Glasgow . . .	2	1,500
Robert Jenkins, Rotherham . . .	1	1,500
Jeyes, Plaistow	2	1,000
George Kent, Luton	4	6,000
D. W. Kent-Jones, Dover . . .	2	5,000
Limmer and Trinidad Lake Asphalt, London	8	3,500
Lister & Co., Bradford . . .	6	2,000
Mirrlees Watson, Glasgow . . .	1	500
National Benzole, London, S.W. 1 .	6	5,000 to 10,000
National Smelting, Avonmouth . .	6	6,000
Pressed Steel, Oxford	3	2,500
Riley, Coventry	3	1,500
Sheffield Smelting	4	2,500
Standfast Dyers and Printers, Lancaster .	4	2,000
Stanton Ironworks, Nottingham . .	22	1,000
United Steel, Sheffield	7	20,000
Warner & Sons, London, E.C. 1 . .	1	750
Total	159	119,330

Average expenditure per worker . . £750

Taken from *Industrial Research Laboratories* (Allen and Unwin, 1936), compiled by the Association of Scientific Workers.

These figures are not satisfactory as they stand. It is clear that the estimates made by different firms for research expenditure are based on different principles. Similarly, the figures for the number of scientific staff in some cases represent only scientists with degrees, and in others include untrained assistants. Nevertheless it is the only statistical picture we have of industrial expenditure on scientific research, and is worth citing as giving a rough idea of the situation.

APPENDIX IV

WAR RESEARCH EXPENDITURE

The following figures are taken from the Estimates for the three Services for 1937.

	No. of Scientists.	Reduced Figures. £	£	Gross. £
Scientific Research in the Air Force.				
Upkeep of research stations, salaries of scientists and assistants . . .		310,000		
Amount spent during the year on construction of stations		148,000		
Components and accessories, grants to other bodies, rewards to inventors, etc.		247,000		
Meteorological Research . . .		2,500		
Air Ministry staff for research . .		20,000		
	110	727,500	727,500	974,000
Scientific Research in the Army.				
Upkeep and salaries of scientists and assistants		395,000		
Amount spent during the year on construction of research stations . .		57,000		
Grants to other bodies and rewards to inventors.		10,500		
Administration		20,000		
	506	482,500		
Less contributions from Air Ministry and Admiralty		91,000		
			391,500	1,030,000
Scientific Research in the Navy.				
Upkeep and salaries of scientists and assistants		274,000		
Amount spent during the year on construction of research stations . .		90,000		
Grants to other bodies, miscellaneous expenses		84,000		
	226	448,000		
Less contributions from the War Office and Air Ministry		31,500		
			416,500	760,000
Total number of scientists .	842			
Total for the three services . . .		1,535,500	2,764,000

These figures were arrived at by taking out from the Estimates everything relating to scientific research. Usually technical work and research is carried on at the same station. In these cases the total amount spent in salaries on the scientific and technical staff was calculated and the cost of upkeep and administration of the station was divided in proportion between the two. In the Navy Estimates, for example, Vote 6, which covers the Scientific Services, is for £586,000, and this was reduced in this way to £274,000. To the reduced figure for the cost of the scientific stations was added the cost of the construction of new research stations, cost of headquarters staff, grants to other bodies for research, etc.

The two sets of figures, the net expenditure on purely scientific research for military purposes and that of the gross total expenditure on research and development, have a different significance. The first represents the amount of scientific work actually diverted to war purposes, the second the sum which might be available for the development of science if it were not for the need for war preparations. Both figures should be compared with those of sums available for non-military government science.

APPENDIX V

REPORT OF PARLIAMENTARY SCIENCE COMMITTEE

The following documents are taken from a "Memorandum on the development and finance of the Department of Scientific and Industrial Research, including Research Associations, based on the preliminary memorandum of the Joint Committee of the British Science Guild and the Association of Scientific Workers."

(*A*) SOME ECONOMIES EFFECTED AS A RESULT OF RESEARCHES CARRIED OUT BY THE DEPARTMENT OF SCIENTIFIC AND INDUSTRIAL RESEARCH

Research carried out by	Nature of Research.	*Total* Government Grant to R.A.	Number of years paid.	Estimated Annual Saving to Industry.	
		£		£	£
Group I— Iron and Steel Industrial Research Council	Blast furnace coke and coal utilization	23,000	4		1,700,000
Cast Iron R.A.	Moulding Sands Balanced blast Cupola Furnace	42,000	12	100,000 200,000 ————	300,000
Non-ferrous Metals R.A.	Fire-box stays and bolts	72,000	13		800,000
Group II— Electrical Industries R.A.	Cable loading Overhead Transmission Insulator Oils Turbine steam nozzles Other Investigations	106,000	12	100,000 300,000 100,000 140,000 360,000 ————	1,000,000
Group III— Refractories R.A.	Saggar replacement	25,000	13		150,000
Group IV— Food Investigations Board	Apple disease Bloom on Meat	44,000		250,000 100,000 ————	350,000
Group V— Cotton R.A.	Miscellaneous Investigations	171,000	16		300,000
	Total	440,000			3,250,000

Remarks.—This table is necessarily of an extremely approximate character. It is impossible with present systems of accounting to discover the precise amount expended on a particular research or still more even the approximate savings effected in industry. In any case the precise economic value of scientific research is essentially unmeasurable. The figures must be taken only as representing an order of magnitude. It must also be realized that they represent merely an arbitrary selection of researches. Only six Research Associations are referred to and each of these has carried on many other researches besides those given. On a conservative estimate not more than half the money spent on the Associations has been used for these researches, and allowing for the direct contribution of industry we may say that a *total expenditure of not more than* £400,000 on industrial research has yielded economies of *not less than* £3,200,000 per annum, a return on money invested of 800 per cent. per annum.

(*B*) Proposals for Development of Scientific Research in Industry

In the following table is found a survey of the existing Government or Government-aided research institutions connected with industry. These are grouped according to the industries they serve. If the list of industries be completed to cover the principal industries and services of the country, it can be seen that there are several gaps in the existing scheme. An attempt to sketch the new research associations, research boards and research institutions which would be required to complete the scheme is made in the last column of the table. These are actually entirely of a provisional nature and would require far more detailed consideration than it has been possible to give them. No account is taken in this table of research carried out by Government departments for their own purposes or by individual firms; in making an effective comprehensive survey of research facilities and research needs in this country this would have to be taken into account.

In the detailed recommendations, however, which follow the table, some attempt is made to allow for these factors, and to point out that the chief needs of development are in those industries which do not carry out research to any extent on their own account but to whom research would be of an undoubtedly practical value.

TABLE I

R.A.=Research Association.　　N.P.L.=National Physical Laboratory.
D.S.I.R.=Department of Scientific and Industrial Research.

Industry or Service.	Yield of levy 1/10 per cent. on net product £000.	Government or Government-aided Research Institutions existing in 1935.	Research Institutions desirable.
I. Heavy Industry. Mining and Quarrying	155	Geological Survey and Museum. Scottish Shale Oil R.A.* Colliery Owners R.A.* Fuel Research Board.	Mining and Quarrying Research Board. Geophysical Institute. (1) Metalliferous Mining R.A.(2) Quarry Products R.A. (3)
Iron and Steel.	92	Metallurgy Research Board. Industrial Research Council. Cast Iron R.A. Metallurgy Dept., N.P.L.	Metal Research Institute for fundamental Research.
Non-ferrous Metallurgy.	24	Non-ferrous Metals R.A.	
II. Engineering. Mechanical	93	Engineering Dept., N.P.L.	Engineering Research Board. Mechanical Engineering R.A. (4)
Power Production.		Fuel Research Board Heat Dept., N.P.L.	
Shipbuilding.	28	Froude Tank, N.P.L.	Shipbuilding R.A.
Railway.	24		
Automobile.	54	Research and Standardization Committee.	
Aeroplane.	6	Air Ministry Aerodynamics Dept., N.P.L.	
Electrical.	45	Electrical and Allied Industries R.A. Electrical Dept., N.P.L.	

* Does not at present receive a Government Grant.

TABLE I—*continued*

Industry or Service.	Yield of levy 1/10 per cent. on net product £000.	Government or Government-aided Research Institutions existing in 1935.	Research Institutions desirable.
Light . . .			Machine Construction and Light Engineering R.A. (4)
Civil . . .	152	(Some investigations by Building Research Board.)	Civil Engineering R.A. (4)
III. *Building & Building Materials.* Brick and Cement .	25	(Some investigations by Building Research Board.)	Silicate Reseach Institute for fundamental Research. Brick and Cement R.A.
Potteries and Glass .	18	Refractories R.A.	Pottery R.A.† Glass R.A.
Building Industries .	130	Building Research Board.	Domestic Engineering Research Institute. (5)
IV. *Chemical Industry.* Heavy . . .	46	Chemistry Research Board.	Extension of National Chemical Laboratory. (6) Chemical Manufacturers R.A.
Fine . . .	15	Chemistry Research Board.	Fine Chemical and Pharmaceutical Manufacturers R.A.
Food Industries .	90	Food Investigation Board. Food Manufacturers R.A. Cocoa, Jam, etc., R.A. Flour Millers R.A.	
Brewing and Tobacco Industries . .	96		Brewers and Distillers R.A. Tobacco R.A.

† Now in existence 1938.

TABLE I—*continued*

Industry or Service.	Yield of levy 1/10 per cent. on net product £000.	Government or Government-aided Research Institutions existing in 1935.	Research Institutions desirable.
V. *Paint, Rubber, Plastics, Leather.*			
Paint Industries .	9	Paint, Colour and Varnish Manufacturers R.A.	⎧ Plastics, Rubber and Leather Research Board.
Rubber and Plastics	17	Rubber Manufacturers R.A.	⎨ Plastics Institute for fundamental Research.
Leather Industries .	26	Leather Manufacturers R.A. Boot and Shoe R.A.	⎩
VI. *Textile Industries.*			
Textile Industries .	143	Wool R.A., Cotton R.A. (Rayon Dept.) Linen R.A.	Fibre Institute (for fundamental research).
Clothing Industries .	70	Launderers R.A.	Clothing Industries R.A.
VII. *Wood, Paper and Printing.*			
Woodworking and Furniture Industries	32	Forest Products Research Board.	(Extension of F.P.R.B. to coordinate Wood, Paper and Cellulose trades research.) Woodworking and Furniture R.A.
Paper Industries .	29	..	Paper Industries R.A.
Printing Industries .	74	Printing Industry R.A.*	
Miscellaneous Light Industries . .	22	..	Light Industries R.A.

* Does not at present receive a Government Grant.

TABLE I—*continued*

Industry or Service.	Yield of levy 1/10 per cent. on net product £000	Government or Government-aided Research Institutions existing in 1935.	Research Institutions desirable.
VIII. *Transport.*			Transport Research Board under direction jointly of D.S.I.R. transport companies and authorities and Ministry of Transport with separate research institutes for Road,†Rail,† Marine and Air transport.
Road . . .	105	Road Research Board.	
Rail . . .	100	..	
Sea and River . .	60	..	
Air . . .		Air Ministry.	
IX. *Communications.*			
Telegraph and Telephone . .		Post Office Research Laboratories.	
Radio . . .		Radio Research Board.	
Cinema, Gramophone and Photographic Industries . .		National Film Institute.	Optical Research Institute. Cinematograph and Allied Industries R.A.
Scientific Instrument Industry . .		Scientific Instrument R.A.	
X. *Distribution and Administration.*			
Distributive Industries . .	570	..	Distributive Trades R.A.
Clerical and Administrative Work .		..	Business Welfare and Efficiency R.A.

† Already in existence.

(1) This would naturally become part of the Geological Survey and Museum.

(2) Instead of a Research Institution this purpose might be met by an increased grant from the department to the Royal School of Mines together with a guaranteed contribution from Mining Interests. In either case co-ordination with other mining research in the Empire would be desirable.

(3) Quarry products research might alternatively be carried out by the Building Research Board with the aid of an increased grant and a guaranteed contribution from quarrying interests.

(4) The functions of these Research Associations might be taken over by the proposed Engineering Research Board working in conjunction with the Institute of Mechanical Engineers and the Institute of Civil Engineers respectively, with guaranteed support from the industries concerned.

(5) Might be combined with the proposed Cookery Research Institute. These would need to be supported mainly by Government grants though contributions might be made by Hotel Managers' Associations, Local Authorities, etc.

(6) The National Chemical Laboratory needs to be developed to something like the same degree as the National Physical Laboratory and should resemble analogous institutions abroad. It should contain some autonomous departments of Inorganic Chemistry, Organic Chemistry, Physical Chemistry (including photochemistry and study of reactions), Electro-chemistry, Photo-chemistry, Structural Chemistry (analysis of matter by spectroscopic, X-ray and electron methods), Geochemistry (in collaboration with the Geological Survey) and Industrial Biochemistry (in collaboration with the Medical Research Council).

TABLE II

Suggested New Research Associations

Metalliferous Mining	*a* [1]
Quarry Products	*a*
Mechanical Engineering	*a*
Machine Construction	*a*
Civil Engineering	*d*
Shipbuilding	*d*
Bricks and Cement	*d*
Pottery	*d*
Glass	*d*
Chemical Manufacture	*b*
Fine Chemical and Pharmaceutical	*b*
Brewing and Distilling	*c*
Tobacco	*b*
Clothing Industries	*c*
Woodworking and Furniture	*c*
Paper and Allied Industries	*d*
Light Industries	*c*

[1] See notes following on pp. 436-7.

Suggested New Research Associations—continued

Cinematograph and Photographic Industries　　.　*b*
Distributing　.　.　.　.　.　.　.　*c*
Business Welfare and Efficiency　.　.　.　.　*c*

Suggested New Research Boards

Mining and Quarrying.
Engineering.
Plastics, Rubber and Leather.
Textile.
Transport.
Consumers' Research Council.

Suggested New Research Institutes

Geophysics.
Optics.
Metals.
Silicates.
Plastics.
Fibres.
Cookery.
Domestic Engineering.
Expansions of National Chemical Laboratory with
　subsidiary Institutes.

It would appear from the survey of the research facilities in industry, shown in the table, that there is need for the formation of twenty new Research Associations, seven institutions for fundamental researches in problems closely connected with industry, and six Research Boards with co-ordinating functions. These needs, however, are not of the same urgency and in some cases might be met without the immediate creation of new bodies.

(*a*) New Research Associations (see Table II) are by no means all on the same footing: thus of the twenty suggested Research Associations, those of Metalliferous Mining, Mechanical Engineering, Light Engineering and Civil Engineering might have their research needs met by providing from Government and industrial sources guaranteed grants for research to professional institutions. For two more, Quarry Products and Ship-building, the work might be done by extending the scope of the Building Research Station and the Froude Tank of the National Physical Laboratory, respectively. The desirability of Research Associations in both these cases is largely because it appears that in this way closer contact between science and industry can be obtained than in the case of purely governmental or institutional activity.

(*b*) The Heavy Chemical, the Tobacco and the Cinematograph and Photographic industries, are controlled relatively by few firms, all of whom carry out research on their own account. Research Associations are called for in these cases only if it is considered in the national interest that the results of industrial research in any field should not be entirely under private control. The work of the Electrical and Allied Industries Research Association has shown how valuable such a body can be even in an industry at least as highly organized as some of those referred to.

(*c*) Of the remaining industries and services six are largely traditional in character: Brewing, Clothing Industry, Woodworking and Furniture, Light Industries (box-making, toys and fancy goods, etc.), Distributive Trades and Business (office technique and administration). It may take some time in these cases for the value of scientific research to be properly appreciated and contributions from the industries cannot be expected on a large scale. It might be wise here to form small Research Associations mainly supported by Government grants (in the first case the whole cost might be borne by a levy on Excise returns). The functions of these Research Associations would be, to start with, mainly to distribute information and act as general consultants to the industry.

(*d*) In the Brick and Cement, Pottery, Glass and Paper indu: .ies, however, there is an urgent need of Research Associations of the type already existing in other industries. These industries are of considerable importance both for domestic and export markets,[1] and if the latter has declined in recent years it is largely because of failure to keep up with modern methods and neglect of scientific methods (except, of course, in the case of fine chemicals). The work of the Refractories Association in this field and the immense savings effected at little cost (saggar research savings per annum, £160,000) show what might be done in all these industries. Even if at the beginning the proportion of the cost falling to the Government is large, it should only need five or six years before the value of research was appreciated by the industry at large.

NOTE.—Proposals for setting up a Research Association for the Pottery and Brick-making industries as an extension of the British Refractories Research Association have been made by the Department of the D.S.I.R. since this report was first drawn up. It may be that further developments of the kind indicated are also under consideration. The slowness with which these schemes have been put into operation has not been due to any lack of desire on the part of the Department but to an extreme conservatism exhibited by those engaged in the industries, particularly when they are of the type consisting of a large number of small firms. It would be in these cases that some levy or tariff scheme would probably be the most successful.

Research Boards

It is also suggested that, for the better co-ordination of industrial research work already in progress as well as for proposed expansion, five new Research Boards (see Table II) should be formed similar to those already in existence for Metallurgy, Building, Road and Food Research. If research is to develop in an efficient way it is essential not only that the work carried out by the Department and Research Associations should be co-ordinated, but that it should also be linked with research carried out by other ministries and by professional associations. Thus, for example, the Transport Research

[1] For pottery alone, value of net product £9,500,000 (1930), exports £3,556,701 (1935).

Board would be composed of representatives of the Ministry of Transport, of the Air Ministry, of the D.S.I.R., of the Institute of Transport and of the research services of transport organizations. Its main function would be to initiate research in the general interest of transport efficiency to eliminate overlap in detailed transport research and to collect, summarize and distribute information as to progress in transport research. Similar arrangements would be made in the case of the other proposed Research Boards, but the Consumers' Research Council stands in a separate category. It would need to be more broadly representative, containing, besides those of the three Government Research Departments, direct representatives of consumers of various income categories. It should have the important function of balancing the natural concern of the D.S.I.R. in production processes and costs with a concern for consumers' needs and preferences and the prices at which these can be most effective.

Research Institutes

This country has lagged far behind others, notably Germany, the U.S.A., and the U.S.S.R., in providing tne type of research institute which stands between the pure research carried out in the universities, and the practical research which is the function of Research Associations and the laboratories of individual firms. To a certain extent this function is fulfilled by certain departments of the National Physical Laboratory, but on a very limited scale. The Royal Society, Mond Laboratory and the Davy-Faraday Research Laboratory are the only institutes of the kind proposed already in existence. What is needed are institutes in which are grouped together sets of researches bearing on different aspects of the properties of the basic raw materials or the characteristic processes of an industry or group of industries. Institutes of this type would serve to solve general problems of a more long-range and fundamental character and to suggest new raw materials and processes, the practical utilities of which could be tested out in the laboratories of the Research Associations. Such institutes as those proposed for Geophysics, Optics, Metals, Silicates, Plastics and Fibres have already been in existence for several years in other countries—notably the Kaiser Wilhelm group of institutes in Berlin, the Geophysical Institute in Washington and the Optical Institute in Leningrad, and have proved of marked value to science and industry.

Up till now we have, apart from such laboratories as the Wellcome Foundation or the Davy-Faraday Laboratory of the Royal Institution, few such institutes in this country. More conservative-minded people consequently are likely to look with suspicion upon their foundation and to prefer the proposal to subsidize existing university departments. It should be realized, however, that for semi-industrial research much larger and more expensive types of laboratory are required than for purely scientific research, and the setting up of such laboratories would be beyond the means of all but the wealthiest universities. That there should be some connection between institutes and universities is obviously desirable, but at the same time there is much to be said for preserving in them a certain degree of autonomy, particularly if their contacts with industry are to be kept close enough to be of full practical value.

The development of the National Chemical Laboratory to a size in keeping with its scientific and industrial importance would be an integral part of such a scheme of research institutes. The separate institutes might well be dependent on the National Physical or Chemical Laboratories, or they might be directly administered by the department. In either case it would be convenient to distribute them in relation to the industries served, *i.e.* the Metal Institute might be at Sheffield or Birmingham, the Fibre Institute at Manchester or Leeds, the Silicate Institute in Staffordshire.

The research institutes might be financed directly by the department, or in certain cases also by contributions from industry. A certain proportion of the grants to the Research Associations of an industry might be earmarked for the common research institute.

Cost of Suggested Developments

A rough estimate of the cost of these developments can be got from existing figures. If the full scheme proposed was put into force it would mean creating six large and fourteen small Research Associations. Taking the gross annual income of these at £20,000 and £10,000 respectively, the total would be £260,000. If we assume that during the first five years the cost of these is borne by the Government and subsequently the figure stands at about one-third, the annual grant would fall from £130,000 to £90,000, or about the same as that of the first nineteen Research Associations.

As the full scheme would probably not be immediately practicable from organizational difficulties or the backwardness of the industries, we may take initially about two-thirds as feasible, rising to the full expenditure of £80,000, with a steadily increasing expenditure from industry as the benefits of the new associations began to be felt. The creation of seven Research Institutions would also involve an expenditure of between £70,000 and £100,000, and the National Chemical Laboratory with its dependent institutes might cost another £100,000 per annum. The total new expenditure involved would then be £250,000 and £300,000 gross, or between £200,000 and £250,000 net (allowing for fees, royalties, etc.). The present net expenditure of the department is £550,000, so that the proposals would involve its increase by between 35 per cent. and 45 per cent.

It is impossible to estimate the capital expenditure; this could be met by a special grant or raised by loans. We may feel confident, however, from the results already achieved that this increased expenditure would be amply repaid by the benefits obtained by rounding off and integrating a research scheme for the whole of British Industry.

(*C*) THE RECOMMENDATIONS WHICH ACCOMPANIED THE COMMITTEE'S REPORT TRANSMITTED TO THE LORD PRESIDENT OF THE COUNCIL ON 29TH APRIL 1937

A

1. That the contributions from Government sources to the Research Institutions (National Physical Laboratory, etc.) and to Research Associations take the form of block grants for a period of five to ten years in advance.

2. That the Department of Scientific and Industrial Research, together with the Medical and Agricultural Research Councils, endeavour to obtain by negotiations with industrial firms, associations of such firms or other bodies, an agreement guaranteeing contributions to Research Associations, Research Stations, etc., for a corresponding period.

3. That the Department should open negotiations with industries for which research facilities are at present inadequate with a view to providing a comprehensive system of government-aided industrial research.

4. That the aggregate sum made available for existing and new scientific research, laboratories and investigations be graduated to increase annually according to a prepared scheme, with allowance for extraordinary expenses.

B

5. That in order to secure continuity and adequate expansion of scientific research (according to recommendations 1, 2, 3, 4) in periods of variable industrial prosperity, a *National Scientific Research Endowment Fund* be established.

6. That the Fund receive from the Exchequer an annual sum of £3,000,000 (or £2,000,000–£4,000,000), or 10 per cent. of the value of Customs Receipts.

7. That part of the annual receipts be used to defray the Government contribution to scientific research.

8. That the accumulated reserve of the Fund be invested in trust securities (except as under Recommendation 10) and the income thereof be used to defray part, and ultimately all, of the expenditure on scientific research.

9. That the Department endeavour to secure contributions from industry and agriculture to the Fund which need not be regular in amount, but should provide over a number of years an aggregate equivalent to that provided from Government funds.

10. That legislation be amended to permit contributions or legacies from individuals or corporations to the Fund to be free from income tax, super tax, or death duties, and that the Fund be permitted to accept stocks or shares in industrial concerns.

11. That the control of the Fund and the payments from it to scientific research be vested in a Scientific Research Endowment Board, an autonomous authority with representation from Government Departments, Industries, Agriculture, Scientific and Medical bodies, Universities, and the Public.

NOTE.—Recommendations A (1, 2, 3, 4) are independent of the adoption of the scheme contained in Recommendations B (5–11). If the latter scheme were adopted, Recommendations A would refer merely to the control of expenditure for the maintenance and development of scientific research, and not for the provision of finance.

See also article by J. D. Bernal in *Ninteenth Century*, January 1938.

APPENDIX VI

THE ORGANIZATION OF SCIENCE IN FRANCE

The general scheme for the organization of science in France is not yet complete, but the two chief sections of government controlled research have already been set up officially. "Le Service central de la Recherche scientifique" and "Le Centre national de la recherche scientifique appliquée" deal respectively with fundamental and applied research. The control of these bodies is vested in two "Conseils supérieurs" composed of eminent scientists and nominees of interested ministries, and their work is co-ordinated by an "haut comité" directly responsible to the minister. They are financed principally by the government and also by various levies and taxes on industry.

In the "Service Central" the chief innovation is that of creating a service of workers whose principal function is research and who are assured of suitable possibilities of promotion and economic security. The service is divided into four grades which are given below, with their corresponding grade on university teaching staff and rough English equivalents in brackets:

Directeur de Recherches	Professeur.
(Director of Laboratory or Institute) .	(Professor.)
Maître de Recherches	Maître de Conférences.
(Assistant Director)	(Reader.)
Chargé de Recherches	Chef de Travaux.
(Research Fellow)	(Lecturer.)
Boursier de Recherches	Assistant.
(Research Student)	(Demonstrator.)

Corresponding grades receive approximately the same salary and pension rights. There is also free interchange for long or short periods between them and possibly of promotion to a higher rank in a different service. The functions of "Conseil supérieur de la Recherche" are advisory, co-ordinating and financial, the actual direction of the research undertaken remains in the hands of the senior research workers. The council is partly nominated by the Ministry of Education and partly elected by the eleven sections of scientists. In each section, of the five elected members, three are chosen from those above forty years of age, and two from those below.

The "Centre national de la Recherche scientifique appliquée" has only recently been called into existence. (Decrees of 24th May and 10th September 1938.) Its purpose is stated in the first decree as follows:

1. To facilitate scientific researches or undertakings of interest to the national defence in establishing all possible links between the research services of the corresponding ministries, those of national education and, eventually, qualified private organizations.

2. To contribute to these researches or undertakings by initiating, co-ordinating, or encouraging applied scientific research carried out by the research workers in the service of the Ministry of Education, or eventually, of private organizations.

3. To carry out all justifiable researches for which its co-operation shall be asked by private enterprise or by individuals.

It is divided into twenty sections: (1) water power; (2) mines; (3) agriculture and fisheries; (4) metallurgy; (5) chemical industry; (6) utilization of fuel (boilers, steam engines, motors, etc.); (7) machinery; (8) textiles, wood and leather; (9) building construction; (10) lighting and heating; (11) civil engineering; (12) transport; (13) communications; (14) national defence; (15) printing, cinemas, etc.; (16) light industry, furniture, and domestic engineering; (17) hygiene; (18) nutrition; (19) working conditions; and (20) physical education and sport. The members of each section are nominated by the Minister of National Education after consultation with the Haut Comité or by other ministries. Each section contains an equal number of persons drawn from the following categories: (a) scientific workers; (b) persons from industry, commerce, agriculture, or Government departments; (c) members of the Haut Comité. No one can belong to more than one section, though arrangements can be made for collaboration. The Conseil supérieur itself contains a representative of the President of the Council and one from each interested ministries. No members are paid. The Council has very considerable financial and administrative powers.

It is naturally too early yet to speak of the work of this organization, but it is interesting on account of its comprehensive structure and its power of initiative. Little information is available as to the budget of scientific research in France. For pure research the sum available for current expenditure in 1938 was 31,000,000 francs, and for construction and apparatus a special grant was made of 53,000,000 francs; in all, therefore, 84,000,000 francs or approximately £480,000. This seems a small sum, but it is not strictly comparable to any of the figures already given for other countries because it does not include technical research of any kind such as that carried on at the National Physical Laboratory or the sums spent on research in universities. The initial grant for applied science is 30,000,000 francs, or approximately £170,000; but this is obviously merely a provisional figure. Nevertheless it is clear that even with these allowances the scale of scientific enterprise in France, relative to the importance of the country, is very much less than that in Britain or Germany. Men of science in France are well aware of this and are making every effort to change this condition.

For a further account of research in France, see *L'Organisation de la Recherche Scientifique en France*, by Jean Perrin.

APPENDIX VII

NOTE ON SCIENCE IN THE U.S.S.R.

By Dr. M. Ruhemann, Ph.D., formerly Assistant Research Director,
Physico-Technical Institute, Kharkov

1. Introduction

The Soviet Union differs from all other countries in that the means of production have become the property of the community. Socialization, which began immediately after the revolution and is now completed, is essential for the successful planning of industry, agriculture and the social services, and therefore for the planning of science which, in the U.S.S.R., is considered an integral part of the production process.

The view prevailing in the Soviet Union as to the social function of science is roughly as follows: In the U.S.S.R., as in all other countries, science is the product of the economical conditions of society, and its social function is to benefit the ruling classes of this society. Since here the ruling classes are the workers and peasants, i.e. practically the entire population, there are no fears of a technocracy detrimental to the community at large. On the contrary, everyone has everything to gain and nothing to lose from a swift development of production. At the very outset technical development was recognized as essential for the Soviet State. "Not until the country is electrified," said Lenin in 1920, "and our industry, agriculture and transport are built up on the foundations of up-to-date large-scale production, shall we be finally victorious." [1] The value of science in bringing about and accelerating this development appears obvious to everyone in the U.S.S.R. and to need no explanation. Just as industry must be developed to increase production and guarantee the amenities of life, so science must be developed to raise the productivity of industry.

"Soviet scientific research has brought forth remarkable achievements. The results of its multifarious efforts are reflected in the growth of our industrial power and have made possible the extraordinary progress that the country has made." This is from an editorial of the journal *Coke and Chemistry*, which appeared in October 1936. Commenting on certain shortcomings of industrial research institutes, the same author continues: "It is essential that the scientific research institutes shall become the most important factor in the progress of heavy industry. . . . The reorganization of scientific research is one of the greatest problems of the country. To a great extent the rate of subsequent development of Soviet economy and national defence depends on the successful solution of this problem."

In spite of this conscious interdependence of science and industry, plenty of work is being done in Soviet laboratories which would in western Europe be termed "pure science." But this term is not required in the U.S.S.R. as it is unnecessary to justify curiosity regarding the laws of nature with the help of idealistic doctrines. Even in England some firms find it worth

[1] Eighth Soviet Conference, 22nd December 1920.

their while to carry on long distance research. In the U.S.S.R. it is common knowledge that the laws of nature have some bearing on human activities and that if neutrinos and superconductivity are to-day inapplicable to the satisfaction of human needs, there is no reason to suppose that they will be to-morrow.

2. The Structure of Science in the U.S.S.R.

The structure of science in the Soviet Union is changing so rapidly that every description is obsolete before it is published. The accompanying chart shows schematically how research was co-ordinated with administration towards the close of 1937. To understand it a few words must be said regarding the structure of the executive. The highest assembly is the Supreme Council, which is elected by the people. Apart from the Council of People's Commissars (corresponding roughly to our Cabinet), several other bodies are directly responsible to the Supreme Council. One of these is the Academy of Sciences, another is the State Planning Commission. I have simplified the picture by ignoring the fact that some of the commissariats are federal and some are not. Thus the Commissar of Health for the Ukraine is responsible, not to the Supreme Council at Moscow, but to that at Kiev. But this is not essential for our subject.

Now the chief feature in the structure of science in the Soviet Union is that scientific research is not confined to one department or one commissariat but is an integral part of every department. The innovation, as against capitalist countries, is that science is and must be universal. Every problem is to be attacked by scientific thought and method.

Research is carried out in most departments of the State machinery, and the further a department is removed from the top of the ladder, the more specialized is its research.

In the chart the picture is given in greatest detail for the People's Commissariat of Heavy Industry, the structure of which I know best. The Commissariat is divided into several "sectors," the directors of which are responsible to the Commissar. A sector administrates a certain branch of industry, such as coal, ferrous metals, oil, etc. Responsible to the sector are State Trusts, organizations directly concerned with production or distribution. The trusts administer mines, factories, oil wells and other means of production.

Each factory has its research laboratory, which treats questions of interest to the particular factory. Some of these laboratories are highly developed, like that of the "Svetlana" works in Leningrad, and contribute fundamental results to the scientific periodicals; others are narrower and treat matters of purely local interest.

Passing one step higher we find that most departments of the Commissariat possess research institutes of their own, which are directly responsible to them and carry on research in the entire field of interest of the department and not only of a particular factory. One of these is the Nitrogen Institute at Moscow, which belongs to Glavazot, the nitrogen department of the Commissariat of Heavy Industry, and works on all questions pertaining to bound nitrogen. This institute has published a number of scientific papers, such as the thermodynamical work of Krishevski and his co-workers.

Apart from their research institutes several departments also have research stations or trial plants, where research is carried on upon the plant itself, more especially when new processes are being evolved and tested.

The Scientific Research Sector is itself a department of the Commissariat of Heavy Industry and as such directly responsible to the Commissar. It controls a number of large research laboratories, such as the Physico-technical Institutes at Leningrad, Kharkov, Dnepropetrovsk and Sverdlovsk, and the Karpov Institute of Chemistry at Moscow. These establishments are concerned with research on subjects which are of interest to the commissariat as a whole, and here most of the fundamental research work of the U.S.S.R. has been carried out.

The highest scientific body in the U.S.S.R. is the Academy of Science, which is now directly responsible to the Supreme Council. The Academy runs numerous laboratories mainly engaged in long-distance research. The principal function of the Academy is to co-ordinate all the scientific activities of all the commissariats, more especially in their relations to the planned development of the country.

According to the practice, now universal in the U.S.S.R., of making one man responsible for each structural unit, the director is fully responsible for his institute. If there are any deputy or assistant directors these are responsible to the principal director and not to the superior organization (trust, sector, etc.). All correspondence between a research institute and its governing body must be signed by the director.

A research institute, if large, is itself composed of several departments. These are the various laboratories, workshops, administrative offices and the book-keeping and planning departments. All these departments have their managers, who are responsible to the director. The managers of the laboratories are themselves senior research workers, the manager of the work-shops is a trained engineer. Each institute has a Party Committee, and a local trade union group concerned with the health, welfare, social life and amusements of all the employees. The party and trade union committees are not concerned with the administration of the institute as such, but their influence on the director may be considerable, and the latter will usually confer with them before taking any important administrative measures. Employees who consider themselves unfairly treated by the director or other members of the administrative staff can apply to the local trade union group or, if they are still not satisfied, to the borough committee of the trade union.

3. THE PLANNING OF RESEARCH

The planning of research work throughout the Union is one of the principal functions of the Academy of Science. The Academy is expected to study continuously, in collaboration with the several commissariats, the situation of the country as a whole, i.e. the condition of industry, agriculture, transport, medical service, national defence, etc., and, on the basis of these investigations, to indicate the main high-roads along which research is to be directed. In this way the relative weight is determined of separate branches of science in their value to the community at the moment and their potential value in the future.

The Academy has further to decide what types of problems are to be reserved for its own research institutions, what subjects are to be treated in the research institutes of the various commissariats and what kind of work is to be done in the factory laboratories. *E.g.* the large physico-technical institutes of the Commissariat of Heavy Industry are warned not to waste time in attacking small-scale technical questions which can be treated just as well in the factory laboratories, but to keep to more fundamental objects of research. On the other hand, every research organization is made responsible for the immediate transmission of any important results, discoveries or inventions it may make to the proper channels, so as to secure its prompt utilization. A piece of research work does not generally end in the publication of facts and figures in a scientific periodical, but, if the results are of technical importance, they must like-wise be presented to the trusts and factory staffs interested in the subject in a comprehensible form, together with suggestions for suitable exploitation. The research workers and directors of scientific laboratories are required to keep up close personal contacts with industrial organizations and factories and to carry on active propaganda for the utilization of new facts and ideas.

Usually the research plans are strictly annual. In 1937, in preparation for the third five-year plan, in which science is to play an exclusive rôle, an attempt was made to formulate a general plan of research, on broad lines, to cover the period from 1938–42. This plan had not been completed when I left, so that I cannot give any definite information as to how it worked.

On the basis of general directives given by the government, in collaboration with the Academy of Science and the State Planning Committee, next year's plan is discussed in the autumn by the managers of the various laboratories with their co-workers and a plan is drawn up and delivered to the director of the institute. The director then discusses these plans with the depart-ment managers and, very frequently, with each individual research worker, after which a general plan is drawn up with the help of the institute's planning department, which makes a fairly accurate estimate of costs, and this plan is sent to the governing body. On a certain date the directors of the institutes run by this body are summoned, and the plans of the various institutes are discussed together and co-ordinated. Of course, a good deal of this work has been accomplished beforehand by personal contacts. The estimates of costs are checked by the accountants of the governing body and co-ordinated with the sum that has been allotted to scientific research for the coming year. Usually this sum is almost sufficient to cover the expenses of any work that it is in the power of the laboratories to accomplish. Cuttings for want of funds rarely exceed 10 per cent. of the plan.

The plan of a research institute is composed as follows: The work is grouped firstly into branches of research corresponding to the separate laboratories, though occasionally these branches overlap and research is carried on jointly by several laboratories. In a physical institute we might have laboratories treating "nuclear physics," "low temperature research," etc. In the next group of the plan certain "problems" are set forth and explained. *E.g.* in nuclear physics we might have "The nature of cosmic rays," "beta-decay," etc. The final groups are "subjects," *i.e.* the actual pieces of work that are to be done in the coming year, and which form part-solutions of the "problems" named. The "subject" and its scope are expected to be so clear in the mind of the research worker that he is in a position to state fairly accurately what equipment he requires, how many persons should be engaged on the work, how much money will be needed and when the work will be completed. The period is not necessarily limited to the current year; subjects may be spread over two years or more if needed. An experienced Soviet research worker, who has drawn up plans for a number of consecutive years, will have no great difficulty in gauging all these points, though it may take him some time and cause him considerable annoyance. But even the time needed for a piece of work can be worked out fairly accurately ·if you know the conditions of work in the laboratory and really give your mind to the question.

4. SCIENCE AND THE COMMUNITY

Science in the Soviet Union cannot be considered an activity distinct from the everyday pursuits of the community at large, but is expected to and actually does permeate general life. What does this signify and how does it become apparent?

The Soviet Government is concerned with teaching the community not so much science as the scientific outlook. It is this outlook which is beginning to dominate the everyday life of the Soviet citizen, more especially of the younger generation. The stupendous gulf which, in this country, separates the scientist from his greengrocer, is rapidly disappearing in the U.S.S.R.

A typical example of this is the so-called Stakhanov movement, named after an enterprising young miner who succeeded in rationalizing his work in the pits, and whose lead was followed by many thousands of workers in all branches of industry and agriculture. It is nowhere contended that these "Stakhanovites" are particularly clever, and probably their results might have been attained by any normally intelligent person giving his mind to the question. The point is that the kind of reasoning applied by Stakhanov and his followers is in no way different from the reasoning of a scientist confronted by a problem in his own sphere. To be a Stakhanovite requires not so much cleverness or even an undue stock of intelligence; what it does require is just the scientific outlook of which we have been speaking. The fact that many thousands of persons are beginning to share this outlook is a momentous fact in Soviet history: not only does it bear out Marxist theory and justify the government policy, but it enables things to be done from below which could never have been done from above.

A survey of the social function of science in the U.S.S.R. would be incomplete without a short description of how this scientific outlook is being cultivated. The most striking measures are probably the following:

(1) Great attention is given to natural science in the schools, and scientific reasoning is everywhere applied even in school subjects not strictly involving natural science.

(2) The "Pioneer Houses" (children's clubs) are equipped with excellent science laboratories and exhibits, and the children are encouraged in every way to develop scientific interests.

(3) Every Soviet newspaper prints leading articles on scientific and technical subjects and the results of science and engineering are front-page news. The production figures of the leading industries, coal, ferrous metals, transport and motor cars are published daily in the central and local press, and are keenly studied by the public who know very well that all the amenities of their daily life depend on these figures.

(4) Well-stocked scientific and technical bookshops are as frequent in Soviet towns as tobacconists are in London. The books are good and cheap, and everyone buys them. Every factory and every State and Collective Farm has an extensive library of popular and advanced scientific and technical literature.

(5) Everyone who is interested in scientific knowledge has ample opportunity to develop it. He may pass from the elementary school to the factory school, from here to the workers' evening school and thence to the university or technical college without paying a penny, simply by passing the examinations in which each course of education culminates. The directors of the organization at which the man or woman is working are obliged to give them every chance of improving their knowledge.

(6) In every factory all employees are obliged to attend classes at which the particular branch of industry in which they are engaged is expounded and discussed, including the scientific facts on which the process is based. Everyone is required to pass an examination in his particular trade on the basis of these classes. Wages are adjusted to the results of these examinations, which are repeated at regular intervals. In 1935, 797,000 workers, administrative functionaries and economists went through these courses alone in the Commissariat of Heavy Industry. In 1937 the number was certainly much greater.

(7) The Stakhanov movement is actively encouraged by all those in authority. Any form of rationalization brings immediate emolument to the workers and every "Stakhanovite" is entitled to particular facilities for increasing his knowledge and broadening his outlook. The importance attached to the Stakhanov movement may be gauged from the fact that, during the first six months of 1936, the fortnightly periodical *Journal of Chemical Industry*, which contains very valuable research results on applied chemistry and physico-chemistry, printed six leading articles on this subject.

These are some of the facts that engender the scientific outlook in the peoples of the U.S.S.R. There are many more, which are perhaps just as important, from the unemotional simplicity of Marxian philosophy to the direct experience of every man and woman that it pays to think.

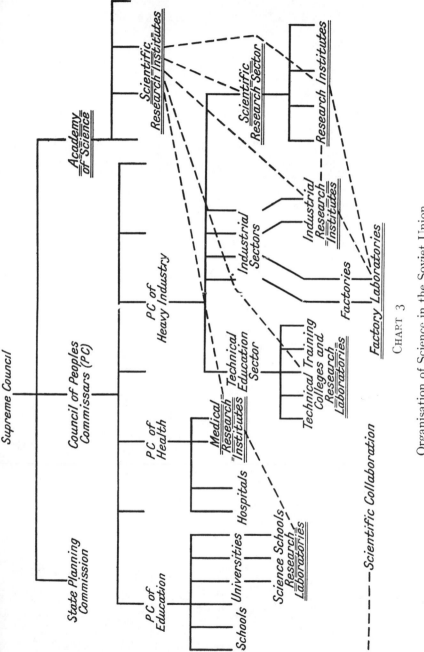

CHART 3

Organisation of Science in the Soviet Union

APPENDIX VIII

PROJECT FOR SCIENTIFIC PUBLICATION AND BIBLIOGRAPHY

(Scientific Information Institute)

It is suggested that there be investigated the possibility of bringing all the bibliographical and abstracting services for science and many of the journals of original publication, which are now having financial struggles, under one central organization (tentatively called Scientific Information Institute or S.I.I.). An essential part of such centralization would be the utilization and development of methods of publishing, duplicating, indexing, selecting and distributing scientific information and bibliography that are novel in their application to this problem.

Details are discussed in the following paragraphs. Essential factors in the project are: (1) Centralization of scientific publication and bibliography with resulting economy of operation and improvement of service. (2) Substitution of photographic (in the broad sense) duplication from printing-from-type duplication. Preferably, the development of reduced size microphotographic duplication, although it is realized that in the beginning the ultimate reduction in size may not be possible from the standpoint of consumer psychology and immediate technical application. Printing is not adapted to small editions, while photographic duplication is. (3) The utilization of a comprehensive scheme of numerical indexing and automatic finding and sorting devices for filing and selecting bibliography.

The S.I.I. would be organized as a non-profit, educational, scientific organization, under joint control through trustees of scientific organizations. It should be self-liquidating in the true sense of the word. It could take over the publication functions of many existing societies and journals, it would charge nominal but sufficient prices for publications and bibliography issued, it would receive regular assured support from memberships in it through societies, etc.

There should be no illusions as to the size of the project. The success of S.I.I. will depend upon incorporating into it most of the existing media of scientific publication and bibliography. It will be a monopoly in the same sense that the post office department is a monopoly, operated for public benefit without profit. If it is not practically all-inclusive, it will fail.

The recording, distribution and preserving of the results of science research in the most effective and efficient manner is a necessary function of the scientific world nearly co-ordinate with the continuance of scientific research itself.

Form of Organization of S.I.I.

The following practical form of organization called, for convenience, Scientific Information Institute, abbreviated hereafter S.I.I., is tentatively outlined.

S.I.I. would be a non-profit institution for the diffusion, publication and recording of scientific literature. It would be formed with the assistance of national and local scientific societies, both general and specialized, universities, research institutions, foundations and, if possible, the United States Government, through appropriations or loan grants. Under present world economic conditions it is probable that it would of necessity begin as a national enterprise rather than as an international enterprise, but its plans should be so laid that it can become international when the opportunity arises. Geographically, S.I.I. would most logically be located in Washington, D.C., in order to utilize the library facilities of the Library of Congress, the Surgeon-General's Library, etc.

Its primary function would be to act as a medium of publication for original scientific research and to compile and distribute bibliography of scientific publications. There would be numerous incidental functions that would be developed and co-ordinated with these primary functions.

S.I.I. would not duplicate existing media of publication and bibliography but would absorb existing media, eliminating duplication and thus preventing waste. S.I.I. would utilize the existing personnel of scientific publication and bibliographical effort, and through coverage of the whole scientific field would confer upon all scientists throughout the country the advantages that would accrue from centralized large-scale operation.

S.I.I. would operate to the advancement of scientific research and scientific personnel in general by establishing a more efficient medium of publication of scientific research and an adequate scientific bibliography service.

Present economic conditions and the growth of scientific literature justify serious consideration of an improved system of scientific publication and bibliography.

Workers in science should be unafraid of change and willing to evaluate present mechanisms and methods in the distribution and exchange of scientific knowledge and research results.

Publication Function of S.I.I.

The following tentative mechanism of original scientific research publication through the medium of S.I.I. is suggested:

The research worker when an investigation is ready for report would submit his report to S.I.I. in just the same way that he now submits it to a specialized scientific journal. Upon arrival at S.I.I. the research reports would be given the same editorial reading that is now given to articles submitted for publication in the conventional scientific journals. The research report when accepted for publication would be typed in uniform style upon uniform permanent paper and assembled together with graphical and illustrative material. Instead of sending this manuscript and illustrative material to the printer and the engraver for the setting of type and the making of half-tones and line-cuts for the illustrative material, the article would be reproduced by some means other than printing more adapted economically to the production of small editions or small numbers of copies. (See discussion on methods of duplication or reproduction below.) The complete paper and its illustrative material would not be duplicated or reproduced in large quantity in anticipation of distribution, but an essentially novel method of distribution would be utilized. Each author of a research report to be distributed by S.I.I. would provide a summary abstract of approximately two hundred words such as now appear at the head of research reports printed in many scientific journals. These abstracts at suitable intervals (weekly or monthly) would be assembled and reproduced by the most economical means depending upon the number of copies needed (printing, lithographing, etc.), and these abstracts in the form of this weekly or monthly journal would be sent to all scientists working or desiring information in the particular field covered. For instance, all physicists would receive the weekly or monthly journal containing the abstracts of research reports on various phases of physics. Appended to each abstract of a research report would be a serial number and a price, say, twenty-five cents. The scientist desiring to have a full copy of the research report abstracted would order such a copy individually, paying the price indicated for this copy. The S.I.I. receiving this order would manufacture to order a copy of the research report and send it to the scientist transmitting the price indicated.

Upon first inspection this mechanism of distributing only abstracts to the large group of scientists and furnishing complete copies of research reports only upon individual order may seem more costly and wasteful than the existing methods of publication in the form of scientific journals. However, with the utilization of methods of reproduction and duplication peculiarly adapted for the production of small numbers of copies, it will be found that the distribution of research reports suggested is much more economical than the method in use at present. (See section on methods of duplication or reproduction.)

The suggested method of distribution of research reports would remedy most of the problems listed in the section headed "Publication Deficiencies."

Bibliographical Activity, S.I.I.

With the purpose of making available without library research of any sort references to scientific literature and bibliographies upon particular research subjects, S.I.I. would operate a bibliographical file and production service which would absorb existing bibliographical schemes in all fields of science and provide bibliographical material in those fields of science which are now not easily accessible.

Publication Deficiencies

The present method of publication by printing in specialized journals monographs and bulletins has the following deficiencies:

1. Research results cannot be reported promptly.

2. Research results cannot be reported completely with all necessary data, illustrations (photographic or diagrammatic), discussion, background and other pertinent details.

3. Waste is widespread in that only a small number of the subscribers of any specialized journal are interested in even the abbreviated details contained in any particular research report as now published.

4. Increasing volume of the scientific literature is increasing the financial burden upon individual scientific workers and upon institutions. Multiplication of journals in a given field increases the cost of receiving the complete literature in any field, and as the expenditures for journals cannot usually keep pace with this growth and often must remain constant, the birth of a new journal operates to reduce the number of subscribers to all competing or supplementing journals unless the growth of workers in the field is increasing sufficiently rapidly to compensate for this loss (which is not the case at the present time).

5. The multiplication of journals, the decrease in funds available for libraries and research publications by institutions and deficiency (4) above, are operating to reduce further the facility and distribution of scientific publication. Failure of libraries to subscribe to journals due to measures of economy will result in serious hindrances to the availability of requisite scientific literature.

6. Editing and business management of specialized journals usually undertaken on an unpaid volunteer basis by scientists constitute impositions that detract from the essential research work in which the scientist-editors or scientist-business-managers are primarily engaged.

7. Articles in printed periodical journals are limited in total number of copies available to the extent of the particular edition of journal in which they appear, plus the number of author's reprints. Individual copies of duplications after exhaustion of these copies are practically impossible to obtain.

8. The present custom of author's reprints places an unjustified financial and time burden upon the author-scientist, who is expected to act as patron and mail clerk in the furnishing of copies of his published articles to all who may desire them.

9. Printing from type which must be set (casting or assembling letter by letter about a cubic inch of metal for each square inch of printed area) is an extremely expensive and uneconomical method of duplication or reproduction for small editions. Use of some method of photographic duplication, or microphotographic duplication, is indicated.

Bibliography Deficiencies

The present diverse, constantly multiplying bibliographical and abstracting efforts have the following deficiencies:

1. Nowhere can all the bibliography on any given subject be found.

2. Only by laborious and time-wasting reference to abstract journals, reviews, articles can even an incomplete bibliography of a subject be obtained.

3. The difficulty of access to the past research in a given subject often results in research being planned and conducted without an adequate knowledge of past achievements, resulting in wasteful duplication.

4. The time lag between original publication and abstracting bibliographical journals and services is so great that often the bibliographical reference is of purely historical value and does not aid other research workers in a field that is very active.

5. No method exists for calling the attention of workers in a related or diverse field to achievements in another field which may relate pertinently to their work, *i.e.* bibliographies are not adequately cross-indexed between sciences.

6. The mechanical aspects of handling, filing or shelving the existing limited bibliographies or abstract services makes it nearly impossible for an individual worker to maintain his own bibliographical files, and the facilities of all libraries, especially the smaller ones, are being taxed as time goes on.

7. If the abstract or bibliographical journal is issued serially, it is necessary to look in every issue to obtain the complete bibliography of any given subject (or every index and then numerous issues if the journal be indexed). If the abstracts or bibliographies are issued on cards, whether classified or not, the work of filing them is thrust upon every subscriber and there is a consequent duplication of this clerical effort with a multiplying factor equal to the number of subscribers.

8. Classifications while worked out in more or less detail for given special fields are in general inadequate and unsatisfactory, with nearly as many fundamental plans as there are bibliographical efforts.

9. Due to inadequate bibliography and lack of availability of published articles, there is a tendency upon the part of every research worker to collect and file for himself all references, reprints, articles upon the subject in which he may be working. This clerical work detracts from his research efforts.

10. Issuance of bibliography in journals or upon card results in the delivery to every worker in a broad field of all the entries in that field, whereas he may be interested in only a small number. This results in waste. (See deficiency (3) under "Publication" above.

11. The factors stressed in deficiencies 4, 5, 6, 7 and under "Publication" above apply with equal force to bibliographical efforts.

This listing of inherent deficiencies is not a criticism of the aims and operation of the many existing journals or bibliographic efforts. It is a constructive attempt to suggest a further evolution of scientific literature methods which will react to the benefit of scientists and the advancement of science. In the project proposed below all the splendid work of the present journals and bibliographies can be utilized. Not the scrapping of present enthusiasms and efforts, but the improving of their scopes, mechanisms and effectiveness is proposed.

Duplication Method

The principal barrier to adequate scientific publication and bibliography is the printing press. Printing from type for text and from half-tone and line-cuts for illustrations is not economically adapted to small edition duplication.

Some method of photographic duplication, capable of producing economically a dozen to two hundred copies at lowest possible over-all cost, must be utilized.   Under the S.I.I. plan complete research reports will not be widely distributed on the present "scatter" principle of scientific publication in journals, but will be supplied or "planted" with economy in the hands of those who actually need and order the specific research report.

The following factors, essentially novel in this application, are needed:

1. Reproduction of text from typewritten copy (specially typewritten, special type style for legibility, special size of paper), obviating the necessity for expensive setting in type as in printing.

2. Reproduction of illustrations of all sorts from original photographs, diagrams, etc., obviating the necessity for expensive half-tones and line-cuts.

3. Photoprinting or photolithographing the copies to be supplied the users.

4. Greatly reduced size photographic reproductions (microphotographs) to read through a lens or reading machine or projected like a lantern slide or slide film.

Complete bibliographical work is very difficult, due to the mechanical difficulty of handling a large and constantly growing volume of material. Anything approaching individual service is out of question because of the cost of typesetting, proof-reading and printing.   Yet a volume of bibliographical references such as those put out by the abstract periodicals and the Engineering Index is not put to complete use by the receiver, on account of the trouble of clipping, sorting and filing necessary.   The proposed scheme obviates these difficulties by correlating the use of methods and machines already perfected and in use for other purposes.

	Present Practice.	Proposed Method.
Reference to literature reaches user by . .	Journal of Abstracts.	Roll of Film.
Method of reproduction .	Printing.	Photography.
Chances of error . .	In typesetting and in proof-reading.	None.
Economical number of copies . . .	Not less than several hundred.	As few as desired.
Individual selection .	To a whole class—a large percentage of the material does not interest the receiver.	As individual as desired. Bibliographies may be made up easily for one person.
Ability to reissue . .	Almost impossible, due to printing cost.	As easy as original issue, at any time.
Bringing subject up to date by correlating new with old data . .	Very difficult, due to mechanical trouble of filing in new material.	Reissue of all material on a subject, in any desired sequence, as easy as original issue. Filing done mechanically.

Financing

A considerable capital expenditure would be necessary to launch S.I.I. These funds might be obtained: (1) Commercially. (2) From U.S. appropriation or loan funds. (3) From foundations.

Once the S.I.I. was placed in operation, it should be capable of being self-supporting, with the following sources of income: (1) Sale of product. (2) Subsidy from societies, institutions, whose publication functions it would exercise to a large degree. (3) Subventions from foundations, etc.

Any detailed budget or financial estimate of the large project is obviously impossible at the present time, but it should be emphasized that there is a good chance of making the project pay a large portion of its own way, and the economies that it would bring to the field of scientific publication and bibliography should return a large financial saving to the scientific world and the world at large. The great economic value of S.I.I. will lie not so much in the saving of the cost of the publication and distribution of scientific information, although that will be important, but in the economy of time and effort on the part of producing scientists that will result from its activities.

WATSON DAVIS.

Science Service, Washington, D.C.
August 19, 1933.

Reissued
October 17, 1933.

As was anticipated the full scheme indicated here has proved too ambitious for immediate acceptance. One important part of it, however, is in operation, that of microfilm reproduction of existing literature. The American Documentation Institute has started a Bibliofilm Service in Washington which can already reproduce to order almost every part of world literature.

The following quotations, taken from *Microfilms make Information Accessible*, by Watson Davis, indicate the scope of the service:

"Microfilms have been used successfully by thousands of persons and institutions. The Bibliofilm Service, now operated by American Documentation Institute, has been microfilming in the Library of the U.S. Department of Agriculture since 1934 and scores of thousands of pages have been serviced. Bibliofilm Service now has access to some 90 per cent. of the world's literature through cameras in the Library of the U.S. Department of Agriculture, the Library of Congress and the Army Medical Library in Washington.

For little more than a cent a page the research and information worker can get what he wants by the simple process of filling out an order blank. This is no more trouble than filling out a call card in a library merely to borrow a book. Microfilming is far cheaper than photostating. When material must be borrowed by mail or express the cost of microfilms is usually less than transportation costs.

The practical nature of this project is indicated by the successful operation of Bibliofilm Service in Washington.

Supplementary to the problem of making available existing literature is the securing of publication for all the material that should be recorded and made available to the intellectual workers of the world. In this microfilm can play an important role, giving publication with economy and effectiveness.

The microfilm can be used to secure what can be called "auxiliary publication." It will supplement other forms of publication and make accessible material of all sorts that cannot now be printed because of economic factors. It will make available valuable research data that now go unrecorded. It will make available out-of-print and rare books. It is adapted to the publication of photographs and other illustrations. Auxiliary publication service (which might be named Docufilm Service) is auxiliary to established channels of scholarly publication and aids and does not hinder journals. Editors of journals and institutions act as intermediaries between the authors of papers and the "Docufilm Service."

Auxiliary publication service is in actual operation. A journal editor can publish as much or as little of a technical paper as he wishes. In the case of a very specialized paper it may be only an abstract or summary. He appends to the notice or article a note saying that the full article with diagrams, pictures, etc., can be obtained by remitting a certain price and specifying the document number under which this full article has been deposited at the central agency operating the auxiliary publication service. Orders are sent by readers directly to this central agency, which is the American Documentation Institute at Washington, D.C. Microfilms of the document are made only if and when ordered. In this way the document is perpetually "in print" but no extensive, space-consuming stocks need be stored, only the document itself and the microfilm negative from which positives are made for distribution. The operation of the plan is simple and uncomplicated and editors may use it when, how and if they find it helpful. No financial participation or guarantees on the part of the editor or author are required.

While the plan of auxiliary publication suggested could be used with other methods of duplication, microfilm is the least expensive and most universal in that it will handle text and illustration of any sort.

Microfilms can aid another documentation project of importance to the world that will need much planning, development and international co-operation. This is the possibility of a world bibliography, beginning in the field of science but eventually extending to all fields.

The economy and compactness of microfilm gives new hope that a world science bibliography may be accomplished without ambitious hopes and promising plans being drowned in a sea of cards and smothered in a maze of details. It is possible to visualize the creation in some world centre of a card file with a card for every article, paper, book or document published in science that is important to the written record of science. Each card could be given multiple classifications. Now if for each of these classifications the card were microfilmed, with a pattern representing that classification, and if selection from microfilm is developed so that a roll of microfilm is run through a selector which prints only microfilm bearing a predetermined classification pattern, we shall have the mechanism whereby a great world file of bibliography can be made to produce special bibliographies in any subject to order. And this should be done at a cost that would allow its use by every scientific research worker.

The American Documentation Institute, formed on behalf of some fifty of America's leading scientific and scholarly societies, councils and institutions, arose out of the need for a broad, energetic and intellectually motivated development of all phases of documentation, particularly microphotographic duplication and its ramifications, in the fields of physical, natural, social and historical sciences and the general sphere of libraries and information services. In its operational aspects, A.D.I. is now primarily concerned with microfilming. It should be recognized, however, that the scientific and scholarly agencies of America have in A.D.I. an institution that is capable of doing what they wish in the broad field of documentation. Without the burden of private profit, with control solidly vested in America's organized intellectual world, A.D.I. will be able to administer, organize or operate activities that would be uneconomical for any one institution. Significantly A.D.I. brings into the same community of interest sectors of the intellectual world that otherwise do not often co-operate; in its councils and activities physicists, astronomers, biologists, economists, librarians, historians, bibliographers, archivists and many other varieties of specialists come together to solve problems common to all."

American Documentation Institute,
Washington, D.C.

APPENDIX IX

RASSEMBLEMENT UNIVERSEL POUR LA PAIX

Brussels 1936

International Peace Campaign

Report of Science Sub-Commission

It was resolved to set up a Science Commission of the I.P.C. with the general object of uniting all scientists in the struggle for peace.

The following should be its immediate tasks:

1. To co-ordinate the activities of existing peace organizations of scientists, and to create new ones in those countries in which they do not already exist.

2. To undertake an active propaganda among all scientists individually and through existing organizations.

3. To oppose the utilization of science for war ends and to support any scientists who are made to suffer for their refusal to take part in such research.

4. To carry on propaganda in universities and technical schools against the utilization of science in war.

5. To assist in the formation of a joint committee of enquiry on the causes of war. This committee should comprise:

Biologists.	Doctors.
Psychologists.	Historians.
Anthropologists.	Economists.

Its tasks should be:

(*a*) To combat pseudo-scientific and pseudo-historical theories used for war propaganda, such as those of the biological necessity of war, the existence of superior and inferior races, etc.

(*b*) To study, from the standpoint of social and biological science, the causes of war and the most useful way in which scientists can help to eliminate them. It is essential that there should be some positive statement, however tentative, on this point in order to counter pseudo-scientific propaganda for war.

The main work of this Commission would be to produce as quickly as possible an authoritative but short and simple statement or statements on these points.

Subsidiary functions would be:

(*a*) To issue critical bibliographies of works both for and against these theories.

(*b*) To conduct a continuous propaganda in the popular and scientific Press against these theories.

(*c*) To expose and combat the teaching of such theories in schools and universities.

(*d*) To influence learned societies to defend scientific truth against these distortions.

6. To assist in the formation of a joint commission on science and war. This Commission should comprise:

Aeroplane technicians.	Geologists.
Military experts.	Engineers.
Bacteriologists.	Chemists.
Physicists.	Doctors.

Its tasks should be:

(*a*) To discover, as far as possible, the objective facts about modern war technique and its probable effects on the military and civil populations.

In particular, to examine various means proposed for protecting the civil population, in regard to their probable efficacy, without neglecting their economic, political and moral aspects.

(*b*) To work for the effective international suppression of chemical and biological warfare.

(*c*) To publish the results of its investigations as soon as possible, simply stated, without minimizing or exaggerating the dangers of modern war or seeking to claim an unobtainable accuracy.

(*d*) To publish critical bibliographies on the technique of warfare and other special studies on this subject.

(*e*) To counter false technical war propaganda by reasoned exposures.

(*f*) To bring home to scientists themselves the part they are playing directly or indirectly in preparations for war, and particularly to draw attention to the utilization for military purposes of funds intended for civil research.

(*g*) To serve as an information bureau on technical military questions to all peace organizations.

Science Sub-Commission Resolution

We recognize that war is fatal to science, not only by breaking up its fundamental international character, but even more by destroying its ultimate purpose of benefiting the human race.

We are therefore resolved to do our utmost as scientists for the preservation of peace. We realize that such a general resolution is by itself of little use and requires to be implemented by definite practical activity.

We have to consider how we, as scientists, can best assist both in the preventing of an immediate outbreak of war, and in permanently removing its fundamental causes.

The I.P.C. offers us the great opportunity of working effectively for both these ends. Through it we can join our forces, which individually are not strong enough to resist war effectively, with greater and more organized popular forces. We can contribute our influence, our technical knowledge and our abilities to this movement, so as in some way to redress the contribution which science has made, and is still making, to war.

At the same time we can assist in the task of removing the causes of war by subjecting them to scientific and historical analysis and by exposing the theories of those who strive to excuse and justify war.

APPENDIX X

ASSOCIATIONS OF SCIENTIFIC WORKERS

(*A*) Policy of the British Association of Scientific Workers

The main objects of the Association are to promote the interests of the Scientific Worker and to secure the wider application of science and scientific method for the welfare of society.

To accomplish these objects the Association seeks to develop a professional society of qualified scientific men and women. This society must be a central unifying body sufficiently powerful to advance the interests of science and scientific workers as essential elements in the life and progress of the nation.

I

In the professional sphere, the Association seeks to promote a spirit of unity amongst scientific workers and to do what the British Medical Association and the Law Society have in fact done for members of the medical and legal professions. Where general qualifying bodies exist for the purpose of maintaining high standards of professional competence and conduct, the Association offers whatever support and co-operation it can give. Where special organizations exist to watch the professional interests, status and conditions of service of particular groups of scientific workers, the Association offers collaboration and aims at facilitating joint consultation and action on matters of common interest. Where the interests of any class of scientific workers are not yet provided for by special organizations, the Association proposes to act directly in their interests.

II

In the social sphere the Association seeks to ensure:

(*a*) That scientific research is adequately financed.

(*b*) That scientific education is improved and its advantages made more widely accessible.

(*c*) That science should be intelligently organized, both internally and in its applications, to ensure the maximum of initiative and the minimum of waste and confusion.

(*d*) That scientific research should be directed primarily to the improvement of the conditions of life.

The Association is in a position to carry out this programme because it is the only organization open to all qualified scientific workers and to no others.

To attain these ends the Association proposes the following detailed actions:

I

In the Professional and Financial Interest of Scientific Workers.

1. To secure that the practice of science for remuneration shall be restricted to persons possessing adequate qualifications.

2. To secure in the interests of national efficiency that all scientific and technical workers in the public service, in industry and in the academic world should be under the direct control of persons of adequate scientific attainments.

3. To secure direct representation of scientific experts upon Royal Commissions, Inter-Departmental and Departmental Committees, and all public and other bodies whose findings may affect the interests of those engaged in the practice of science for remuneration.

4. To secure a far wider application in practice of the admitted principle that scientific and technical training is no disqualification for appointment to the highest administrative posts in all public services, particularly in the Colonial services.

5. To secure a systematic grading of scientific and technical workers in State service and to secure parity of status and remuneration between the highest scientific and the highest administrative posts.

6. To secure that scientific workers in industry shall be assured of security of tenure, definite leave, superannuation, regular increments of salary and all other conditions of employment appropriate to their professional status.

7. To obtain concessions from the Commissioners of Inland Revenue for the abatement of Income Tax on the professional expenses of individual scientific workers.

8. To establish and maintain a complete register of qualified scientific workers.

9. To maintain an employment bureau by means of a register of posts and vacancies collected from all available sources.

10. To provide members with information and advice and to secure their protection in matters concerning publishers' contracts, conditions of appointment, patent law, etc.

11. To take up individual cases of unsatisfactory remuneration and conditions of employment brought to the notice of the Association by members, and to assist those members to obtain better conditions.

12. To assist members to obtain advice on legal matters.

13. To assist students by supplying information and advice about matters relating to their future employment.

II

(a) *In the Finance of Scientific Research*

14. To press for the provision of funds adequate for the present needs and future development of scientific research and teaching.

15. To secure the abolition of death duties on bequests for research and scientific education.

16. To secure that income tax procedure should be so amended as to encourage a maximum expenditure by industrial concerns on scientific research.

17. To secure that government aid to university and research organizations be made by means of block grants for a period of years, and not by fluctuating annual allotments conditioned by the circumstances of the moment.

18. To investigate the conditions determining the price of scientific instruments and apparatus and to promote measures to reduce their cost to scientific institutions.

19. To examine the possibility of further income for science from patents, inventions and discoveries.

(b) *In Relation of Science to Education*

20. To press for the development of the scholarship system until the opportunity for a scientific education depends upon merit alone.

21. To secure the correlation of the number of students in different branches of science with the prospects of employment in those branches.

22. To emphasize the value of scientific research in public administration and industry with the object of increasing the openings available in these fields.

23. To prevent any suppression of the teaching of science by limitation of number of students or by arbitrary impositions on curricula.

24. To press for a fuller recognition of the economic and cultural value of science in general education.

(c) *In the Organization of Scientific Research*

25. To assist Governmental and other authorities to draw up a comprehensive and rational scheme for the organization of scientific research, and to criticize such schemes as are advanced in a constructive manner.

26. To urge that scientists actively engaged in research should be enabled to play a greater part in its organization.

27. To urge the immediate undertaking of a comprehensive rationalization of scientific publications and archives.

28. To further the interchange of scientific workers between institutions at home and abroad, and to press for increased facilities for travel and hospitality.

29. To maintain and extend the international character of scientific research.

(d) *In the Application of Scientific Research*

30. To study the existing mechanism for the application of science and to study means of improving this for the benefit of human welfare.

31. To endeavour to secure that the results of scientific research are not applied for purely destructive purposes.

32. To study the protection of inventors by Patent Law.

To achieve these aims the Association proposes:

1. To arrange for periodical meetings of the Association and public meetings of the profession generally for the discussion of matters concerning the general or sectional interests of scientific workers.

2. To issue a journal, which shall be the official organ of the Association, as a medium for the expression of the attitude of scientific workers on matters of public importance and as an instrument of general propaganda on behalf of science.

3. To supply to the Press accurate information concerning the professional activities and interests of scientific workers and to urge through this medium the importance of fundamental research to the welfare of the community.

4. To organize among its members a thorough study of the questions involved with the object of issuing detailed practicable recommendations.

5. To collaborate in any of the fields in question by representation of the Association on special committees concerned with the organization of science and its applications.

6. To assist in the drawing up and promoting such legislation as concerns science and scientific workers.

7. To co-operate with other bodies in undertaking general publicity on behalf of science and scientific workers, by the calling of public conferences, the holding of public meetings, the drafting of parliamentary bills, the framing of questions to be asked in the Houses of Parliament, the conduct of Press correspondence, and all other suitable means.

8. To provide speakers for and otherwise assist the Parliamentary Science Committee.

(This is an all-party committee of members of both Houses of Parliament formed in 1929 on the initiative of the Association. It arranges periodical meetings in the House of Commons to discuss scientific matters of current legislative interest.)

(B) Provisional Programme of the American Association of Scientific Workers

Scientists all over the world are faced with a number of serious problems.

1. Except for a small number of unusually successful and fortunate people, their economic position is very unsatisfactory. Considering the expenses and duration of their professional training, their salaries are usually low, and hardly ever as high as those of people of equal rank in other fields. There is considerable unemployment among scientists and the positions of many of them are insecure. Pension provisions for scientists are rare.

2. They are particularly concerned by the misapplication of scientific discovery and the inefficiency with which the benefits of scientific knowledge and invention are made available to the general public.

3. They suffer not only from economic insecurity but also from insecurity in the prosecution of their work for science. Loss of the facilities for work is often as serious a matter for a scientist as is loss of salary. Financial retrenchment takes the form, not only of restriction of personnel, but also of poor provision for equipment and assistance. The tendency towards restriction of freedom of speech frequently involves the restriction of scientific freedom.

4. Accompanying certain trends of reaction there is a marked tendency to make use of pseudo-scientific ideas to excuse war and to attack reason and democracy.

(a) *Description of the Association*

The Scientists Association is an organization open for all people who are occupied in any branch of pure or applied—natural, social or philosophical—science and who possess at least a bachelor's degree or equivalent qualification. Its main objects are to promote the interests of science and scientists and to secure a wider application of science and the scientific method for the welfare of society.

The aim of the Scientists Association is to be a unifying body for all progressive-minded scientists. It seeks to co-operate with other organizations such as the various scientific and medical societies in so far as these deal with social scientific problems and the welfare of scientists. Recognizing that the effectiveness of even a strong association of scientific workers would be limited if it were to act in isolation from the non-scientific world, the Scientists Association seeks to co-operate with labour and other progressive organizations wherever their aims and those of the scientist coincide.

(b) *Objectives*

The programme of the American Association of Scientific Workers may be arranged under the following headings:

I. Professional and Financial Interests of Scientific Workers.
II. Finance of Scientific Research.
III. Organization and Application of Science.
IV. Relation of Science to Education.

I. Professional and Financial Interests of Scientific Workers.

The Association will work:

(*a*) To ensure for scientific workers in general, security of tenure, regular vacations, pensions, proper increases in salary and participation in Government security provisions.

(*b*) To take up individual cases of unsatisfactory remuneration and conditions of employment of members and to assist such members to obtain better conditions.

(*c*) To set up an advisory and employment bureau to provide members with information and advice with regard to contracts, conditions of employment, patent law, etc., and to maintain a register of vacant positions collected from all available sources.

(*d*) To secure the public advertisement of vacant positions.

(*e*) To secure that administrative positions requiring scientific understanding shall be filled by people with scientific qualifications.

(*f*) To secure that scientific workers shall be under the direct control of persons of adequate scientific attainments.

(*g*) To secure parity of status and remuneration between scientific and administrative posts of equal standing.

(*h*) To study methods for improving the position of graduate students and fellows with regard to remuneration, prospects and continuity of study and research.

II. Finance of Scientific Research.

The Association will work:

(*a*) To secure the provision of funds adequate for the present needs and future development of scientific research and teaching. To stress especially the need for Government programmes of research.

(*b*) To secure that governmental and other aid to research organizations be made by endowment or long-period grants, and not by fluctuating annual appropriations.

(*c*) To study the possibility of securing that more of the fruits of research are returned to science in the form of income from patents and similar sources.

(*d*) To investigate the conditions determining the price of scientific apparatus and materials, and to promote measures to reduce their cost, particular attention to be given to the high customs duties levied on instruments and materials from abroad which do not compete with the products of American firms.

III. Organization and Application of Science.

The Association will work:

(*a*) To promote and extend the application of science for the welfare of society. To emphasize the value of scientific research in industry and in public administration:

(*b*) To combat all tendencies to limit scientific investigation or suppress conclusions drawn therefrom.

(*c*) To extend the open interchange of all scientific knowledge and discovery. To maintain and extend the international character of scientific research.

(*d*) To study and expose unsocial organization and application of science. Particularly to oppose the suppression of technical advance by systematic shelving of scientific discoveries, and to counteract the application of scientific research for purely destructive purposes.

(*e*) To secure that scientists actively engaged in research should be enabled to play a greater part in its organization.

(*f*) To secure direct representation of scientific experts upon all Government Commissions and Committees and upon all public bodies whose findings may affect the interests of scientists or the application of science to society.

IV. Relation of Science to Education.

The Association will work:

(*a*) To develop a fuller recognition in education of the economic and cultural value of science.

(*b*) To improve and extend the scholarship and fellowship system until opportunity for scientific training depends upon aptitude alone.

(*c*) To expose pseudo-scientific theories, particularly where such are used as justification for anti-social, anti-democratic, anti-labour, or pro-war policies.

(c) *Methods*

Among other methods for achieving these aims, the American Association of Scientific Workers proposes:

(*a*) To build a strong national organization and to promote the formation of active local groups recruited from industries, universities and other institutions.

(*b*) To participate in public meetings of the profession and other groups when matters of individual and social interest to scientists are discussed.

(*c*) To collaborate on special committees concerned with the problems with which the Association is concerned.

(*d*) To supply to the Press accurate information concerning the social and scientific interests of scientific workers. To urge through the Press the importance of fundamental research to the welfare of the community.

(*e*) To issue a journal as a medium for the expression of the attitude of scientific workers on matters of public importance and as an instrument of general propaganda on behalf of science.

(*f*) To encourage the formulation in federal and state legislatures of volunteer Science Committees consisting of all legislators interested in science and to assist such committees with information and recommendations.

(*g*) To assist in the drawing up and promoting of such legislation as concerns science and scientific workers.

(*h*) To maintain contact with labour unions so that expert advice and help may be provided them on scientific questions, and support from them may be obtained for social and economic programmes advocated by the Scientists Association.

(*i*) To organize among its members thorough study of problems of the Association with the object of recommending detailed practical action.

INDEX

(The heavy type indicates a sub-section in which the subject is considered)